ELECTRONIC DEVICES
AND CIRCUITS

McGRAW-HILL ELECTRICAL AND ELECTRONIC ENGINEERING SERIES

Frederick Emmons Terman, *Consulting Editor*
W. W. Harman and J. G. Truxal, *Associate Consulting Editors*

ELECTRONIC DEVICES AND CIRCUITS

Jacob Millman, Ph.D.

Professor of Electrical Engineering
Columbia University

Christos C. Halkias, Ph.D.

Associate Professor of Electrical Engineering
Columbia University

McGRAW-HILL BOOK COMPANY
New York   St. Louis   San Francisco
Toronto   London   Sydney

ELECTRONIC DEVICES AND CIRCUITS

Library of Congress Catalog Card Number 67-16934

42380

67891011 HDBP 7543210

PREFACE

This book, intended as a text for a first course in electronics for electrical engineering or physics students, has two primary objectives: to present a clear, consistent picture of the internal physical behavior of many electronic devices, and to teach the reader how to analyze and design electronic circuits using these devices.

Only through a study of physical electronics, particularly solid-state science, can the usefulness of a device be appreciated and its limitations be understood. From such a physical study, it is possible to deduce the external characteristics of each device. This characterization allows us to exploit the device as a circuit element and to determine its large-signal (nonlinear) behavior. A small-signal (linear) model is also obtained for each device, and analyses of many circuits using these models are given. The approach is to consider a circuit first on a physical basis, in order to provide a clear understanding and intuitive feeling for its behavior. Only after obtaining such a qualitative insight into the circuit is mathematics (through simple differential equations) used to express quantitative relationships

Methods of analysis and features which are common to many different devices and circuits are emphasized. For example, Kirchhoff's, Thévenin's, Norton's, and Miller's theorems are utilized throughout the text. The concepts of the load line and the bias curve are used to establish the quiescent operating conditions in many different circuits. Calculations of input and output impedances, as well as current and voltage gains, using small-signal models, are made for a wide variety of amplifiers.

A great deal of attention is paid to the effects of feedback on input and output resistance, nonlinear distortion, frequency response, and the stabilization of voltage or current gains of the various devices and circuits studied. In order that the student appreciate the different applications of these circuits, the basic building blocks (such as untuned amplifiers, power amplifiers, feedback amplifiers, oscillators, and power suppliers) are discussed in detail.

For the most part, real (commercially available) device characteristics are employed. In this way the reader may become familiar with the order of magnitude of device parameters, the variability of these parameters within a given type and with a change of temperature, the effect of the inevitable shunt capacitances in circuits, and the effect of input and output resistances and loading on circuit operation. These

vii

considerations are of utmost importance to the student or the practicing engineer since the circuits to be designed must function properly and reliably in the physical world, rather than under hypothetical or ideal circumstances.

There are over 600 homework problems, which will test the student's grasp of the fundamental concepts enunciated in the book and will give him experience in the analysis and design of electronic circuits. In almost all numerical problems realistic parameter values and specifications have been chosen. An answer book is available for students, and a solutions manual may be obtained from the publisher by an instructor who has adopted the text.

This book was planned originally as a second edition of Millman's "Vacuum-tube and Semiconductor Electronics" (McGraw-Hill Book Company, New York, 1958). However, so much new material has been added and the revisions have been so extensive and thorough that a new title for the present text seems proper. The changes are major and have been made necessary by the rapid developments in electronics, and particularly by the continued shift in emphasis from vacuum tubes to transistors and other semiconductor devices. Less than 25 percent of the coverage relates to vacuum tubes; the remainder is on solid-state devices, particularly the bipolar transistor. In recognition of the growing importance of integrated circuits and the field-effect transistor, an entire chapter is devoted to each of these topics. But to avoid too unwieldy a book, it was decided not to consider gas tubes, silicon-controlled rectifiers, polyphase rectifiers, tuned amplifiers, modulation, or detection circuits. The companion volume to this book, Millman and Taub's "Pulse, Digital, and Switching Waveforms" (McGraw-Hill Book Company, New York, 1965), gives an extensive treatment of the generation and processing of nonsinusoidal waveforms.

Considerable thought was given to the pedagogy of presentation, to the explanation of circuit behavior, to the use of a consistent system of notation, to the care with which diagrams are drawn, and to the many illustrative examples worked out in detail in the text. It is hoped that these will facilitate the use of the book in self-study and that the practicing engineer will find the text useful in updating himself in this fast-moving field.

The authors are very grateful to P. T. Mauzey, Professor H. Taub, and N. Voulgaris, who read portions of the manuscript and offered constructive criticism. We thank Dr. Taub also because some of our material on the steady-state characteristics of semiconductor devices and on transistor amplifiers parallels that in Millman and Taub's "Pulse, Digital, and Switching Waveforms." We acknowledge with gratitude the influence of Dr. V. Johannes and of the book "Integrated Circuits" by Motorola, Inc. (McGraw-Hill Book Company, New York, 1965) in connection with Chapter 15. We express our particular appreciation to Miss S. Silverstein, administrative assistant of the Electrical Engineering Department of The City College, for her most skillful service in the preparation of the manuscript. We also thank J. T. Millman and S. Thanos for their assistance.

Jacob Millman
Christos C. Halkias

CONTENTS

chapter 13

The High-frequency Transistor   363

14

Field-effect Transistors   384

15

Integrated Circuits   418

chapter 19

Photoelectric Devices   566

20

Rectifiers and Power Supplies   592

1/ELECTRON BALLISTICS AND APPLICATIONS

In this chapter we present the fundamental physical and mathematical theory of the motion of charged particles in electric and magnetic fields of force. In addition, we discuss a number of the more important electronic devices that depend on this theory for their operation.

The motion of a charged particle in electric and magnetic fields is presented, starting with simple paths and proceeding to more complex motions. First a uniform electric field is considered, and then the analysis is given for motions in a uniform magnetic field. This discussion is followed, in turn, by the motion in parallel electric and magnetic fields and in perpendicular electric and magnetic fields.

1-1   CHARGED PARTICLES

The charge, or quantity, of negative electricity of the electron has been found by numerous experiments to be 1.602×10^{-19} C (coulomb). The values of many important physical constants are given in Appendix A. Some idea of the number of electrons per second that represents current of the usual order of magnitude is readily possible. For example, since the charge per electron is 1.602×10^{-19} C, the number of electrons per coulomb is the reciprocal of this number, or approximately, 6×10^{18}. Further, since a current of 1 A (ampere) is the flow of 1 C/sec, then a current of only 1 pA (1 picoampere, or 10^{-12} A) represents the motion of approximately 6 million electrons per second. Yet a current of 1 pA is so small that considerable difficulty is experienced in attempting to measure it.

In addition to its charge, the electron possesses a definite mass. A direct measurement of the mass of an electron cannot be made, but the ratio e/m of the charge to the mass has been determined by a number of experimenters using independent methods. The most probable value for this ratio is 1.759×10^{11} C/kg. From this value of e/m and the value of e, the charge on the electron, the mass of the electron is calculated to be 9.109×10^{-31} kg.

The charge of a positive ion is an integral multiple of the charge of the electron, although it is of opposite sign. For the case of singly ionized particles, the charge is equal to that of the electron. For the case of doubly ionized particles, the ionic charge is twice that of the electron.

The mass of an atom is expressed as a number that is based on the choice of the atomic weight of oxygen equal to 16. The mass of a hypothetical atom of atomic weight unity is, by this definition, one-sixteenth that of the mass of monatomic oxygen. This has been calculated to be 1.660×10^{-27} kg. Hence, *in order to calculate the mass in kilograms of any atom, it is necessary only to multiply the atomic weight of the atom by* 1.660×10^{-27} *kg.* A table of atomic weights is given in Appendix C.

The radius of the electron has been estimated as 10^{-15} m, and that of an atom as 10^{-10} m. These are so small that all charges are considered as mass points in the following sections.

Classical and Wave-mechanical Models of the Electron   The foregoing description of the electron (or atom) as a tiny particle possessing a definite charge and mass is referred to as the *classical model*. If this particle is subjected to electric, magnetic, or gravitational fields, it experiences a force, and hence is accelerated. The trajectory can be determined precisely using Newton's laws, provided that the forces acting on the particle are known. In this chapter we make exclusive use of the classical model to study electron ballistics. The term *electron ballistics* is used because of the existing analogy between the motion of charged particles in a field of force and the motion of a falling body in the earth's gravitational field.

For large-scale phenomena, such as electronic trajectories in a vacuum tube, the classical model yields accurate results. For small-scale systems, however, such as an electron in an atom or in a crystal, the classical model treated by Newtonian mechanics gives results which do not agree with experiment. To describe such subatomic systems properly it is found necessary to attribute to the electron a wavelike property which imposes restrictions on the exactness with which the electronic motion can be predicted. This wave-mechanical model of the electron is considered in Chap. 2.

1-2   THE FORCE ON CHARGED PARTICLES IN AN ELECTRIC FIELD

The force on a unit positive charge at any point in an electric field is, by definition, *the electric field intensity ε at that point.* Consequently, the force on a positive charge q in an electric field of intensity ε is given by $q\varepsilon$, the resulting force being in the direction of the electric field.   Thus,

$$\mathbf{f}_q = q\boldsymbol{\mathcal{E}}$$ (1-1)

where $\mathbf{f}_q$ is in newtons, q is in coulombs, and $\boldsymbol{\mathcal{E}}$ is in volts per meter.   Boldface type is employed wherever vector quantities (those having both magnitude and direction) are encountered.

The mks (meter-kilogram-second) rationalized system of units is found most convenient for the subsequent studies.   Therefore, unless otherwise stated, this system of units is employed.

In order to calculate the path of a charged particle in an electric field, the force, given by Eq. (1-1), must be related to the mass and the acceleration of the particle by Newton's second law of motion.   Hence

$$\mathbf{f}_q = q\boldsymbol{\mathcal{E}} = m\mathbf{a} = m\frac{d\mathbf{v}}{dt}$$ (1-2)

where m = mass, kg
    $\mathbf{a}$ = acceleration, m/sec^2
    $\mathbf{v}$ = velocity, m/sec

The solution of this equation, subject to appropriate initial conditions, gives the path of the particle resulting from the action of the electric forces.   If the magnitude of the charge on the electron is e, the force on an electron in the field is

$$\mathbf{f} = -e\boldsymbol{\mathcal{E}}$$ (1-3)

The minus sign denotes that the force is in the direction opposite to the field.

In investigating the motion of charged particles moving in externally applied force fields of electric and magnetic origin, it is implicitly assumed that the number of particles is so small that their presence does not alter the field distribution.

1-3   CONSTANT ELECTRIC FIELD

Suppose that an electron is situated between the two plates of a parallel-plate capacitor which are contained in an evacuated envelope, as illustrated in Fig. 1-1.   A difference of potential is applied between the two plates, the direction of the electric field in the region between the two plates being as shown.   If the distance between the plates is small compared with the dimensions of the plates, the electric field may be considered to be uniform, the lines of force pointing along the negative X direction.   That is, the only field that is present is $\boldsymbol{\mathcal{E}}$ along the $-X$ axis.   It is desired to investigate the characteristics of the motion, subject to the initial conditions

$$v_x = v_{ox} \qquad x = x_o \qquad \text{when } t = 0$$ (1-4)

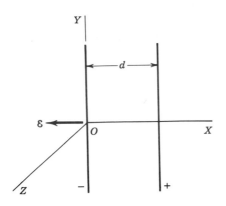

Fig. 1-1 The one-dimensional electric field between the plates of a parallel-plate capacitor.

This means that the initial velocity v_{ox} is chosen along $\mathcal{E}$, the lines of force, and that the initial position x_o of the electron is along the X axis.

Since there is no force along the Y or Z directions, Newton's law states that the acceleration along these axes must be zero. However, zero acceleration means constant velocity; and since the velocity is initially zero along these axes, the particle will not move along these directions. That is, the only possible motion is one-dimensional, and the electron moves along the X axis.

Newton's law applied to the X direction yields

$$e\mathcal{E} = ma_x$$

or

$$a_x = \frac{e\mathcal{E}}{m} = \text{const} \qquad (1\text{-}5)$$

where $\mathcal{E}$ represents the *magnitude* of the electric field. This analysis indicates that the electron will move with a constant acceleration in a uniform electric field. Consequently, the problem is analogous to that of a freely falling body in the uniform gravitational field of the earth. The solution of this problem is given by the well-known expressions for the velocity and displacement, viz.,

$$v_x = v_{ox} + a_x t \qquad x = x_o + v_{ox}t + \tfrac{1}{2}a_x t^2 \qquad (1\text{-}6)$$

provided that $a_x = $ const, independent of the time.

It is to be emphasized that, if the acceleration of the particle is not a constant but depends upon the time, Eqs. (1-6) are no longer valid. Under these circumstances the motion is determined by integrating the equations

$$\frac{dv_x}{dt} = a_x \qquad \text{and} \qquad \frac{dx}{dt} = v_x \qquad (1\text{-}7)$$

These are simply the definitions of the acceleration and the velocity, respectively. Equations (1-6) follow directly from Eqs. (1-7) by integrating the latter equations subject to the condition of a constant acceleration.

EXAMPLE An electron starts at rest on one plate of a plane-parallel capacitor whose plates are 5 cm apart. The applied voltage is zero at the instant the electron is released, and it increases linearly from zero to 10 V in 0.1 μsec.†

  a. If the opposite plate is positive, what speed will the electron attain in 50 nsec?

  b. Where will it be at the end of this time?

  c. With what speed will the electron strike the positive plate?

Solution Assume that the plates are oriented with respect to a cartesian system of axes as illustrated in Fig. 1-1. The magnitude of the electric field intensity is

  a. $\mathcal{E} = \dfrac{10}{5 \times 10^{-2}} \times \dfrac{t}{10^{-7}} = 2 \times 10^9 t \quad$ V/m

whence

$$a_x = \frac{dv_x}{dt} = \frac{f_x}{m} = \frac{e\mathcal{E}}{m} = (1.76 \times 10^{11})(2 \times 10^9 t)$$

$$= 3.52 \times 10^{20} t \quad \text{m/sec}^2$$

Upon integration, we obtain for the speed

$$v_x = \int_0^t a_x \, dt = 1.76 \times 10^{20} t^2$$

At $t = 5 \times 10^{-8}$ sec, $v_x = 4.40 \times 10^5$ m/sec.

  b. Integration of v_x with respect to t, subject to the condition that $x = 0$ when $t = 0$, yields

$$x - \int_0^t v_x \, dt = \int_0^t 1.76 \times 10^{20} t^2 \, dt = 5.87 \times 10^{19} t^3$$

At $t = 5 \times 10^{-8}$ sec, $x = 7.32 \times 10^{-3}$ m = 0.732 cm.

  c. To find the speed with which the electron strikes the positive plate, we first find the time t it takes to reach that plate, or

$$t = \left(\frac{x}{5.87 \times 10^{19}}\right)^{\frac{1}{3}} = \left(\frac{0.05}{5.87 \times 10^{19}}\right)^{\frac{1}{3}} = 9.46 \times 10^{-8} \text{ sec}$$

Hence

$$v_x = 1.76 \times 10^{20} t^2 = 1.76 \times 10^{20} (9.46 \times 10^{-8})^2 = 1.58 \times 10^6 \text{ m/sec}$$

1-4   POTENTIAL

The discussion to follow need not be restricted to uniform fields, but $\mathcal{E}_x$ may be a function of distance. However, it is assumed that $\mathcal{E}_x$ is *not a function*

† 1 μsec = 1 microsecond = 10^{-6} sec. 1 nsec = 1 nanosecond = 10^{-9} sec. Conversion factors and prefixes are given in Appendix B.

of time.   Then, from Newton's second law,

$$- \frac{e \mathcal{E}_x}{m} = \frac{dv_x}{dt}$$

Multiply this equation by $dx = v_x \, dt$, and integrate.   This leads to

$$- \frac{e}{m} \int_{x_o}^{x} \mathcal{E}_x \, dx = \int_{v_{ox}}^{v_x} v_x \, dv_x \tag{1-8}$$

The definite integral

$$\int_{x_o}^{x} \mathcal{E}_x \, dx$$

is an expression for the work done by the field in carrying a unit positive charge from the point x_o to the point x.

By definition, *the potential V (in volts) of point x with respect to point x_o is the work done* against *the field in taking a unit positive charge from x_o to x.*   Thus†

$$V \equiv - \int_{x_o}^{x} \mathcal{E}_x \, dx \tag{1-9}$$

By virtue of Eq. (1-9), Eq. (1-8) integrates to

$$eV = \tfrac{1}{2} m (v_x^2 - v_{ox}^2) \tag{1-10}$$

where the energy eV is expressed in joules.   Equation (1-10) shows that an electron that has "fallen" through a certain difference of potential V in going from point x_o to point x has acquired a specific value of kinetic energy and velocity, independent of the form of the variation of the field distribution between these points and dependent only upon the magnitude of the potential difference V.

Although this derivation supposes that the field has only one component, namely, $\mathcal{E}_x$ along the X axis, the final result given by Eq. (1-10) is simply a statement of the law of conservation of energy.   This law is known to be valid even if the field is multidimensional.   This result is extremely important in electronic devices.   Consider any two points A and B in space, with point B at a higher potential than point A by V_{BA}.   Stated in its most general form, Eq. (1-10) becomes

$$qV_{BA} = \tfrac{1}{2} m v_A^2 - \tfrac{1}{2} m v_B^2 \tag{1-11}$$

where q is the charge in coulombs, qV_{BA} is in joules, and v_A and v_B are the corresponding initial and final speeds in meters per second at the points A and B, respectively.   By definition, *the potential energy between two points equals the potential multiplied by the charge in question.*   Thus the left-hand side of Eq. (1-11) is the *rise* in *potential energy* from A to B.   The right-hand side represents the *drop* in *kinetic energy* from A to B.   Thus Eq. (1-11) states that the rise in potential energy equals the drop in kinetic energy, which is equivalent to the statement that the total energy remains unchanged.

† The symbol $\equiv$ is used to designate "equal to by definition."

It must be emphasized that *Eq. (1-11) is not valid if the field varies with time.*

If the particle is an electron, then $-e$ must be substituted for q. If the electron starts at rest, its final speed v, as given by Eq. (1-11) with $v_A = 0$, $v_B = v$, and $V_{BA} = V$, is

$$v = \left(\frac{2eV}{m}\right)^{\frac{1}{2}} \tag{1-12}$$

or

$$v = 5.93 \times 10^5 V^{\frac{1}{2}} \tag{1-13}$$

Thus, if an electron "falls" through a difference of only 1 V, its final speed is 5.93×10^5 m/sec, or approximately 370 miles/sec. Despite this tremendous speed, the electron possesses very little kinetic energy, because of its minute mass.

It must be emphasized that *Eq. (1-13) is valid only for an electron starting at rest.* If the electron does not have zero initial velocity or if the particle involved is not an electron, the more general formula [Eq. (1-11)] must be used.

1-5   THE eV UNIT OF ENERGY

The joule (J) is the unit of energy in the mks system. In some engineering power problems this unit is very small, and a factor of 10^3 or 10^6 is introduced to convert from watts (1 W = 1 J/sec) to kilowatts or megawatts, respectively. However, in other problems, the joule is too large a unit, and a factor of 10^{-7} is introduced to convert from joules to ergs. For a discussion of the energies involved in electronic devices, even the erg is much too large a unit. This statement is not to be construed to mean that only minute amounts of energy can be obtained from electron devices. It is true that each electron possesses a tiny amount of energy, but as previously pointed out (Sec. 1-1), an enormous number of electrons is involved even in a small current, so that considerable power may be represented.

A unit of work or energy, called the *electron volt* (eV), is defined as follows:

$$1 \text{ eV} \equiv 1.60 \times 10^{-19} \text{ J}$$

Of course, any type of energy, whether it be electric, mechanical, thermal, etc., may be expressed in electron volts.

The name *electron volt* arises from the fact that, if an electron falls through a potential of one volt, its kinetic energy will increase by the decrease in potential energy, or by

$$eV = (1.60 \times 10^{-19} \text{ C})(1 \text{ V}) = 1.60 \times 10^{-19} \text{ J} = 1 \text{ eV}$$

However, as mentioned above, the electron-volt unit may be used for any type of energy, and is not restricted to problems involving electrons.

The abbreviations MeV and BeV are used to designate 1 million and 1 billion electron volts, respectively.

1-6 RELATIONSHIP BETWEEN FIELD INTENSITY AND POTENTIAL

The definition of potential is expressed mathematically by Eq. (1-9). If the electric field is uniform, the integral may be evaluated to the form

$$- \int_{x_o}^{x} \mathcal{E}_x \, dx = -\mathcal{E}_x(x - x_o) = V$$

which shows that the electric field intensity resulting from an applied potential difference V between the two plates of the capacitor illustrated in Fig. 1-1 is given by

$$\mathcal{E}_x = \frac{-V}{x - x_o} = -\frac{V}{d} \tag{1-14}$$

where $\mathcal{E}_x$ is in volts per meter, and d is the distance between plates, in meters.

In the general case, where the field may vary with the distance, this equation is no longer true, and the correct result is obtained by differentiating Eq. (1-9). We obtain

$$\mathcal{E}_x = -\frac{dV}{dx} \tag{1-15}$$

The minus sign shows that the electric field is directed from the region of higher potential to the region of lower potential.

1-7 TWO–DIMENSIONAL MOTION

Suppose that an electron enters the region between the two parallel plates of a parallel-plate capacitor which are oriented as shown in Fig. 1-2 with an initial velocity in the $+X$ direction. It will again be assumed that the electric field between the plates is uniform. Then, as chosen, the electric field $\mathcal{E}$ is in the direction of the $-Y$ axis, no other fields existing in this region.

The motion of the particle is to be investigated, subject to the initial conditions

$$\left. \begin{array}{ll} v_x = v_{ox} & x = 0 \\ v_y = 0 & y = 0 \\ v_z = 0 & z = 0 \end{array} \right\} \quad \text{when } t = 0 \tag{1-16}$$

Since there is no force in the Z direction, the acceleration in that direction is

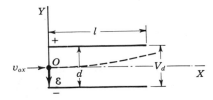

Fig. 1-2 Two-dimensional electronic motion in a uniform electric field.

zero.   Hence the component of velocity in the Z direction remains constant. Since the initial velocity in this direction is assumed to be zero, the motion must take place entirely in one plane, the plane of the paper.

For a similar reason, the velocity along the X axis remains constant and equal to v_{ox}.   That is,

$$v_x = v_{ox}$$

from which it follows that

$$x = v_{ox}t \tag{1-17}$$

On the other hand, a constant acceleration exists along the Y direction, and the motion is given by Eqs. (1-6), with the variable x replaced by y:

$$v_y = a_y t \qquad y = \tfrac{1}{2}a_y t^2 \tag{1-18}$$

where

$$a_y = -\frac{e\mathcal{E}_y}{m} = \frac{eV_d}{md} \tag{1-19}$$

and where the potential across the plates is $V = V_d$.   These equations indicate that in the region between the plates the electron is accelerated upward, the velocity component v_y varying from point to point, whereas the velocity component v_x remains unchanged in the passage of the electron between the plates.

The path of the particle with respect to the point O is readily determined by combining Eqs. (1-17) and (1-18), the variable t being eliminated.   This leads to the expression

$$y = \left(\frac{1}{2}\frac{a_y}{v_{ox}^2}\right) x^2 \tag{1-20}$$

which shows that the particle moves in a parabolic path in the region between the plates.

EXAMPLE   Hundred-volt electrons are introduced at A into a uniform electric field of 10^4 V/m, as shown in Fig. 1-3.   The electrons are to emerge at the point B in time 4.77 nsec.

　　a. What is the distance AB?

　　b. What angle does the electron beam make with the horizontal?

Fig. 1-3 Parabolic path of an electron in a uniform electric field.

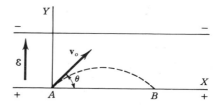

Solution   The path of the electrons will be a parabola, as shown by the dashed curve in Fig. 1-3.   This problem is analogous to the firing of a gun in the earth's gravitational field.   The bullet will travel in a parabolic path, first rising because of the muzzle velocity of the gun and then falling because of the downward attractive force of the earth.   The source of the charged particles is called an *electron gun*, or an *ion gun*.

The initial electron velocity is found using Eq. (1-13).

$$v_o = 5.93 \times 10^5 \sqrt{100} = 5.93 \times 10^6 \text{ m/sec}$$

Since the speed along the X direction is constant, the distance $AB = x$ is given by

$$x = (v_o \cos \theta)t = (5.93 \times 10^6 \cos \theta)(4.77 \times 10^{-9}) = 2.83 \times 10^{-2} \cos \theta$$

Hence we first must find θ before we can solve for x.   Since the acceleration a_y in the Y direction is constant, then

$$y = (v_o \sin \theta)t - \tfrac{1}{2}a_y t^2$$

and $y = 0$ at point B, or

$$v_o \sin \theta = \frac{1}{2} a_y t = \frac{1}{2}\left(\frac{e\mathcal{E}}{m}\right) t$$

$$= \tfrac{1}{2}(1.76 \times 10^{11})(10^4)(4.77 \times 10^{-9}) = 4.20 \times 10^6 \text{ m/sec}$$

$$b. \ \sin \theta = \frac{4.20 \times 10^6}{5.93 \times 10^6} = 0.707 \qquad \text{or} \qquad \theta = 45°$$

and

$$a. \ x = 2.83 \times 10^{-2} \times 0.707 = 2.00 \times 10^{-2} \text{ m} = 2.00 \text{ cm}$$

1-8   ELECTROSTATIC DEFLECTION IN A CATHODE–RAY TUBE

The essentials of a cathode-ray tube for electrostatic deflection are illustrated in Fig. 1-4.   The hot cathode K emits electrons which are accelerated toward the anode by the potential V_a.   Those electrons which are not collected by the anode pass through the tiny anode hole and strike the end of the glass envelope.   This has been coated with a material that fluoresces when bom-

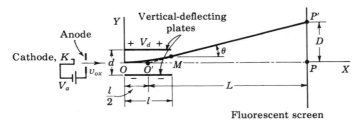

Fig. 1-4   Electrostatic deflection in a cathode-ray tube.

barded by electrons. Thus the positions where the electrons strike the screen are made visible to the eye. The displacement D of the electrons is determined by the potential V_d (assumed constant) applied between the deflecting plates, as shown. The velocity v_{ox} with which the electrons emerge from the anode hole is given by Eq. (1-12), viz.,

$$v_{ox} = \sqrt{\frac{2eV_a}{m}} \tag{1-21}$$

on the assumption that the initial velocities of emission of the electrons from the cathode are negligible.

Since no field is supposed to exist in the region from the anode to the point O, the electrons will move with a constant velocity v_{ox} in a straight-line path. In the region between the plates the electrons will move in the parabolic path given by $y = \frac{1}{2}(a_y/v_{ox}^2)x^2$ according to Eq. (1-20). The path is a straight line from the point of emergence M at the edge of the plates to the point P' on the screen, since this region is field-free.

The straight-line path in the region from the deflecting plates to the screen is, of course, tangent to the parabola at the point M. The slope of the line at this point, and so at every point between M and P', is [from Eq. (1-20)]

$$\tan \theta = \frac{dy}{dx}\bigg]_{x=l} = \frac{a_y l}{v_{ox}^2}$$

From the geometry of the figure, the equation of the straight line MP' is found to be

$$y = \frac{a_y l}{v_{ox}^2}\left(x - \frac{l}{2}\right) \tag{1-22}$$

since $x = l$ and $y = \frac{1}{2}a_y l^2/v_{ox}^2$ at the point M.

When $y = 0$, $x = l/2$, which indicates that when the straight line MP' is extended backward, it will intersect the tube axis at the point O', the center point of the plates. This result means that O' is, in effect, a virtual cathode, and regardless of the applied potentials V_a and V_d, the electrons appear to emerge from this "cathode" and move in a straight line to the point P'.

At the point P', $y = D$, and $x = L + \frac{1}{2}l$. Equation (1-22) reduces to

$$D = \frac{a_y l L}{v_{ox}^2}$$

By inserting the known values of a_y ($= eV_d/dm$) and v_{ox}, this becomes

$$D = \frac{lLV_d}{2dV_a} \tag{1-23}$$

This result shows that the deflection on the screen of a cathode-ray tube is directly proportional to the deflecting voltage V_d applied between the plates. Consequently, a cathode-ray tube may be used as a linear-voltage indicating device.

The *electrostatic-deflection sensitivity* of a cathode-ray tube is defined as the deflection (in meters) on the screen per volt of deflecting voltage. Thus

$$S \equiv \frac{D}{V_d} = \frac{lL}{2dV_a} \qquad (1\text{-}24)$$

An inspection of Eq. (1-24) shows that the sensitivity is independent of both the deflecting voltage V_d and the ratio e/m. Furthermore, the sensitivity varies inversely with the accelerating potential V_a.

The idealization made in connection with the foregoing development, viz., that the electric field between the deflecting plates is uniform and does not extend beyond the edges of the plates, is never met in practice. Consequently, the effect of fringing of the electric field may be enough to necessitate corrections amounting to as much as 40 percent in the results obtained from an application of Eq. (1-24). Typical measured values of sensitivity are 1.0 to 0.1 mm/V, corresponding to a voltage requirement of 10 to 100 V to give a deflection of 1 cm.

1-9   THE CATHODE–RAY OSCILLOSCOPE

An electrostatic tube has two sets of deflecting plates which are at right angles to each other in space (as indicated in Fig. 1-5). These plates are referred to as the *vertical-deflection* and *horizontal-deflection* plates because the tube is oriented in space so that the potentials applied to these plates result in vertical and horizontal deflections, respectively. The reason for having two sets of plates is now discussed.

Suppose that the *sawtooth* waveform of Fig. 1-6 is impressed across the horizontal-deflection plates. Since this voltage is used to sweep the electron beam across the screen, it is called a *sweep voltage*. The electrons are deflected

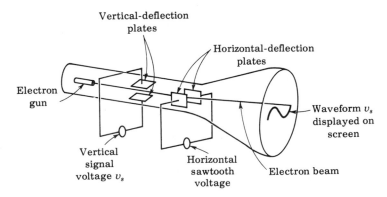

Fig. 1-5 A waveform to be displayed on the screen of a cathode-ray tube is applied to the vertical-deflection plates, and simultaneously a sawtooth voltage is applied to the horizontal-deflection plates.

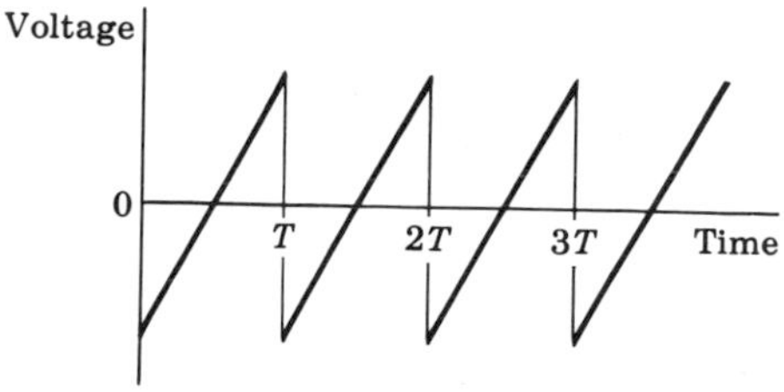

Fig. 1-6   Sweep or sawtooth voltage
for a cathode-ray tube.

linearly with time in the horizontal direction for a time T.   Then the beam
returns to its starting point on the screen very quickly as the sawtooth voltage
rapidly falls to its initial value at the end of each period.

If a sinusoidal voltage is impressed across the vertical-deflection plates
when, simultaneously, the sweep voltage is impressed across the horizontal-
deflection plates, the sinusoidal voltage, which of itself would give rise to a
vertical line, will now be spread out and will appear as a sinusoidal trace on
the screen.   The pattern will appear stationary only if the time T is equal to,
or is some multiple of, the time for one cycle of the wave on the vertical plates.
It is then necessary that the frequency of the sweep circuit be adjusted to
synchronize with the frequency of the applied signal.

Actually, of course, the voltage impressed on the vertical plates may have
any waveform.   Consequently, a system of this type provides an almost
inertialess oscilloscope for viewing arbitrary waveshapes.   This is one of the
most common uses for cathode-ray tubes.   If a nonrepeating sweep voltage is
applied to the horizontal plates, it is possible to study transients on the screen.
This requires a system for synchronizing the sweep with the start of the
transient.[1]†

A commercial oscilloscope has many refinements not indicated in the
schematic diagram of Fig. 1-5.   The sensitivity is greatly increased by means
of a high-gain amplifier interposed between the input signal and the deflection
plates.   The electron gun is a complicated structure which allows for accelerating the electrons through a large potential, for varying the intensity of the
beam, and for focusing the electrons into a tiny spot.   Controls are also provided for positioning the beam as desired on the screen.

1-10   RELATIVISTIC VARIATION OF MASS WITH VELOCITY

The theory of relativity postulates an equivalence of mass and energy according to the relationship

$$W = mc^2 \qquad\qquad (1\text{-}25)$$

where W = total energy, J
    m = mass, kg
    c = velocity of light in vacuum, m/sec

† Superscript numerals are keyed to the References at the end of the chapter.

According to this theory, the mass of a particle will increase with its energy, and hence with its speed.

If an electron starts at the point A with zero velocity and reaches the point B with a velocity v, then the increase in energy of the particle must be given by the expression eV, where V is the difference of potential between the points A and B. Hence

$$eV = mc^2 - m_o c^2 \qquad (1\text{-}26)$$

where $m_o c^2$ is the energy possessed at the point A. The quantity m_o is known as the *rest mass*, or the *electrostatic mass*, of the particle, and is a constant, independent of the velocity. The total mass m of the particle is given by

$$m = \frac{m_o}{\sqrt{1 - v^2/c^2}} \qquad (1\text{-}27)$$

This result, which was originally derived by Lorentz and then by Einstein as a consequence of the theory of special relativity, predicts an increasing mass with an increasing velocity, the mass approaching an infinite value as the velocity of the particle approaches the velocity of light. From Eqs. (1-26) and (1-27), the decrease in potential energy, or equivalently, the increase in kinetic energy, is

$$eV = m_o c^2 \left(\frac{1}{\sqrt{1 - v^2/c^2}} - 1 \right) \qquad (1\text{-}28)$$

This expression enables one to find the velocity of an electron after it has fallen through any potential difference V. By defining the quantity v_N as the velocity that would result if the relativistic variation in mass were neglected, i.e.,

$$v_N \equiv \sqrt{\frac{2eV}{m_o}} \qquad (1\text{-}29)$$

then Eq. (1-28) can be solved for v, the true velocity of the particle. The result is

$$v = c \left[1 - \frac{1}{(1 + v_N^2/2c^2)^2} \right]^{\frac{1}{2}} \qquad (1\text{-}30)$$

This expression looks imposing at first glance. It should, of course, reduce to $v = v_N$ for small velocities. That it does so is seen by applying the binomial expansion to Eq. (1-30). The result becomes

$$v = v_N \left(1 - \frac{3}{8} \frac{v_N^2}{c^2} + \cdots \right) \qquad (1\text{-}31)$$

From this expression it is seen that, if the speed of the particle is much less than the speed of light, the second and all subsequent terms in the expansion can be neglected, and then $v = v_N$, as it should. This equation also serves as a criterion to determine whether the simple classical expression or the more formidable relativistic one must be used in any particular case. For example, if the speed of the electron is one-tenth of the speed of light, Eq. (1-31) shows that an error of only three-eighths of 1 percent will result if the speed is taken as v_N instead of v.

For an electron, the potential difference through which the particle must fall in order to attain a velocity of $0.1c$ is readily found to be 2,560 V. Thus, if an electron falls through a potential in excess of about 3 kV, the relativistic corrections should be applied. If the particle under question is not an electron, the value of the nonrelativistic velocity is first calculated. If this is greater than $0.1c$, the calculated value of v_N must be substituted in Eq. (1-30) and the true value of v then calculated. In cases where the speed is not too great, the simplified expression (1-31) may be used.

The accelerating potential in high-voltage cathode-ray tubes is sufficiently high to require that relativistic corrections be made in order to calculate the velocity and mass of the particle. Other devices employing potentials that are high enough to require these corrections are x-ray tubes, the cyclotron, and other particle-accelerating machines. Unless specifically stated otherwise, nonrelativistic conditions are assumed in what follows.

1-11   FORCE IN A MAGNETIC FIELD

To investigate the force on a moving charge in a magnetic field, the well-known *motor law* is recalled. It has been verified by experiment that, if a conductor of length L, carrying a current of I, is situated in a magnetic field of intensity B, the force f_m acting on this conductor is

$$f_m = BIL \tag{1-32}$$

where f_m is in newtons, B is in webers per square meter (Wb/m^2),† I is in amperes, and L is in meters. Equation (1-32) assumes that the directions of I and B are perpendicular to each other. The direction of this force is perpendicular to the plane of I and B and has the direction of advance of a right-handed screw which is placed at O and is rotated from I to B through 90°, as illustrated in Fig. 1-7. *If I and B are not perpendicular to each other, only the component of I perpendicular to B contributes to the force.*

Some caution must be exercised with regard to the meaning of Fig. 1-7. If the particle under consideration is a positive ion, then I is to be taken along the direction of its motion. This is so because the conventional direction of the current is taken in the direction of flow of positive charge. If the current is due to the flow of electrons, the direction of I is to be taken as opposite to the direction of the motion of the electrons. If, therefore, a negative charge

---

† One weber per square meter (also called a *tesla*) equals 10^4 G. A unit of more practical size in most applications is the milliweber per square meter (mWb/m^2), which equals 10 G. Other conversion factors are given in Appendix B.

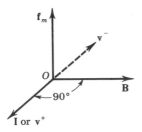

Fig. 1-7 Pertaining to the determination of the direction of the force f_m on a charged particle in a magnetic field.

moving with a velocity v^- is under consideration, one must first draw I antiparallel to v^- as shown and then apply the "direction rule."

If N electrons are contained in a length L of conductor (Fig. 1-8) and if it takes an electron a time T sec to travel a distance of L m in the conductor, the total number of electrons passing through any cross section of wire in unit time is N/T. Thus the total charge per second passing any point, which, by definition, is the current in amperes, is

$$I = \frac{Ne}{T} \tag{1-33}$$

The force in newtons on a length L m (or the force on the N conduction charges contained therein) is

$$BIL = \frac{BNeL}{T}$$

Furthermore, since L/T is the average, or *drift*, speed v m/sec of the electrons, the force per electron is

$$f_m = eBv \tag{1-34}$$

The subscript m indicates that the force is of magnetic origin.   To summarize: *The force on a negative charge e (coulombs) moving with a component of velocity v^- (meters per second) normal to a field B (webers per square meter) is given by eBv^- (newtons) and is in a direction perpendicular to the plane of* B *and* v^-, *as noted in Fig. 1-7.*†

1-12   CURRENT DENSITY

Before proceeding with the discussion of possible motions of charged particles in a magnetic field, it is convenient to introduce the concept of current density.

† In the cross-product notation of vector analysis, $f_m = eB \times v^-$. For a positive ion moving with a velocity v^+, the force is $f_m = ev^+ \times B$.

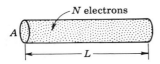

Fig. 1-8 Pertaining to the determination of the magnitude of the force f_m on a charged particle in a magnetic field.

This concept is very useful in many later applications. By definition, the current density, denoted by the symbol J, is the current per unit area of the conducting medium. That is, assuming a uniform current distribution,

$$J \equiv \frac{I}{A} \tag{1-35}$$

where J is in amperes per square meter, and A is the cross-sectional area (in meters) of the conductor. This becomes, by Eq. (1-33),

$$J = \frac{Ne}{TA}$$

But it has already been pointed out that $T = L/v$. Then

$$J = \frac{Nev}{LA} \tag{1-36}$$

From Fig. 1-8 it is evident that LA is simply the volume containing the N electrons, and so N/LA is the electron concentration n (in electrons per cubic meter). Thus

$$n = \frac{N}{LA} \tag{1-37}$$

and Eq. (1-36) reduces to

$$J = nev = \rho v \tag{1-38}$$

where $\rho \equiv ne$ is the charge density, in coulombs per cubic meter, and v is in meters per second.

This derivation is independent of the form of the conducting medium. Consequently, Fig. 1-8 does not necessarily represent a wire conductor. It may represent equally well a portion of a gaseous-discharge tube or a volume element in the space-charge cloud of a vacuum tube or a semiconductor. Furthermore, neither ρ nor v need be constant, but may vary from point to point in space or may vary with time. Numerous occasions arise later in the text when reference is made to Eq. (1-38).

1-13   MOTION IN A MAGNETIC FIELD

The path of a charge particle that is moving in a magnetic field is now investigated. Consider an electron to be placed in the region of the magnetic field. If the particle is at rest, $f_m = 0$ and the particle remains at rest. If the initial velocity of the particle is along the lines of the magnetic flux, there is no force acting on the particle, in accordance with the rule associated with Eq. (1-34). Hence *a particle whose initial velocity has no component normal to a uniform magnetic field will continue to move with constant speed along the lines of flux.*

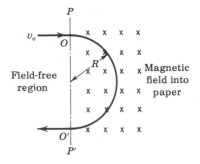

Fig. 1-9 Circular motion of an electron in a transverse magnetic field.

Now consider an electron moving with a speed v_o to enter a constant uniform magnetic field normally, as shown in Fig. 1-9. Since the force f_m is perpendicular to v and so to the motion at every instant, *no work is done on the electron*. This means that its kinetic energy is not increased, and so its speed remains unchanged. Further, since v and B are each constant in magnitude, then f_m is constant in magnitude and perpendicular to the direction of motion of the particle. This type of force results in motion in a circular path with constant speed. It is analogous to the problem of a mass tied to a rope and twirled around with constant speed. The force (which is the tension in the rope) remains constant in magnitude and is always directed toward the center of the circle, and so is normal to the motion.

To find the radius of the circle, it is recalled that a particle moving in a circular path with a constant speed v has an acceleration toward the center of the circle of magnitude v^2/R, where R is the radius of the path in meters. Then

$$\frac{mv^2}{R} = eBv$$

from which

$$R = \frac{mv}{eB} \tag{1-39}$$

The corresponding angular velocity in radians per second is given by

$$\omega = \frac{v}{R} = \frac{eB}{m} \tag{1-40}$$

The time in seconds for one complete revolution, called the *period*, is

$$T = \frac{2\pi}{\omega} = \frac{2\pi m}{eB} \tag{1-41}$$

For an electron, this reduces to

$$T = \frac{3.57 \times 10^{-11}}{B} \tag{1-42}$$

In these equations, e/m is in coulombs per kilogram and B in webers per square meter.

It is noticed that the radius of the path is directly proportional to the speed of the particle. Further, *the period and the angular velocity are independent of speed or radius.* This means, of course, that faster-moving particles will traverse larger circles in the same time that a slower particle moves in its smaller circle. This very important result is the basis of operation of numerous devices, for example, the cyclotron and magnetic-focusing apparatus.

EXAMPLE Calculate the deflection of a cathode-ray beam caused by the earth's magnetic field. Assume that the tube axis is so oriented that it is normal to the field, the strength of which is 0.6 G. The anode potential is 400 V; the anode-screen distance is 20 cm (Fig. 1-10).

Solution According to Eq. (1-13), the velocity of the electrons will be

$$v_{ox} = 5.93 \times 10^5 \sqrt{400} = 1.19 \times 10^7 \text{ m/sec}$$

Since 1 Wb/m² = 10^4 G, then $B = 6 \times 10^{-5}$ Wb/m². From Eq. (1-39) the radius of the circular path is

$$R = \frac{v_{ox}}{(e/m)B} = \frac{1.19 \times 10^7}{1.76 \times 10^{11} \times 6 \times 10^{-5}} = 1.12 \text{ m} = 112 \text{ cm}$$

Furthermore, it is evident from the geometry of Fig. 1-10 that (in centimeters)

$$112^2 = (112 - D)^2 + 20^2$$

from which it follows that

$$D^2 - 224D + 400 = 0$$

The evaluation of D from this expression yields the value $D = 1.8$ cm.

This example indicates that the earth's magnetic field can have a large effect on the position of the cathode-beam spot in a low-voltage cathode-ray tube. If

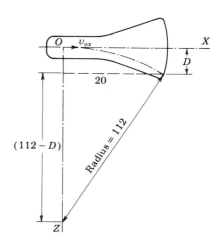

Fig. 1-10 The circular path of an electron in a cathode-ray tube, resulting from the earth's transverse magnetic field (normal to the plane of the paper). This figure is not drawn to scale.

the anode voltage is higher than the value used in this example, or if the tube is not oriented normal to the field, the deflection will be less than that calculated. In any event, this calculation indicates the advisability of carefully shielding a cathode-ray tube from stray magnetic fields.

1-14   MAGNETIC DEFLECTION IN A CATHODE–RAY TUBE

The illustrative example in Sec. 1-13 immediately suggests that a cathode-ray tube may employ a magnetic as well as an electric field in order to accomplish the deflection of the electron beam. However, since it is not feasible to use a field extending over the entire length of the tube, a short coil furnishing a transverse field in a limited region is employed, as shown in Fig. 1-11. The magnetic field is taken as pointing out of the paper, and the beam is deflected upward. It is assumed that the magnetic field intensity B is uniform in the restricted region shown and is zero outside of this area. Hence the electron moves in a straight line from the cathode to the boundary O of the magnetic field. In the region of the uniform magnetic field the electron experiences a force of magnitude eBv, where v is the speed.

The path OM will be the arc of a circle whose center is at Q. The speed of the particles will remain constant and equal to

$$v = v_{ox} = \sqrt{\frac{2eV_a}{m}} \tag{1-43}$$

The angle φ is, by definition of radian measure, equal to the length of the arc OM divided by R, the radius of the circle. If we assume a small angle of deflection, then

$$\varphi \approx \frac{l}{R} \tag{1-44}$$

where, by Eq. (1-39),

$$R = \frac{mv}{eB} \tag{1-45}$$

In most practical cases, L is very much larger than l, so that little error will

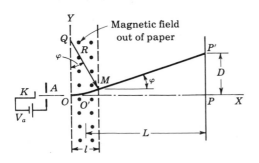

Fig. 1-11 Magnetic deflection in a cathode-ray tube.

be made in assuming that the straight line MP', if projected backward, will pass through the center O' of the region of the magnetic field. Then

$$D \approx L \tan \varphi \approx L\varphi \tag{1-46}$$

By Eqs. (1-43) to (1-45), Eq. (1-46) now becomes

$$D \approx L\varphi = \frac{lL}{R} = \frac{lLeB}{mv} = \frac{lLB}{\sqrt{V_a}} \sqrt{\frac{e}{2m}}$$

The deflection per unit magnetic field intensity, D/B, given by

$$\frac{D}{B} = \frac{lL}{\sqrt{V_a}} \sqrt{\frac{e}{2m}} \tag{1-47}$$

is called the *magnetic-deflection sensitivity* of the tube. It is observed that this quantity is independent of B. This condition is analogous to the electric case for which the electrostatic sensitivity is independent of the deflecting potential. However, in the electric case, the sensitivity varies inversely with the anode voltage, whereas it here varies inversely with the square root of the anode voltage. Another important difference is in the appearance of e/m in the expression for the magnetic sensitivity, whereas this ratio did not enter into the final expression for the electric case. Because the sensitivity increases with L, the deflecting coils are placed as far down the neck of the tube as possible, usually directly after the accelerating anode.

Deflection in a Television Tube A modern TV tube has a screen diameter comparable with the length of the tube neck. Hence the angle φ is too large for the approximation $\tan \varphi \approx \varphi$ to be valid. Under these circumstances it is found that the deflection is no longer proportional to B (Prob. 1-24). If the magnetic-deflection coil is driven by a sawtooth current waveform (Fig. 1-6), the deflection of the beam on the face of the tube will *not* be linear with time. For such wide-angle deflection tubes, special linearity-correcting networks must be added.

A TV tube has two sets of magnetic-deflection coils mounted around the neck at right angles to each other, corresponding to the two sets of plates in the oscilloscope tube of Fig. 1-5. Sweep currents are applied to both coils, with the horizontal signal much higher in frequency than that of the vertical sweep. The result is a rectangular raster of closely spaced lines which cover the entire face of the tube and impart a uniform intensity to the screen. When the video signal is applied to the electron gun, it modulates the intensity of the beam and thus forms the TV picture.

1-15   MAGNETIC FOCUSING

As another application of the theory developed in Sec. 1-13, one method of measuring e/m is discussed. Imagine that a cathode-ray tube is placed in a constant longitudinal magnetic field, the axis of the tube coinciding with the direction of the magnetic field.   A magnetic field of the type here considered is obtained through the use of a long solenoid, the tube being placed within the coil.   Inspection of Fig. 1-12 reveals the motion.   The Y axis represents the axis of the cathode-ray tube.   The origin O is the point at which the electrons emerge from the anode.   The velocity at the origin is v_o, the initial transverse velocity due to the mutual repulsion of the electrons being v_{ox}.   It is now shown that the resulting motion is a helix, as illustrated.

The electronic motion can most easily be analyzed by resolving the velocity into two components, v_y and v_θ, along and transverse to the magnetic field, respectively.   Since the force is perpendicular to B, there is no acceleration in the Y direction.   *Hence v_y is constant and equal to v_{oy}.*   A force eBv_θ normal to the path will exist, resulting from the transverse velocity.   *This force gives rise to circular motion,* the radius of the circle being mv_θ/eB, with v_θ a constant, and equal to v_{ox}.   *The resultant path is a helix* whose axis is parallel to the Y axis and displaced from it by a distance R along the Z axis, as illustrated.

The pitch of the helix, defined as the distance traveled along the direction of the magnetic field in one revolution, is given by

$$p = v_{oy}T$$

where T is the period, or the time for one revolution.   It follows from Eq. (1-41) that

$$p = \frac{2\pi m}{eB} v_{oy} \tag{1-48}$$

If the electron beam is defocused, a smudge is seen on the screen when the applied magnetic field is zero.   This means that the various electrons in the beam pass through the anode hole with different transverse velocities v_{ox}, and so strike the screen at different points.   This accounts for the appearance of a broad, faintly illuminated area instead of a bright point on the screen. As the magnetic field is increased from zero the electrons will move in helices of different radii, since the velocity v_{ox} that controls the radius of the path will be different for different electrons.   However, the period, or the time to trace out the path, is independent of v_{ox}, and so the period will be the same for all electrons.   If, then, the distance from the anode to the screen is made equal to one pitch, all the electrons will be brought back to the Y axis (the point O' in Fig. 1-12), since they all will have made just one revolution. Under these conditions an image of the anode hole will be observed on the screen.

As the field is increased from zero, the smudge on the screen resulting from the defocused beam will contract and will become a tiny sharp spot (the image of the anode hole) when a critical value of the field is reached. This critical field is that which makes the pitch of the helical path just equal to the anode-screen distance, as discussed above.   By continuing to increase

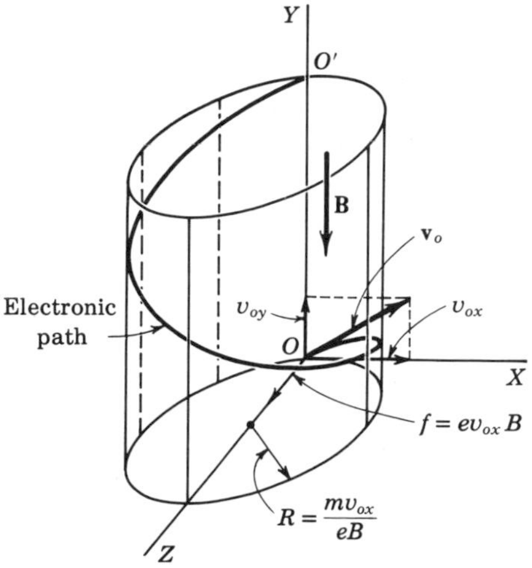

Fig. 1-12 The helical path of an electron introduced at an angle (not 90°) with a constant magnetic field.

the strength of the field beyond this critical value, the pitch of the helix decreases, and the electrons travel through more than one complete revolution. The electrons then strike the screen at various points, so that a defocused spot is again visible. A magnetic field strength will ultimately be reached at which the electrons make two complete revolutions in their path from the anode to the screen, and once again the spot will be focused on the screen. This process may be continued, numerous foci being obtainable. In fact, the current rating of the solenoid is the factor that generally furnishes a practical limitation to the order of the focus.

The foregoing considerations may be generalized in the following way: If the screen is perpendicular to the Y axis at a distance L from the point of emergence of the electron beam from the anode, then, for an anode-cathode potential equal to V_a, the electron beam will come to a focus at the center of the screen provided that L is an integral multiple of p. Under these conditions, Eq. (1-48) may be rearranged to read

$$\frac{e}{m} = \frac{8\pi^2 V_a n^2}{L^2 B^2} \tag{1-49}$$

where n is an integer representing the order of the focus. It is assumed, in this development, that $eV_a = \frac{1}{2}mv_{oy}^2$, or that the only effect of the anode potential is to accelerate the electron along the tube axis. This implies that the transverse velocity x_{oz}, which is variable and unknown, is negligible in comparison with v_{oy}. This is a justifiable assumption.

This arrangement was suggested by Busch, and has been used[2] to measure the ratio e/m for electrons very accurately.

A Short Focusing Coil The method described above of employing a longitudinal magnetic field over the entire length of a commercial tube is not too practical. Hence, in a commercial tube, a short coil is wound around

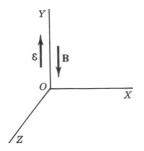

Fig. 1-13 Parallel electric and magnetic fields.

the neck of the tube. Because of the fringing of the magnetic lines of flux, a radial component of B exists in addition to the component along the tube axis. Hence there are now two components of force on the electron, one due to the axial component of velocity and the radial component of the field, and the second due to the radial component of the velocity and the axial component of the field. The analysis is complicated,[3] but it can be seen qualitatively that the motion will be a rotation about the axis of the tube and, if conditions are correct, the electron on leaving the region of the coil may be turned sufficiently so as to move in a line toward the center of the screen. A rough adjustment of the focus is obtained by positioning the coil properly along the neck of the tube. The fine adjustment of focus is made by controlling the coil current.

1-16   PARALLEL ELECTRIC AND MAGNETIC FIELDS

Consider the case where both electric and magnetic fields exist simultaneously, the fields being in the same or in opposite directions. If the initial velocity of the electron either is zero or is directed along the fields, *the magnetic field exerts no force on the electron*, and the resultant motion depends solely upon the electric field intensity ε. In other words, the electron will move in a direction parallel to the fields with a constant acceleration. If the fields are chosen as in Fig. 1-13, the complete motion is specified by

$$v_y = v_{oy} - at \qquad y = v_{oy}t - \tfrac{1}{2}at^2 \qquad\qquad (1\text{-}50)$$

where $a = e\varepsilon/m$ is the magnitude of the acceleration. The negative sign results from the fact that the direction of the acceleration of an electron is opposite to the direction of the electric field intensity ε.

If, initially, a component of velocity v_{ox} perpendicular to the magnetic field exists, this component, together with the magnetic field, will give rise to circular motion, the radius of the circular path being independent of ε. However, because of the electric field ε, the velocity along the field changes with time. Consequently, the resulting path is helical with a pitch that changes with the time. That is, the distance traveled along the Y axis per revolution increases with each revolution.

EXAMPLE Given a uniform electric field of 1.10×10^3 V/m parallel to and opposite in direction to a magnetic field of 7.50×10^{-4} Wb/m². An electron gun in the XY plane directed at an angle $\varphi = \arctan \frac{3}{4}$ with the direction of the electric field introduces electrons into the region of the fields with a velocity $v_o = 5.00 \times 10^6$ m/sec. Find:

  a. The time for an electron to reach its maximum height above the XZ plane

  b. The position of the electron at this time

  c. The velocity components of the electron at this time

Solution *a.* As discussed above, the path is a helix of variable pitch. The acceleration is downward, and for the coordinate system of Fig. 1-14,

$$y = v_{oy}t - \tfrac{1}{2}at^2 \qquad v_y = v_{oy} - at$$

The electron starts moving in the $+Y$ direction, but since the acceleration is along the $-Y$ direction, its velocity is reduced to zero at a time $t = t'$. The particle will then reverse its Y-directed motion. At maximum height $v_y = 0$ and $t' = v_{oy}/a$. Since $v_{oy} = v_o \cos \varphi = (5 \times 10^6)(0.8) = 4 \times 10^6$ m/sec and

$$a_y = \frac{e\mathcal{E}}{m} = (1.76 \times 10^{11})(1.10 \times 10^3) = 1.94 \times 10^{14} \text{ m/sec}^2$$

we find

$$t' = \frac{v_{oy}}{a} = \frac{4 \times 10^6}{1.94 \times 10^{14}} = 2.06 \times 10^{-8} \text{ sec} = 20.6 \text{ nsec}$$

  b. The distance traveled in the $+Y$ direction to the position at which the reversal occurs is

$$y = v_{oy}t - \tfrac{1}{2}at^2 = (4 \times 10^6)(2.06 \times 10^{-8}) - \tfrac{1}{2}(1.94 \times 10^{14})(4.24 \times 10^{-16})$$

$$= 4.13 \times 10^{-2} \text{ m} = 4.13 \text{ cm}$$

It should be kept in mind that the term reversal refers only to the Y-directed motion, not to the direction in which the electron traverses the circular component of its path. The helical rotation is determined entirely by the quantities B and v_{ox}. The angular velocity remains constant and equal to

$$\omega = \frac{eB}{m} = (1.76 \times 10^{11})(7.50 \times 10^{-4}) = 1.32 \times 10^8 \text{ rad/sec}$$

Fig. 1-14 A problem illustrating helical electronic motion of variable pitch.

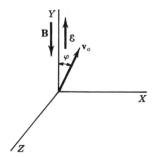

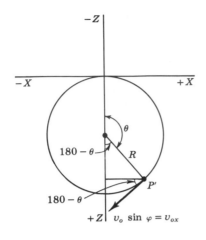

Fig. 1-15 The projection of the path in the XZ plane is a circle.

By use of either the relationship $T = 2\pi/\omega$ or Eq. (1-42), there is obtained $T = 4.75 \times 10^{-8}$ sec, and hence less than one revolution is made before the reversal.

The point P' in space at which the reversal takes place is obtained by considering the projection of the path in the XZ plane (since the Y coordinate is already known). The angle θ in Fig. 1-15 through which the electron has rotated is

$$\theta = \omega t = 1.32 \times 10^8 \times 2.06 \times 10^{-8} = 2.71 \text{ rad} = 155°$$

The radius of the circle is

$$R = \frac{v_{ox}}{\omega} = \frac{(5 \times 10^6)(0.6)}{1.32 \times 10^8} \text{ m} = 2.27 \text{ cm}$$

From the figure it is clear that

$$X = R \sin (180 - \theta) = 2.27 \sin 25° = 0.957 \text{ cm}$$

$$Z = R + R \cos (180 - \theta) = 2.27 + 2.05 = 4.32 \text{ cm}$$

c. The velocity is tangent to the circle, and its magnitude equals $v_o \sin \varphi = 5 \times 10^6 \times 0.6 = 3 \times 10^6$ m/sec. At $\theta = 155°$, the velocity components are

$$v_x = -v_{ox} \cos (180 - \theta) = -3 \times 10^6 \cos 25° = -2.71 \times 10^6 \text{ m/sec}$$

$$v_y = 0$$

$$v_z = v_{ox} \sin (180 - \theta) = 3 \times 10^6 \sin 25° = 1.26 \times 10^6 \text{ m/sec}$$

1-17   PERPENDICULAR ELECTRIC AND MAGNETIC FIELDS

The directions of the fields are shown in Fig. 1-16. The magnetic field is directed along the $-Y$ axis, and the electric field is directed along the $-X$ axis. The force on an electron due to the electric field is directed along the $+X$ axis. Any force due to the magnetic field is always normal to $\mathbf{B}$, and

Fig. 1-16 Perpendicular electric and magnetic fields.

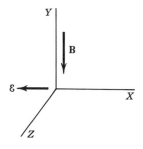

hence lies in a plane parallel to the XZ plane. Thus there is no component of force along the Y direction, and the Y component of acceleration is zero. Hence the motion along Y is given by

$$f_y = 0 \qquad v_y = v_{oy} \qquad y = v_{oy}t \tag{1-51}$$

assuming that the electron starts at the origin.

If the initial velocity component parallel to **B** *is zero, the path lies entirely in a plane perpendicular to* **B**.

It is desired to investigate the path of an electron *starting at rest* at the origin. The initial magnetic force is zero, since the velocity is zero. The electric force is directed along the $+X$ axis, and the electron will be accelerated in this direction. As soon as the electron is in motion, the magnetic force will no longer be zero. There will then be a component of this force which will be proportional to the X component of velocity and will be directed along the $+Z$ axis. The path will thus bend away from the $+X$ direction toward the $+Z$ direction. Clearly, the electric and magnetic forces interact with one another. In fact, the analysis cannot be carried along further, profitably, in this qualitative fashion. The arguments given above do, however, indicate the manner in which the electron starts on its path. This path will now be shown to be a cycloid.

To determine the path of the electron quantitatively, the force equations must be set up. The force due to the electric field ε is $e\varepsilon$ along the $+X$ direction. The force due to the magnetic field is found as follows: At any instant, the velocity is determined by the three components v_x, v_y, and v_z along the three coordinate axes. Since **B** is in the Y direction, no force will be exerted on the electron due to v_y. Because of v_x, the force is eBv_x in the $+Z$ direction, as can be verified by the direction rule of Sec. 1-11. Similarly, the force due to v_z is eBv_z in the $-X$ direction. Hence Newton's law, when expressed in terms of the three components, yields

$$f_x = m \frac{dv_x}{dt} = e\varepsilon - eBv_z \qquad f_z = m \frac{dv_z}{dt} = eBv_x \tag{1-52}$$

By writing for convenience

$$\omega \equiv \frac{eB}{m} \qquad \text{and} \qquad u \equiv \frac{\varepsilon}{B} \tag{1-53}$$

the foregoing equations may be written in the form

$$\frac{dv_x}{dt} = \omega u - \omega v_z \qquad \frac{dv_z}{dt} = +\omega v_x \tag{1-54}$$

A straightforward procedure is involved in the solution of these equations. If the first equation of (1-54) is differentiated and combined with the second, we obtain

$$\frac{d^2 v_x}{dt^2} = -\omega \frac{dv_z}{dt} = -\omega^2 v_x \tag{1-55}$$

This linear differential equation with constant coefficients is readily solved for v_x. Substituting this expression for v_x in Eq. (1-54), this equation can be solved for v_z. Subject to the initial conditions $v_x = v_z = 0$, we obtain

$$v_x = u \sin \omega t \qquad v_z = u - u \cos \omega t \tag{1-56}$$

In order to find the coordinates x and z from these expressions, each equation must be integrated. Thus, subject to the initial conditions $x = z = 0$,

$$x = \frac{u}{\omega}(1 - \cos \omega t) \qquad z = ut - \frac{u}{\omega} \sin \omega t \tag{1-57}$$

If, for convenience,

$$\theta \equiv \omega t \qquad \text{and} \qquad Q \equiv \frac{u}{\omega} \tag{1-58}$$

then

$$x = Q(1 - \cos \theta) \qquad z = Q(\theta - \sin \theta) \tag{1-59}$$

where u and ω are as defined in Eqs. (1-53).

Cycloidal Path   Equations (1-59) are the parametric equations of a *common cycloid*, defined as *the path generated by a point on the circumference of a circle of radius Q which rolls along a straight line*, the Z axis. This is illustrated in Fig. 1-17. The point P, whose coordinates are x and z ($y = 0$), represents the position of the electron at any time. The dark curve is the locus of the point P. The reference line CC' is drawn through the center of the generating circle parallel to the X axis. Since the circle rolls on the Z axis, then OC' represents the length of the circumference that has already come in contact with the Z axis. This length is evidently equal to the arc PC' (and equals $Q\theta$). The angle θ gives the number of radians through which the circle has rotated. From the diagram, it readily follows that

$$x = Q - Q \cos \theta \qquad z = Q\theta - Q \sin \theta \tag{1-60}$$

which are identical with Eqs. (1-59), thus proving that the path is cycloidal as predicted.

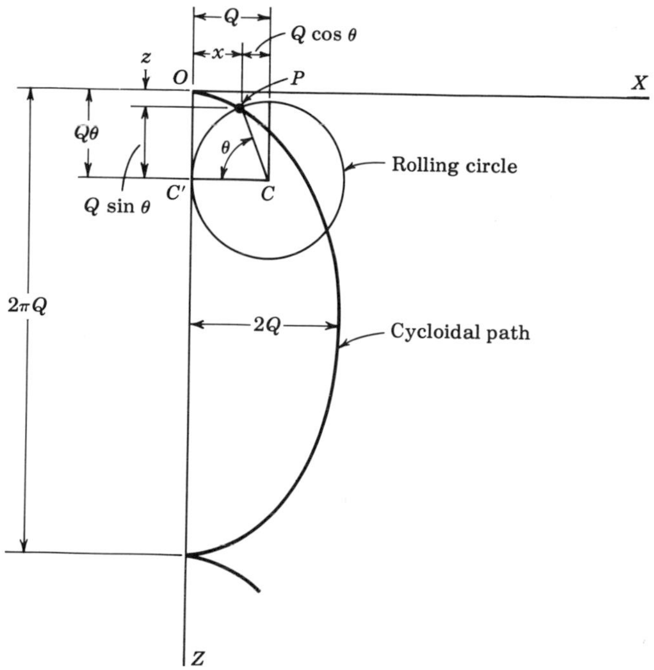

Fig. 1-17 The cycloidal path of an electron in perpendicular electric and magnetic fields when the initial
velocity is zero.

The physical interpretation of the symbols introduced above merely
as abbreviations is as follows:

ω represents the angular velocity of rotation of the rolling circle.
θ represents the number of radians through which the circle has rotated.
Q represents the radius of the rolling circle.
Since $u = \omega Q$, then u represents the velocity of translation of the center of
the rolling circle.

From these interpretations and from Fig. 1-17 it is clear that the maximum
displacement of the electron along the X axis is equal to the diameter of the
rolling circle, or $2Q$. Also, the distance along the Z axis between cusps is
equal to the circumference of the rolling circle, or $2\pi Q$. At each cusp the
speed of the electron is zero, since at this point the velocity is reversing its
direction (Fig. 1-17). This is also seen from the fact that each cusp is along
the Z axis, and hence at the same potential. Therefore the electron has gained
no energy from the electric field, and its speed must again be zero.
If an initial velocity exists that is directed parallel to the magnetic field,
the projection of the path on the XZ plane will still be a cycloid but the
particle will now have a constant velocity normal to the plane. This path

might be called a "cycloidal helical motion." The path is described by Eqs. (1-59), with the addition of Eqs. (1-51).

Straight Line Path As a special case of importance, consider that the electron is released perpendicular to both the electric and magnetic fields so that $v_{ox} = v_{oy} = 0$ and $v_{oz} \neq 0$. The electric force is $e\mathcal{E}$ along the $+X$ direction (Fig. 1-16), and the magnetic force is eBv_{oz} along the $-X$ direction. If the net force on the electron is zero, it will continue to move along the Z axis with the constant speed v_{oz}. This conditions is realized when

$$e\mathcal{E} = eBv_{oz}$$

or

$$v_{oz} = \frac{\mathcal{E}}{B} = u \tag{1-61}$$

from Eqs. (1-53).

This discussion gives another interpretation to u. It represents that velocity with which an electron may be injected into perpendicular electric and magnetic fields and suffer no deflection, the net force being zero. Note that this velocity u is independent of the charge or mass of the ions. Such a system of perpendicular fields will act as a *velocity filter* and allow only those particles whose velocity is given by the ratio $\mathcal{E}/B$ to be selected.

EXAMPLE A magnetic field of 0.01 Wb/m² is applied along the axis of a cathode-ray tube. A field of 10^4 V/m is applied to the deflecting plates. If an electron leaves the anode with a velocity of 10^6 m/sec along the axis, how far from the axis will it be when it emerges from the region between the plates? The length l of the deflecting plates along the tube axis is 2.0 cm.

Solution Choose the system of coordinate axes illustrated in Fig. 1-16. Then

$$v_{ox} = v_{oz} = 0 \qquad v_{oy} = 10^6 \text{ m/sec}$$

As shown above, the projection of the path is a cycloid in the XZ plane, and the electron travels with constant velocity along the Y axis. The electron is in the region between the plates for the time

$$\frac{l}{v_{oy}} = \frac{2 \times 10^{-2}}{10^6} = 2 \times 10^{-8} \text{ sec}$$

Then, from Eqs. (1-53) and (1-58), it is found that

$$\omega = \frac{eB}{m} = 1.76 \times 10^{11} \times 10^{-2} = 1.76 \times 10^9 \text{ rad/sec}$$

$$u = \frac{\mathcal{E}}{B} = \frac{10^4}{10^{-2}} = 10^6 \text{ m/sec}$$

$$Q = \frac{u}{\omega} = \frac{10^6}{1.76 \times 10^9} = 5.68 \times 10^{-4} \text{ m} = 0.0568 \text{ cm}$$

$$\theta = \omega t = (1.76 \times 10^9)(2 \times 10^{-8}) = 35.2 \text{ rad}$$

Since there are 2π rad/revolution, the electron goes through five complete cycles and enters upon the sixth before it emerges from the plate. Thus

$$35.2 \text{ rad} = 10\pi + 3.8 \text{ rad}$$

Since 3.8 rad equals 218°, then Eqs. (1-59) yield

$$x = Q(1 - \cos\theta) = 0.0568(1 - \cos 218°) = 0.103 \text{ cm}$$

$$z = Q(\theta - \sin\theta) = 0.0568(35.2 - \sin 218°) = 2.03 \text{ cm}$$

so that the distance from the tube axis is

$$r = \sqrt{x^2 + z^2} = 2.03 \text{ cm}$$

Trochoidal Paths If the initial-velocity component in the direction perpendicular to the magnetic field is not zero, it can be shown[4] that the path is a *trochoid*.[5] This curve is the locus of a point on a "spoke" of a wheel rolling on a straight line, as illustrated in Fig. 1-18. If the length Q' of the spoke is greater than the radius Q of the rolling circle, the trochoid is called a *prolate cycloid*[5] and has subsidiary loops (Fig. 1-19a). If $Q' = Q$, the path is called a *common cycloid*, illustrated in Fig. 1-17 or 1-19b. If Q' is less than Q, the path is called a *curtate cycloid*,[5] and has blunted cusps, as indicated in Fig. 1-19c.

1-18   THE CYCLOTRON

The principles of Sec. 1-13 were first employed by Lawrence and Livingston to develop an apparatus called a *magnetic resonator*, or *cyclotron*.[6] This device imparts very high energies (tens of millions of electron volts) to positive ions. These high-energy positive ions are then allowed to bombard some substances, which become radioactive and generally disintegrate. Because of this, the cyclotron has popularly become known as an *atom smasher*.

The basic principles upon which the cyclotron operates are best understood with the aid of Fig. 1-20. The essential elements are the "dees," the

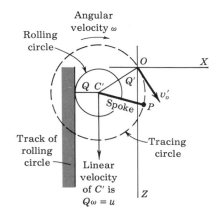

Fig. 1-18 The locus of the point P at the end of a "spoke" of a wheel rolling on a straight line is a trochoid.

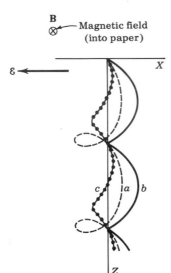

Fig. 1-19 The trochoidal paths of electrons in perpendicular electric and magnetic fields.

two halves of a shallow, hollow, metallic "pillbox" which has been split along a diameter as shown; a strong magnetic field which is parallel to the axis of the dees; and a high-frequency ac potential applied to the dees.

A moving positive ion released near the center of the dees will be accelerated in a semicircle by the action of the magnetic field and will reappear at point 1 at the edge of dee I. Assume that dee II is negative at this instant with respect to dee I. Then the ion will be accelerated from point 1 to point 2 across the gap, and will gain an amount of energy corresponding to the potential difference between these two points. Once the ion passes inside the metal dee II, the electric field is zero, and the magnetic field causes it to move in the semicircle from point 2 to point 3. If the frequency of the applied ac potential is such that the potential has reversed in the time necessary for the ion to

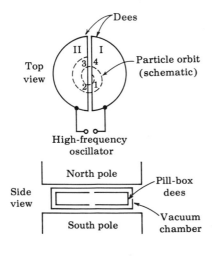

Fig. 1-20 The cyclotron principle.

go from point 2 to point 3, then dee I is now negative with respect to dee II, and the ion will be accelerated across the gap from point 3 to point 4. With the frequency of the accelerating voltage properly adjusted to this "resonance" value, the ion continues to receive pulses of energy corresponding to this difference of potential again and again.

Thus, after each half revolution, the ion gains energy from the electric field, resulting, of course, in an increased velocity. The radius of each semicircle is then larger than the preceding one, in accordance with Eq. (1-39), so that the path described by the whirling ion will approximate a planar spiral.

EXAMPLE Suppose that the oscillator that supplies the power to the dees of a given cyclotron imparts 50,000 eV to heavy hydrogen atoms (deuterons), each of atomic number 1 and atomic weight 2.0147, at each passage of the ions across the accelerating gap. Calculate the magnetic field intensity, the frequency of the oscillator, and the time it will take for an ion introduced at the center of the chamber to emerge at the rim of the dee with an energy of 5 million electron volts (5 MeV). Assume that the radius of the last semicircle is 15 in.

Solution The mass of the deuteron is

$$m = 2.01 \times 1.66 \times 10^{-27} = 3.34 \times 10^{-27} \text{ kg}$$

The velocity of the 5-MeV ions is given by the energy equation

$$\tfrac{1}{2}mv^2 = (5 \times 10^6)(1.60 \times 10^{-19}) = 8.00 \times 10^{-13} \text{ J}$$

or

$$v = \left(\frac{2 \times 8.00 \times 10^{-13}}{3.34 \times 10^{-27}} \right)^{\frac{1}{2}} = 2.20 \times 10^7 \text{ m/sec}$$

The magnetic field, given by Eq. (1-39),

$$B = \frac{mv}{eR} = \frac{(3.34 \times 10^{-27})(2.20 \times 10^7)}{(1.60 \times 10^{-19})(15 \times 2.54 \times 0.01)} = 1.20 \text{ Wb/m}^2$$

is needed in order to bring these ions to the edge of the dees.

The frequency of the oscillator must be equal to the reciprocal of the time of revolution of the ion. This is, from Eq. (1-41),

$$f = \frac{1}{T} = \frac{eB}{2\pi m} = \frac{1.60 \times 10^{-19} \times 1.20}{2\pi \times 3.34 \times 10^{-27}}$$

$$= 9.15 \times 10^6 \text{ Hz}^\dagger = 9.15 \text{ MHz}$$

Since the ions receive 5 MeV energy from the oscillator in 50-keV steps, they must pass across the accelerating gap 100 times. That is, the ion must make 50 complete revolutions in order to gain the full energy. Thus, from Eq. (1-41), the time of flight is

$$t = 50T = \frac{50 \times 1}{9.15 \times 10^6} = 5.47 \times 10^{-6} \text{ sec} = 5.47 \text{ } \mu\text{sec}$$

† Hz = hertz = cycles per second. MHz = megahertz (Appendix B).

In order to produce a uniform magnetic field of 1.2 Wb/m² over a circular area whose radius is at least 15 in., with an air gap approximately 6 in. wide, an enormous magnet is required, the weight of such a magnet being of the order of 60 tons. Also, the design of a 50-kV oscillator for these high frequencies and the method of coupling it to the dees present some difficulties, since the dees are in a vacuum-tight chamber. Further, means must be provided for introducing the ions into the region at the center of the dees and also for removing the high-energy particles from the chamber, if desired, or for directing them against a target.

The bombardment of the elements with the high-energy protons, deuterons, or helium nuclei which are normally used in the cyclotrons renders the bombarded elements radioactive. These radioactive elements are of the utmost importance to physicists, since they permit a glimpse into the constitution of nuclei. They are likewise of extreme importance in medical research, since they offer a substitute for radium. Radioactive substances can be followed through any physical or chemical changes by observing their emitted radiations. This "tracer," or "tagged-atom," technique is used in industry, medicine, physiology, and biology.

F-M Cyclotron and Synchrotron   It is shown in Sec. 1-10 that if an electron falls through a potential of more than 3 kV, a relativistic mass correction must be made, indicating that its mass increases with its energy. Thus, if electrons were used in a cyclotron, their angular velocity would decrease as their energy increased, and they would soon fall out of step with the high-frequency field. For this reason electrons are not introduced into the cyclotron.

For positive ions whose mass is several thousand times that of the electron, the relativistic correction becomes appreciable when energies of a few tens of millions of electron volts are reached. For greater energies than these, the ions will start to make their trip through the dees at a slower rate and slip behind in phase with respect to the electric field. This difficulty is overcome in the *synchrocyclotron*, or *f-m cyclotron*, by decreasing the frequency of the oscillator (frequency modulation) in accordance with the decrease in the angular velocity of the ion. With such an f-m cyclotron, deuterons, α particles, and protons have been accelerated to several hundred million electron volts.[7]

It is possible to give particles energies in excess of those for which the relativistic correction is important even if the oscillator frequency is fixed, provided that the magnetic field is slowly increased in step with the increase in the mass of the ions so as to maintain a constant angular velocity. Such an instrument is called a *synchrotron*. The particles are injected from a gun, which gives them a velocity approaching that of light. Since the radius of the orbit is given by $R = mv/Be$ and since the ratio m/B is kept constant and v changes very little, there is not much of an increase in the orbit as the energy of the electron increases. The vacuum chamber is built in the form of a doughnut instead of the cyclotron pillbox. The magnet has the form of a hollow cylinder, since there is need for a magnetic field only transverse to the path. This results in a great saving in weight and expense. The dees of the cyclotron are replaced by a single-cavity resonator. Electrons and protons have been accelerated to the order of a billion electron volts (Bev) in synchrotrons.[8] The larger the number of revolutions the particles make, the higher will be their energy. The defocusing of the beam limits the number of allowable cycles. With the discovery of *alternating-gradient magnetic field focusing*,[9] higher-energy-particle accelerators (70 BeV) have been constructed.[10]

REFERENCES

1. Millman, J., and H. Taub: "Pulse, Digital, and Switching Waveforms," chaps. 14 and 19, McGraw-Hill Book Company, New York, 1965.

2. Goedicke, E.: Eine Neubestimmung der spezifischen Ladung des Electrons nach der Methode von H. Busch, *Physik. Z.*, vol. 36, no. 1, pp. 47–63, 1939.

3. Cosslett, V. E.: "Introduction to Electron Optics," Oxford University Press, Fair Lawn, N.J., 1946.

4. Millman, J., and S. Seely: "Electronics," 2d ed., p. 35, McGraw-Hill Book Company, New York, 1951.

5. James, G., and R. C. James: "Mathematics Dictionary," D. Van Nostrand Company, Inc., Princeton, N.J., 1949.

6. Livingston, M. S.: The Cyclotron, I, *J. Appl. Phys.*, vol. 15, pp. 2–19, January, 1944; The Cyclotron, II, *ibid.*, pp. 128–147, February, 1944.
   Livingston, M. S.: Particle Accelerators, *Advan. Electron., Electrochem. Eng.*, vol. 1, pp. 269–316, 1948.

7. Brobeck, W. M., E. O. Lawrence, K. R. MacKenzie, E. M. McMillan, R. Serber, D. C. Sewell, K. M. Simpson, and R. L. Thornton: Initial Performance of the 184-inch Cyclotron of the University of California, *Phys. Rev.*, vol. 71, pp. 449–450, April, 1947.

8. Livingston, M. S., J. P. Blewett, G. K. Green, and L. J. Haworth: Design Study for a Three-Bev Proton Accelerator, *Rev. Sci. Instr.*, vol. 21, pp. 7–22, January, 1950.

9. Courant, E. D., M. S. Livingston, and H. S. Snyder: The Strong-focusing Synchrotron: A New High Energy Accelerator, *Phys. Rev.*, vol. 88, pp. 1190–1196, December, 1952.

10. Livingston, M. S., and J. P. Blewett: "Particle Accelerators," chap. 15, McGraw-Hill Book Company, New York, 1962.

2/ENERGY LEVELS AND ENERGY BANDS

In this chapter we begin with a review of the basic atomic properties of matter leading to discrete electronic energy levels in atoms. We also examine some selected topics in quantum physics, such as the wave properties of matter, the Schrödinger wave equation, and the Pauli exclusion principle. We find that atomic energy levels are spread into energy bands in a crystal. This band structure allows us to distinguish between an insulator, a semiconductor, and a metal.

2-1 THE NATURE OF THE ATOM

In order to explain many phenomena associated with conduction in gases, metals, and semiconductors and the emission of electrons from the surface of a metal, it is necessary to assume that the atom has loosely bound electrons which can be torn away from it.

Rutherford,[1] in 1911, found that the atom consists of a nucleus of positive charge that contains nearly all the mass of the atom. Surrounding this central positive core are negatively charged electrons. As a specific illustration of this atomic model, consider the hydrogen atom. This atom consists of a positively charged nucleus (a proton) and a single electron. The charge on the proton is positive and is equal in magnitude to the charge on the electron. Therefore the atom as a whole is electrically neutral. Because the proton carries practically all the mass of the atom, it will remain substantially immobile, whereas the electron will move about it in a closed orbit. The force of attraction between the electron and the proton follows Coulomb's law. It can be shown from classical mechanics that the resultant closed path will be a circle or an ellipse under the action of such a force. This motion is exactly analogous to that of the planets about the sun, because in both cases the force varies inversely as the square of the distance between the particles.

Assume, therefore, that the orbit of the electron in this planetary model of the atom is a circle, the nucleus being supposed fixed in space. It is a simple matter to calculate its radius in terms of the total energy W of the electron. The force of attraction between the nucleus and the electron is $e^2/4\pi\epsilon_0 r^2$, where the electronic charge e is in coulombs, the separation r between the two particles is in meters, the force is in newtons, and ϵ_0 is the permittivity of free space.† By Newton's second law of motion, this must be set equal to the product of the electronic mass m in kilograms and the acceleration v^2/r toward the nucleus, where v is the speed of the electron in its circular path, in meters per second. Then

$$\frac{e^2}{4\pi\epsilon_0 r^2} = \frac{mv^2}{r} \tag{2-1}$$

Furthermore, the potential energy of the electron at a distance r from the nucleus is $-e^2/4\pi\epsilon_0 r$, and its kinetic energy is $\frac{1}{2}mv^2$. Then, according to the conservation of energy,

$$W = \tfrac{1}{2}mv^2 - \frac{e^2}{4\pi\epsilon_0 r} \tag{2-2}$$

where the energy is in joules. Combining this expression with (2-1) produces

$$W = -\frac{e^2}{8\pi\epsilon_0 r} \tag{2-3}$$

which gives the desired relationship between the radius and the energy of the electron. This equation shows that the total energy of the electron is always negative. The negative sign arises because the potential energy has been chosen to be zero when r is infinite. This expression also shows that the energy of the electron becomes smaller (i.e., more negative) as it approaches closer to the nucleus.

The foregoing discussion of the planetary atom has been considered only from the point of view of classical mechanics, using the classical model for the electron. However, an accelerated charge must radiate energy, in accordance with the classical laws of electromagnetism. If the charge is performing oscillations of a frequency f, the radiated energy will also be of this frequency. Hence, classically, it must be concluded that the frequency of the emitted radiation equals the frequency with which the electron is rotating in its circular orbit.

There is one feature of this picture that cannot be reconciled with experiment. If the electron is radiating energy, its total energy must decrease by the amount of this emitted energy. As a result the radius r of the orbit must decrease, in accordance with Eq. (2-3). Consequently, as the atom radiates energy, the electron must move in smaller and smaller orbits, eventually fall-

† The numerical value of ϵ_0 is in Appendix B.

ing into the nucleus. Since the frequency of oscillation depends upon the size of the circular orbit, the energy radiated would be of a gradually changing frequency. Such a conclusion, however, is incompatible with the sharply defined frequencies of spectral lines.

The Bohr Atom The difficulty mentioned above was resolved by Bohr in 1913.[2] He postulated the following three fundamental laws:

1. Not all energies as given by classical mechanics are possible, but the atom can possess only certain discrete energies. While in states corresponding to these discrete energies, the electron does *not* emit radiation, and the electron is said to be in a *stationary*, or nonradiating, state.

2. In a transition from one stationary state corresponding to a definite energy W_2 to another stationary state, with an associated energy W_1, radiation will be emitted. The frequency of this radiant energy is given by

$$f = \frac{W_2 - W_1}{h} \tag{2-4}$$

where h is Planck's constant in joule-seconds, the W's are expressed in joules, and f is in cycles per second, or hertz.

3. A stationary state is determined by the condition that the angular momentum of the electron in this state is quantized and must be an integral multiple of $h/2\pi$. Thus

$$mvr = \frac{nh}{2\pi} \tag{2-5}$$

where n is an integer.

Combining Eqs. (2-1) and (2-5), we obtain the radii of the stationary states (Prob. 2-1), and from Eq. (2-3) the energy level in joules of each state is found to be

$$W_n = -\frac{me^4}{8h^2\epsilon_o^2}\frac{1}{n^2} \tag{2-6}$$

Then, upon making use of Eq. (2-4), the exact frequencies found in the hydrogen spectrum are obtained, a remarkable achievement. The radius of the lowest state is found to be 0.5 Å.

2-2 ATOMIC ENERGY LEVELS

Though it is theoretically possible to calculate the various energy states of the atoms of the simpler elements, these levels must be determined indirectly from spectroscopic and other data for the more complicated atoms. The experimentally determined *energy-level diagram* for mercury is shown in Fig. 2-1.

The numbers to the left of the horizontal lines give the energy of these levels in electron volts. The arrows represent some of the transitions that

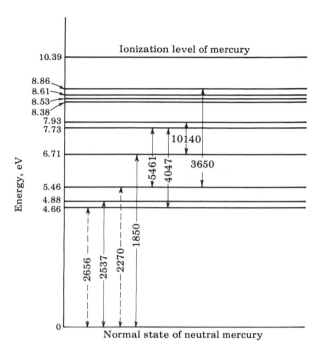

Fig. 2-1 The lower energy levels of atomic mercury.

have been found to exist in actual spectra, the attached numbers giving the wavelength of the emitted radiation, expressed in angstrom units (10^{-10} m). The light emitted in these transitions gives rise to the luminous character of the gaseous discharge. However, all the emitted radiation need not appear in the form of visible light, but may exist in the ultraviolet or infrared regions. The meaning of the broken lines is explained in Sec. 2-7.

It is customary to express the energy value of the stationary states in electron volts E rather than in joules W. Also, it is more common to specify the emitted radiation by its wavelength λ in angstroms rather than by its frequency f in hertz. In these units, Eq. (2-4) may be rewritten in the form

$$\lambda = \frac{12,400}{E_2 - E_1} \tag{2-7}$$

Since only differences of energy enter into this expression, the zero state may be chosen at will. It is convenient and customary to choose the lowest energy state as the zero level. This was done in Fig. 2-1. The lowest energy state is called the *normal* level, and the other stationary states of the atom are called *excited, radiating, critical,* or *resonance* levels.

The most intense line in the mercury spectrum is that resulting from the transition from the 4.88-eV level to the zero state. The emitted radiation, as calculated from Eq. (2-7), is $12,400/4.88 = 2,537$ Å, as indicated in the diagram. It is primarily this line that is responsible for the ultraviolet burns which arise from mercury discharges.

2-3   THE PHOTON NATURE OF LIGHT

The mean life of an excited state ranges from 10^{-7} to 10^{-10} sec, the excited electron returning to its previous state after the lapse of this time.[3]   In this transition, the atom must lose an amount of energy equal to the difference in energy between the two states that it has successively occupied, this energy appearing in the form of radiation.   According to the postulates of Bohr, this energy is emitted in the form of a photon of light, the frequency of this radiation being given by Eq. (2-4).   The term *photon* denotes an amount of radiant energy equal to the constant h times the frequency.   This quantized nature of an electromagnetic wave was first introduced by Planck,[3] in 1901, in order to verify theoretically the blackbody radiation formula obtained experimentally.

The photon concept of radiation may be difficult to comprehend at first. Classically, it was believed that the atoms were systems that emitted radiation *continuously* in all directions.   According to the foregoing theory, however, this is not true, the emission of light by an atom being a discontinuous process.   That is, the atom radiates only when it makes a transition from one energy level to a lower energy state.   In this transition, it emits a definite amount of energy of one particular frequency, namely, one photon hf of light. Of course, when a luminous discharge is observed, this discontinuous nature of radiation is not suspected because of the enormous number of atoms that are radiating energy and, correspondingly, because of the immense number of photons that are emitted in unit time.

EXAMPLE   Given a 50-W mercury-vapor lamp.   Assume that 0.1 percent of the electric energy supplied to the lamp appears in the ultraviolet line, 2,537 Å.   Calculate the number of photons per second of this wavelength emitted by the lamp.

Solution   The energy per photon is, according to Eq. (2-7),

$$E = \frac{12,400}{2,537} = 4.88 \text{ eV/photon}$$

The total power being transformed to the 2,537-Å line is 0.05 W, or 0.05 J/sec. Since 1 eV $= 1.60 \times 10^{-19}$ J, the power radiated is

$$\frac{0.05 \text{ J/sec}}{1.60 \times 10^{-19} \text{ J/eV}} = 3.12 \times 10^{17} \text{ eV/sec}$$

Hence the number of photons per second is

$$\frac{3.12 \times 10^{17} \text{ eV/sec}}{4.88 \text{ eV/photon}} = 6.40 \times 10^{16} \text{ photons/sec}$$

This is an extremely large number.

2-4   IONIZATION

As the most loosely bound electron of an atom is given more and more energy, it moves into stationary states which are farther and farther away from the nucleus. When its energy is large enough to move it completely out of the field of influence of the ion, it becomes "detached" from it. The energy required for this process to occur is called the *ionization potential* and is represented as the highest state in the energy-level diagram. From an inspection of Fig. 2-1, this is seen to be 10.39 eV for mercury. The alkali metals have the lowest ionization potentials, whereas the inert gases have the highest values, the ionizing potentials ranging from approximately 4 to 25 eV.

2-5   COLLISIONS OF ELECTRONS WITH ATOMS

The foregoing discussion has shown that, in order to excite or ionize an atom, energy must be supplied to it. This energy may be supplied to the atom in various ways, one of the most important of which is electron impact. Other methods of ionization or excitation of atoms are considered below.

Suppose that an electron is accelerated by the potential applied to a discharge tube. When this electron collides with an atom, one of several effects may occur. A slowly moving electron suffers an "elastic" collision, i.e., one that entails an energy loss only as required by the laws of conservation of energy and momentum. The direction of travel of the electron will be altered by the collision although its energy remains substantially unchanged. This follows from the fact that the mass of the gas molecule is large compared with that of the electron.

If the electron possesses sufficient energy, the amount depending upon the particular gas present, it may transfer enough of its energy to the atom to elevate it to one of the higher quantum states. The amount of energy necessary for this process is the excitation, or radiation, potential of the atom. If the impinging electron possesses a higher energy, say, an amount at least equal to the ionization potential of the gas, it may deliver this energy to an electron of the atom and completely remove it from the parent atom. Three charged particles result from such an ionizing collision: two electrons and a positive ion.

It must not be presumed that the incident electron must possess an energy corresponding exactly to the energy of a stationary state in an atom in order to raise the atom into this level. If the bombarding electron has gained more than the requisite energy from the electric field to raise an atom into a particular energy state, the amount of energy in excess of that required for excitation will be retained by the incident electron as kinetic energy after the collision. Or if the process of ionization has taken place, the excess energy divides between the two electrons.

2-6   COLLISIONS OF PHOTONS WITH ATOMS

Another important method by which an atom may be elevated into an excited energy state is to have radiation fall on the gas. An atom may absorb a photon of frequency f and thereby move from the level of energy W_1 to the higher energy level W_2, where $W_2 = W_1 + hf$.

An extremely important feature of excitation by photon capture is that *the photon will not be absorbed unless its energy corresponds exactly to the energy difference between two stationary levels of the atom with which it collides.* Consider, for example, the following experiment: The 2,537-Å mercury radiation falls on sodium vapor in the normal state. What is the result of this irradiation? The impinging photons have an energy of 12,400/2,537 = 4.88 eV, whereas the first excitation potential of sodium is only 2.09 eV. It is conceivable that the sodium atom might be excited and that the excess energy 4.88 − 2.09 = 2.79 eV would appear as another photon of wavelength 12,400/2.79 = 4,440 Å. Actually, however, the 2,537-Å line is transmitted without absorption through the sodium vapor, neither of the two lines appearing. We conclude, therefore, that the probability of excitation of a gas by photon absorption is negligible unless the energy of the photon corresponds exactly to the energy difference between two stationary states of the atoms of the gas.

When a photon is absorbed by an atom, the excited atom may return to its normal state in one jump, or it may do so in several steps. If the atom falls into one or more excitation levels before finally reaching the normal state, it will emit several photons. These will correspond to energy differences between the successive excited levels into which the atom falls. None of the emitted photons will have the frequency of the absorbed radiation! This *fluorescence* cannot be explained by classical theory, but is readily understood once Bohr's postulates are accepted.

If the frequency of the impinging photon is sufficiently high, it may have enough energy to ionize the gas. The photon vanishes with the appearance of an electron and a positive ion. Unlike the case of photoexcitation, the photon need not possess an energy corresponding exactly to the ionizing energy of the atom. It need merely possess *at least* this much energy. If it possesses more than ionizing energy, the excess will appear as the kinetic energy of the emitted electron and positive ion. It is found by experiment, however, that the maximum probability of photoionization occurs when the energy of the photon is equal to the ionization potential, the probability decreasing rapidly for higher photon energies.

2-7   METASTABLE STATES

Stationary states may exist which can be excited by electron bombardment but not by photoexcitation. Such levels are called *metastable states*. A transition from a metastable level to the normal state *with the emission of radiation* has a very low probability of taking place. The 4.66- and 5.46-eV levels in Fig. 2-1 are metastable states. The forbidden transitions are indicated by dashed arrows on the energy-level diagram. Transitions from a higher level to a metastable state are permitted, and several of these are shown in Fig. 2-1.

The mean life of a metastable state is found to be very much longer than the mean life of a radiating level. Representative times are 10^{-2} to 10^{-4} sec for metastable states and 10^{-7} to 10^{-10} sec for radiating levels. The long lifetime of the metastable states arises from the fact that a transition to the normal state with the emission of a photon is forbidden. How then can the energy of a metastable state be expended so that the atom may return to its normal state? One method is for the metastable atom to collide with another molecule and give up its energy to the other molecule as kinetic energy of translation, or potential energy of excitation. Another method is that by which the electron in the metastable state receives additional energy by any of the processes enumerated in the preceding sections. The metastable atom may thereby be elevated to a higher energy state from which a transition to the normal level can take place, or else it may be ionized. If the metastable atom diffuses to the walls of the discharge tube or to any of the electrodes therein, either it may expend its energy in the form of heat or the metastable atoms might induce secondary emission.

2-8   THE WAVE PROPERTIES OF MATTER

In Sec. 2-6 we find that an atom may absorb a photon of frequency f and move from the energy level W_1 to the higher energy level W_2, where

$$W_2 = W_1 + hf$$

Since a photon is absorbed by only one atom, the photon acts as if it were concentrated in one point in space, in contradiction to the concept of a wave associated with radiation. In Chap. 19, where we discuss the photoelectric effect, it is again necessary to assign to a photon the property of a particle in order to explain the results of experiments involving the interaction of radiation and matter.

According to a hypothesis of De Broglie,[3] in 1924, the dual character of wave and particle is not limited to radiation alone, but is also exhibited by particles such as electrons, atoms, molecules, or macroscopic masses. He calculated that a particle of mass m traveling with a velocity v has a wavelength λ associated with it given by

$$\lambda = \frac{h}{mv} = \frac{h}{p} \tag{2-8}$$

where p is the momentum of the particle. The existence of such matter waves was demonstrated experimentally by Davisson and Germer in 1927 and Thomson in 1928. We can make use of the wave properties of a moving electron to establish Bohr's postulate that a stationary state is determined by the condition that the angular momentum must be an integral multiple of $h/2\pi$. It seems reasonable to assume that an orbit of radius r will correspond to a stationary state if it contains a standing-wave pattern. In other words, a stable orbit is one whose circumference is exactly equal to the electronic wavelength λ, or to $n\lambda$, where n is an integer (but not zero).   Thus

$$2\pi r = n\lambda = \frac{nh}{mv} \tag{2-9}$$

Clearly, Eq. (2-9) is identical with the Bohr condition [Eq. (2-5)].

Wave Mechanics Schrödinger carried the implication of the wave nature of the electron further and developed a branch of physics called *wave mechanics*, or *quantum mechanics*. He argued that, if De Broglie's concept is correct, it should be possible to deduce the properties of an electron system from a mathematical relationship such as the wave equation of electromagnetic theory, optics, mechanical vibrations, etc.   Such a wave equation is

$$\nabla^2\phi - \frac{1}{v^2}\frac{\partial^2\phi}{\partial t^2} = 0 \tag{2-10}$$

where

$$\nabla^2 \equiv \frac{\partial^2}{\partial x^2} + \frac{\partial^2}{\partial y^2} + \frac{\partial^2}{\partial z^2}$$

and v is the velocity of the wave, and t is time.   The physical meaning of ϕ depends upon the problem under consideration.   It may be one component of electric field, the mechanical displacement, the pressure, etc., depending upon the physical problem.   We can eliminate the time variable by assuming a solution of the form

$$\phi(x, y, z, t) = \psi(x, y, z)\epsilon^{j\omega t} \tag{2-11}$$

where $\omega = 2\pi f$ is the angular frequency.   Then Eq. (2-10) becomes

$$\nabla^2\psi + \frac{4\pi^2}{\lambda^2}\psi = 0 \tag{2-12}$$

where $\lambda \equiv v/f =$ the wavelength.   From De Broglie's relationship [Eq. (2-8)],

$$\frac{1}{\lambda^2} = \frac{p^2}{h^2} = \frac{2m}{h^2}(W - U) \tag{2-13}$$

where use has been made of the fact that the kinetic energy $p^2/2m$ is the difference between the total energy W and the potential energy U.   Substituting Eq. (2-13) in (2-12) gives the time-independent Schrödinger equation

$$\nabla^2\psi + \frac{8\pi^2 m}{h^2}(W - U)\psi = 0 \tag{2-14}$$

The ψ in Eq. (2-14) is called the *wave function*, and it must describe the behavior of the particle.   But what is the physical meaning of ψ?   It is found that the proper interpretation of ψ is that it is a quantity whose square gives the probability of finding the electron.   In other words, $|\psi|^2\,dx\,dy\,dz$ is proportional to the probability that the electron is in the volume $dx\,dy\,dz$ at the point $P(x, y, z)$ in space.   The wave function ψ must be normalized, that is, $\iiint|\psi|^2\,dx\,dy\,dz$ over all space equals unity, indicating that the probability of finding the electron somewhere must be unity. Quantum mechanics makes no attempt to locate a particle at a precise point P in space, but rather the Schrödinger equation determines only the probability that the electron is to be found in the neighborhood of P.

The potential energy $U(x, y, z)$ specifies the physical problem at hand. For the electron in the hydrogen atom, $U = -e^2/4\pi\epsilon_o r$, whereas for a crystal, it is a complicated periodic function of space. The solution of Schrödinger's equation, subject to the proper boundary conditions, yields the allowed total energies W_n (called *characteristic values*, or *eigenvalues*) of the particle and the corresponding wave functions ψ_n (called *eigenfunctions*). Except for the very simplest potential functions (as in Sec. 3-6), there is considerable mathematical complexity in solving for ψ. Hence we shall not obtain the solution of the Schrödinger equation for the hydrogen atom, but shall state the important result that such a solution leads to precisely the energy levels given in Eq. (2-3) which were obtained from the simpler Bohr picture of the atom.

2-9   ELECTRONIC STRUCTURE OF THE ELEMENTS

The solution of the Schrödinger equation for hydrogen or any multielectron atom need not have radial symmetry. The wave functions may be a function of the azimuthal and polar angles as well as of the radial distance. It turns out that, in the general case, four quantum numbers are required to define the wave function. The total energy, the orbital angular momentum, the component of this angular momentum along a fixed axis in space, and the electron spin are quantized. The four quantum numbers are identified as follows:

1. The *principal quantum number n* is an integer 1, 2, 3, . . . and determines the total energy associated with a particular state. This number may be considered to define the size of the classical elliptical orbit, and it corresponds to the quantum number n of the Bohr atom.

2. *The orbital angular momentum quantum number l* takes on the values 0, 1, 2, . . . , $(n-1)$. This number indicates the shape of the classical orbit. The magnitude of this angular momentum is $\sqrt{(l)(l+1)}\,(h/2\pi)$.

3. *The orbital magnetic number m_l* may have the values 0, ± 1, ± 2, . . . , $\pm l$. This number gives the orientation of the classical orbit with respect to an applied magnetic field. The magnitude of the component of angular momentum along the direction of the magnetic field is $m_l(h/2\pi)$.

4. *Electron spin.* In order to explain certain spectroscopic and magnetic phenomena, Uhlenbeck and Goudsmit, in 1925, found it necessary to assume that, in addition to traversing its orbit around the nucleus, the electron must also rotate about its own axis. This intrinsic electronic angular momentum is called *electron spin.* When an electron system is subjected to a magnetic field, the spin axis will orient itself either parallel or antiparallel to the direc-

tion of the field. The spin is thus quantized to one of two possible values. The electronic angular momentum is given by $m_s(h/2\pi)$, where the *spin quantum number* m_s may assume only two values, $+\frac{1}{2}$ or $-\frac{1}{2}$.

The Exclusion Principle The periodic table of the chemical elements (given in Appendix C) may be explained by invoking a law enunciated by Pauli in 1925. He stated that *no two electrons in an electronic system can have the same set of four quantum numbers, n, l, m_l, and m_s.* This statement that no two electrons may occupy the same quantum state is known as the *Pauli exclusion principle.*

Electronic Shells All the electrons in an atom which have the same value of n are said to belong to the same *electron shell.* These shells are identified by the letters K, L, M, N, . . . , corresponding to $n = 1, 2, 3, 4, . . . ,$ respectively. A shell is divided into *subshells* corresponding to different values of l and identified as s, p, d, f, . . . , corresponding to $l = 0, 1, 2, 3, . . . ,$ respectively. Taking account of the exclusion principle, the distribution of electrons in an atom among the shells and subshells is indicated in Table 2-1. Actually, seven shells are required to account for all the chemical elements, but only the first four are indicated in the table.

There are two states for $n = 1$ corresponding to $l = 0$, $m_l = 0$, and $m_s = \pm\frac{1}{2}$. These are called the $1s$ states. There are two states corresponding to $n = 2$, $l = 0$, $m_l = 0$, and $m_s = \pm\frac{1}{2}$. These constitute the $2s$ subshell. There are, in addition, six energy levels corresponding to $n = 2$, $l = 1$, $m_l = -1$, 0, or $+1$, and $m_s = \pm\frac{1}{2}$. These are designated as the $2p$ subshell. Hence, as indicated in Table 2-1, the total number of electrons in the L shell is $2 + 6 = 8$. In a similar manner we may verify that a d subshell contains a maximum of 10 electrons, an f subshell a maximum of 14 electrons, etc.

The atomic number Z gives the number of electrons orbiting about the nucleus. Let us use superscripts to designate the number of electrons in a particular subshell. Then sodium, Na, for which $Z = 11$, has an electronic configuration designated by $1s^2 2s^2 2p^6 3s^1$. Note that Na has a single electron in the outermost unfilled subshell, and hence is said to be monovalent. This

TABLE 2-1　　　Electron shells and subshells

Shell	K	L		M			N			
n	1	2		3			4			
l . . . . Subshell	0 s	0 s	1 p	0 s	1 p	2 d	0 s	1 p	2 d	3 f
Number of electrons	2	2	6	2	6	10	2	6	10	14
	2	8		18			32			

TABLE 2-2   Electronic configuration in Group IVA

Element	Atomic number	Configuration
C	6	$1s^2 2s^2 2p^2$
Si	14	$1s^2 2s^2 2p^6 3s^2 3p^2$
Ge	32	$1s^2 2s^2 2p^6 3s^2 3p^6 3d^{10} 4s^2 4p^2$
Sn	50	$1s^2 2s^2 2p^6 3s^2 3p^6 3d^{10} 4s^2 4p^6 4d^{10} 5s^2 5p^2$

same property is possessed by all the alkali metals (Li, Na, K, Rb, and Cs), which accounts for the fact that these elements in the same group in the periodic table (Appendix C) have similar chemical properties.

The inner-shell electrons are very strongly bound to an atom, and cannot be easily removed. That is, the electrons closest to the nucleus are the most tightly bound, and so have the lowest energy. Also, atoms for which the electrons exist in closed shells form very stable configurations. For example, the inert gases He, Ne, A, Kr, and Xe all have either completely filled shells or, at least, completely filled subshells.

Carbon, silicon, germanium, and tin have the electronic configurations indicated in Table 2-2. Note that each of these elements has completely filled subshells except for the outermost p shell, which contains only two of the six possible electrons. Despite this similarity, carbon in crystalline form (diamond) is an insulator, silicon and germanium solids are semiconductors, and tin is a metal. This apparent anomaly is explained in the next section.

2-10   THE ENERGY–BAND THEORY OF CRYSTALS

X-ray and other studies reveal that most metals and semiconductors are crystalline in structure. A crystal consists of a space array of atoms or molecules (strictly speaking, ions) built up by regular repetition in three dimensions of some fundamental structural unit. The electronic energy levels discussed for a single free atom (as in a gas, where the atoms are sufficiently far apart not to exert any influence on one another) do not apply to the same atom in a crystal. This is so because the potential U in Eq. (2-14), characterizing the crystalline structure, is now a periodic function in space whose value at any point is the result of contributions from every atom. When atoms form crystals it is found that the energy levels of the inner-shell electrons are not affected appreciably by the presence of the neighboring atoms. However, the levels of the outer-shell electrons are changed considerably, since these electrons are shared by more than one atom in the crystal. The new energy levels of the outer electrons can be determined by means of quantum mechanics, and it is found that coupling between the outer-shell electrons of the atoms results in a *band* of closely spaced energy states instead of the widely separated energy levels of the isolated atom (Fig. 2-2). A qualitative discussion of this energy-band structure follows.

Consider a crystal consisting of N atoms of one of the elements in Table 2-2. Imagine that it is possible to vary the spacing between atoms without altering the type of fundamental crystal structure. If the atoms are so far apart that the interaction between them is negligible, the energy levels will coincide with those of the isolated atom. The outer two subshells for each element in Table 2-2 contain two s electrons and two p electrons. Hence, if we ignore the inner-shell levels, then, as indicated to the extreme right in Fig. 2-2a, there are $2N$ electrons completely filling the $2N$ possible s levels, all at the same energy. Since the p atomic subshell has six possible states, our imaginary crystal of widely spaced atoms has $2N$ electrons, which fill only one-third of the $6N$ possible p states, all at the same level.

If we now decrease the interatomic spacing of our imaginary crystal (moving from right to left in Fig. 2-2a), an atom will exert an electric force on its neighbors. Because of this coupling between atoms, the atomic-wave functions overlap, and the crystal becomes an electronic *system* which must obey the Pauli exclusion principle. Hence the $2N$ degenerate s states must spread out in energy. The separation between levels is small, but since N is very large ($\sim 10^{23}$ cm^{-3}), the total spread between the minimum and maximum energy may be several electron volts if the interatomic distance is decreased sufficiently. This large number of discrete but closely spaced energy levels is called an *energy band*, and is indicated schematically by the lower shaded

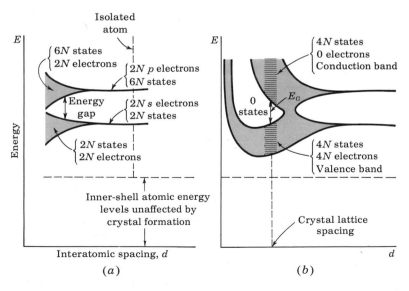

Fig. 2-2 Illustrating how the energy levels of isolated atoms are split into energy bands when these atoms are brought into close proximity to form a crystal.

region in Fig. 2-2a. The $2N$ states in this band are completely filled with $2N$ electrons. Similarly, the upper shaded region in Fig. 2-2a is a band of $6N$ states which has only $2N$ of its levels occupied by electrons.

Note that there is an energy gap (a forbidden band) between the two bands discussed above and that this gap decreases as the atomic spacing decreases. For small enough distances (not indicated in Fig. 2-2a but shown in Fig. 2-2b) these bands will overlap. Under such circumstances the $6N$ upper states merge with the $2N$ lower states, giving a total of $8N$ levels, half of which are occupied by the $2N + 2N = 4N$ available electrons. At this spacing each atom has given up four electrons to the band; these electrons can no longer be said to orbit in s or p subshells of an isolated atom, but rather they belong to the crystal as a whole. In this sense the elements in Table 2-2 are tetravalent, since they contribute four electrons each to the crystal. The band these electrons occupy is called the *valence band*.

If the spacing between atoms is decreased below the distance at which the bands overlap, the interaction between atoms is indeed large. The energy-band structure then depends upon the orientation of the atoms relative to one another in space (the crystal structure) and upon the atomic number, which determines the electrical constitution of each atom. Solutions of Schrödinger's equation are complicated, and have been obtained approximately for only relatively few crystals. These solutions lead us to expect an energy-band diagram somewhat as pictured[4] in Fig. 2-2b. At the crystal-lattice spacing (the dashed vertical line), we find the valence band *filled* with $4N$ electrons separated by a forbidden band (no allowed energy states) of extent E_G from an *empty* band consisting of $4N$ additional states. This upper vacant band is called the *conduction band*, for reasons given in the next section.

2-11   INSULATORS, SEMICONDUCTORS, AND METALS

A very poor conductor of electricity is called an *insulator;* an excellent conductor is a *metal;* and a substance whose conductivity lies between these extremes is a *semiconductor*. A material may be placed in one of these three classes, depending upon its energy-band structure.

Insulator The energy-band structure of Fig. 2-2b at the normal lattice spacing is indicated schematically in Fig. 2-3a. For a diamond (carbon) crystal the region containing no quantum states is several electron volts high ($E_G \approx 6$ eV). This large forbidden band separates the filled valence region from the vacant conduction band. The energy which can be supplied to an electron from an applied field is too small to carry the particle from the filled into the vacant band. Since the electron cannot acquire externally applied energy, conduction is impossible, and hence diamond is an *insulator*.

Semiconductor A substance for which the width of the forbidden energy region is relatively small (~ 1 eV) is called a *semiconductor*. Graphite, a

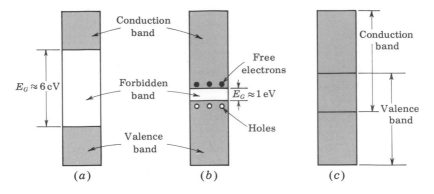

Fig. 2-3 Energy-band structure of (a) an insulator, (b) a semiconductor, and (c) a metal.

crystalline form of carbon but having a crystal symmetry which is different from diamond, has such a small value of E_G, and it is a semiconductor. The most important practical semiconductor materials are germanium and silicon, which have values of E_G of 0.785 and 1.21 eV, respectively, at 0°K. Energies of this magnitude normally cannot be acquired from an applied field. Hence the valence band remains full, the conduction band empty, and these materials are insulators at low temperatures. However, the conductivity increases with temperature, as we explain below, and for this reason these substances are known as *intrinsic semiconductors*.

As the temperature is increased, some of these valence electrons acquire *thermal* energy greater than E_G and hence move into the conduction band. These are now free electrons in the sense that they can move about under the influence of even a small applied field. These free, or conduction, electrons are indicated schematically by dots in Fig. 2-3b. The insulator has now become slightly conducting; it is a *semiconductor*. The absence of an electron in the valence band is represented by a small circle in Fig. 2-3b, and is called a *hole*. The phrase "holes in a semiconductor" therefore refers to the empty energy levels in an otherwise filled valence band.

The importance of the hole is that it may serve as a carrier of electricity, comparable in effectiveness with the free electron. The mechanism by which a hole contributes to conductivity is explained in Sec. 5-1. We also show in Chap. 5 that if certain impurity atoms are introduced into the crystal, these result in allowable energy states which lie in the forbidden energy gap. We find that these impurity levels also contribute to the conduction. A semiconductor material where this conduction mechanism predominates is called an *extrinsic (impurity) semiconductor*.

Since the band-gap energy of a crystal is a function of interatomic spacing (Fig. 2-2), it is not surprising that E_G depends somewhat on temperature. It has been determined experimentally that E_G for silicon decreases with temperature at the rate of 3.60×10^{-4} eV/°K. Hence, for silicon,[5]

$$E_G(T) = 1.21 - 3.60 \times 10^{-4}T \tag{2-15}$$

and at room temperature (300°K), $E_G = 1.1$ eV. Similarly, for germanium,[6]

$$E_G(T) = 0.785 - 2.23 \times 10^{-4}T \tag{2-16}$$

and at room temperature, $E_G = 0.72$ eV.

Metal The band structure of a crystal may contain no forbidden energy region, so that the valence band merges into an empty band, as indicated in Fig. 2-3c. Under the influence of an applied electric field the electrons may acquire additional energy and move into higher energy states. Since these mobile electrons constitute a current, this substance is a conductor, and the empty region is the conduction band. A *metal* is characterized by a band structure containing overlapping valence and conduction bands.

REFERENCES

1. Rutherford, E.: The Scattering of α and β Particles by Matter and the Structure of the Atom, *Phil. Mag.*, vol. 21, pp. 669–688, May, 1911.

2. Bohr, N.: On the Constitution of Atoms and Molecules, Part 2: Systems Containing Only a Single Nucleus, *Phil. Mag.*, vol. 26, pp. 476–502, September, 1913.

3. Richtmyer, F. K., E. H. Kennard, and T. Lauritsen: "Introduction to Modern Physics," McGraw-Hill Book Company, New York, 1955.

4. Adler, R. B., A. C. Smith, and R. L. Longini: "Introduction to Semiconductor Physics," vol. 1, p. 78, Semiconductor Electronics Education Committee, John Wiley & Sons, Inc., New York, 1964.

5. Morin, F. J., and J. P. Maita: Electrical Properties of Silicon Containing Arsenic and Boron, *Phys. Rev.*, vol. 96, pp. 28–35, October, 1954.

6. Morin, F. J., and J. P. Maita: Conductivity and Hall Effect in the Intrinsic Range of Germanium, *Phys. Rev.*, vol. 94, pp. 1525–1529, June, 1954.

3 / CONDUCTION IN METALS

In this chapter we describe the interior of a metal and present the basic principles which characterize the movement of electrons within the metal. The laws governing the emission of electrons from the surface of a metal are also considered.

3-1   MOBILITY AND CONDUCTIVITY

In the preceding chapter we presented an energy-band picture of metals, semiconductors, and insulators. In a metal the outer, or valence, electrons of an atom are as much associated with one ion as with another, so that the electron attachment to any individual atom is almost zero. In terms of our previous discussion this means that the band occupied by the valence electrons may not be completely filled and that there are no forbidden levels at higher energies. Depending upon the metal, at least one, and sometimes two or three, electrons per atom are free to move throughout the interior of the metal under the action of applied fields.

Figure 3-1 shows the charge distribution within a metal, specifically, sodium.[1] The plus signs represent the heavy positive sodium nuclei of the individual atoms. The heavily shaded regions represent the electrons in the sodium atom that are tightly bound to the nucleus. These are inappreciably disturbed as the atoms come together to form the metal. The unshaded volume contains the outer, or valence, electrons in the atom. It is these electrons that cannot be said to belong to any particular atom; instead, they have completely lost their individuality and can wander freely about from atom to atom in the metal. Thus a metal is visualized as a region containing a periodic three-dimensional array of heavy, tightly bound ions permeated with

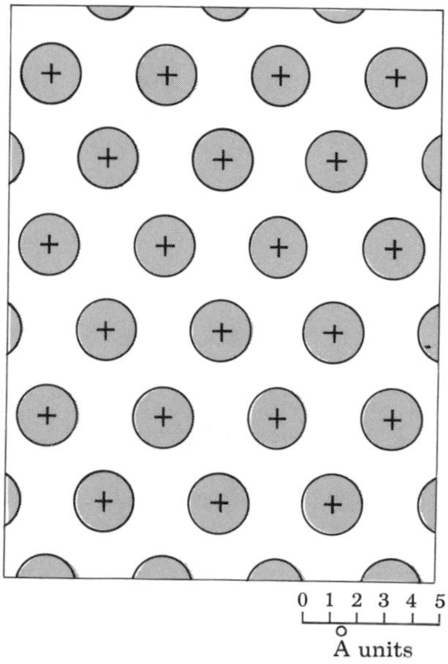

Fig. 3-1   Arrangement of the sodium atoms in one plane of the metal.

0 1 2 3 4 5

$\overset{\circ}{A}$ units

a swarm of electrons that may move about quite freely.   This picture is known as the *electron-gas* description of a metal.

According to the electron-gas theory of a metal, the electrons are in continuous motion, the direction of flight being changed at each collision with the heavy (almost stationary) ions.   The average distance between collisions is called the *mean free path*.   Since the motion is random, then, on an average, there will be as many electrons passing through unit area in the metal in any direction as in the opposite direction in a given time.   Hence the average current is zero.

Let us now see how the situation is changed if a constant electric field ε (volts per meter) is applied to the metal.   As a result of this electrostatic force, the electrons would be accelerated and the velocity would increase indefinitely with time, were it not for the collisions with the ions.   However, at each inelastic collision with an ion, an electron loses energy, and a steady-state condition is reached where a finite value of *drift speed* v is attained. This drift velocity is in the direction opposite to that of the electric field, and its magnitude is proportional to ε.   Thus

$$v = \mu\varepsilon \tag{3-1}$$

where μ (square meters per volt-second) is called the *mobility* of the electrons.

According to the foregoing theory, a steady-state drift speed has been superimposed upon the random thermal motion of the electrons.   Such a directed flow of electrons constitutes a current.   If the concentration of free electrons is n (electrons per cubic meter), the current density J (amperes per square meter) is (Sec. 1-12)

$$J = nev = ne\mu\varepsilon = \sigma\varepsilon \tag{3-2}$$

where

$$\sigma = ne\mu \tag{3-3}$$

is the *conductivity* of the metal in (ohm-meter)$^{-1}$. Equation (3-2) is recognized as Ohm's law, namely, the conduction current is proportional to the applied voltage. As already mentioned, the energy which the electrons acquire from the applied field is, as a result of collisions, given to the lattice ions. Hence power is dissipated within the metal by the electrons, and the power density (Joule heat) is given by $J\mathcal{E} = \sigma\mathcal{E}^2$ (watts per cubic meter).

3-2 THE ENERGY METHOD OF ANALYZING THE MOTION OF A PARTICLE

A method is considered in Chap. 1 by which the motion of charged particles may be analyzed. It consists in the solution of Newton's second law, in which the forces of electric and magnetic origin are equated to the product of the mass and the acceleration of the particle. Obviously, this method is not applicable when the forces are as complicated as they must be in a metal. Furthermore, it is neither possible nor desirable to consider what happens to each individual electron.

It is necessary, therefore, to consider an alternative approach. This method employs the law of the conservation of energy, use being made of the potential-energy curve corresponding to the field of force. The principles involved may best be understood by considering specific examples of the method.

EXAMPLE An idealized diode consists of plane-parallel electrodes, 5 cm apart. The anode A is maintained 10 V negative with respect to the cathode K. An electron leaves the cathode with an initial energy of 2 eV. What is the maximum distance it can travel from the cathode?

Solution This problem is analyzed by the energy method. Figure 3-2a is a linear

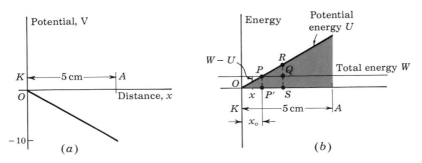

Fig. 3-2 (a) Potential vs. distance in a plane-parallel diode. (b) The potential-energy barrier encountered by an electron in the retarding field.

plot of potential vs. distance, and in Fig. 3-2b is indicated the corresponding potential energy vs. distance. Since potential is the potential energy per unit charge (Sec. 1-4), curve b is obtained from curve a by multiplying each ordinate by the charge on the electron (a negative number). Since the total energy W of the electron remains constant, it is represented as a horizontal line. The kinetic energy at any distance x equals the difference between the total energy W and the potential energy U at this point. This difference is greatest at O, indicating that the kinetic energy is a maximum when the electron leaves the cathode. At the point P this difference is zero, which means that no kinetic energy exists, so that the particle is at rest at this point. This distance x_o is the maximum that the electron can travel from the cathode. At point P it comes momentarily to rest, and then reverses its motion and returns to the cathode. From geometry it is seen that $x_o/5 = \frac{2}{10}$, or $x_o = 1$ cm.

Consider a point such as S which is at a greater distance than 1 cm from the cathode. Here the total energy QS is less than the potential energy RS, so that the difference, which represents the kinetic energy, is negative. This is an impossible physical condition, however, since negative kinetic energy ($\frac{1}{2}mv^2 < 0$) implies an imaginary velocity. We must conclude that the particle can never advance a distance greater than OP' from the cathode.

The foregoing analysis leads to the very important conclusion that the shaded portion of Fig. 3-2b can never be penetrated by the electron. Thus, at point P, the particle acts *as if* it had collided with a solid wall, hill, or barrier and the direction of its flight had been altered. *Potential-energy barriers* of this sort play important roles in the analyses to follow.

It must be emphasized that the words "collides with" or "rebounds from" a potential "hill" are convenient descriptive phrases and that an actual encounter between two material bodies is not implied.

As a second illustration, consider a mathematical pendulum of length l, consisting of a "point" bob of mass m that is free to swing in the earth's gravitational field. If the lowest point of the swing (point O, Fig. 3-3) is chosen as the origin, the potential energy of the mass at any point P corresponding to any angle θ of the swing is given by

$$U = mgy = mgl(1 - \cos\theta)$$

where g is the acceleration of gravity. This potential-energy function is illustrated graphically in Fig. 3-4.

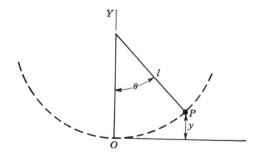

Fig. 3-3 Point P represents the mass m of a mathematical pendulum swinging in the earth's gravitational field.

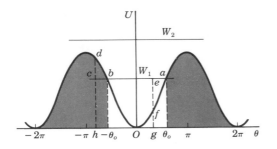

Fig. 3-4 The potential energy of the mass m in Fig. 3-3 plotted as a function of the angle of swing.

Consider the resultant motion of the bob if it is given a potential energy U_1 by raising it through an angle θ_o and releasing it with zero initial velocity. If dissipation is neglected, the particle will swing back and forth through the angle $2\theta_o$, going from θ_o on one side to θ_o on the other side of the vertical axis. How might we analyze the motion of the physical system if only the potential-energy field of Fig. 3-4 were given without specifying the physical character of the system?

The procedure is the same as that followed in the simple diode problem considered above. A horizontal line $aebc$ is drawn at a height equal to the total energy W_1 of the particle. At any point, such as e, the total energy is represented by $eg = W_1$, and the potential energy is represented by fg. The difference between these two, namely, ef, represents the kinetic energy of the particle when the angle of swing, given by the intercept of eg on the axis, corresponds to Og. In other words, the difference between the total-energy line and the potential-energy curve at any angle represents the kinetic energy of the particle under these conditions. This difference is greatest at O, indicating that the kinetic energy is a maximum at the bottom of the swing, an almost evident result. At the points a and b this difference is zero. This condition means that no kinetic energy exists, or that the particle is at rest at these points. This result is evident, since corresponding to the points a ($\theta = \theta_o$) and b ($\theta = -\theta_o$), the particle is about to reverse its motion.

Consider a point in the shaded region outside the range $-\theta_o$ to $+\theta_o$, such as h. Here the total energy ch is less than the potential energy dh. This impossible condition is interpreted by our previous reasoning to mean that the particle whose total energy is W_1 can never swing to the angle Oh, so that the motion must be confined to the region ab. The shaded portions of Fig. 3-4 represent the potential-energy barrier which can never be penetrated by the bob, if its total energy is no greater than W_1. This type of constrained motion about a point O is closely analogous to that of the so-called "bound" electrons in a metal, as shown in Sec. 3-4.

Now consider the case when the mass has a total energy equal to W_2, which is greater than the maximum of the potential-energy curve. Clearly, from Fig. 3-4, the horizontal line corresponding to this energy cannot intersect the curve at any point. Consequently, the particle does not "collide" with the potential-energy barrier, and its course is never altered, so that it moves through an ever-increasing angle. Of course, its kinetic energy varies over wide limits, being maximum for $\theta = 0$, 2π, 4π, . . . and minimum for $\theta = \pi$, 3π, 5π, ... Physically, this type of motion results when the bob has enough energy to set it spinning completely around in a circular path. This type of motion is somewhat analogous to that experienced by the so-called "free" electrons in a metal.

This simple but powerful energy method facilitates the discussion of the motion of a particle in a conservative field of force, such as that found in the body of a metal. It is also applied to many other types of problem. For example, the method of analysis just considered is extremely useful in determining whether electrons will possess sufficient energy to pass through grids and reach the various electrodes in a vacuum tube, whether or not electrons will be able to penetrate electron clouds in a vacuum tube, and whether charge carriers can cross a semiconductor junction. This method is now applied to the analysis of the motion of electrons in metals.

3-3   THE POTENTIAL–ENERGY FIELD IN A METAL

It is desired to set up the potential-energy field for the three-dimensional array of atoms that exists in the interior of a metal and to discuss the motion of electrons in this field. The resultant potential energy at any point in the metal is simply the sum of the potential energies produced at this point by all the ions of the lattice. To determine the potential energy due to one ion, it is noted that an atom of atomic number Z has a net positive charge Ze on its nucleus. Surrounding this nucleus is an approximately spherical cloud, or shell, of Z electrons. By Gauss' law the potential at a point at a distance r from the nucleus varies inversely as r and directly as the total charge enclosed within a sphere of radius r. Since the potential V equals the potential energy U per unit charge (Sec. 1-4), then $U = -eV$. The minus sign is introduced since e represents the magnitude of the (negative) electronic charge.

The potential of any point may be chosen as the zero reference of potential because it is only differences of potential that have any physical significance. For the present discussion it is convenient to choose zero potential at infinity, and then the potential energy at any point is negative. Enough has been said to make plausible the potential-energy curve illustrated in Fig. 3-5. Here α represents a nucleus, the potential energy of which is given by the curve $\alpha_1\alpha_2$. The vertical scale represents U, and the horizontal scale gives the distance r from the nucleus. It must be emphasized that r represents a radial distance from the nucleus, and hence can be taken in any direction. If the direction is horizontal but to the left of the nucleus, the dashed curve represents the potential energy.

To represent the potential energy at every point in space requires a four-dimensional picture, three dimensions for the three space coordinates and a fourth for the potential-energy axis. This difficulty is avoided by plotting U

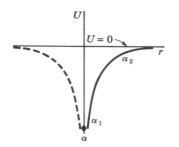

Fig. 3-5 The potential energy of an electron as a function of radial distance from an isolated nucleus.

along some chosen line through the crystal, say, through a row of ions.   From this graph and the method by which it is constructed it is easy to visualize what the potential energy at any other point might be.   In order to build up this picture, consider first two adjacent ions, and neglect all others.   The construction is shown in Fig. 3-6. $\alpha_1\alpha_2$ is the U curve for nucleus α, and $\beta_1\beta_2$ is the corresponding U curve for the adjacent nucleus β.   If these were the only nuclei present in the metal, the resultant U curve in the region between α and β would be the sum of these two curves, as shown by the dashed curve $\alpha_1 d\beta_1$ (since $ad = ab + ac$).   It is seen that the resultant curve is very nearly the same as the original curves in the immediate vicinity of a nucleus, but it is lower and flatter than either individual curve in the region between the nuclei.

Let us now single out an entire row of nuclei α, β, γ, δ, ϵ, . . . from the metallic lattice (Figs. 3-1 and 3-7) and sketch the potential energy as we proceed along this line from one nucleus to the other, until the surface of the metal is reached.   Following the same type of construction as above, but considering the small influence of other nearby nuclei, an energy distribution somewhat as illustrated in Fig. 3-7 is obtained.

According to classical electrostatics, which does not take the atomic structure into account, the interior of a metal is an equipotential region. The present, more accurate, picture shows that the potential energy varies appreciably in the immediate neighborhoods of the nuclei and actually tends to $-\infty$ in these regions.   However, the potential is approximately constant

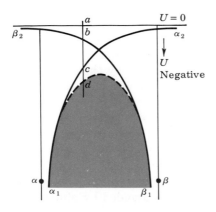

Fig. 3-6 The potential energy resulting from two nuclei, α and β.

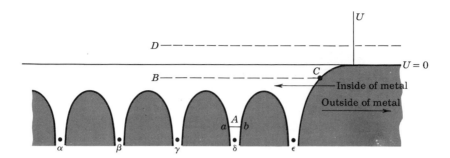

Fig. 3-7 The potential-energy distribution within and at the surface of a metal.

for a very large *volume* of the metal, as indicated by the slowly varying portions of the diagram in the regions between the ions.

Consider the conditions that exist near the surface of the metal. It is evident, according to the present point of view, that the exact position of the "surface" cannot be defined. It is located at a small distance from the last nucleus ϵ in the row. It is to be noted that, since no nuclei exist to the right of ϵ, there can be no lowering and flattening of the potential-energy curve such as prevails in the region between the nuclei. This leads to a most important conclusion: *A potential-energy "hill," or "barrier," exists at the surface of the metal.*

3-4   BOUND AND FREE ELECTRONS

The motion of an electron in the potential-energy field of Fig. 3-7 is now discussed by the method given in Sec. 3-2. Consider an electron in the metal that possesses a total energy corresponding to the level A in Fig. 3-7. This electron collides with, and rebounds from, the potential walls at a and b. It cannot drift very far from the nucleus, but can move about only in the neighborhood ab of the nucleus. Obviously, this electron is strongly bound to the nucleus, and so is a *bound electron*. This particle is one of the inner-shell electrons of an isolated atom, discussed in Sec. 2-9. It is evident that these bound electrons do not contribute to the conductivity of the metal since they cannot drift in the metal, even under the stimulus of an externally applied electric field. These electrons are responsible for the heavy shading in the neighborhood of the nuclei of Fig. 3-1.

Our present interest is in the *free* electrons in the metal rather than in the bound ones. A free electron is one having an energy such as level B of Fig. 3-7, corresponding to an energy in the conduction band. At no point *within* the metal is its total energy entirely converted into potential energy. Hence, at no point is its velocity zero, and the electron travels more or less

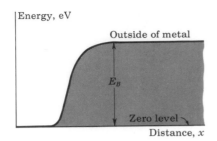

Fig. 3-8 For the free electrons, the interior of a metal may be considered an equipotential volume, but there is a potential barrier at the surface.

freely throughout the body of the metal. However, when the electron reaches the surface of the metal, it collides with the potential-energy barrier there. At the point C, its kinetic energy is reduced to zero, and the electron is turned back into the body of the metal. An electron having an energy corresponding to the level D collides with no potential walls, not even the one at the surface, and so it is capable of leaving the metal.

Simplified Potential-energy Picture of a Metal In our subsequent discussions the bound electrons are neglected completely since they in no way contribute to the phenomena to be studied. Attention is focused on the free electrons. The region in which they find themselves is essentially a potential plateau, or equipotential region. It is only for distances close to an ion that there is any appreciable variation in potential. Since the regions of rapidly varying potential represent but a very small portion of the total volume of the metal, we henceforth assume that the field distribution within the metal is equipotential and the free electrons are subject to no forces whatsoever. The present viewpoint is therefore essentially that of classical electrostatics.

Figure 3-7 is redrawn in Fig. 3-8, all potential† variations within the metal being omitted, with the exception of the potential barrier at the surface. For the present discussion, the zero of energy is chosen at the level of the plateau of this diagram. This choice of the zero-energy reference level is valid since, as has already been emphasized, only difference of potential has physical significance. The region outside the metal is now at a potential equal to E_B, the height of the potential-energy barrier in electron volts.

3-5 ENERGY DISTRIBUTION OF ELECTRONS

In order to be able to escape, an electron inside the metal must possess an amount of energy at least as great as that represented by the surface barrier

---

† This figure really represents potential energy, and not potential. However, the phrase "potential barrier" is much more common in the literature than the phrase "potential-energy barrier." When no confusion is likely to arise, these two expressions are used interchangeably. These barriers are measured in electron volts, and hence the symbol E replaces the U of the preceding sections. It must be emphasized that one unit of E represents 1.60×10^{-19} J of energy.

E_R. It is therefore important to know what energies are possessed by the electrons in a metal. This relationship is called the *energy distribution function*. We here digress briefly in order to make clear what is meant by a distribution function.

Age Density   Suppose that we were interested in the distribution in age of the people in the United States. A sensible way to indicate this relationship is shown in Fig. 3-9, where the abscissa is *age* and the ordinate is ρ_A, the *density* of the population in age. This density gives the number dn_A of people whose ages lie in the range between A and $A + dA$, or

$$dn_A = \rho_A \, dA \qquad\qquad (3\text{-}4)$$

The data for such a plot are obtained from census information. We see, for example, that the number of persons of ages between 10 and 12 years is represented by dn_A, with $\rho_A = 2.25$ million per year chosen as the mean ordinate between 10 and 12 years, and dA is taken as $12 - 10 = 2$ years. Thus $dn_A = \rho_A \, dA = 4.50$ million. Geometrically, this is the shaded area of Fig. 3-9. Evidently, the total population n is given by

$$n = \int dn_A = \int \rho_A \, dA \qquad\qquad (3\text{-}5)$$

or simply the total area under the curve.

Energy Density   We are now concerned with the distribution in energy of the free electrons in a metal. By analogy with Eq. (3-4), we may write

$$dn_E = \rho_E \, dE \qquad\qquad (3\text{-}6)$$

where dn_E represents the number of free electrons per cubic meter whose energies lie in the energy interval dE, and ρ_E gives the density of electrons in this interval. Since our interests are confined only to the free electrons, it is assumed that there are no potential variations within the metal. Hence there must be, a priori, the same number of electrons in each cubic meter of the metal. That is, the density in space (electrons per cubic meter) is

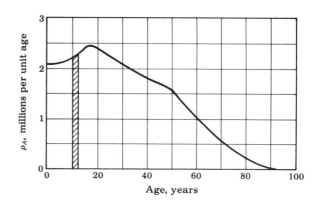

Fig. 3-9 The distribution function in age of people in the United States.

a constant.   However, within each unit volume of metal there will be electrons having all possible energies.   It is this distribution in energy that is expressed by ρ_E (number of electrons per electron volt per cubic meter of metal).

The function ρ_E may be expressed as the product

$$\rho_E = f(E)N(E) \tag{3-7}$$

where $N(E)$ is the density of states (number of states per electron volt per cubic meter) in the conduction band, and $f(E)$ is the probability that a quantum state with energy E is occupied by an electron.

The expression for $N(E)$ is derived in the following section and is given by

$$N(E) = \gamma E^{\frac{1}{2}} \tag{3-8}$$

where γ is a constant defined by

$$\gamma \equiv \frac{4\pi}{h^3}(2m)^{\frac{3}{2}}(1.60 \times 10^{-19})^{\frac{3}{2}} = 6.82 \times 10^{27} \tag{3-9}$$

The dimensions of γ are $(m^{-3})(eV)^{-\frac{3}{2}}$; m is the mass of the electron in kilograms; and h is Planck's constant in joule-seconds.

The Fermi-Dirac Function   The equation for $f(E)$ is called *the Fermi-Dirac probability function*, and specifies the fraction of all states at energy E (electron volts) occupied under conditions of thermal equilibrium.   From quantum statistics it is found[2,3] that

$$f(E) = \frac{1}{1 + \epsilon^{(E-E_F)/kT}} \tag{3-10}$$

where k = Boltzmann constant, eV/°K
        T = temperature, °K
        E_F = Fermi level, or *characteristic energy*, for the crystal, eV

The Fermi level represents the energy state with 50 percent probability of being filled if no forbidden band exists.   The reason for this last statement is that, if $E = E_F$, then $f(E) = \frac{1}{2}$ for any value of temperature.   A plot of $f(E)$ versus $E - E_F$ is given in Fig. 3-10a and of $E - E_F$ versus $f(E)$ in Fig. 3-10b, both for $T = 0°K$ and for larger values of temperature.   When $T = 0°K$, two possible conditions exist: (1) If $E > E_F$, the exponential term becomes infinite and $f(E) = 0$.   Consequently, *there is no probability of finding an occupied quantum state of energy greater than E_F at absolute zero*.   (2) If $E < E_F$, the exponential in Eq. (3-10) becomes zero and $f(E) = 1$.   *All quantum levels with energies less than E_F will be occupied at $T = 0°K$.*

From Eqs. (3-7), (3-8), and (3-10), we obtain at *absolute zero temperature*

$$\rho_E = \begin{cases} \gamma E^{\frac{1}{2}} & \text{for } E < E_F \\ 0 & \text{for } E > E_F \end{cases} \tag{3-11}$$

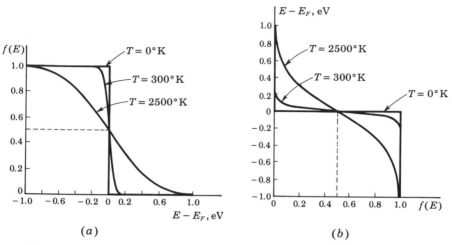

Fig. 3-10 The Fermi-Dirac distribution function $f(E)$ gives the probability that a state of energy E is occupied.

Clearly, there are no electrons at 0°K which have energies in excess of E_F. That is, the Fermi energy is the maximum energy that any electron may possess at absolute zero. The relationship represented by Eq. (3-11) is called the *completely degenerate energy distribution function*. Classically, all particles should have zero energy at 0°K. The fact that the electrons actually have energies extending from 0 to E_F at absolute zero is a consequence of the Pauli exclusion principle, which states that no two electrons may have the same set of quantum numbers (Sec. 2-9). Hence not all electrons can have the same energy even at 0°K. The application of Fermi-Dirac statistics to the theory of metals is due primarily to Sommerfeld.[3]

A plot of the distribution in energy given by Eqs. (3-7) and (3-11) for metallic tungsten at $T = 0°$K and $T = 2500°$K is shown in Fig. 3-11. The area under each curve is simply the total number of particles per cubic meter of the metal; hence the two areas must be equal. Also, the curves for all temperatures must pass through the same ordinate, namely, $\rho_E = \gamma E_F^{\frac{1}{2}}/2$, at the point $E = E_F$, since, from Eq. (3-10), $f(E) = \frac{1}{2}$ for $E = E_F$.

A most important characteristic is to be noted, viz., the distribution function changes only very slightly with temperature, even though the tem-

Fig. 3-11 Energy distribution in metallic tungsten at 0 and 2500°K.

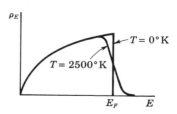

perature change is as great as 2500°K. The effect of the high temperature is merely to give those electrons having the high energies at absolute zero (those in the neighborhood of E_F) still higher energies, whereas those having lower energies have been left practically undisturbed. Since the curve for $T = 2500°K$ approaches the energy axis asymptotically, a few electrons will have large values of energy.

The Fermi Level An expression for E_F may be obtained on the basis of the completely degenerate function. The area under the curve of Fig. 3-11 represents the total number of free electrons (as always, per cubic meter of the metal). Thus

$$n = \int_0^{E_F} \gamma E^{\frac{1}{2}} dE = \frac{2}{3}\gamma E_F^{\frac{3}{2}}$$

or

$$E_F = \left(\frac{3n}{2\gamma}\right)^{\frac{2}{3}} \tag{3-12}$$

Inserting the numerical value (6.82×10^{27}) of the constant γ in this expression, there results

$$E_F = 3.64 \times 10^{-19} n^{\frac{2}{3}} \tag{3-13}$$

Since the density n varies from metal to metal, E_F will also vary among metals. Knowing the specific gravity, the atomic weight, and the number of free electrons per atom, it is a simple matter to calculate n, and so E_F. For most metals the numerical value of E_F is less than 10 eV.

EXAMPLE The specific gravity of tungsten is 18.8, and its atomic weight is 184.0.† Assume that there are two free electrons per atom. Calculate the numerical value of n and E_F.

Solution A quantity of any substance equal to its molecular weight in grams is a *mole* of that substance. Further, one mole of any substance contains the same number of molecules as one mole of any other substance. This number is *Avogadro's number* and equals 6.02×10^{23} molecules per mole. Thus

$$n = 6.02 \times 10^{23} \frac{\text{molecules}}{\text{mole}} \times \frac{1 \text{ mole}}{184 \text{ g}} \times 18.8 \frac{\text{g}}{\text{cm}^3} \times \frac{2 \text{ electrons}}{\text{atom}} \times \frac{1 \text{ atom}}{\text{molecule}}$$

$$= 12.3 \times 10^{22} \frac{\text{electrons}}{\text{cm}^3} = 1.23 \times 10^{29} \frac{\text{electrons}}{\text{m}^3}$$

since for tungsten the atomic and the molecular weights are the same. Therefore, for tungsten,

$$E_F = 3.64 \times 10^{-19} (123 \times 10^{27})^{\frac{2}{3}} = 8.95 \text{ eV}$$

---

† The atomic weights of the elements are given in the periodic table (Appendix C).

3-6   THE DENSITY OF STATES

As a preliminary step in the derivation of the density function $N(E)$ we first show that the components of the momentum of an electron in a metal are quantized. Consider a metal in the form of a cube, each side of which has a length L. Assume that the interior of the metal is at a constant (zero) potential but that the potential-energy barrier (Fig. 3-8) at the surface is arbitrarily high, so that no electrons can escape. Hence the wave functions representing the electrons must be zero outside the metal and at the surface. A one-dimensional model of the potential-energy diagram is given in Fig. 3-12a, and two possible wave functions are indicated in Fig. 3-12b and c. Clearly, this situation is possible only if the dimension L is a half-integral multiple of the De Broglie wavelength λ, or

$$L = n_x \frac{\lambda}{2} \tag{3-14}$$

where n_x is a positive integer (not zero). From the De Broglie relationship (2-8), $\lambda = h/p_x$ and the x component of momentum is

$$p_x = \frac{n_x h}{2L} \tag{3-15}$$

Hence the momentum is quantized since p_x can assume only values which are integral multiples of $h/2L$.

The energy W (in joules) of the electron in this one-dimensional problem is

$$W = \frac{p_x{}^2}{2m} = \frac{n_x{}^2 h^2}{8mL^2} \tag{3-16}$$

The wave nature of the electron has led to the conclusion that its energy must also be quantized. Since $n_x = 1, 2, 3, \ldots$, the lowest possible energy is $h^2/8mL^2$, the next energy level is $h^2/2mL^2$, etc.

The Schrödinger Equation   The above results may be obtained directly by solving the one-dimensional Schrödinger equation with the potential

Fig. 3-12 (a) A one-dimensional problem in which the potential U is zero for a distance L but rises abruptly toward infinity at the boundaries $x = 0$ and $x = L$. (b, c) Two possible wave functions for an electron in the system described by (a).

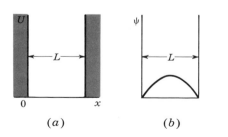

(a) (b) (c)

energy U set equal to zero. Under these circumstances Eq. (2-14) may be written

$$\frac{d^2\psi}{dx^2} + \frac{8\pi^2 m W \psi}{h^2} = 0 \tag{3-17}$$

The general solution of this second-order linear differential equation has two arbitrary constants, C_1 and C_2, and in the interval $0 \le x \le L$ is given by

$$\psi = C_1 \sin ax + C_2 \cos ax \tag{3-18}$$

where

$$a^2 \equiv \frac{8\pi^2 m W}{h^2} \tag{3-19}$$

Since for $x = 0$, $\psi = 0$, then $C_2 = 0$. Since for $x = L$, $\psi = 0$, $\sin aL = 0$, or

$$aL = n_x \pi \tag{3-20}$$

where n_x is an integer. Substituting from Eq. (3-20) into Eq. (3-19) and solving for W, we again obtain the quantized energies given in Eq. (3-16).

The wave function is $\psi = C_1 \sin (n_x \pi x / L)$. Since the probability of finding the electron somewhere in the metal is unity, then from Sec. 2-8,

$$\int_0^L \psi^2 \, dx = 1 = \int_0^L C_1^2 \sin^2 \frac{n_x \pi x}{L} \, dx = \frac{C_1^2 L}{2}$$

or $C_1 = (2/L)^{\frac{1}{2}}$, and

$$\psi = \left(\frac{2}{L}\right)^{\frac{1}{2}} \sin \frac{n_x \pi x}{L} \tag{3-21}$$

Note that n_x cannot be zero since, if it were, ψ would vanish everywhere. For $n_x = 1$ the function ψ is plotted in Fig. 3-12b, and for $n_x = 2$ the wave function ψ is as shown in Fig. 3-12c. Note also that a negative value of n_x gives a value of ψ which is the negative of the value of ψ for the corresponding positive value of n_x. Since only $|\psi|^2$ has a physical meaning (Sec. 2-8), the state described by $-n_x$ is the same as that for $+n_x$. Hence only positive integers are to be used for n_x.

The Uncertainty Principle We digress for a moment to make the point that the measurement of a physical quantity is characterized in an essential way by a lack of precision. For example, in the one-dimensional electronic problem discussed above, there is an inherent uncertainty Δp_x in momentum because n_x can have only integral values. The smallest value of $\Delta n_x = 1$, and hence $\Delta p_x = h/2L$. Since the electron is somewhere between $x = 0$ and $x = L$, the uncertainty in position is $\Delta x = L$. Therefore

$$\Delta p_x \, \Delta x = \frac{h}{2} \tag{3-22}$$

This equation is a statement of the *uncertainty principle*, first enunciated by Heisenberg. He postulated that, for all physical systems (not limited to electrons in a metal), there is always an uncertainty in the position and in the momentum of a particle and that the product of these two uncertainties is of the order of magnitude of Planck's constant h.

Quantum States in a Metal   The above results may be generalized to three dimensions.   For an electron in a cube of metal, each component of momentum is quantized.   Thus

$$p_x = n_x\rho \qquad p_y = n_y\rho \qquad p_z = n_z\rho \qquad\qquad (3\text{-}23)$$

where $\rho \equiv h/2L$, and n_x, n_y, and n_z are positive integers.   A convenient pictorial representation may be obtained by constructing three mutually perpendicular axes labeled p_x, p_y, and p_z.   This "volume" is called *momentum space*. The only possible points which may be occupied by an electron in momentum space are those given by Eq. (3-23).   These are indicated in Fig. 3-13, where for clarity we have indicated points only in a plane for a fixed value of p_z (say, $p_z = 2\rho$).   By the Pauli exclusion principle (Sec. 2-9), no two electrons in a metal may have the same four quantum numbers, n_x, n_y, n_z, and the spin number s.   Hence each dot in Fig. 3-13 represents two electrons, one for $s = \frac{1}{2}$ and the other for $s = -\frac{1}{2}$.

We now find the energy density function $N(E)$.   Since in Fig. 3-13 there is one dot per volume ρ^3 of momentum space, the density of electrons in this space is $2/\rho^3$.   The magnitude of the momentum is $p = (p_x{}^2 + p_y{}^2 + p_z{}^2)^{\frac{1}{2}}$. The number of electrons with momentum between p and $p + dp$ is those

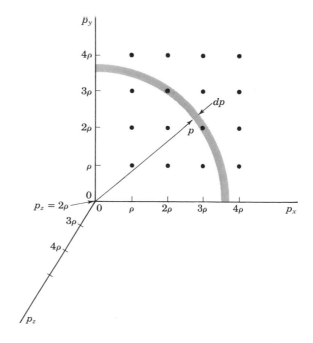

Fig. 3-13   Momentum space.
Each dot represents three
quantum numbers, n_x, n_y,
and n_z.   There are two
electrons per dot, corre-
sponding to the two possible
values of spin.

lying in the shaded spherical shell of Fig. 3-13.   This number is

$$\left(\frac{2}{\rho^3}\right)(4\pi p^2\, dp)\left(\frac{1}{8}\right) = \frac{\pi p^2\, dp}{(h/2L)^3} = \frac{8\pi L^3 p^2\, dp}{h^3} \tag{3-24}$$

The factor $\frac{1}{8}$ introduced in the above equation is due to the fact that only positive values of n_x, n_y, and n_z are permissible, and hence only that part of the shell in the first octant may be used.

If W is the energy (in joules), then $W = p^2/2m$.   Hence

$$p = (2mW)^{\frac{1}{2}} \qquad p\, dp = m\, dW \qquad p^2\, dp = 2^{\frac{1}{2}}m^{\frac{3}{2}}W^{\frac{1}{2}}\, dW \tag{3-25}$$

If $N(W)$ is the density of states (per cubic meter), then, since the volume of the metal is L^3, it follows from Eq. (3-24) that

$$N(W)\, dW = \frac{8\pi p^2\, dp}{h^3} \tag{3-26}$$

gives the number of electrons with momenta between p and $p + dp$, corresponding to energies between W and $W + dW$.   Substituting for $p^2\, dp$ from Eq. (3-25) in Eq. (3-26), we finally obtain

$$N(W)\, dW = \frac{4\pi}{h^3}(2m)^{\frac{3}{2}}W^{\frac{1}{2}}\, dW \tag{3-27}$$

If we use electron volts E instead of joules W as the unit of energy, then since $W = 1.60 \times 10^{-19}\, E$ (Sec. 1-5), the energy density $N(E)$ is given by Eq. (3-8), with γ defined in Eq. (3-9).

3-7   WORK FUNCTION

In Fig. 3-14, Fig. 3-11 has been rotated 90° counterclockwise and combined with Fig. 3-8, so that the vertical axis represents energy for both sets of curves. At 0°K it is impossible for an electron to escape from the metal because this requires an amount of energy equal to E_B, and the maximum energy possessed by any electron is only E_F.   It is necessary to supply an additional amount of energy equal to the difference between E_B and E_F in order to make this escape possible.   This difference, written E_W, is known as the *work function* of the metal.

$$E_W \equiv E_B - E_F \tag{3-28}$$

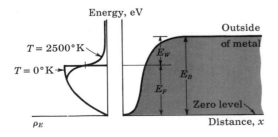

Fig. 3-14   Energy diagram used to define the work function.

Thus the work function of a metal represents the minimum amount of energy that must be given to the fastest-moving electron at the absolute zero of temperature in order for this electron to be able to escape from the metal.

The experiments of Davisson and Germer[4] on the diffraction of electrons in passing through matter have verified the existence of the potential-energy barrier at the surface of the metal. In fact, based on the results of these experiments, together with experimentally determined values of E_W, it is possible to calculate the values of E_F for the metals used. These data show fair agreement between the experimental and theoretical values.

A second physical meaning of the term work function may be obtained by considering what happens to an electron as it escapes from a metal, without particular regard to the conditions within the interior of the metal. A negative electron will induce a positive charge on a metal from which it escapes. There will then be a force of attraction between the induced charge and the electron. Unless the electron possesses sufficient energy to carry it out of the region of influence of this image force of attraction, it will be returned to the metal. The energy required for the electron to escape from the metal is the work function E_W (based upon this classical electrostatic model).

3-8   THERMIONIC EMISSION

The curves of Fig. 3-14 show that the electrons in a metal at absolute zero are distributed among energies which range in value from zero to the maximum energy E_F. Since an electron must possess an amount of energy at least as great as E_B in order to be able to escape, no electrons can leave the metal. Suppose now that the metal, in the form of a filament, is heated by sending a current through it. Thermal energy is then supplied to the electrons from the lattice of the heated metal crystal. The energy distribution of the electrons changes, because of the increased temperature, as indicated in Fig. 3-14. Some of the electrons represented by the tail of the curve will have energies greater than E_B and so may be able to escape from the metal.

Using the analytical expression from the distribution function, it is possible to calculate the number of electrons which strike the surface of the metal per second with sufficient energy to be able to surmount the surface barrier and hence escape. Based upon such a calculation,[3,5] the thermionic current in amperes is given by

$$I_{th} = SA_oT^2\epsilon^{-E_W/kT} \tag{3-29}$$

where S = area of filament, m²
$\quad A_o$ = a constant, whose dimensions are A/(m²)(°K²)
$\quad T$ = temperature, °K
$\quad k$ = Boltzmann constant, eV/°K
$\quad E_W$ = work function, eV

Equation (3-29) is called the *thermionic-emission, Dushman,* or *Richardson* equation. The work function E_W is known also as the "latent heat of evaporation of electrons" from the metal, from the analogy of electron emission with the evaporation of molecules from a liquid.

The thermionic-emission equation has received considerable experimental verification.[6] The graphical representation between the thermionic-emission current and the temperature is generally obtained by taking the logarithm of Eq. (3-29), viz.,

$$\log I_{th} - 2 \log T = \log SA_o - 0.434 \frac{E_W}{kT} \tag{3-30}$$

where the factor 0.434 represents $\log \epsilon$. Hence, if we plot $\log I_{th} - 2 \log T$ versus $1/T$, the result should be a straight line having a slope equal to $-0.434E_W/k$, from which the work function may be determined.

By taking the derivative of the natural logarithm of Eq. (3-29), we obtain

$$\frac{dI_{th}}{I_{th}} = \left(2 + \frac{E_W}{kT}\right) \frac{dT}{T} \tag{3-31}$$

For tungsten, $E_W = 4.52$ eV, and we calculate that at a normal operating temperature of 2400°K, the fractional change in current dI_{th}/I_{th} is $2 + 22$ times the fractional change in the temperature. It is to be noted that the term 22 arises from the exponential term in the Dushman equation, and the term 2 arises from the T^2 term. We observe that the thermionic current is a very sensitive function of the temperature, since a 1 percent change in T results in a 24 percent change in I_{th}.

It must be emphasized that Eq. (3-29) gives the electron emission from a metal at a given temperature provided that there are no external fields present. If there are either accelerating or retarding fields at the surface, the actual current collected will be greater or less than the emission current, respectively. The effect of such surface fields is discussed later in this chapter.

3-9   CONTACT POTENTIAL

Consider two metals in contact with each other, as at the junction C in Fig. 3-15. The contact difference of potential between these two metals is defined as the potential difference V_{AB} between a point A just outside metal 1 and a

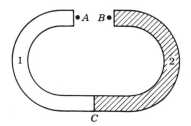

Fig. 3-15   Two metals in contact at the junction C.

point B just outside metal 2. The reason for the existence of the difference of potential is easily understood. When the two metals are joined at the boundary C, electrons will flow from the lower-work-function metal, say 1, to the other metal, 2. This flow will continue until metal 2 has acquired so much negative charge that a retarding field has built up which repels any further electrons. A detailed analysis[5] of the requirement that the number of electrons traveling from metal 1 across junction C into metal 2 is the same as that in the reverse direction across C leads to the conclusion that this equilibrium condition is attained when the Fermi energies E_F of the two metals are located at the same height on the energy-level diagram. To satisfy this condition, the potential-energy difference E_{AB} between points A and B is given by (Prob. 3-16)

$$E_{AB} = E_{W2} - E_{W1} \qquad (3\text{-}32)$$

which means that *the contact difference of potential energy between two metals equals the difference between their work functions.* This result has been verified experimentally by numerous investigators. Corresponding to the potential energy E_{AB}, there is a contact potential (volts) which we designate by $V_{AB} \equiv V'$ and which is numerically equal to E_{AB}.

If metals 1 and 2 are similar, the contact potential between them is evidently zero. If they are dissimilar metals, the metal having the lower work function becomes charged positively and the higher-work-function metal becomes charged negatively. In a vacuum tube the cathode is usually the lowest-work-function metal. If it is connected to any other electrode externally by means of a wire, the effective voltage between the two electrodes is not zero, but equals the difference in the work functions. This potential difference is in such a direction as to *repel* the electrons being emitted from the cathode. If a battery is connected between the two electrodes, the effective potential is the algebraic sum of the applied voltage and the contact potential.

3-10   ENERGIES OF EMITTED ELECTRONS

Since the electrons inside a metal have a distribution of energies, those which escape from the metal will also have an energy distribution. It is easy to demonstrate this experimentally. Thus consider a plane emitter and a plane-parallel collector. The current is measured as a function of the retarding voltage V_r (the emitter positive with respect to the collector). If all the electrons left the cathode with the same energy, the current would remain constant until a definite voltage was reached and then it would fall abruptly to zero. For example, if they all had 2 eV energy, then, when the retarding voltage was greater than 2 V, the electrons could not surmount the potential barrier between cathode and anode and no particles would be collected. Experimentally, no such sudden falling off of current is found, but instead there is an exponential decrease of current I with voltage according to the equation

$$I = I_{th}\epsilon^{-V_r/V_T} \tag{3-33}$$

where V_T is the "volt equivalent of temperature," defined by

$$V_T \equiv \frac{\bar{k}T}{e} = \frac{T}{11,600} \tag{3-34}$$

where $\bar{k}$ is the Boltzmann constant in joules per degree Kelvin.   Note the distinction between $\bar{k}$ and k; the latter is the Boltzmann constant in electron volts per degree Kelvin.   (Numerical values of $\bar{k}$ and k are given in Appendix A.   From Sec. 1-5 it follows that $\bar{k} = 1.60 \times 10^{-19}k$.)

The Volt-Ampere Characteristic   Equation (3-33) may be obtained theoretically as follows: Since I_{th} is the current for zero retarding voltage, the current obtained when the barrier height is increased by E_r is determined from the right-hand side of Eq. (3-29) by changing E_W to $E_W + E_r$.   Hence

$$I = SA_oT^2\epsilon^{-(E_W+E_r)/kT} = I_{th}\epsilon^{-E_r/kT} \tag{3-35}$$

where use was made of Eq. (3-29).   Since V_r is numerically equal to E_r, and V_T is numerically equal to kT, then

$$\frac{E_r}{kT} = \frac{V_r}{V_T} \tag{3-36}$$

Hence Eq. (3-33) follows from Eq. (3-35).

If V is the applied (accelerating) anode potential and if V' is the (retarding) contact potential, then $V_r = V' - V$, and Eq. (3-33) becomes

$$I = I_o\epsilon^{+V/V_T} \tag{3-37}$$

where

$$I_o \equiv I_{th}\epsilon^{-V'/V_T} \tag{3-38}$$

represents the current which is collected at zero applied voltage.   Since $V' > V_T$, this current I_o is a small fraction of I_{th}.   If V is increased from zero, the current I increases exponentially until the magnitude of the applied voltage V equals the contact potential V'.   At this voltage $V_r = 0$, and the thermionic current is collected.   If $V > V'$, the field acting on the emitted electrons is in the accelerating direction and the current remains at the value I_{th}.   A plot of the term log I versus V should be of the form shown in Fig. 3-16. The nonzero slope of this broken-line curve is $(11,600 \log \epsilon)/T = 5,030/T$. From the foregoing considerations, the potential represented by the distance from O to O' is the contact potential V'.   Because most commercial diodes do not even approximate a plane cathode with a plane-parallel anode, the volt-ampere characteristic indicated in Fig. 3-16 is only approached in practice.

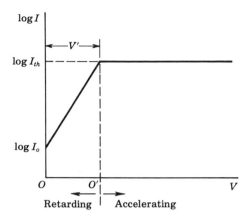

Fig. 3-16   To verify the retarding-
potential equation, $\log I$ is plotted
versus V.

Furthermore, since the effect of space charge (Chap. 4) has been completely
neglected, Eq. (3-33) is valid only for low values (microamperes) of current.
For larger values of I, the current varies as the three-halves power of the
plate potential (Sec. 4-4).

EXAMPLE   What percentage of the electrons leaving a tungsten filament at,
2700°K can surmount a barrier whose height is 1 eV?

Solution   Using Eq. (3-33), with $V_r = 1$, and remembering that $V_T - T/11{,}600$,
yields

$$\frac{I}{I_{th}} = \epsilon^{-(11{,}600 \times 1)/2{,}700} = \epsilon^{-4.28} = 0.014$$

Hence only about 1.4 percent of the electrons have surface-directed energies in
excess of 1 eV.

If the emitter is an oxide-coated cathode operating at 1000°K, a calculation similar to the above gives the result that only about 0.001 percent of
the electrons have a surface-directed energy in excess of 1 eV.

A statistical analysis[3,5] shows that the average energy of the escaping
electrons is given by the expression

$$\bar{E} = 2kT \tag{3-39}$$

For operating temperatures of 2700 and 1000°K, the average energies of the
emitted electrons are 0.47 and 0.17 eV, respectively.

These calculations demonstrate the validity of the assumption made in
Chap. 1 in the discussion of the motion of electrons in electric and magnetic
fields, viz., that the electrons begin their motions with very small initial velocities.   In most applications the initial velocities are of no consequence.

3-11   ACCELERATING FIELDS

Under normal operating conditions, the field applied between the cathode and
the collecting anode is accelerating rather than retarding, and so the field aids
the electrons in overcoming the image force at the surface of the metal. This
accelerating field tends, therefore, to lower the work function of the metal,
and so results in an increased thermionic emission from the metal. It can be
shown[5] that the current I under the condition of an accelerating field of ε
(volts per meter) at the surface of the emitter is

$$I = I_{th}\epsilon^{+0.440\varepsilon^{\frac{1}{2}}/T} \tag{3-40}$$

where I_{th} is the zero-field thermionic current, and T is the cathode temperature in degrees Kelvin. The fact that the measured thermionic currents continue to increase as the applied potential between the cathode and the anode is
increased is often referred to as the *Schottky effect*, after the man who first predicted this effect. Some idea of the order of magnitude of this increase can be
obtained from the following illustration.

EXAMPLE Consider a cylindrical cathode of radius 0.01 cm and a coaxial
cylindrical anode of radius 1.0 cm. The temperature of the cathode is 2500°K.
If an accelerating potential of 500 V is applied between the cathode and the anode,
calculate the percentage increase in the zero-external-field thermionic-emission
current because of the Schottky effect.

Solution The electric field intensity (volts per meter) at any point r (meters)
in the region between the electrodes of a cylindrical capacitor, according to
classical electrostatics, is given by the formula

$$\varepsilon = \frac{V}{\ln (r_a/r_k)} \frac{1}{r} \tag{3-41}$$

where ln = logarithm to the natural base ϵ
    V = plate voltage
    r_a = anode radius
    r_k = cathode radius
Thus the electric field intensity at the surface of the cathode is

$$\varepsilon = \frac{500}{2.303 \log 100} \frac{1}{10^{-4}} = 1.085 \times 10^6 \text{ V/m}$$

It follows from Eq. (3-40) that

$$\log \frac{I}{I_{th}} = \frac{(0.434)(0.44)(1.085 \times 10^6)^{\frac{1}{2}}}{2,500} = 0.0795$$

Hence $I/I_{th} = 1.20$, which shows that the Schottky theory predicts a 20 percent
increase over the zero-field emission current.

3-12   HIGH–FIELD EMISSION

Suppose that the accelerating field at the surface of a "cold" cathode (one for which the thermionic-emission current is negligible) is very intense. Then, not only is the potential-energy barrier at the surface of the cathode lowered, but also it is reduced in thickness. For fields of the order of 10^9 V/m, the barrier may become so thin ($\sim$100 Å) that an electron, considered as a De Broglie wave, may penetrate, or "tunnel," through the barrier (Sec. 6-13). Under these circumstances the variation of the emission-current density with the strength of the electric field intensity at the surface of the metal has been calculated by several investigators.[7]

This tunneling effect is called *high-field, cold-cathode,* or *autoelectronic emission.* The electric field intensity at an electrode whose geometry includes a sharp point or edge may be very high even if the applied voltage is moderate. Hence, if high-field emission is to be avoided, it is very important to shape the electrodes in a tube properly so that a concentration of electrostatic lines of flux does not take place on any metallic surface. On the other hand, the cold-cathode effect has been used to provide several thousand amperes in an x-ray tube used for high-speed radiography.

3-13   SECONDARY EMISSION[8]

The number of secondary electrons that are emitted from a material, either a metal or a dielectric, when subjected to electron bombardment has been found experimentally to depend upon the following factors: the number of primary electrons, the energy of the primary electrons, the angle of incidence of the electrons on the material, the type of material, and the physical condition of the surface. The *yield,* or *secondary-emission ratio* δ, defined as the ratio of the number of secondary electrons per primary electron, is small for pure metals, the maximum value being between 1.5 and 2. It is increased markedly by the presence of a contaminating layer of gas or by the presence of an electropositive or alkali metal on the surface. For such composite surfaces, secondary-emission ratios as high as 10 or 15 have been detected. Most secondary electrons are emitted with small (less than 3 eV) energies.

The ratio δ is a function of the energy E of the impinging primary electrons, and a plot of δ versus E exhibits a maximum, usually at a few hundred electron volts. This maximum can be explained qualitatively as follows: For low-energy primaries, the number of secondaries that are able to overcome the surface attraction is small. As the energy of the impinging electrons increases, more energetic secondaries are produced and the yield increases. Since, however, the depth of penetration increases with the energy of the incident electron, the secondaries must travel a greater distance in the metal before they reach the surface. This increases the probability of collision in the metal, with a consequent loss of energy of these secondaries. Thus, if the primary energy is increased too much, the secondary-emission ratio must pass through a maximum.

REFERENCES

1. Shockley, W.: The Nature of the Metallic State, *J. Appl. Phys.*, vol. 10, pp. 543–555, 1939.

2. Fermi, E.: Zur Quantelung des idealen einatomigen Gases, *Z. Physik*, vol. 36, pp. 902–912, May, 1926.
   Dirac, P. A. M.: On the Theory of Quantum Mechanics, *Proc. Roy. Soc. (London)*, vol. 112, pp. 661–677, October, 1926.

3. Sommerfeld, A., and H. Bethe: Elektronentheorie der Metalle, in "Handbuch der Physik," 2d ed., vol. 24, pt. 2, pp. 333–622, Springer Verlag OHG, Berlin, 1933.
   Darrow, K. K.: Statistical Theories of Matter, Radiation and Electricity, *Bell System Tech. J.*, vol. 8, pp. 672–748, October, 1929.

4. Davisson, C. J., and L. H. Germer: Reflection and Refraction of Electrons by a Crystal of Nickel, *Proc. Natl. Acad. Sci. U.S.*, vol. 14, pp. 619–627, August, 1928.

5. Millman, J., and S. Seely: "Electronics," 2d ed., McGraw-Hill Book Company, New York, 1951.

6. Dushman, S.: Thermionic Emission, *Rev. Mod. Phys.*, vol. 2, pp. 381–476, October, 1930.

7. Dyke, W. P., and W. W. Dolan: Field Emission, "Advances in Electronics," vol. 8, Academic Press Inc., New York, 1956.
   Fowler, R. H., and L. Nordheim: Electron Emission in Intense Electric Fields, *Proc. Roy. Soc. (London)*, vol. 119, pp. 173–181, May, 1928.
   Oppenheimer, J. R.: On the Quantum Theory of Autoelectric Field Circuits, *Proc. Natl. Acad. Sci. U.S.*, vol. 14, pp. 363–365, May, 1928.

8. Spangenberg, K. R.: "Vacuum Tubes," McGraw-Hill Book Company, New York, 1948.
   McKay, K. G.: Secondary Electron Emission, "Advances in Electronics," vol. 1, pp. 65–130, Academic Press Inc., New York, 1948.   An extensive review.

4 / VACUUM–DIODE CHARACTERISTICS

The properties of practical thermionic cathodes are discussed in this chapter. In order to collect the emitted electrons, a plate or anode is placed close to the cathode in an evacuated envelope. If an accelerating field is applied, it is found that the plate current increases as the anode voltage is increased. When a large enough plate potential is applied to collect the thermionic-emission current I_{th}, the anode current will remain constant at the value I_{th} even though the plate voltage is increased further. The limitation of the current which can be collected in a diode at a given voltage because of the space charge of the electrons is discussed in detail in this chapter.

Finally, practical diode volt-ampere characteristics are considered, and an analysis of a circuit containing a diode is given.

4-1   CATHODE MATERIALS

The three most important practical emitters are pure tungsten, thoriated tungsten, and oxide-coated cathodes. The most important properties of these emitters are now discussed, and are summarized in Table 4-1.

Tungsten   Unlike the other cathodes discussed below, tungsten does not have an active surface layer which can be damaged by positive-ion bombardment. Hence tungsten is used as the cathode in high-voltage high-vacuum tubes. These include x-ray tubes, diodes for use as rectifiers above about 5,000 V, and large power-amplifier tubes for use in communication transmitters.

Tungsten has the disadvantage that the *cathode-emission efficiency*, defined as the ratio of the emission current, in amperes, to the heating

TABLE 4-1   Comparison of thermionic emitters

Type of cathode	$A_o \times 10^{-4}$, A/(m²)(°K²)	E_W, eV	Approximate operating temperature, °K	Efficiency,† mA/W	Plate voltage, V	Gas or vacuum tube
Tungsten....	60.2	4.52	2,500	20–100	Above 5,000	Vacuum
Thoriated tungsten ..	3.0	2.63	1,900	50–1,000	750–5,000	Vacuum
Oxide-coated	0.01	1.0	1,000	100–10,000	Below 750	Vacuum or gas

† K. R. Spangenberg, "Vacuum Tubes," McGraw-Hill Book Company, New York, 1948.

power, in watts, is small.   However, a copious supply of electrons can be provided by operating the cathode at a sufficiently high temperature.   The higher the temperature, the greater will be the evaporation of the filament during its operation and the sooner it will burn out.   Economic considerations dictate that the temperature of the filament be about 2500°K, which gives it a life of approximately 2,000 hr.   The melting point of tungsten is 3650°K.

Thoriated Tungsten[1]   In order to obtain copious emission of electrons at moderately low temperatures, it is necessary for the material to have a low work function.   Unfortunately, the low-work-function metals, such as cesium, rubidium, and barium, in some cases melt and in other cases boil at temperatures necessary for appreciable thermionic emission.   However, it is possible to apply a very thin (monatomic) layer of low-work-function material, such as thorium, on a filament of tungsten.   Thoriated-tungsten filaments are obtained by adding a small amount (1 or 2 percent by weight) of thorium oxide to the tungsten.   The base metal holds the adsorbed layer at high temperatures, even above the point at which the pure thorium would normally evaporate. Such a filament possesses emission properties that are considerably better than those of the pure tungsten.

The limitation to the use of thoriated-tungsten emitters is the deactivation due to positive-ion bombardment.   The effect of even a few ions is severe at high potentials, so that these filaments are confined to use in tubes that operate with potentials of less than about 5,000 V.   Thoriated-tungsten filaments are used in a number of moderate-voltage transmitting tubes as well as in high-power beam-type microwave tubes.

EXAMPLE   At what temperature will a thoriated-tungsten filament give 5,000 times as much emission as a pure tungsten filament at the same temperature? The filament dimensions of the two emitters are the same.

Solution   It is required that $I_{T-W} = 5{,}000 I_W$. From Eq. (3-15) and Table 4-1,

$$I_{T-W} = (S)(3.0 \times 10^4)(T^2)\epsilon^{-2.63/kT}$$

and

$$I_W = (S)(60.2 \times 10^4)(T^2)\epsilon^{-4.52/kT}$$

Upon dividing these two equations, there results

$$\frac{I_{T-W}}{I_W} = 5{,}000 = \frac{3}{60.2}\,\epsilon^{(4.52-2.63)/(8.62\times10^{-5}T)}$$

$$= \frac{1}{20.1}\,\epsilon^{21{,}900/T}$$

where the value of k in electron volts per degree Kelvin given in Appendix A was used. We can solve for T with the aid of logarithms. Thus

$$\frac{(0.434)(21{,}900)}{T} = \log\,(5{,}000)(20.1) = 5.00$$

or

$$T = 1900°K$$

Oxide-coated Cathodes[2]   The modern oxide-coated cathode is the most efficient type of emitter that has been developed commercially. It consists of a metallic base of platinum, nickel, nickel with a few percent of cobalt or silicon, or Konal metal. Konal metal is an alloy consisting of nickel, cobalt, iron, and titanium. Konal-metal sleeves are used very extensively as the indirectly heated cathode of radio receiving tubes. The wire filaments or the metallic sleeves are coated with oxides of the alkaline-earth group, especially barium and strontium oxides.

Four characteristics of the coating account for its extensive use: (1) It has a long life, several thousand hours under normal operating conditions being common. At reduced filament power, several hundred thousand hours has been obtained. (2) It can easily be manufactured in the form of the indirectly heated cathode. (3) It gives tremendous outputs under pulsed conditions. Thus it has been found that for (microsecond) pulses current densities in excess of 10^8 A/m^2 may be obtained.[3] (4) It has very high cathode efficiency.

Oxide-coated cathodes are subject to deactivation by positive-ion bombardment, and so are generally used in low-voltage tubes only. The emission properties of an oxide-coated cathode are influenced by many factors, for example, the proportion of the contributing oxides, the thickness of the oxide coating, possibly the core material, and the details of the processing. Hence the emission characteristics change with the age of the cathode and vary markedly from tube to tube. How then can tubes using oxide-coated cathodes serve satisfactorily in any circuit? It is shown in Sec. 4-4 that tubes usually operate under conditions of space-charge limitation and not under conditions of temperature limitation. This statement means that *the current is determined by the plate voltage and not by the cathode temperature.* Thus, despite their rather unpredictable emission characteristics, oxide-coated cathodes make excellent tube elements, provided only that their thermionic-emission current never falls below that required by the circuit.

Oxide-coated cathodes are used in the greatest percentage of commercial electron tubes. Almost all receiving tubes, many low-voltage transmitting tubes, and practically all gas tubes use such cathodes.

4-2   COMMERCIAL CATHODES

The cathodes used in thermionic tubes are sometimes directly heated filaments in the form of a V, a W, or a straight wire, although most tubes use indirectly heated cathodes.

The indirectly heated cathode was developed so as to minimize the hum (Sec. 16-11) arising from the various effects of ac heater operation. The heater wire (tungsten) is contained in a ceramic insulator (oxides of beryllium and aluminum) enclosed by a nickel or Konal-metal sleeve on which the oxide coating is placed. The cathode as a unit is so massive that its temperature does not vary appreciably with instantaneous variations in the magnitude of the heater currents. Further, since the sleeve is the emitting surface, the cathode is essentially equipotential. The ceramic insulator which acts to isolate electrically the heater wire from the cathode must, of course, be a good heat conductor. Under normal conditions of operation, the heater is maintained at about 1000°C, which results in the cathode temperature being at approximately 850°C.

Heaterless Cathodes   Vacuum diode and multielectrode tubes have been constructed which contain no heater. The *Thermionic Integrated Micro-Module*, known as TIMM (General Electric trade name), obtains the heat needed to develop thermionic emission by conserving the normal dissipations of both active and passive components and containing this energy within a suitable insulated enclosure.

A TIMM is constructed of special ceramic materials, with electrodes of titanium, and is operated at approximately 600°C. The oxide cathode coating is deposited upon platinum base metal, leading to chemical stability and long emitter life.

4-3   THE POTENTIAL VARIATION BETWEEN THE ELECTRODES

Consider a simple thermionic diode whose cathode can be heated to any desired temperature and whose anode or plate potential is maintained at V_P. It will be assumed that the cathode is a plane equipotential surface and that the collecting plate is also a plane parallel to it. The potential variations between

Fig. 4-1 The potential variation between plane-parallel electrodes for several values of cathode temperature.

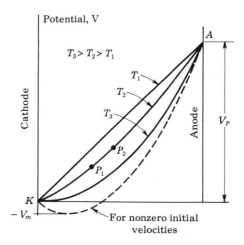

the electrodes for various temperatures of the cathode are given in Fig. 4-1. The general shape of these curves may be explained as follows: At the temperature T_1 at which no electrons are emitted, the potential gradient is constant, so that the potential variation is a linear function of the distance from the cathode to the anode.

At the higher temperature T_2, an appreciable density of electrons exists in the interelectrode space. The potential variation will be somewhat as illustrated by the curve marked T_2 in Fig. 4-1. The increase in temperature can change neither the potential of the cathode nor the potential of the anode. Hence all the curves must pass through the fixed end points K and A. Since negative charge (electrons) now exists in the space between K and A, then, by Coulomb's law, the potential at any point will be lowered. The greater the space charge, the lower will be the potential. Thus, as the temperature is increased, the potential curves become more and more concave upward. At T_3, the curve has drooped so far that it is tangent to the X axis at the origin. That is, the electric field intensity at the cathode for this condition is zero. One may sketch the broken curve of Fig. 4-1 to represent the potential variation at a temperature higher than T_3. This curve contains a potential minimum. Such a condition is physically impossible if the initial velocities of the emitted electrons are assumed negligible. That this is so follows from the discussion given below.

The Potential-energy Curves Since the potential energy is equal to the product of the potential V and the charge $-e$, the curves of Fig. 4-2 are simply those of Fig. 4-1 inverted, the unit of the ordinates being changed to electron volts. It is immediately evident that the broken curve represents a potential-energy barrier at the surface of the cathode. Several such potential-energy barriers have already been considered in Chap. 3. On the basis of our previous discussions, it is clear that only those electrons which possess an initial energy greater than E_m, the maximum height of the barrier, can escape from the cathode and reach the anode. Consequently, the assumed condition of zero initial velocities of the emitted electrons precludes the possibility of any electrons being emitted. As a result, the barrier will be broken down, since the applied field will cause those electrons which produce the barrier to leave the interelectrode space and become part of the anode current. This automatic growth and collapse of the potential barrier outside the cathode may be considered as a self-regulating valve that allows a certain definite number of electrons per second to escape from the cathode and reach the anode, for a given value of plate voltage.

The Field Intensity at the Cathode It can be inferred from the foregoing argument that the maximum current that can be drawn from a diode for a fixed plate voltage and any temperature whatsoever is obtained under the condition of zero electric field at the surface of the cathode. Thus, for optimum conditions,

$$\mathcal{E} = -\frac{dV}{dx} = 0 \qquad \text{at } x = 0 \tag{4-1}$$

This condition is based on the assumption that the emitted electrons have zero initial energies. Because the initial velocities are not truly zero, the potential variation within the tube may actually acquire the form illustrated by the broken curve of Fig. 4-1. However, since the potential minimum in Fig. 4-1 is usually small in comparison with the applied potential, it is neglected, and condition (4-1) is assumed to represent the true status when space-charge current is being drawn.

4-4   SPACE–CHARGE CURRENT

We shall now obtain the analytical relationship between the current and voltage in a diode. The electrons flowing from the cathode to the anode consti-

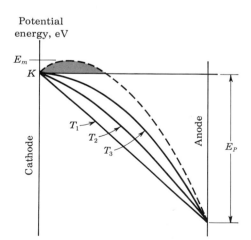

Fig. 4-2 The potential-energy variations corresponding to the curves of Fig. 4-1.

tute the current.   The magnitude of the current density J in amperes per square meter is given by Eq. (1-38), viz.,

$$J = \rho v \tag{4-2}$$

where v is the drift velocity of these electrons in meters per second, and ρ is the volume density of electric charge in coulombs per cubic meter.   Both ρ and v are functions of the distance from the origin (the cathode).   However, the product is constant, since the number of electrons passing through unit area per second must be the same for all points between a plane cathode and a parallel anode.   This statement expresses the principle of *conservation of electric charge*.   Therefore, at the cathode, where the velocity of the electrons is very small (the velocities being the initial velocities), the charge density must be very large.   In the neighborhood of the anode, the velocity is a maximum; hence the charge density is a minimum.   If the initial velocities are neglected, the velocity of the electrons at any point in the interelectrode space may be determined from the equation that relates the kinetic energy of the particle with the potential through which it has fallen, viz.,

$$\tfrac{1}{2}mv^2 = eV \tag{4-3}$$

Poisson's equation is

$$\frac{d^2V}{dx^2} = \frac{\rho}{\epsilon_o} \tag{4-4}$$

where x = distance from cathode, m
  V = potential, V
  ρ = *magnitude* of *electronic* volume charge density, C/m³
  ϵ_o = permittivity of free space, mks system
There results, from Eqs. (4-2) to (4-4),

$$\frac{d^2V}{dx^2} = \frac{\rho}{\epsilon_o} = \frac{J}{v\epsilon_o} = \frac{J}{[2(e/m)]^{\frac{1}{2}}\epsilon_o} V^{-\frac{1}{2}} = KV^{-\frac{1}{2}} \tag{4-5}$$

where

$$K \equiv \frac{J}{[2(e/m)]^{\frac{1}{2}}\epsilon_o} \tag{4-6}$$

is a constant, independent of x.

The Solution of Eq. (4-5)   Let $y \equiv dV/dx$, and this nonlinear differential equation may be solved by the separation-of-variables method.   Thus

$$\frac{dy}{dx} = KV^{-\frac{1}{2}}$$

or

$$dy = KV^{-\frac{1}{2}}\,dx = KV^{-\frac{1}{2}}\frac{dV}{y}$$

Hence

$$y\,dy = KV^{-\frac{1}{2}}\,dV$$

which integrates to

$$\frac{y^2}{2} = 2KV^{\frac{1}{2}} + C_1 \tag{4-7}$$

The constant of integration C_1 is zero because, at the cathode, $V = 0$ and $y = dV/dx = 0$, from Eq. (4-1). By taking the square root of Eq. (4-7) there results

$$y = \frac{dV}{dx} = 2K^{\frac{1}{2}}V^{\frac{1}{4}} \qquad \text{and} \qquad V^{-\frac{1}{4}}\,dV = 2K^{\frac{1}{2}}\,dx$$

This equation integrates to

$$\tfrac{4}{3}V^{\frac{3}{4}} = 2K^{\frac{1}{2}}x + C_2$$

The constant of integration C_2 is zero because $V = 0$ at $x = 0$. Finally,

$$V = (\tfrac{3}{2})^{\frac{4}{3}}K^{\frac{2}{3}}x^{\frac{4}{3}} \tag{4-8}$$

It is seen that the potential depends upon the four-thirds power of the interelectrode spacing. For example, the curve marked T_3 in Fig. 4-1 is expressed by the relation

$$V = \alpha x^{\frac{4}{3}} \tag{4-9}$$

where α is readily found in terms of constants and the current density J from the foregoing equations. However, α may also be written as $V_P/d^{\frac{4}{3}}$, where d is the separation of the electrode and V_P is the plate potential. This is so because Eq. (4-9) is valid for the entire interelectrode space, including the boundary $x = d$, where $V = V_P$.

The Three-halves-power Law The complete expression for the current density is obtained by combining Eqs. (4-8) and (4-6). The result is

$$J = \frac{4}{9}\left(2\frac{e}{m}\right)^{\frac{1}{2}}\epsilon_o\frac{V^{\frac{3}{2}}}{x^2} \tag{4-10}$$

In terms of the boundary values, this becomes, upon inserting the value of e/m for electrons and $\epsilon_o = 10^{-9}/36\pi$,

$$J = 2.33 \times 10^{-6}\frac{V_P^{\frac{3}{2}}}{d^2} \tag{4-11}$$

Therefore *the plate current varies as the three-halves power of the plate potential.* This result was established by Langmuir,[4] although it had been previously published in a different connection by Child.[5] It is known by several different names, for example, the *Langmuir-Child law,* the *three-halves-power law,* or simply, the *space-charge equation.*

It will be noticed that this equation relates the current density, and so the current, in terms only of the applied potential and the geometry of the tube. The space-charge current does not depend upon either the temperature or the work function of the cathode. Hence, no matter how many electrons a cathode may be able to supply, the geometry of the tube and the potential applied thereto will determine the maximum current that can be collected by the anode. Of course, it may be less than the value predicted by Eq. (4-11) if the electron supply from the cathode is restricted (because the temperature is too low). To summarize, the *plate current in a given diode depends only upon the applied potential*, provided that this current is less than the temperature-limited current.

The velocity of the electrons as a function of position between the cathode and anode can be found from Eq. (4-3) with the aid of Eq. (4-10). Then the charge density as a function of x can be obtained from Eq. (4-2). It is found (Prob. 4-6) that v varies as the two-thirds power of x and that ρ varies inversely as the two-thirds power of x. This physically impossible result that at the cathode the charge density is infinite is a consequence of the assumption that the electrons emerging from the cathode all do so with zero initial velocity. Actually, of course, the initial velocities are small, but nonzero, and the charge density is large, though finite.

Systems that possess plane-parallel electrodes were considered above because the simplicity of this geometry made it easy to understand the physical principles involved. However, such tube geometry is almost never met in practice. More frequently, tubes are constructed with cylindrical symmetry, the anode being in the form of a cylinder that is coaxial with a cathode of either the directly or the indirectly heated type. It is possible to demonstrate[6] that *an expression of the form*

$$I_P = G V_P^{\frac{3}{2}} \tag{4-12}$$

where I_P is the plate current, applies for any geometrical arrangement of cathode and anode, provided that initial velocities are neglected. The specific value of the constant G, called the *perveance*, that exists in this expression depends upon the geometry of the system.

4-5   FACTORS INFLUENCING SPACE–CHARGE CURRENT

Several factors modify the equations for space charge given above, particularly at low plate voltages. Among these factors are:

1. Filament Voltage Drop   The space-charge equations are derived on the assumption that the cathode is an equipotential surface. This is not a valid assumption for a directly heated emitter, and the voltage across the ends of the filament causes a deviation from the three-halves-power equation. In fact, the results depend on whether the plate current is returned to the positive or to the negative end of the filament. Usually, the filament is heated with a transformer, and the plate is returned to the center tap of the secondary winding.

2. Contact Potential   In every space-charge equation, the symbol V_P must be understood to mean the sum of the applied voltage from plate to cathode plus the contact potential between the two.   For plate voltages of only a few volts, this effect may be quite appreciable.

3. Asymmetries in Tube Structure   Commercial tubes seldom possess the ideal geometry assumed in deriving the space-charge equations.

4. Gas   The presence of even minute traces of gas in a tube can have marked effects on the tube characteristics.   If the voltage is sufficiently high to cause ionization of the residual gas molecules, the plate current will rise above that demanded by the space-charge equations because the positive ions that are formed neutralize the electronic-charge density.   Modern vacuum tubes are exhausted to pressures of about 10^{-6} mm Hg.

5. Initial Velocities of Emitted Electrons   If the initial velocities of the electrons are not neglected, the variations of potential with interelectrode spacing will be somewhat as depicted by the broken curve of Fig. 4-1, which is reproduced in Fig. 4-3 for convenience.   This represents a potential-energy barrier at the cathode surface, and so it is only those electrons whose energies are greater than the height $E_m = eV_m$ of this barrier that can escape from the cathode.   The height of this barrier is, from the results of Sec. 3-10, a fraction of 1 eV.

At a distance x_m from the surface of the thermionic emitter, the point of the potential minimum, the electric field intensity passes through zero.   Hence the point M may be considered as the position of a "virtual" cathode.   Evidently, the distance that will enter into the resulting space-charge equation will be $d - x_m$, and not d.   Likewise, the effective plate potential will be $V_P + V_m$, and not V_P alone.   Both of these factors will tend to increase the current above that which exists when the initial velocities are neglected.   The exact mathematical formulation of the volt-ampere equation, taking into account the energy distribution of the electrons, is somewhat involved.[7]   To

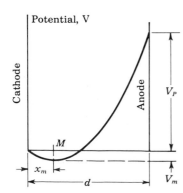

Fig. 4-3   The potential variation in a plane-parallel space-charge diode, with the initial velocities of the electrons taken into account.

summarize, the space-charge current in a diode is not strictly a function of the plate potential only, but does depend, to a small extent, upon the temperature of the cathode.

4-6   DIODE CHARACTERISTICS

The two most important factors that determine the characteristics of diodes are thermionic emission and space charge. The first gives the temperature-saturated value, i.e., the maximum current that can be collected at a given cathode temperature, regardless of the magnitude of the applied accelerating potential. The second gives the space-charge-limited value, or the voltage-saturated value, and specifies the maximum current that can be collected at a given voltage regardless of the temperature of the filament.

Large-voltage Characteristics   The volt-ampere curves obtained experimentally for an oxide-coated cathode are shown in Fig. 4-4. It should be noted that the space-charge currents corresponding to the different temperatures do not coincide, but that the currents decrease slightly as the temperature decreases. Further, there is no abrupt transition between the space-charge-limited and the temperature-limited portions of the curves, but rather a gradual transition occurs. Also, the current for the temperature-limited regions gradually rises with increased anode potentials (because of the Schottky effect, Sec. 3-11). The shapes of these curves are determined by the factors mentioned in the preceding section.

Low-voltage Characteristic   The diode curve does not follow Eq. (4-12) for small currents or voltages because the initial velocities of the electrons and the contact potential cannot be neglected in this region. An expanded view of the volt-ampere curve near the origin is given in Fig. 4-5. Space charge is negligible at these small currents, and the volt-ampere relationship is given by Eq. (3-37), namely,

$$I_P = I_o \epsilon^{V_P/V_T} \tag{4-13}$$

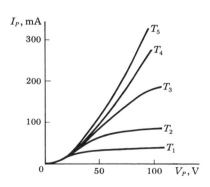

Fig. 4-4 Volt-ampere diode characteristics for various filament temperatures. $T_5 > T_4 > T_3 > T_2 > T_1$.

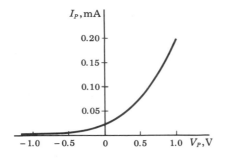

Fig. 4-5 The volt-ampere characteristic of a vacuum diode for small voltages.

where I_o is the plate current at zero applied voltage V, and $V_T = T/11,600$ [Eq. (3-34)] is the volt equivalent of temperature. Note that the curve does *not* pass through the origin.

4-7 AN IDEAL DIODE VERSUS A THERMIONIC DIODE

An ideal diode is defined as a two-terminal circuit element having the following characteristics: (1) It offers no resistance to current flow if the plate is positive with respect to cathode (zero forward resistance). (2) There is no current if the plate is negative with respect to the cathode (infinite reverse resistance). (3) The capacitance shunting the diode is zero. (4) These characteristics are independent of temperature. The volt-ampere characteristic of an ideal diode is shown in Fig. 4-6.

A physical thermionic diode differs in the following important respects from the ideal diode:

1. The forward resistance is not zero, but lies in the approximate range of 100 to 1,000 Ω.
2. The value of the resistance is not constant, but depends upon the applied voltage. Hence a distinction must be made between *static* and *dynamic* resistance. The static resistance R is defined as the ratio V_P/I_P. At any point P on the volt-ampere characteristic of the diode, R is the reciprocal of the slope of the line joining P to the origin. The static resistance varies widely with voltage, and hence is seldom used. For small-signal operation,

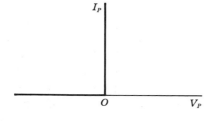

Fig. 4-6 An ideal-diode characteristic.

an important parameter is the *dynamic, incremental,* or *plate resistance,* defined by

$$r_p \equiv \frac{dV_P}{dI_P} \tag{4-14}$$

This dynamic forward resistance will also be designated by R_f. Of course, if the volt-ampere characteristic were a straight line passing through the origin, R_f would equal R. Although r_p varies with current, it is reasonable to treat this parameter as a constant in a small-signal model.

3. The back, or reverse, resistance R_r is not infinite, although values of hundreds or even thousands of megohms are attainable even for small negative applied voltages.

4. The "break" in the characteristic (the division between the high- and low-resistance regions) is not sharp, and may not occur at zero applied voltage.

5. As already mentioned in Sec. 4-5, the volt-ampere characteristic is not strictly space-charge-limited, but does depend somewhat upon the filament temperature. Experiment reveals that there is a shift in the voltage at constant current of about -0.1 V *for a* 10 *percent increase in the heater voltage.* The higher the filament voltage, the more the curves shift to the left, because the increase in the initial velocities of the electrons with increase in temperature results in higher currents at a given voltage. The shift with tube replacement or tube aging is found in practice to be of the order of ± 0.25 V.

6. Since a diode consists of two metallic electrodes (a cathode and an anode) separated by a dielectric (a vacuum), this device constitutes a capacitor. The order of magnitude of this capacitance is 5 pF To this value must be added the wiring capacitance introduced when the diode is inserted into a circuit.

4-8   RATING OF VACUUM DIODES

The rating of a vacuum diode, i.e., the maximum current that it may normally carry and the maximum potential difference that may be applied between the cathode and the anode, is influenced by a number of factors.

1. The plate current cannot exceed the thermionic-emission current.

2. In order that the gas adsorbed by the glass walls should not be liberated, the temperature of the envelope must not be allowed to exceed the temperature to which the tube was raised in the outgassing process.

3. The most important factor limiting the rating of a tube is the allowable temperature rise of the anode. When a diode is in operation, the anode becomes heated to a rather high temperature because of the power ($I_P V_P$) that must be dissipated by the anode. The temperature of the anode will rise until the rate at which the energy supplied to the anode just equals the rate at which the heat is dissipated from the anode in the form of radiation. Conse-

quently, the temperature will depend upon the area of the anode and the material of which it is constructed. The most common metals used for anodes are nickel and iron for receiving tubes and tantalum, molybdenum, and graphite for transmitting tubes. The surfaces are often roughened or blackened in order to increase the thermal emissivity and permit higher-power operation. These anodes may be operated at a cherry-red heat without excessive gas emission or other deleterious effects. For the larger tubes, it is necessary that the anodes be cooled either by circulating water through special cooling coils or by forced-air-cooling radiator fins attached to the anode.

4. The voltage limitation of a high-vacuum diode is not always determined by the permissible heating of the anode. Conduction may take place between the filament leads and the anode lead through the glass itself, if the voltage between these leads is high. For this reason, high-voltage rectifiers are generally constructed with the filament leads and the anode lead at opposite ends of the glass envelope.

Peak Inverse Voltage The separation of the leads of high-voltage rectifiers must be large enough to preclude flashover through the air. In fact, it is the highest voltage that may be safely impressed across the electrodes with no flow of charge which determines the safe voltage rating of a tube. Since, with an alternating potential applied between the cathode and anode, no current must exist during the portion of the cycle when the anode is negative with respect to the cathode, the maximum safe rating of a rectifying diode is known as the *peak-inverse-voltage rating.*

Commercial vacuum diodes are made to rectify currents at very high voltages, up to about 200,000 V. Such units are used with x-ray equipment, high-voltage cable-testing equipment, and high-voltage equipment for nuclear-physics research.

Semiconductor Diodes Because of their small size and long life and because no filament power is required, semiconductor diodes (Chap. 6) are replacing vacuum rectifiers in many applications. The tube must be used, however, if very high voltage or power is involved, if extremely low reverse currents are necessary, or if the diode is located in an unusual environment (high nuclear radiation or high ambient temperature).

4-9 THE DIODE AS A CIRCUIT ELEMENT

The basic diode circuit of Fig. 4-7 consists of the tube in series with a load resistance R_L and an input-signal source v_i. Since the heater plays no part in the analysis of the circuit, it has been omitted from Fig. 4-7, and the diode is indicated as a two-terminal device. This circuit is now analyzed to find the instantaneous plate current i_P and the instantaneous voltage across the diode v_P when the instantaneous input voltage is v_i.

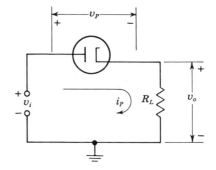

Fig. 4-7 The basic diode circuit.

The Load Line From Kirchhoff's voltage law,

$$v_P = v_i - i_P R_L \qquad\qquad (4\text{-}15)$$

where R_L is the magnitude of the load resistance. This one equation is not sufficient to determine the two unknowns v_P and i_P in this expression. However, a second relation between these two variables is given by the static plate characteristic of the diode (Fig. 4-4). In Fig. 4-8a is indicated the simultaneous solution of Eq. (4-15) and the diode plate characteristic. The straight line, which is represented by Eq. (4-15), is called the *load line*. The load line passes through the points $i_P = 0$, $v_P = v_i$, and $i_P = v_i/R_L$, $v_P = 0$. That is, the intercept with the voltage axis is v_i, and with the current axis is v_i/R_L. The slope of this line is determined, therefore, by R_L. It may happen that $i_P = v_i/R_L$ is too large to appear on the printed volt-ampere characteristic supplied by the manufacturer. If I' does appear on this characteristic, one point on the load line is $i_P = I'$, $v_P = v_i - I'R_L$, and the second point is $i_P = 0$, $v_P = v_i$. The point of intersection A of the load line and the static curve gives the current i_A that will flow under these conditions. This construction determines the current in the circuit when the instantaneous input potential is v_i.

The Dynamic Characteristic Consider now that the input voltage is allowed to vary. Then the above procedure must be repeated for each voltage value. A plot of current vs. input voltage, called the *dynamic characteristic*, may be obtained as follows: The current i_A is plotted vertically above v_i at point B in Fig. 4-8b. As v_i changes, the slope of the load line does not vary since R_L is fixed. Thus, when the applied potential has the value v_i', the corresponding current is $i_{A'}$. This current is plotted vertically above v_i' at B'. The resulting curve $OB'B$ that is generated as v_i varies is the dynamic characteristic.

It is to be emphasized that, regardless of the shape of the static characteristic or the waveform of the input voltage, the resulting waveform of the current in the output circuit can always be found graphically from the dynamic characteristic. This construction is indicated in Fig. 4-9. The input-signal waveform (not necessarily sinusoidal) is drawn with its time axis vertically

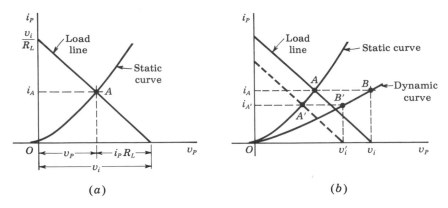

(a)   (b)

Fig. 4-8   (a) The intersection A of the load line with the diode static characteristic gives the current i_A corresponding to an instantaneous input voltage v_i.
(b) The method of constructing the dynamic curve from the static curve and
the load line.

downward, so that the voltage axis is horizontal. Suppose that the input
voltage has the value indicated by the point A at an instant t'. The corresponding current is obtained by drawing a vertical line through A and noting
the current a where this line intersects the dynamic curve. This current is
then plotted at an instant of time equal to t'. Similarly, points b, c, d, . . .
of the current waveform correspond to points B, C, D, . . . of the input-
voltage waveform.

Diode Applications   The construction of Fig. 4-9 indicates that, for
negative input voltages, zero output current is obtained. If the dynamic

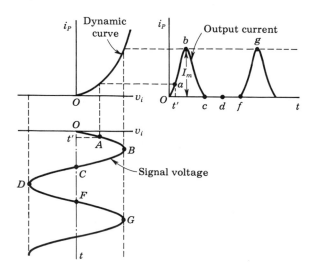

Fig. 4-9   The method of
obtaining the output-current
waveform from the dynamic
curve for a given input-
voltage waveform.

characteristic is linear, the output voltage $v_o = i_P R_L$ is an exact replica of the input voltage v_i except that the negative portion of v_i is missing. In this application the diode acts as a *clipper*. If the diode polarity is reversed, the positive portion of the input voltage is clipped. The clipping level need not be at zero (or ground) potential. For example, if a reference battery V_R is added in series with R_L of Fig. 4-7 (with the negative battery terminal at ground), signal voltages smaller than V_R will be clipped. Many other wave-shaping circuits[8] employ diodes.

One of the most important applications of a diode is rectification. If the input voltage is sinusoidal, the output consists of only positive sections (resembling half sinusoids). The important fact to note is that, whereas the average value of the input is zero, the output contains a nonzero dc value. Hence rectification, or the conversion from alternating to direct voltage, has taken place. Practical rectifier circuits are discussed in Chap. 20. Diodes also find extensive application in digital computers[8] and in circuits used to detect radio-frequency signals.

REFERENCES

1. Dushman, S., and J. W. Ewald: Electron Emission from Thoriated Tungsten, *Phys. Rev.*, vol. 29, pp. 857–870, June, 1927.

2. Blewett, J. P.: Oxide Coated Cathode Literature, 1940–1945, *J. Appl. Phys.*, vol. 17, pp. 643–647, August, 1946.
   Eisenstein, A. S.: Oxide Coated Cathodes, "Advances in Electronics," vol. 1, pp. 1–64, Academic Press Inc., New York, 1948.
   Hermann, G., and S. Wagner: "The Oxide-coated Cathode," vols. 1 and 2, Chapman & Hall, Ltd., London, 1951.
   Gewartowski, J. W., and H. A. Watson: "Principles of Electron Tubes," D. Van Nostrand Company, Inc., Princeton, N.J., 1965.

3. Coomes, E. A.: The Pulsed Properties of Oxide Cathodes, *J. Appl. Phys.*, vol. 17, pp. 647–654, August, 1946.
   Sproull, R. L.: An Investigation of Short-time Thermionic Emission from Oxide-coated Cathodes, *Phys. Rev.*, vol. 67, pp. 166–178, March, 1945.

4. Langmuir, I.: The Effect of Space Charge and Residual Gases on Thermionic Currents in High Vacuum, *Phys. Rev.*, vol. 2, pp. 450–486, December, 1913.

5. Child, C. D.: Discharge from Hot CaO, *Phys. Rev.*, vol. 27, pp. 492–511, May, 1911.

6. Langmuir, I., and K. T. Compton: Electrical Discharges in Gases, Part II: Fundamental Phenomena in Electrical Discharges, *Rev. Mod. Phys.*, vol. 3, pp. 191–257, April, 1931.

7. Fry, T. C.: The Thermionic Current between Parallel Plane Electrodes; Velocities of Emission Distributed According to Maxwell's Law, *Phys. Rev.*, vol. 17, pp. 441–452, April, 1921.

Fry, T. C.: Potential Distribution between Parallel Plane Electrodes, *ibid.*, vol. 22, pp. 445–446, November, 1923.

Langmuir, I.: The Effect of Space Charge and Initial Velocities on the Potential Distribution and Thermionic Current between Parallel Plane Electrodes, *ibid.*, vol. 21, pp. 419–435, April, 1923.

8. Millman, J., and H. Taub: "Pulse, Digital, and Switching Waveforms," McGraw-Hill Book Company, New York, 1965.

5 / CONDUCTION IN SEMICONDUCTORS

In Chap. 2 we consider the energy-band structure of crystals and the classification of materials as insulators, conductors, and semiconductors. Because of their importance we examine semiconductors in this chapter, with special emphasis on the determination of hole and electron concentrations. The effect of carrier concentrations on the Fermi level and the transport of holes and electrons by conduction or diffusion are also investigated.

5-1   ELECTRONS AND HOLES IN AN INTRINSIC SEMICONDUCTOR[1]

From Eq. (3-3) we see that the conductivity is proportional to the concentration n of free electrons. For a good conductor, n is very large ($\sim 10^{28}$ electrons/m³); for an insulator, n is very small ($\sim 10^7$); and for a semiconductor, n lies between these two values. The valence electrons in a semiconductor are not free to wander about as they are in a metal, but rather are trapped in a bond between two adjacent ions, as explained below.

Germanium and silicon are the two most important semiconductors used in electronic devices. The crystal structure of these materials consists of a regular repetition in three dimensions of a unit cell having the form of a tetrahedron with an atom at each vertex. This structure is illustrated symbolically in two dimensions in Fig. 5-1. Germanium has a total of 32 electrons in its atomic structure, arranged in shells as indicated in Table 2-2. As explained in Sec. 2-10, each atom in a germanium crystal contributes four valence electrons, so that the atom is tetravalent. The inert ionic core of the germanium atom carries a positive charge of $+4$ measured in units

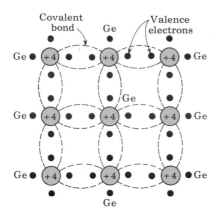

Fig. 5-1 Crystal structure of germanium, illustrated symbolically in two dimensions.

of the electronic charge. The binding forces between neighboring atoms result from the fact that each of the valence electrons of a germanium atom is shared by one of its four nearest neighbors. This *electron-pair*, or *covalent*, *bond* is represented in Fig. 5-1 by the two dashed lines which join each atom to each of its neighbors. The fact that the valence electrons serve to bind one atom to the next also results in the valence electron being tightly bound to the nucleus. Hence, in spite of the availability of four valence electrons, the crystal has a low conductivity.

At a very low temperature (say 0°K) the ideal structure of Fig. 5-1 is approached, and the crystal behaves as an insulator, since no free carriers of electricity are available. However, at room temperature, some of the covalent bonds will be broken because of the thermal energy supplied to the crystal, and conduction is made possible. This situation is illustrated in Fig. 5-2. Here an electron, which for the far greater period of time forms part of a covalent bond, is pictured as being dislodged and therefore free to wander in a random fashion throughout the crystal. The energy E_G required to break such a covalent bond is about 0.72 eV for germanium and 1.1 eV for silicon at room temperature. The absence of the electron in the covalent bond is represented by the small circle in Fig. 5-2, and such an incomplete covalent

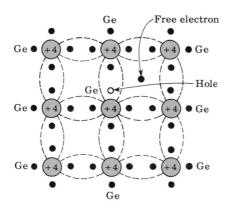

Fig. 5-2 Germanium crystal with a broken covalent bond.

Fig. 5-3   The mechanism by
which a hole contributes to
the conductivity.

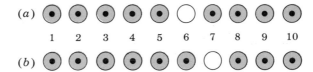

(a)

1 2 3 4 5 6 7 8 9 10

(b)

bond is called a *hole*. The importance of the hole is that it may serve as a carrier of electricity comparable in effectiveness to the free electron.

The mechanism by which a hole contributes to the conductivity is qualitatively as follows: When a bond is incomplete so that a hole exists, it is relatively easy for a valence electron in a neighboring atom to leave its covalent bond to fill this hole. An electron moving from a bond to fill a hole leaves a hole in its initial position. Hence the hole effectively moves in the direction opposite to that of the electron. This hole, in its new position, may now be filled by an electron from another covalent bond, and the hole will correspondingly move one more step in the direction opposite to the motion of the electron. Here we have a mechanism for the conduction of electricity which does not involve *free* electrons. This phenomenon is illustrated schematically in Fig. 5-3, where a circle with a dot in it represents a completed bond, and an empty circle designates a hole. Figure 5-3a shows a row of 10 ions, with a broken bond, or hole, at ion 6. Now imagine that an electron from ion 7 moves into the hole at ion 6, so that the configuration of Fig. 5-3b results. If we compare this figure with Fig. 5-3a, it looks as if the hole in (a) has moved toward the right in (b) (from ion 6 to ion 7). This discussion indicates that the motion of the hole in one direction actually means the transport of a negative charge an equal distance in the opposite direction. So far as the flow of electric current is concerned, the hole behaves like a positive charge equal in magnitude to the electronic charge. We can consider that the holes are physical entities whose movement constitutes a flow of current.

In a pure semiconductor the number of holes is equal to the number of free electrons. Thermal agitation continues to produce new hole-electron pairs, whereas other hole-electron pairs disappear as a result of recombination.

5-2   CONDUCTIVITY OF A SEMICONDUCTOR

With each hole-electron pair created, two charge-carrying "particles" are formed. One is negative (the free electron), of mobility μ_n, and the other is positive (the hole), of mobility μ_p. These particles move in opposite directions in an electric field $\mathcal{E}$, but since they are of opposite sign, the current of each is in the same direction. Hence the current density J is given by (Sec. 3-1)

$$J = (n\mu_n + p\mu_p)e\mathcal{E} = \sigma\mathcal{E} \qquad (5\text{-}1)$$

where n = magnitude of free-electron (negative) concentration
p = magnitude of hole (positive) concentration
σ = conductivity

Hence

$$\sigma = (n\mu_n + p\mu_p)e \tag{5-2}$$

For the pure (called *intrinsic*) semiconductor considered here, $n = p = n_i$, where n_i is the intrinsic concentration.

In pure germanium at room temperature there is about one hole-electron pair for every 2×10^9 germanium atoms. With increasing temperature, the density of hole-electron pairs increases [Eq. (5-21)], and correspondingly, the conductivity increases. In the following section it is found that the intrinsic concentration n_i varies with temperature in accordance with the relationship

$$n_i{}^2 = A_o T^3 \epsilon^{-E_{GO}/kT} \tag{5-3}$$

The constants E_{GO}, μ_n, μ_p, and many other important physical quantities for germanium and silicon are given in Table 5-1.

The conductivity of germanium (silicon) is found from Eq. (5-3) to increase approximately 6 (8) percent per degree increase in temperature. Such a large change in conductivity with temperature places a limitation upon the use of semiconductor devices in some circuits. On the other hand, for some applications it is exactly this property of semiconductors that is used to advantage. A semiconductor used in this manner is called a *thermistor*.[2] Such a device finds extensive application in thermometry, in the measurement of microwave-frequency power, as a thermal relay, and in control devices actuated by changes in temperature. Silicon and germanium are not used as thermistors because their properties are too sensitive to impurities. Commercial thermistors consist of sintered mixtures of such oxides as NiO, Mn_2O_3, and Co_2O_3.

TABLE 5-1   Properties of germanium and silicon†

Property	Ge	Si
Atomic number	32	14
Atomic weight	72.6	28.1
Density, g/cm³	5.32	2.33
Dielectric constant (relative)	16	12
Atoms/cm³	4.4×10^{22}	5.0×10^{22}
E_{GO}, eV, at 0°K	0.785	1.21
E_G, eV, at 300°K	0.72	1.1
n_i at 300°K, cm⁻³	2.5×10^{13}	1.5×10^{10}
Intrinsic resistivity at 300°K, Ω-cm	45	230,000
μ_n, cm²/V-sec	3,800	1,300
μ_p, cm²/V-sec	1,800	500
D_n, cm²/sec $= \mu_n V_T$	99	34
D_p, cm²/sec $= \mu_p V_T$	47	13

† G. L. Pearson and W. H. Brattain, History of Semiconductor Research, *Proc. IRE*, vol. 43, pp. 1794–1806, December, 1955. E. M. Conwell, Properties of Silicon and Germanium, Part II, *Proc. IRE*, vol. 46, no. 6, pp. 1281–1299, June, 1958.

The exponential decrease in resistivity (reciprocal of conductivity) of a semiconductor should be contrasted with the small and almost linear increase in resistivity of a metal. An increase in the temperature of a metal results in greater thermal motion of the ions, and hence decreases slightly the mean free path of the free electrons. The result is a decrease in the mobility, and hence in conductivity. For most metals the resistance increases about 0.4 percent/°C increase in temperature. It should be noted that a thermistor has a negative coefficient of resistance, whereas that of a metal is positive and of much smaller magnitude. By including a thermistor in a circuit it is possible to compensate for temperature changes over a range as wide as 100°C.

5-3   CARRIER CONCENTRATIONS IN AN INTRINSIC SEMICONDUCTOR

In order to calculate the conductivity of a semiconductor from Eq. (5-2) it is necessary to know the concentration of free electrons n and the concentration of holes p. From Eqs. (3-6) and (3-7), with E in electron volts,

$$dn = N(E)f(E)\, dE \tag{5-4}$$

where dn represents the number of conduction electrons per cubic meter whose energies lie between E and $E + dE$. The density of states $N(E)$ is derived in Sec. 3-6 on the assumption that the bottom of the conduction band is at zero potential. In a semiconductor the lowest energy in the conduction band is E_C, and hence Eq. (3-8) must be generalized as follows:

$$N(E) = \gamma(E - E_C)^{\frac{1}{2}} \tag{5-5}$$

The Fermi function $f(E)$ is given by Eq. (3-10), namely,

$$f(E) = \frac{1}{1 + \epsilon^{(E-E_F)/kT}} \tag{5-6}$$

At room temperature $kT \approx 0.03$ eV, so that $f(E) = 0$ if $E - E_F \gg 0.03$ and $f(E) = 1$ if $E - E_F \ll 0.03$ (Fig. 3-10). We shall show that the Fermi level lies in the region of the energy gap midway between the valence and conduction bands, as indicated in Fig. 5-4. This diagram shows the Fermi-Dirac distribution of Eq. (5-6) superimposed on the energy-band diagram of a semiconductor. At absolute zero ($T = 0°K$) the function is as shown in Fig. 5-4a. At room temperature some electrons are excited to higher energies and some states near the bottom of the conduction band E_C will be filled. Similarly, near the top of the valence band E_V, the probability of occupancy is decreased from unity since some electrons have escaped from their covalent bond and are now in the conduction band. For a further increase in temperature the function is as shown by the curve in Fig. 5-4b marked "$T = 1000°K$."

The concentration of electrons in the conduction band is, from Eq. (5-4),

$$n = \int_{E_C}^{\infty} N(E)f(E)\, dE \tag{5-7}$$

For $E \geq E_C$, $E - E_F \gg kT$ and Eq. (5-6) reduces to

$$f(E) = \epsilon^{-(E-E_F)/kT}$$

and

$$n = \int_{E_C}^{\infty} \gamma(E - E_C)^{\frac{1}{2}} \epsilon^{-(E-E_F)/kT}\, dE \tag{5-8}$$

This integral evaluates to

$$n = N_C \epsilon^{-(E_C-E_F)/kT} \tag{5-9}$$

where

$$N_C = 2\left(\frac{2\pi m_n kT}{h^2}\right)^{\frac{3}{2}} (1.60 \times 10^{-19})^{\frac{3}{2}} = 2\left(\frac{2\pi m_n \bar{k}T}{h^2}\right)^{\frac{3}{2}} \tag{5-10}$$

In deriving this equation the value of γ from Eq. (3-9) is used, k is given in electron volts per degree Kelvin, and $\bar{k}$ is expressed in joules per degree Kelvin. (The relationship between joules and electron volts is given in Sec. 1-5.) The mass m has been replaced by the symbol m_n, which represents the *effective mass* of the electron.

Effective Mass[3] We digress here briefly to discuss the concept of the effective mass of the electron and hole. It is found that, when quantum mechanics is used to specify the motion within the crystal of an electron or hole on which an external field is applied, it is possible to treat the hole and electron as imaginary *classical particles* with effective positive masses m_p and m_n, respectively. This approximation is valid provided that the externally applied fields are much weaker than the internal *periodic* fields produced by

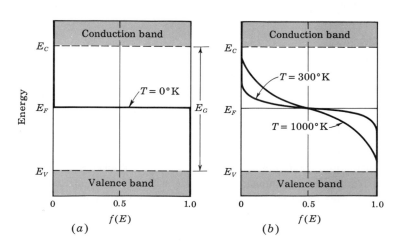

Fig. 5-4 Fermi-Dirac distribution and energy-band diagram for an intrinsic semiconductor. (a) $T = 0°$K and (b) $T = 300°$K and $T = 1000°$K.

the lattice structure. In a perfect crystal these imaginary particles respond only to the external fields.

In conclusion, then, the effective-mass approximation removes the quantum features of the problem and allows us to use Newton's laws to determine the effect of external forces on the electrons and holes within the crystal.

The Number of Holes in the Valence Band Since the top of the valence band (the maximum energy) is E_V, the density of states [analogous to Eq. (5-5)] is given by

$$N(E) = \gamma(E_V - E)^{\frac{1}{2}} \qquad (5\text{-}11)$$

Since a "hole" signifies an empty energy level, the Fermi function for a hole is $1 - f(E)$, where $f(E)$ is the probability that the level is occupied by an electron. For example, if the probability that a particular energy level is occupied by an electron is 0.2, the probability that it is empty (occupied by a hole) is 0.8. Using Eq. (5-6) for $f(E)$, we obtain

$$1 - f(E) = \frac{\epsilon^{(E-E_F)/kT}}{1 + \epsilon^{(E-E_F)/kT}} \approx \epsilon^{-(E_F-E)/kT} \qquad (5\text{-}12)$$

where we have made use of the fact that $E_F - E \gg kT$ for $E \leq E_V$ (Fig. 5-4). Hence the number of holes per cubic meter in the valence band is

$$p = \int_{-\infty}^{E_V} \gamma(E_V - E)^{\frac{1}{2}} \epsilon^{-(E_F-E)/kT} \, dE \qquad (5\text{-}13)$$

This integral evaluates to

$$p = N_V \epsilon^{-(E_F-E_V)/kT} \qquad (5\text{-}14)$$

where N_V is given by Eq. (5-10), with m_n replaced by m_p, the effective mass of a hole.

The Fermi Level in an Intrinsic Semiconductor It is important to note that Eqs. (5-9) and (5-14) apply to both intrinsic and extrinsic or impure semiconductors. In the case of intrinsic material the subscript i will be added to n and p. Since the crystal must be electrically neutral,

$$n_i = p_i \qquad (5\text{-}15)$$

and we have from Eqs. (5-9) and (5-14)

$$N_C \epsilon^{-(E_C-E_F)/kT} = N_V \epsilon^{-(E_F-E_V)/kT}$$

Taking the logarithm of both sides, we obtain

$$\ln \frac{N_C}{N_V} = \frac{E_C + E_V - 2E_F}{kT}$$

Hence

$$E_F = \frac{E_C + E_V}{2} - \frac{kT}{2} \ln \frac{N_C}{N_V} \qquad (5\text{-}16)$$

If the effective masses of a hole and a free electron are the same, $N_C = N_V$, and Eq. (5-16) yields

$$E_F = \frac{E_C + E_V}{2} \tag{5-17}$$

Hence the Fermi level lies in the center of the forbidden energy band, as shown in Fig. 5-4.

The Intrinsic Concentration Using Eqs. (5-9) and (5-14), we have for the product of electron-hole concentrations

$$np = N_C N_V \epsilon^{-(E_C - E_V)/kT} = N_C N_V \epsilon^{-E_G/kT} \tag{5-18}$$

Note that this product is independent of the Fermi level, but does depend upon the temperature and the energy gap $E_G \equiv E_C - E_V$. Equation (5-18) is valid for either an extrinsic or intrinsic material. Hence, writing $n = n_i$ and $p = p_i = n_i$, we have the important relationship (called the *mass-action law*)

$$np = n_i{}^2 \tag{5-19}$$

Note that, regardless of the individual magnitudes of n and p, the product is always a constant at a fixed temperature. Substituting numerical values for the physical constants in Eq. (5-10), we obtain

$$N_C = 4.82 \times 10^{21} \left(\frac{m_n}{m}\right)^{\frac{3}{2}} T^{\frac{3}{2}} \tag{5-20}$$

where N_C has the dimensions of a concentration (number per cubic meter). Note that N_V is given by the right-hand side of Eq. (5-20) with m_n replaced by m_p. From Eqs. (5-18) to (5-20),

$$np = n_i{}^2 = (2.33 \times 10^{43}) \left(\frac{m_n m_p}{m^2}\right)^{\frac{3}{2}} T^3 \epsilon^{-E_G/kT} \tag{5-21}$$

As indicated in Eqs. (2-15) and (2-16), the energy gap decreases linearly with temperature, so that

$$E_G = E_{GO} - \beta T \tag{5-22}$$

where E_{GO} is the magnitude of the energy gap at 0°K. Substituting this relationship into Eq. (5-21) gives an expression of the following form:

$$n_i{}^2 = A_o T^3 \epsilon^{-E_{GO}/kT} \tag{5-23}$$

This result has been verified experimentally.[4] The measured values of n_i and E_{GO} are given in Table 5-1.

5-4 DONOR AND ACCEPTOR IMPURITIES

If, to pure germanium, a small amount of impurity is added in the form of a substance with five valence electrons, the situation pictured in Fig. 5-5 results.

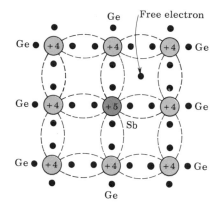

Fig. 5-5 Crystal lattice with a germanium atom displaced by a pentavalent impurity atom.

The impurity atoms will displace some of the germanium atoms in the crystal lattice. Four of the five valence electrons will occupy covalent bonds, and the fifth will be nominally unbound and will be available as a carrier of current. The energy required to detach this fifth electron from the atom is of the order of only 0.01 eV for Ge or 0.05 eV for Si. Suitable pentavalent impurities are antimony, phosphorus, and arsenic. Such impurities donate excess (negative) electron carriers, and are therefore referred to as *donor*, or *n*-type, impurities.

When donor impurities are added to a semiconductor, allowable energy levels are introduced a very small distance below the conduction band, as is shown in Fig. 5-6. These new allowable levels are essentially a discrete level because the added impurity atoms are far apart in the crystal structure, and hence their interaction is small. In the case of germanium, the distance of the new discrete allowable energy level is only 0.01 eV (0.05 eV in silicon) below the conduction band, and therefore at room temperature almost all of the "fifth" electrons of the donor material are raised into the conduction band.

If intrinsic semiconductor material is "doped" with *n*-type impurities, not only does the number of electrons increase, but the number of holes decreases below that which would be available in the intrinsic semiconductor. The reason for the decrease in the number of holes is that the larger number of electrons present increases the rate of recombination of electrons with holes.

If a trivalent impurity (boron, gallium, or indium) is added to an intrinsic

Fig. 5-6 Energy-band diagram of *n*-type semiconductor.

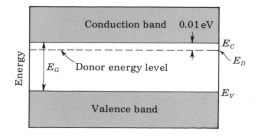

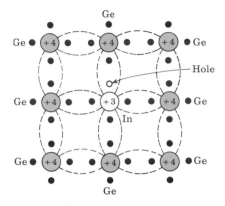

Fig. 5-7 Crystal lattice with a germanium atom displaced by an atom of a trivalent impurity.

semiconductor, only three of the covalent bonds can be filled, and the vacancy that exists in the fourth bond constitutes a hole. This situation is illustrated in Fig. 5-7. Such impurities make available positive carriers because they create holes which can accept electrons. These impurities are consequently known as *acceptor*, or *p*-type impurities. The amount of impurity which must be added to have an appreciable effect on the conductivity is very small. For example, if a donor-type impurity is added to the extent of 1 part in 10^8, the conductivity of germanium at 30°C is multiplied by a factor of 12.

When acceptor, or *p*-type, impurities are added to the intrinsic semiconductor, they produce an allowable discrete energy level which is just above the valence band, as shown in Fig. 5-8. Since a very small amount of energy is required for an electron to leave the valence band and occupy the acceptor energy level, it follows that the holes generated in the valence band by these electrons constitute the largest number of carriers in the semiconductor material.

We have the important result that the doping of an intrinsic semiconductor not only increases the conductivity, but also serves to produce a conductor in which the electric carriers are either predominantly holes or predominantly electrons. In an *n*-type semiconductor, the electrons are called the *majority carriers*, and the holes are called the *minority carriers*. In a *p*-type material, the holes are the majority carriers, and the electrons are the minority carriers.

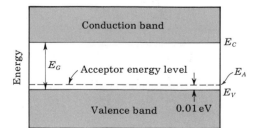

Fig. 5-8 Energy-band diagram of *p*-type semiconductor.

5-5   CHARGE DENSITIES IN A SEMICONDUCTOR

Equation (5-19), namely,

$$np = n_i{}^2 \tag{5-19}$$

gives one relationship between the electron n and the hole p concentrations. These densities are further interrelated by the law of electrical neutrality, which we shall now state in algebraic form: Let N_D equal the concentration of donor atoms.   Since, as mentioned above, these are practically all ionized, N_D positive charges per cubic meter are contributed by the donor ions.   Hence the total positive-charge density is $N_D + p$.   Similarly, if N_A is the concentration of acceptor ions, these contribute N_A negative charges per cubic meter. The total negative-charge density is $N_A + n$.   Since the semiconductor is electrically neutral, the magnitude of the positive-charge density must equal that of the negative concentration, or

$$N_D + p = N_A + n \tag{5-24}$$

Consider an n-type material having $N_A = 0$.   Since the number of electrons is much greater than the number of holes in an n-type semiconductor $(n \gg p)$, then Eq. (5-24) reduces to

$$n \approx N_D \tag{5-25}$$

In an n-type material the free-electron concentration is approximately equal to the density of donor atoms.

In later applications we study the characteristics of n- and p-type materials connected together.   Since some confusion may arise as to which type is under consideration at a given moment, we add the subscript n or p for an n-type or a p-type substance, respectively.   Thus Eq. (5-25) is more clearly written

$$n_n \approx N_D \tag{5-26}$$

The concentration p_n of holes in the n-type semiconductor is obtained from Eq. (5-19), which is now written $n_n p_n = n_i{}^2$.   Thus

$$p_n = \frac{n_i{}^2}{N_D} \tag{5-27}$$

Similarly, for a p-type semiconductor,

$$n_p p_p = n_i{}^2 \qquad p_p \approx N_A \qquad n_p = \frac{n_i{}^2}{N_A} \tag{5-28}$$

5-6   FERMI LEVEL IN A SEMICONDUCTOR HAVING IMPURITIES

From Eqs. (5-1) and (5-2) it is seen that the electrical characteristics of a semiconductor material depend on the concentration of free electrons and holes.

The expressions for n and p are given by Eqs. (5-9) and (5-14), respectively, and these are valid for both intrinsic semiconductors and semiconductors with impurities. The only parameter in Eqs. (5-9) and (5-14) which changes with impurities is the Fermi level E_F. In order to see how E_F depends on temperature and impurity concentration, we recall that, in the case of no impurities (an intrinsic semiconductor), E_F lies in the middle of the energy gap, indicating equal concentrations of free electrons and holes. If a donor-type impurity is added to the crystal, then, at a given temperature and assuming all donor atoms are ionized, the first N_D states in the conduction band will be filled. Hence it will be more difficult for the electrons from the valence band to bridge the energy gap by thermal agitation. Consequently, the number of electron-hole pairs thermally generated for that temperature will be reduced. Since the Fermi level is a measure of the probability of occupancy of the allowed energy states, it is clear that E_F must move closer to the conduction band to indicate that many of the energy states in that band are filled by the donor electrons, and fewer holes exist in the valence band. This situation is pictured in Fig. 5-9a for an n-type material. The same kind of argument leads to the conclusion that E_F must move from the center of the forbidden gap closer to the valence band for a p-type material, as indicated in Fig. 5-9b. If for a given concentration of impurities the temperature of, say, the n-type material increases, more electron-hole pairs will be formed, and since all donor atoms are ionized, it is possible that the concentration of thermally generated electrons in the conduction band may become much larger than the concentration of donor electrons. Under these conditions the concentrations of holes and electrons become almost equal and the crystal becomes essentially intrinsic. We can conclude that as the temperature of either n-type or p-type material increases, the Fermi level moves toward the center of the energy gap.

A calculation of the exact position of the Fermi level in an n-type material

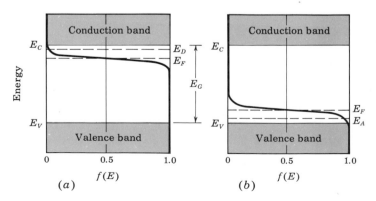

Fig. 5-9 Positions of Fermi level in (a) n-type and (b) p-type semiconductors.

can be made if we substitute $n = N_D$ from Eq. (5-25) into Eq. (5-9).   We obtain

$$N_D = N_C \epsilon^{-(E_C - E_F)/kT} \tag{5-29}$$

or solving for E_F,

$$E_F = E_C - kT \ln \frac{N_C}{N_D} \tag{5-30}$$

Similarly, for p-type material, from Eqs. (5-28) and (5-14) we obtain

$$E_F = E_V + kT \ln \frac{N_V}{N_A} \tag{5-31}$$

Note that, if $N_A = N_D$, Eqs. (5-30) and (5-31) added together (and divided by 2) yield Eq. (5-16).

5-7   DIFFUSION

In addition to a conduction current, the transport of charges in a semiconductor may be accounted for by a mechanism called *diffusion*, not ordinarily encountered in metals.   The essential features of diffusion are now discussed.

We see later that it is possible to have a nonuniform concentration of particles in a semiconductor.   Under these circumstances the concentration p of holes varies with distance x in the semiconductor, and there exists a concentration gradient dp/dx in the density of carriers.   The existence of a gradient implies that, if an imaginary surface is drawn in the semiconductor, the density of holes immediately on one side of the surface is larger than the density on the other side.   The holes are in a random motion as a result of their thermal energy.   Accordingly, holes will continue to move back and forth across this surface.   We may then expect that, in a given time interval, more holes will cross the surface from the side of greater concentration to the side of smaller concentration than in the reverse direction.   This net transport of charge across the surface constitutes a flow of current.   It should be noted that this net transport of charge is not the result of mutual repulsion among charges of like sign, but is simply the result of a statistical phenomenon.   This diffusion is exactly analogous to that which occurs in a neutral gas if a concentration gradient exists in the gaseous container.   The diffusion hole-current density J_p (amperes per square meter) is proportional to the concentration gradient, and is given by

$$J_p = -eD_p \frac{dp}{dx} \tag{5-32}$$

where D_p (square meters per second) is called the *diffusion constant* for holes. A similar equation exists for diffusion electron-current density [p is replaced by n, and the minus sign is replaced by a plus sign in Eq. (5-32)].   Since both diffusion and mobility are statistical thermodynamic phenomena, D and μ are not independent. The relationship between them is given by the Einstein equation

$$\frac{D_p}{\mu_p} = \frac{D_n}{\mu_n} = V_T \tag{5-33}$$

where $V_T = \bar{k}T/e = T/11{,}600$ is defined as in Eq. (3-34). At room temperature (300°K), $\mu = 39D$. Measured values of μ and computed values of D for silicon and germanium are given in Table 5-1, on page 98.

5-8   CARRIER LIFETIME

In Sec. 5-1 we see that in a pure semiconductor the number of holes is equal to the number of free electrons. Thermal agitation, however, continues to produce new hole-electron pairs while other hole-electron pairs disappear as a result of recombination. On an average, a hole (an electron) will exist for τ_p (τ_n) sec before recombination. This time is called the *mean lifetime* of the hole and electron, respectively. Carrier lifetimes range from nanoseconds (10^{-9} sec) to hundreds of microseconds. These parameters are very important in semiconductor devices because they indicate the time required for electron and hole concentrations which have been caused to change to return to their equilibrium concentrations.

Consider a bar of n-type silicon illuminated by light of the proper frequency. As a result of this radiation the hole and electron concentrations will increase by the same amount. If p_{no} and n_{no} are the equilibrium concentrations of holes and electrons in the n-type specimen, we have

$$\bar{p}_{no} - p_{no} = \bar{n}_{no} - n_{no} \tag{5-34}$$

where $\bar{p}_{no}$ and $\bar{n}_{no}$ represent the carrier concentrations during steady irradiation.

If we now turn off the source of light, the carrier concentrations will return to their equilibrium values exponentially and with a time constant $\tau = \tau_n = \tau_p$. This result has been verified experimentally, and we can write

$$p_n - p_{no} = (\bar{p}_{no} - p_{no})e^{-t/\tau} \tag{5-35}$$

$$n_n - n_{no} = (\bar{n}_{no} - n_{no})e^{-t/\tau} \tag{5-36}$$

We should emphasize here that majority and minority carriers in a specific region of a given specimen have the same lifetime τ. Using Eqs. (5-35) and (5-36), we can obtain the expressions for the rate of concentration change. For holes, we find from Eq. (5-35)

$$\frac{dp_n}{dt} = -\frac{p_n - p_{no}}{\tau} = \frac{d}{dt}(p_n - p_{no}) \tag{5-37}$$

For electrons, a similar expression with p replaced by n is valid. The quantity $p_n - p_{no}$ represents the *injected*, or *excess*, carrier density. The rate of change of excess density is proportional to the density—an intuitively correct result. The minus sign indicates that the change is a decrease in the case of recombination and an increase when the concentration is recovering from a temporary depletion.

The most important mechanism through which holes and electrons recombine is the mechanism involving *recombination centers*[5,6] which contribute electronic states in the energy gap of the semiconductor material. These new states are associated with imperfections in the crystal. Specifically, metallic impurities in the semiconductor are capable of introducing energy states in the forbidden gap. Recombination is affected not only by volume impurities, but also by surface imperfections in the crystal.

Gold is extensively used as a recombination agent by semiconductor-device manufacturers. Thus the device designer can obtain desired carrier lifetimes by introducing gold into silicon under controlled conditions.[7,8]

5-9   THE CONTINUITY EQUATION

In the preceding section it is seen that if we disturb the equilibrium concentrations of carriers in a semiconductor material, the concentration of holes or electrons will vary with time. In the general case, however, the carrier concentration in the body of a semiconductor is a function of both time and distance. We now derive the differential equation which governs this functional relationship. This equation is based upon the fact that charge can be neither created nor destroyed. Consider the infinitesimal element of volume of area A and length dx (Fig. 5-10) within which the average hole concentration is p, If τ_p is the mean lifetime of the holes, then p/τ_p equals the holes per second lost by recombination per unit volume. If e is the electronic charge, then, because of recombination, the number of coulombs per second

$$Decreases \text{ within the volume} = eA \, dx \, \frac{p}{\tau_p} \qquad (5\text{-}38)$$

If g is the thermal rate of generation of hole-electron pairs per unit volume, the number of coulombs per second

$$Increases \text{ within the volume} = eA \, dx \, g \qquad (5\text{-}39)$$

Fig. 5-10   Relating to the conservation of charge.

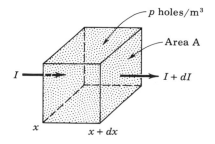

In general, the current will vary with distance within the semiconductor. If, as indicated in Fig. 5-10, the current entering the volume at x is I and leaving at $x + dx$ is $I + dI$, the number of coulombs per second

$$Decreases \text{ within the volume} = dI \tag{5-40}$$

Because of the three effects enumerated above, the hole density must change with time, and the total number of coulombs per second

$$Increases \text{ within the volume} = eA \, dx \, \frac{dp}{dt} \tag{5-41}$$

Since charge must be conserved,

$$eA \, dx \, \frac{dp}{dt} = -eA \, dx \, \frac{p}{\tau_p} + eA \, dx \, g - dI \tag{5-42}$$

The hole current is the sum of the diffusion current [Eq. (5-32)] and the drift current [Eq. (5-1)], or

$$I = -AeD_p \frac{dp}{dx} + Ape\mu_p \varepsilon \tag{5-43}$$

where ε is the electric field intensity within the volume. If the semiconductor is in thermal equilibrium with its surroundings and is subjected to no applied fields, the hole density will attain a constant value p_o. Under these conditions, $I = 0$ and $dp/dt = 0$, so that, from Eq. (5-42),

$$g = \frac{p_o}{\tau_p} \tag{5-44}$$

This equation indicates that the rate at which holes are generated thermally just equals the rate at which holes are lost because of recombination under equilibrium conditions. Combining Eqs. (5-42), (5-43), and (5-44) yields the *equation of conservation of charge*, or the *continuity equation*,

$$\frac{dp}{dt} = -\frac{p - p_o}{\tau_p} + D_p \frac{d^2p}{dx^2} - \mu_p \frac{d(p\varepsilon)}{dx} \tag{5-45}$$

If we are considering holes in the n-type material, the subscript n is added to p and p_o. Also, since p is a function of both t and x, partial derivatives should be used. Making these changes, we have, finally,

$$\frac{\partial p_n}{\partial t} = -\frac{p_n - p_{no}}{\tau_p} + D_p \frac{\partial^2 p_n}{\partial x^2} - \mu_p \frac{\partial(p_n\varepsilon)}{\partial x} \tag{5-46}$$

We now consider three special cases of the continuity equation.

Concentration Independent of x and with Zero Electric Field We now derive Eqs. (5-35) and (5-37) using the continuity equation. Consider a situation in which $\varepsilon = 0$ and the concentration is independent of x. For example, assume that radiation falls uniformly over the surface of a semiconductor and raises the concentration to $\bar{p}_{no}$, which is above the thermal-equilibrium value

p_{no}.   At $t = 0$ the illumination is removed.   How does the concentration vary with time?   The answer to this query is obtained from Eq. (5-46), which now reduces to

$$\frac{dp_n}{dt} = - \frac{p_n - p_{no}}{\tau_p} \tag{5-47}$$

in agreement with Eq. (5-37).   The solution of this equation is

$$p_n - p_{no} = (\bar{p}_{no} - p_{no})\epsilon^{-t/\tau_p} \tag{5-48}$$

which is identical with Eq. (5-35).   We now see that the mean lifetime of the holes τ_p can also be interpreted as the time constant with which the concentration returns to its normal value.   In other words, τ_p is the time it takes the injected concentration to fall to $1/\epsilon$ of its initial value.

Concentration Independent of t and with Zero Electric Field   Let us solve the equation of continuity subject to the following conditions: There is no electric field, so that $\mathcal{E} = 0$, and a steady state has been reached, so that $\partial p_n/\partial t = 0$.   Then

$$\frac{d^2 p_n}{dx^2} = \frac{p_n - p_{no}}{D_p \tau_p} \tag{5-49}$$

The solution of this equation is

$$p_n - p_{no} = K_1 \epsilon^{-x/L_p} + K_2 \epsilon^{+x/L_p} \tag{5-50}$$

where K_1 and K_2 are constants of integration and

$$L_p \equiv \sqrt{D_p \tau_p} \tag{5-51}$$

This solution may be verified by a direct substitution of Eq. (5-50) into Eq. (5-49).   Consider a very long piece of semiconductor extending in the positive X direction from $x = 0$.   Since the concentration cannot become infinite as $x \to \infty$, then K_2 must be zero.   The quantity $p_n - p_{no} \equiv P_n(x)$ by which the density exceeds the thermal-equilibrium value is called the *injected concentration* and is a function of the position x.   We shall assume that at $x = 0$, $P_n = P_n(0) = p_n(0) - p_{no}$.   In order to satisfy this boundary condition, $K_1 = P_n(0)$.   Hence

$$P_n(x) = p_n - p_{no} = P_n(0)\epsilon^{-x/L_p} \tag{5-52}$$

We see that the quantity L_p (called the *diffusion length* for holes) represents the distance into the semiconductor at which the injected concentration falls to $1/\epsilon$ of its value at $x = 0$.

The diffusion length L_p may also be interpreted as the average distance which an injected hole travels before recombining with an electron.   This statement may be verified as follows: From Fig. 5-11 and Eq. (5-52),

$$|dP_n| = \frac{P_n(0)}{L_p} \epsilon^{-x/L_p} \, dx \tag{5-53}$$

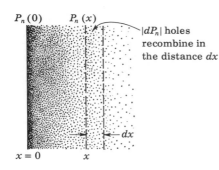

$|dP_n|$ holes recombine in the distance dx

Fig. 5-11   Relating to the injected hole concentration in n-type material.

$|dP_n|$ gives the number of injected holes which recombine in the distance between x and $x + dx$. Since each hole has traveled a distance x, the total distance traveled by $|dP_n|$ holes is $x\,|dP_n|$. Hence the total distance covered by all the holes is $\int_0^\infty x\,|dP_n|$. The average distance $\bar{x}$ equals this total distance divided by the total number $P_n(0)$ of injected holes. Hence

$$\bar{x} \equiv \frac{\int_0^\infty x\,|dP_n|}{P_n(0)} = \frac{1}{L_p} \int_0^\infty x\epsilon^{-x/L_p}\,dx = L_p \tag{5-54}$$

thus confirming that the mean distance of travel of a hole before recombination is L_p.

Concentration Varies Sinusoidally with t and with Zero Electric Field
Let us retain the restriction $\mathcal{E} = 0$ but assume that the injected concentration varies sinusoidally with an angular frequency ω. Then, in phasor notation,

$$P_n(x, t) = P_n(x)\epsilon^{j\omega t} \tag{5-55}$$

where the space dependence of the injected concentration is given by $P_n(x)$. If Eq. (5-55) is substituted into the continuity equation (5-46), the result is

$$j\omega P_n(x) = -\frac{P_n(x)}{\tau_p} + D_p \frac{d^2 P_n(x)}{dx^2}$$

or

$$\frac{d^2 P_n}{dx^2} = \frac{1 + j\omega\tau_p}{L_p{}^2} P_n \tag{5-56}$$

where use has been made of Eq. (5-51). At zero frequency the equation of continuity is given by Eq. (5-49), which may be written in the form

$$\frac{d^2 P_n}{dx^2} = \frac{P_n}{L_p{}^2}$$

A comparison of this equation with Eq. (5-56) shows that the ac solution at frequency $\omega \neq 0$ can be obtained from the dc solution ($\omega = 0$) by replacing L_p by $L_p(1 + j\omega\tau_p)^{-\frac{1}{2}}$. This result is used in Chap. 13.

5-10   THE HALL EFFECT[1]

If a specimen (metal or semiconductor) carrying a current I is placed in a transverse magnetic field **B**, an electric field $\mathcal{E}$ is induced in the direction perpendicular to both I and **B**. This phenomenon, known as the *Hall effect*, is used to determine whether a semiconductor is n- or p-type and to find the carrier concentration. Also, by simultaneously measuring the conductivity σ, the mobility μ can be calculated.

The physical origin of the Hall effect is not difficult to find. If in Fig. 5-12 I is in the positive X direction and **B** is in the positive Z direction, a force will be exerted in the negative Y direction on the current carriers. If the semiconductor is n-type, so that the current is carried by electrons, these electrons will be forced downward toward side 1 in Fig. 5-12, and side 1 becomes negatively charged with respect to side 2. Hence a potential V_H, called the *Hall voltage*, appears between the surfaces 1 and 2. In the equilibrium state the electric field intensity $\mathcal{E}$ due to the Hall effect must exert a force on the carrier which just balances the magnetic force, or

$$e\mathcal{E} = Bev \tag{5-57}$$

where e is the magnitude of the charge on the carrier, and v is the drift speed. From Eq. (1-14), $\mathcal{E} = V_H/d$, where d is the distance between surfaces 1 and 2. From Eq. (1-38), $J = \rho v = I/wd$, where J is the current density, ρ is the charge density, and w is the width of the specimen in the direction of the magnetic field. Combining these relationships, we find

$$V_H = \mathcal{E}d = Bvd = \frac{BJd}{\rho} = \frac{BI}{\rho w} \tag{5-58}$$

If V_H, B, I, and w are measured, the charge density ρ can be determined from Eq. (5-58). If the polarity of V_H is positive at terminal 2, then, as explained above, the carriers must be electrons, and $\rho = ne$, where n is the electron concentration. If, on the other hand, terminal 1 becomes charged positively with respect to terminal 2, the semiconductor must be p-type, and $\rho = pe$, where p is the hole concentration.

It is customary to introduce the Hall coefficient R_H defined by

$$R_H \equiv \frac{1}{\rho} \tag{5-59}$$

Fig. 5-12   Pertaining to the Hall effect. The carriers (whether electrons or holes) are subjected to a force in the negative Y direction.

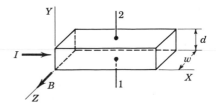

Hence

$$R_H = \frac{V_H w}{BI} \tag{5-60}$$

If conduction is due primarily to charges of one sign, the conductivity σ is related to the mobility μ by Eq. (3-3), or

$$\sigma = \rho\mu \tag{5-61}$$

If the conductivity is measured together with the Hall coefficient, the mobility can be determined from

$$\mu = \sigma R_H \tag{5-62}$$

We have assumed in the foregoing discussion that all particles travel with the mean drift speed v. Actually, the current carriers have a random thermal distribution in speed. If this distribution is taken into account, it is found that Eq. (5-60) remains valid provided that R_H is defined by $3\pi/8\rho$. Also, Eq. (5-62) must be modified to $\mu = (8\sigma/3\pi)R_H$.

REFERENCES

1. Shockley, W.: Electrons and Holes in Semiconductors, D. Van Nostrand Company, Inc., Princeton, N.J., reprinted February, 1963.
   Gibbons, J. F.: "Semiconductor Electronics," McGraw-Hill Book Company, New York, 1966.
   Middlebrook, R. D.: "An Introduction to Junction Transistor Theory," John Wiley & Sons, Inc., New York, 1957.

2. Becker, J. A., C. B. Green, and G. L. Pearson: Properties and Uses of Thermistors—Thermally Sensitive Resistors, *Bell System Tech. J.*, vol. 26, pp. 170–212, January, 1947.

3. Adler, R. B., A. C. Smith, and R. L. Longini: "Introduction to Semiconductor Physics," vol. 1, Semiconductor Electronics Education Committee, John Wiley & Sons, Inc., New York, 1964.

4. Conwell, E. M.: Properties of Silicon and Germanium: II, *Proc. IRE*, vol. 46, pp. 1281–1300, June, 1958.

5. Shockley, W., and W. T. Read, Jr.: Statistics of the Recombination of Holes and Electrons, *Phys. Rev.*, vol. 87, pp. 835–842, September, 1952.

6. Hall, R. N.: Electron-Hole Recombination in Germanium, *Phys. Rev.*, vol. 87, p. 387, July, 1952.

7. Collins, C. B., R. O. Carlson, and C. J. Gallagher: Properties of Gold-doped Silicon, *Phys. Rev.*, vol. 105, pp. 1168–1173, February, 1957.

8. Bemski, G.: Recombination Properties of Gold in Silicon, *Phys. Rev.*, vol. 111, pp. 1515–1518, September, 1958.

6 / SEMICONDUCTOR-DIODE CHARACTERISTICS

In this chapter we demonstrate that if a junction is formed between a sample of p-type and one of n-type semiconductor, this combination possesses the properties of a rectifier. The volt-ampere characteristics of such a junction are derived. Electron and hole currents as a function of distance are studied in detail. The capacitance across the junction is calculated.

Although the transistor is a triode semiconductor, it may be considered as one diode biased by the current from a second diode. Hence most of the theory developed in this chapter is utilized later in connection with our study of the transistor.

6-1 QUALITATIVE THEORY OF THE p-n JUNCTION[1]

If donor impurities are introduced into one side and acceptors into the other side of a single crystal of a semiconductor, say, germanium, a p-n junction is formed. Such a system is illustrated in Fig. 6-1a. The donor ion is indicated schematically by a plus sign because, after this impurity atom "donates" an electron, it becomes a positive ion. The acceptor ion is indicated by a minus sign because, after this atom "accepts" an electron, it becomes a negative ion. Initially, there are nominally only p-type carriers to the left of the junction and only n-type carriers to the right. Because there is a density gradient across the junction, holes will diffuse to the right across the junction, and electrons to the left.

As a result of the displacement of these charges, an electric field will appear across the junction. Equilibrium will be established when the field becomes large enough to restrain the process of diffusion. The general shape of the charge distribution may be as illustrated in

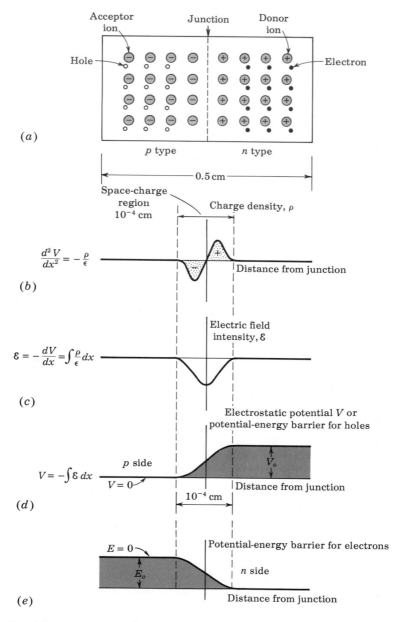

Fig. 6-1   A schematic diagram of a p-n junction, including the charge density, electric field intensity, and potential-energy barriers at the junction.   (Not drawn to scale.)

Fig. 6-1b.   The electric charges are confined to the neighborhood of the junction, and consist of immobile ions.   We see that the positive holes which neutralized the acceptor ions near the junction in the *p*-type germanium have disappeared as a result of combination with electrons which have diffused across the junction.   Similarly, the neutralizing electrons in the *n*-type germanium have combined with holes which have crossed the junction from the *p* material.   The unneutralized ions in the neighborhood of the junction are referred to as *uncovered charges*.   Since the region of the junction is depleted of mobile charges, it is called the *depletion region*, the *space-charge region*, or the *transition region*.   The thickness of this region is of the order of

$$10^{-4} \text{ cm} = 10^{-6} \text{ m} = 1 \text{ micron}$$

The electric field intensity in the neighborhood of the junction is indicated in Fig. 6-1c.   Note that this curve is the integral of the density function ρ in Fig. 6-1b.   The electrostatic-potential variation in the depletion region is shown in Fig. 6-1d, and is the negative integral of the function ε of Fig. 6-1c.   This variation constitutes a potential-energy barrier against the further diffusion of holes across the barrier.   The form of the potential-energy barrier against the flow of electrons from the *n* side across the junction is shown in Fig. 6-1e.   It is similar to that shown in Fig. 6-1d, except that it is inverted, since the charge on an electron is negative.

The necessity for the existence of a potential barrier called the *contact*, or *diffusion, potential* is now considered further.   Under open-circuited conditions the net hole current must be zero.   If this statement were not true, the hole density at one end of the semiconductor would continue to increase indefinitely with time, a situation which is obviously physically impossible.   Since the concentration of holes in the *p* side is much greater than that in the *n* side, a very large diffusion current tends to flow across the junction from the *p* to the *n* material.   Hence an electric field must build up across the junction in such a direction that a drift current will tend to flow across the junction from the *n* to the *p* side in order to counterbalance the diffusion current.   This equilibrium condition of zero resultant hole current allows us to calculate the height of the potential barrier V_o [Eq. (6-8)] in terms of the donor and acceptor concentrations.   The numerical value for V_o is of the order of magnitude of a few tenths of a volt.

6-2   THE *p-n* JUNCTION AS A DIODE

The essential electrical characteristic of a *p-n* junction is that it constitutes a diode which permits the easy flow of current in one direction but restrains the flow in the opposite direction.   We consider now, qualitatively, how this diode action comes about.

Reverse Bias   In Fig. 6-2, a battery is shown connected across the terminals of a *p-n* junction.   The negative terminal of the battery is con-

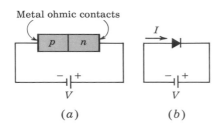

Metal ohmic contacts

(a)   (b)

Fig. 6-2 (a) A p-n junction biased in the reverse direction. (b) The rectifier symbol is used for the p-n diode.

nected to the p side of the junction, and the positive terminal to the n side. The polarity of connection is such as to cause both the holes in the p type and the electrons in the n type to move away from the junction. Consequently, the region of negative-charge density is spread to the left of the junction (Fig. 6-1b), and the positive-charge-density region is spread to the right. However, this process cannot continue indefinitely, because in order to have a steady flow of holes to the left, these holes must be supplied across the junction from the n-type germanium. And there are very few holes in the n-type side. Hence, nominally, zero current results. Actually, a small current does flow because a small number of hole-electron pairs are generated throughout the crystal as a result of thermal energy. The holes so formed in the n-type germanium will wander over to the junction. A similar remark applies to the electrons thermally generated in the p-type germanium. This small current is the diode *reverse saturation current*, and its magnitude is designated by I_o. This reverse current will increase with increasing temperature [Eq. (6-28)], and hence the back resistance of a crystal diode decreases with increasing temperature.

The mechanism of conduction in the reverse direction may be described alternatively in the following way: When no voltage is applied to the p-n diode, the potential barrier across the junction is as shown in Fig. 6-1d. When a voltage V is applied to the diode in the direction shown in Fig. 6-2, the height of the potential-energy barrier is increased by the amount eV. This increase in the barrier height serves to reduce the flow of majority carriers (i.e., holes in p type and electrons in n type). However, the minority carriers (i.e., electrons in p type and holes in n type), since they fall down the potential-energy hill, are uninfluenced by the increased height of the barrier. The applied voltage in the direction indicated in Fig. 6-2 is called the *reverse*, or *blocking, bias*.

Forward Bias An external voltage applied with the polarity shown in Fig. 6-3 (opposite to that indicated in Fig. 6-2) is called a *forward* bias. An ideal p-n diode has zero ohmic voltage drop across the body of the crystal. For such a diode the height of the potential barrier at the junction will be lowered by the applied forward voltage V. The equilibrium initially established between the forces tending to produce diffusion of majority carriers and the restraining influence of the potential-energy barrier at the junction

Fig. 6-3 (a) A *p-n* junction biased in the forward direction. (b) The rectifier symbol is used for the *p-n* diode.

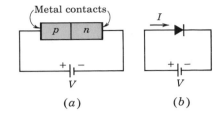

(a)   *(b)*

will be disturbed.   Hence, for a forward bias, the holes cross the junction from the *p* type to the *n* type, and the electrons cross the junction in the opposite direction.   These majority carriers can then travel around the closed circuit, and a relatively large current will flow.

Ohmic Contacts[1]   In Fig. 6-2 (6-3) we show an external reverse (forward) bias applied to a *p-n* diode.   We have assumed that the external bias voltage appears directly across the junction and has the effect of raising (lowering) the electrostatic potential across the junction.   In order to justify this assumption we must specify how electric contact is made to the semiconductor from the external bias circuit.   In Figs. 6-2 and 6-3 we indicate metal contacts with which the homogeneous *p*-type and *n*-type materials are provided.   We thus see that we have introduced two metal-semiconductor junctions, one at each end of the diode.   We naturally expect a contact potential to develop across these additional junctions.   However, we shall assume that the metal-semiconductor contacts shown in Figs. 6-2 and 6-3 have been manufactured in such a way that they are nonrectifying.   In other words, the contact potential across these junctions is approximately independent of the direction and magnitude of the current.   A contact of this type is referred to as an *ohmic contact*.

We are now in a position to justify our assumption that the entire applied voltage appears as a *change* in the height of the potential barrier.   Inasmuch as the metal-semiconductor contacts are low-resistance ohmic contacts and the voltage drop across the bulk of the crystal is neglected, approximately the entire applied voltage will indeed appear as a change in the height of the potential barrier at the *p-n* junction.

The Short-circuited and Open-circuited *p-n* Junction   If the voltage *V* in Fig. 6-2 or 6-3 were set equal to zero, the *p-n* junction would be short-circuited.   Under these conditions, as we show below, no current can flow ($I = 0$) and the electrostatic potential V_o remains unchanged and equal to the value under open-circuit conditions.   If there were a current ($I \neq 0$), the metal would become heated.   Since there is no external source of energy available, the energy required to heat the metal wire would have to be supplied by the *p-n* bar.   The semiconductor bar, therefore, would have to cool off.   Clearly, under thermal equilibrium the simultaneous heating of the metal and cooling of the bar is impossible, and we conclude that $I = 0$. Since under short-circuit conditions the sum of the voltages around the closed loop must be zero, the junction potential V_o must be exactly compensated by the metal-to-semiconductor contact potentials at the ohmic contacts. Since the current is zero, the wire can be cut without changing the situation, and the voltage drop across the cut must remain zero. If in an attempt to measure V_o we connected a voltmeter across the cut, the voltmeter would read zero voltage. In other words, it is not possible to measure contact difference of potential directly with a voltmeter.

Large Forward Voltages Suppose that the forward voltage V in Fig. 6-3 is increased until V approaches V_o. If V were equal to V_o, the barrier would disappear and the current could be arbitrarily large, exceeding the rating of the diode. As a practical matter we can never reduce the barrier to zero because, as the current increases without limit, the bulk resistance of the crystal, as well as the resistance of the ohmic contacts, will limit the current. Therefore it is no longer possible to assume that all the voltage V appears as a change across the p-n junction. We conclude that, as the forward voltage V becomes comparable with V_o, the current through a real p-n diode will be governed by the ohmic-contact resistances and the crystal bulk resistance. Thus the volt-ampere characteristic becomes approximately a straight line.

6-3 BAND STRUCTURE OF AN OPEN–CIRCUITED p-n JUNCTION

As in the previous section, we here consider that a p-n junction is formed by placing p- and n-type materials in intimate contact on an atomic scale. Under these conditions the Fermi level must be constant throughout the specimen at equilibrium. If this were not so, electrons on one side of the junction would have an average energy higher than those on the other side, and there would be a transfer of electrons and energy until the Fermi levels in the two sides did line up. In Sec. 5-6 it is verified that the Fermi level E_F is closer to the conduction band edge E_{Cn} in the n-type material and closer to the valence band edge E_{Vp} in the p side. Clearly, then, the conduction band edge E_{Cp} in the p material cannot be at the same level as E_{Cn}, nor can the valence band edge E_{Vn} in the n side line up with E_{Vp}. Hence the energy-band diagram for a p-n junction appears as shown in Fig. 6-4, where a shift in energy levels E_o is indicated. Note that

$$E_o = E_{Cp} - E_{Cn} = E_{Vp} - E_{Vn} = E_1 + E_2 \tag{6-1}$$

This energy E_o represents the potential energy of the electrons at the junction, as is indicated in Fig. 6-1e.

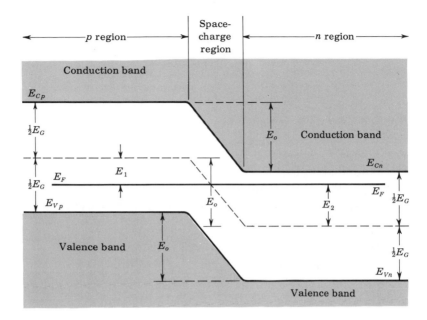

Fig. 6-4 Band diagram for a p-n junction under open-circuit conditions. This sketch corresponds to Fig. 6-1e and represents potential energy for electrons. The width of the forbidden gap is E_G in electron volts.

The Contact Difference of Potential We now obtain an expression for E_o. From Fig. 6-4 we see that

$$E_F - E_{Vp} = \tfrac{1}{2}E_G - E_1 \tag{6-2}$$

and

$$E_{Cn} - E_F = \tfrac{1}{2}E_G - E_2 \tag{6-3}$$

Adding these two equations, we obtain

$$E_o = E_1 + E_2 = E_G - (E_{Cn} - E_F) - (E_F - E_{Vp}) \tag{6-4}$$

From Eqs. (5-18) and (5-19),

$$E_G = kT \ln \frac{N_C N_V}{n_i{}^2} \tag{6-5}$$

From Eq. (5-30),

$$E_{Cn} - E_F = kT \ln \frac{N_C}{N_D} \tag{6-6}$$

From Eq. (5-31),

$$E_F - E_{Vp} = kT \ln \frac{N_V}{N_A} \tag{6-7}$$

Substituting from Eqs. (6-5), (6-6), and (6-7) in Eq. (6-4) yields

$$E_o = kT \left(\ln \frac{N_C N_V}{n_i^2} - \ln \frac{N_C}{N_D} - \ln \frac{N_V}{N_A} \right)$$

$$= kT \ln \left(\frac{N_C N_V}{n_i^2} \frac{N_D}{N_C} \frac{N_A}{N_V} \right) = kT \ln \frac{N_D N_A}{n_i^2} \tag{6-8}$$

We emphasize that, in the above equations, the E's are expressed in electron volts and k has the dimensions of electron volts per degree Kelvin. The contact difference in potential V_o is expressed in volts and is *numerically* equal to E_o. Note that V_o depends only upon the equilibrium concentrations, and not at all upon the charge density in the transition region.

Other expressions for E_o are obtained by substituting Eqs. (5-26), (5-27), and (5-28) in Eq. (6-8). We find

$$E_o = kT \ln \frac{p_{po}}{p_{no}} = kT \ln \frac{n_{no}}{n_{po}} \tag{6-9}$$

where the subscripts o are added to the concentrations to indicate that these are obtained under conditions of thermal equilibrium. Using the reasonable values $p_{po} = 10^{16}$ cm^{-3}, $p_{no} = 10^4$ cm^{-3}, and $kT = 0.026$ eV at room temperature, we obtain $E_o \approx 0.5$ eV.

An Alternative Derivation[2] **for** V_o In Sec. 6-1 we indicate that an application of the equilibrium condition of zero resultant hole current allows a calculation of V_o to be made. We now carry out such an analysis. Since the net hole current density is zero, the negative of the hole diffusion current [Eq. (5-32)] must equal the hole drift current [Eq. (3-2)], or

$$eD_p \frac{dp}{dx} = e\mu_p p \mathcal{E} \tag{6-10}$$

The Einstein relation [Eq. (5-33)] is

$$\frac{D_p}{\mu_p} = V_T \tag{6-11}$$

where the volt equivalent of temperature V_T is defined by Eq. (3-34). Substituting Eq. (6-11) in Eq. (6-10) and remembering the relationship (1-15) between field intensity and potential, we obtain

$$\frac{dp}{p} = \frac{\mathcal{E} \, dx}{V_T} = -\frac{dV}{V_T} \tag{6-12}$$

If this equation is integrated between limits which extend across the junction (Fig. 6-1d) from the p material, where the equilibrium hole concentration is p_{po}, to the n side, where the hole density is p_{no}, the result is

$$p_{po} = p_{no}\epsilon^{V_o/V_T} \tag{6-13}$$

Since $V_o/V_T = E_o/kT$, Eq. (6-13) is equivalent to Eq. (6-9).

Fig. 6-5 The hole- and
electron-current compo-
nents vs. distance in a p-n
junction diode. The space-
charge region at the junction is assumed to be
negligibly small.

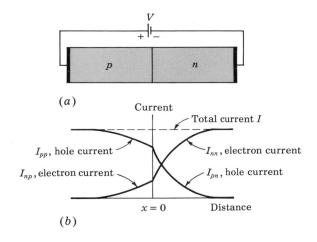

(a)

(b)

6-4   THE CURRENT COMPONENTS IN A p-n DIODE

In Sec. 6-2 it is indicated that when a forward bias is applied to a diode,
holes are injected into the n side and electrons into the p side. The number
of these injected minority carriers falls off exponentially with distance from
the junction [Eq. (5-52)]. Since the diffusion current of minority carriers is
proportional to the concentration gradient [Eq. (5-32)], this current must also
vary exponentially with distance. There are two minority currents, I_{pn} and
I_{np}, and these are indicated in Fig. 6-5. The symbol† $I_{pn}(x)$ represents the
hole current in the n material, and $I_{np}(x)$ indicates the electron current in the
p side as a function of x.

Electrons crossing the junction at $x = 0$ from right to left constitute a
current in the same direction as holes crossing the junction from left to right.
Hence the total current I at $x = 0$ is

$$I = I_{pn}(0) + I_{np}(0) \tag{6-14}$$

Since the current is the same throughout a series circuit, I is independent of x,
and is indicated as a horizontal line in Fig. 6-5. Consequently, in the p side,
there must be a second component of current I_{pp} which, when added to I_{np},
gives the total current I. Hence this hole current in the p side I_{pp} (a majority
carrier current) is given by

$$I_{pp}(x) = I - I_{np}(x) \tag{6-15}$$

This current is plotted as a function of distance in Fig. 6-5, as is also the
corresponding electron current I_{nn} in the n material. This figure is drawn for
an unsymmetrically doped diode, so that $I_{pn} \neq I_{np}$.

Note that deep into the p side the current is a drift (conduction) current
I_{pp} of holes sustained by the small electric field in the semiconductor. As the

† If the letters p and n both appear in a symbol, the first letter refers to the type of
carrier, and the second to the type of material.

holes approach the junction, some of them recombine with the electrons, which are injected into the p side from the n side. Hence part of the current I_{pp} becomes a negative current just equal in magnitude to the diffusion current I_{np}. The current I_{pp} thus decreases toward the junction (at just the proper rate to maintain the total current constant, independent of distance). What remains of I_{pp} at the junction enters the n side and becomes the hole diffusion current I_{pn}. Similar remarks can be made with respect to current I_{nn}. Hence, in a forward-biased p-n diode, the current enters the p side as a hole current and leaves the n side as an electron current of the same magnitude.

We emphasize that the current in a p-n diode is bipolar in character since it is made up of both positive and negative carriers of electricity. The total current is constant throughout the device, but the proportion due to holes and that due to electrons varies with distance, as indicated in Fig. 6-5.

6-5   QUANTITATIVE THEORY OF THE p-n DIODE CURRENTS

We now derive the expression for the total current as a function of the applied voltage (the volt-ampere characteristic). In the discussion to follow we neglect the depletion-layer thickness, and hence assume that the barrier width is zero. If a forward bias is applied to the diode, holes are injected from the p side into the n material. The concentration p_n of holes in the n side is increased above its thermal-equilibrium value p_{no} and, as indicated in Eq. (5-52), is given by

$$p_n(x) = p_{no} + P_n(0)\epsilon^{-x/L_p} \tag{6-16}$$

where the parameter L_p is called the *diffusion length for holes* in the n material, and the *injected*, or *excess*, concentration at $x = 0$ is

$$P_n(0) = p_n(0) - p_{no} \tag{6-17}$$

These several hole-concentration components are indicated in Fig. 6-6, which shows the exponential decrease of the density $p_n(x)$ with distance x into the n material.

From Eq. (5-32) the diffusion hole current in the n side is given by

$$I_{pn} = -AeD_p \frac{dp_n}{dx} \tag{6-18}$$

Taking the derivative of Eq. (6-16) and substituting in Eq. (6-18), we obtain

$$I_{pn}(x) = \frac{AeD_pP_n(0)}{L_p} \epsilon^{-x/L_p} \tag{6-19}$$

This equation verifies that the hole current decreases exponentially with distance. The dependence of I_{pn} upon applied voltage is contained implicitly in the factor $P_n(0)$ because the injected concentration is a function of voltage. We now find the dependence of $P_n(0)$ upon V.

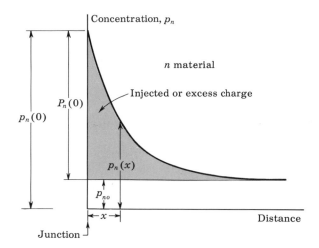

Fig. 6-6 Defining the several components of hole concentration in the n side of a forward-biased diode. The diagram is not drawn to scale since $p_n(0) \gg p_{no}$.

The Law of the Junction If the hole concentrations at the edges of the space-charge region are p_p and p_n in the p and n materials, respectively, and if the barrier potential across this depletion layer is V_B, then

$$p_p = p_n \epsilon^{V_B/V_T} \tag{6-20}$$

This is the Boltzmann relationship of kinetic gas theory. It is valid[2] even under nonequilibrium conditions as long as the net hole current is small compared with the diffusion or the drift hole current. Under this condition, called *low-level injection*, we may to a good approximation again equate the magnitudes of the diffusion and drift currents. Starting with Eqs. (6-10) and (6-12) and integrating over the depletion layer, Eq. (6-20) is obtained.

If we apply Eq. (6-20) to the case of an open-circuited p-n junction, then $p_p = p_{po}$, $p_n = p_{no}$, and $V_B = V_o$. Substituting these values in Eq. (6-20), it reduces to Eq. (6-13), from which we obtain the contact potential V_o.

Consider now a junction biased in the forward direction by an applied voltage V. Then the barrier voltage V_B is decreased from its equilibrium value V_o by the amount V, or $V_B = V_o - V$. The hole concentration throughout the p region is constant and equal to the thermal equilibrium value, or $p_p = p_{po}$. The hole concentration varies with distance into the n side, as indicated in Fig. 6-6. At the edge of the depletion layer, $x = 0$, $p_n = p_n(0)$. The Boltzmann relation (6-20) is, for this case,

$$p_{po} = p_n(0)\epsilon^{(V_o-V)/V_T} \tag{6-21}$$

Combining this equation with Eq. (6-13), we obtain

$$p_n(0) = p_{no}\epsilon^{V/V_T} \tag{6-22}$$

This boundary condition is called the *law of the junction*. It indicates that, for a forward bias ($V > 0$), the hole concentration $p_n(0)$ at the junction is greater than the thermal-equilibrium value p_{no}. A similar law, valid for electrons, is obtained by interchanging p and n in Eq. (6-22).

The hole concentration $P_n(0)$ injected into the n side at the junction is obtained by substituting Eq. (6-22) in Eq. (6-17), yielding

$$P_n(0) = p_{no}(\epsilon^{V/V_T} - 1) \tag{6-23}$$

The Forward Currents The hole current $I_{pn}(0)$ crossing the junction into the n side is given by Eq. (6-19), with $x = 0$. Using Eq. (6-23) for $P_n(0)$, we obtain

$$I_{pn}(0) = \frac{AeD_p p_{no}}{L_p} (\epsilon^{V/V_T} - 1) \tag{6-24}$$

The electron current $I_{np}(0)$ crossing the junction into the p side is obtained from Eq. (6-24) by interchanging n and p, or

$$I_{np}(0) = \frac{AeD_n n_{po}}{L_n} (\epsilon^{V/V_T} - 1) \tag{6-25}$$

Finally, from Eq. (6-14), the total diode current I is the sum of $I_{pn}(0)$ and $I_{np}(0)$, or

$$I = I_o(\epsilon^{V/V_T} - 1) \tag{6-26}$$

where

$$I_o \equiv \frac{AeD_p p_{no}}{L_p} + \frac{AeD_n n_{po}}{L_n} \tag{6-27}$$

If W_p and W_n are the widths of the p and n materials, respectively, the above derivation has implicitly assumed that $W_p \gg L_p$ and $W_n \gg L_n$. If, as sometimes happens in a practical diode, the widths are much smaller than the diffusion lengths, the expression for I_o remains valid provided that L_p and L_n are replaced by W_p and W_n, respectively.

The Reverse Saturation Current In the foregoing discussion a positive value of V indicates a forward bias. The derivation of Eq. (6-26) is equally valid if V is negative, signifying an applied reverse-bias voltage. For a reverse bias whose magnitude is large compared with V_T ($\sim$26 mV at room temperature), $I \rightarrow -I_o$. Hence I_o is called the *reverse saturation current*. Combining Eqs. (5-27), (5-28), and (6-27), we obtain

$$I_o = Ae \left(\frac{D_p}{L_p N_D} + \frac{D_n}{L_n N_A} \right) n_i^2 \tag{6-28}$$

where n_i^2 is given by Eq. (5-23),

$$n_i^2 = A_o T^3 \epsilon^{-E_{Go}/kT} = A_o T^3 \epsilon^{-V_{Go}/V_T} \tag{6-29}$$

where V_{GO} is a voltage which is numerically equal to the forbidden-gap energy E_{GO} in electron volts, and V_T is the volt equivalent of temperature [Eq. (3-34)]. For germanium the diffusion constants D_p and D_n vary approximately[3] inversely proportional to T. Hence the temperature dependence of I_o is

$$I_o = K_1 T^2 \epsilon^{-V_{Go}/V_T} \tag{6-30}$$

where K_1 is a constant independent of temperature.

Throughout this section we have neglected carrier generation and recombination in the space-charge region. Such an assumption is valid for a germanium diode, but not for a silicon device. For the latter, the diffusion current is negligible compared with the transition-layer charge-generation[3,4] current, which is given approximately by

$$I = I_o(\epsilon^{V/\eta V_T} - 1) \tag{6-31}$$

where $\eta \approx 2$ for small (rated) currents and $\eta \approx 1$ for large currents. Also, I_o is now found to be proportional to n_i instead of n_i^2. Hence, if K_2 is a constant,

$$I_o = K_2 T^{1.5} \epsilon^{-V_{Go}/2V_T} \tag{6-32}$$

The practical implications of these diode equations are given in the following sections.

6-6   THE VOLT–AMPERE CHARACTERISTIC

The discussion of the preceding section indicates that, for a p-n junction, the current I is related to the voltage V by the equation

$$I = I_o(\epsilon^{V/\eta V_T} - 1) \tag{6-33}$$

A positive value of I means that current flows from the p to the n side. The diode is forward-biased if V is positive, indicating that the p side of the junction is positive with respect to the n side. The symbol η is unity for germanium and is approximately 2 for silicon.

The symbol V_T stands for the volt equivalent of temperature, and is given by Eq. (3-34), repeated here for convenience:

$$V_T \equiv \frac{T}{11,600} \tag{6-34}$$

At room temperature ($T = 300°K$), $V_T = 0.026$ V $= 26$ mV.

The form of the volt-ampere characteristic described by Eq. (6-33) is shown in Fig. 6-7a. When the voltage V is positive and several times V_T, the unity in the parentheses of Eq. (6-33) may be neglected. Accordingly, except for a small range in the neighborhood of the origin, the current increases exponentially with voltage. When the diode is reverse-biased and $|V|$ is several times V_T, $I \approx -I_o$. The reverse current is therefore constant, independent of the applied reverse bias. Consequently, I_o is referred to as the *reverse saturation current*.

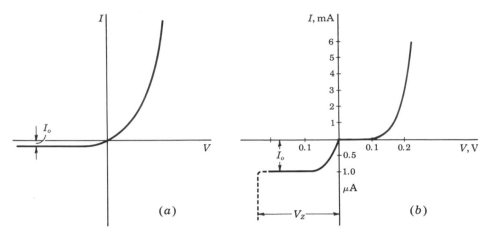

Fig. 6-7 (a) The volt-ampere characteristic of an ideal p-n diode. (b) The volt-ampere characteristic for a germanium diode redrawn to show the order of magnitude of currents. Note the expanded scale for reverse currents. The dashed portion indicates breakdown at V_Z.

For the sake of clarity, the current I_o in Fig. 6-7a has been greatly exaggerated in magnitude. Ordinarily, the range of forward currents over which a diode is operated is many orders of magnitude larger than the reverse saturation current. In order to display forward and reverse characteristics conveniently, it is necessary, as in Fig. 6-7b, to use two different current scales. The volt-ampere characteristic shown in that figure has a forward current scale in milliamperes and a reverse scale in microamperes.

The dashed portion of the curve of Fig. 6-7b indicates that, at a reverse-biasing voltage V_Z, the diode characteristic exhibits an abrupt and marked departure from Eq. (6-33). At this critical voltage a large reverse current flows, and the diode is said to be in the *breakdown* region, discussed in Sec. 6-12.

The Cutin Voltage V_γ Both silicon and germanium diodes are commercially available. A number of differences between these two types are relevant in circuit design. The difference in volt-ampere characteristics is brought out in Fig. 6-8. Here are plotted the forward characteristics at room temperature of a general-purpose germanium switching diode and a general-purpose silicon diode, the 1N270 and 1N3605, respectively. The diodes have comparable current ratings. A noteworthy feature in Fig. 6-8 is that there exists a *cutin, offset, break-point,* or *threshold* voltage V_γ below which the current is very small (say, less than 1 percent of maximum rated value). Beyond V_γ the current rises very rapidly. From Fig. 6-8 we see that V_γ is approximately 0.2 V for germanium and 0.6 V for silicon.

Note that the break in the silicon-diode characteristic is offset about 0.4 V with respect to the break in the germanium-diode characteristic. The

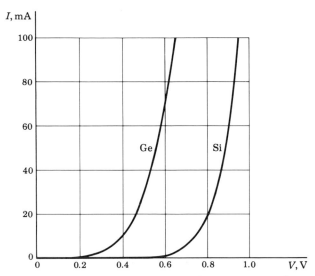

Fig. 6-8 The forward volt-ampere characteristics of a germanium (1N270) and a silicon (1N3605) diode at 25°C.

reason for this difference is to be found, in part, in the fact that the reverse saturation current in a germanium diode is normally larger by a factor of about 1,000 than the reverse saturation current in a silicon diode of comparable ratings. Thus, if I_o is in the range of microamperes for a germanium diode, I_o will be in the range of nanoamperes for a silicon diode.

Since $\eta = 2$ for small currents in silicon, the current increases as $\epsilon^{V/2V_T}$ for the first several tenths of a volt and increases as ϵ^{V/V_T} only at higher voltages. This initial smaller dependence of the current on voltage accounts for the further delay in the rise of the silicon characteristic.

Logarithmic Characteristic It is instructive to examine the family of curves for the silicon diodes shown in Fig. 6-9. A family for a germanium diode of comparable current rating is quite similar, with the exception that corresponding currents are attained at lower voltage.

From Eq. (6-33), assuming that V is several times V_T, so that we may drop the unity, we have $\log I = \log I_o + 0.434V/\eta V_T$. We therefore expect in Fig. 6-9, where $\log I$ is plotted against V, that the plots will be straight lines. We do indeed find that at low currents the plots are linear and correspond to $\eta \approx 2$. At large currents an increment of voltage does not yield as large an increase of current as at low currents. The reason for this behavior is to be found in the ohmic resistance of the diode. At low currents the ohmic drop is negligible and the externally impressed voltage simply decreases the potential barrier at the p-n junction. At high currents the externally

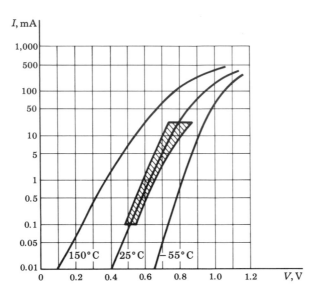

Fig. 6-9 Volt-ampere characteristics at three different temperatures for a silicon diode (planar epitaxial passivated types 1N3605, 1N3606, 1N3608, and 1N3609). The shaded area indicates 25°C limits of controlled conductance. Note that the vertical scale is logarithmic and encompasses a current range of 50,000. (Courtesy of General Electric Company.)

impressed voltage is called upon principally to establish an electric field to overcome the ohmic resistance of the semiconductor material. Therefore, at high currents, the diode behaves more like a resistor than a diode, and the current increases linearly rather than exponentially with applied voltage.

6-7 THE TEMPERATURE DEPENDENCE OF p-n CHARACTERISTICS

Let us inquire into the diode voltage variation with temperature at fixed current. This variation may be calculated from Eq. (6-33), where the temperature is contained implicitly in V_T and also in the reverse saturation current. The dependence of I_o on temperature T is, from Eqs. (6-30) and (6-32), given approximately by

$$I_o = KT^m \epsilon^{-V_{GO}/\eta V_T} \tag{6-35}$$

where K is a constant and eV_{GO} (e is the magnitude of the electronic charge) is the forbidden-gap energy in joules:

For Ge: $\eta = 1$ $m = 2$ $V_{GO} = 0.785$ V
For Si: $\eta = 2$ $m = 1.5$ $V_{GO} = 1.21$ V

Taking the derivative of the logarithm of Eq. (6-35), we find

$$\frac{1}{I_o}\frac{dI_o}{dT} = \frac{d(\ln I_o)}{dT} = \frac{m}{T} + \frac{V_{GO}}{\eta T V_T} \tag{6-36}$$

At room temperature, we deduce from Eq. (6-36) that $d(\ln I_o)/dT = 0.08°\text{C}^{-1}$ for Si and $0.11°\text{C}^{-1}$ for Ge. The performance of commercial diodes is only approximately consistent with these results. The reason for the discrepancy is that, in a physical diode, there is a component of the reverse saturation current due to leakage over the surface that is not taken into account in Eq. (6-35). Since this leakage component is independent of temperature, we may expect to find a smaller rate of change of I_o with temperature than that predicted above. From experimental data we find that the reverse saturation current increases approximately 7 percent/°C for both silicon and germanium. Since $(1.07)^{10} \approx 2.0$, we conclude that the *reverse saturation current approximately doubles for every 10°C rise in temperature.*

From Eq. (6-33), dropping the unity in comparison with the exponential, we find, for constant I,

$$\frac{dV}{dT} = \frac{V}{T} - \eta V_T \left(\frac{1}{I_o} \frac{dI_o}{dT} \right) = \frac{V - (V_{GO} + m\eta V_T)}{T} \tag{6-37}$$

where use has been made of Eq. (6-36). Consider a diode operating at room temperature (300°K) and just beyond the threshold voltage V_γ (say, at 0.2 V for Ge and 0.6 for Si). Then we find, from Eq. (6-37),

$$\frac{dV}{dT} = \begin{cases} -2.1 \text{ mV/°C} & \text{for Ge} \\ -2.3 \text{ mV/°C} & \text{for Si} \end{cases} \tag{6-38}$$

Since these data are based on "average characteristics," it might be well for conservative design to assume a value of

$$\frac{dV}{dT} = -2.5 \text{ mV/°C} \tag{6-39}$$

for either Ge or Si at room temperature. Note from Eq. (6-37) that $|dV/dT|$ decreases with increasing T.

The temperature dependence of forward voltage is given in Eq. (6-37) as the difference between two terms. The positive term V/T on the right-hand side results from the temperature dependence of V_T. The negative term results from the temperature dependence of I_o, and does not depend on the voltage V across the diode. The equation predicts that for increasing V, dV/dT should become less negative, reach zero at $V = V_{GO} + m\eta V_T$, and thereafter reverse sign and go positive. This behavior is regularly exhibited by diodes. Normally, however, the reversal takes place at a current which is higher than the maximum rated current. The curves of Fig. 6-9 also suggest this behavior. At high voltages the horizontal separation between curves of different temperatures is smaller than at low voltages.

Typical reverse characteristics of germanium and silicon diodes are given in Fig. 6-10a and b. Observe the very pronounced dependence of current on reverse voltage, a result which is not consistent with our expectation of a constant saturated reverse current. This increase in I_o results from leakage across the surface of the diode, and also from the additional fact that new current carriers may be generated by collision in the transition region at the junction. On the other hand, there are many commercially available diodes, both germanium and silicon, that do exhibit a fairly constant reverse current with

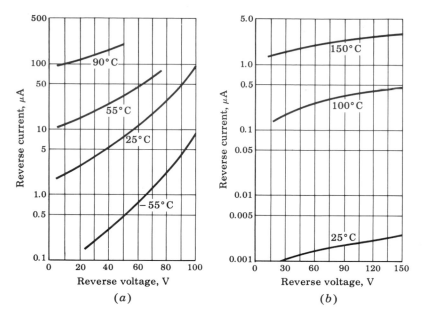

Fig. 6-10 Examples of diodes which do not exhibit a constant reverse saturation current. (a) Germanium diode 1N270; (b) silicon 1N461. (Courtesy of Raytheon Company.)

increasing voltage. The much larger value of I_o for a germanium than for a silicon diode, to which we have previously referred, is apparent in comparing Fig. 6-10a and b. Since the temperature dependence is approximately the same in both types of diodes, at elevated temperatures the germanium diode will develop an excessively large reverse current, whereas for silicon, I_o will be quite modest. Thus we can see that for Ge in Fig. 6-10 an increase in temperature from room temperature (25°C) to 90°C increases the reverse current to hundreds of microamperes, although in silicon at 100°C the reverse current has increased only to some tenths of a microampere.

6-8   DIODE RESISTANCE

The static resistance R of a diode is defined as the ratio V/I of the voltage to the current. At any point on the volt-ampere characteristic of the diode (Fig. 6-7), the resistance R is equal to the reciprocal of the slope of a line joining the operating point to the origin. The static resistance varies widely with V and I and is not a useful parameter. The rectification property of a diode is indicated on the manufacturer's specification sheet by giving the maximum forward voltage V_F required to attain a given forward current I_F and also the maximum reverse current I_R at a given reverse voltage V_R. Typical values for a silicon planar epitaxial diode are $V_F = 0.8$ V at $I_F = 10$ mA (corresponding to $R_F = 80\ \Omega$) and $I_R = 0.1\ \mu$A at $V_R = 50$ V (corresponding to $R_R = 500$ M).

For small-signal operation the *dynamic*, or *incremental, resistance r* is an important parameter, and is defined as the reciprocal of the slope of the volt-ampere characteristic, $r \equiv dV/dI$. The dynamic resistance is not a constant, but depends upon the operating voltage. For example, for a semiconductor diode, we find from Eq. (6-33) that the dynamic conductance $g \equiv 1/r$ is

$$g \equiv \frac{dI}{dV} = \frac{I_o \epsilon^{V/\eta V_T}}{\eta V_T} = \frac{I + I_o}{\eta V_T} \tag{6-40}$$

For a reverse bias greater than a few tenths of a volt (so that $|V/\eta V_T| \gg 1$), g is extremely small and r is very large. On the other hand, for a forward bias greater than a few tenths of a volt, $I \gg I_o$, and r is given approximately by

$$r \approx \frac{\eta V_T}{I} \tag{6-41}$$

The dynamic resistance varies inversely with current; at room temperature and for $\eta = 1$, $r = 26/I$, where I is in milliamperes and r in ohms. For a forward current of 26 mA, the dynamic resistance is 1 Ω. The ohmic body resistance of the semiconductor may be of the same order of magnitude or even much higher than this value. Although r varies with current, in a small-signal model, it is reasonable to use the parameter r as a constant.

A Piecewise Linear Diode Characteristic   A large-signal approximation which often leads to a sufficiently accurate engineering solution is the *piecewise linear representation*. For example, the piecewise linear approximation for a semiconductor diode characteristic is indicated in Fig. 6-11. The break point is not at the origin, and hence V_γ is also called the *offset*, or *threshold, voltage*. The diode behaves like an open circuit if $V < V_\gamma$, and has a constant incremental resistance $r = dV/dI$ if $V > V_\gamma$. Note that the resistance r (also designated as R_f and called the *forward resistance*) takes on added physical

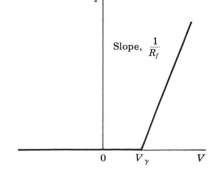

**Fig. 6-11   The piecewise linear character-
ization of a semiconductor diode.**

significance even for this large-signal model, whereas the static resistance $R_F = V/I$ is not constant and is not useful.

The numerical values V_γ and R_f to be used depend upon the type of diode and the contemplated voltage and current swings. For example, from Fig. 6-8 we find that, for a current swing from cutoff to 10 mA with a germanium diode, reasonable values are $V_\gamma = 0.6$ V and $R_f = 15$ Ω. On the other hand, a better approximation for current swings up to 50 mA leads to the following values: germanium, $V_\gamma = 0.3$ V, $R_f = 6$ Ω; silicon, $V_\gamma = 0.65$ V, $R_f = 5.5$ Ω. For an avalanche diode, discussed in Sec. 6-12, $V_\gamma = V_Z$, and R_f is the dynamic resistance in the breakdown region.

6-9   SPACE–CHARGE, OR TRANSITION, CAPACITANCE[1] C_T

As mentioned in Sec. 6-1, a reverse bias causes majority carriers to move away from the junction, thereby uncovering more immobile charges. Hence the thickness of the space-charge layer at the junction increases with reverse voltage. This increase in uncovered charge with applied voltage may be considered a capacitive effect. We may define an incremental capacitance C_T by

$$C_T = \left| \frac{dQ}{dV} \right| \tag{6-42}$$

where dQ is the increase in charge caused by a change dV in voltage. It follows from this definition that a change in voltage dV in a time dt will result in a current $i = dQ/dt$, given by

$$i = C_T \frac{dV}{dt} \tag{6-43}$$

Therefore a knowledge of C_T is important in considering a diode (or a transistor) as a circuit element. The quantity C_T is referred to as the *transition-region, space-charge, barrier,* or *depletion-region, capacitance.* We now consider C_T quantitatively. As it turns out, this capacitance is not a constant, but depends upon the magnitude of the reverse voltage. It is for this reason that C_T is defined by Eq. (6-42) rather than as the ratio Q/V.

An Alloy Junction   Consider a junction in which there is an abrupt change from acceptor ions on one side to donor ions on the other side. Such a junction is formed experimentally, for example, by placing indium, which is trivalent, against n-type germanium and heating the combination to a high temperature for a short time. Some of the indium dissolves into the germanium to change the germanium from n to p type at the junction. Such a junction is called an *alloy,* or *fusion, junction.* It is not necessary that the concentration N_A of acceptor ions equal the concentration N_D of donor impurities. As a matter of fact, it is often advantageous to have an unsymmetrical

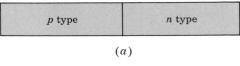

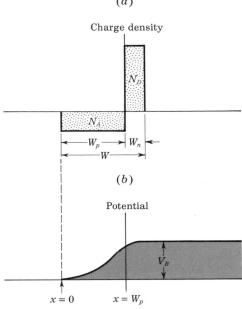

Fig. 6-12 The charge-density and
potential variation at a fusion
p-n junction ($W \approx 10^{-4}$ cm).

junction. Figure 6-12 shows the charge density as a function of distance from
an alloy junction in which the acceptor impurity density is assumed to be
much smaller than the donor concentration. Since the net charge must be
zero, then

$$eN_A W_p = eN_D W_n \qquad (6\text{-}44)$$

If $N_A \ll N_D$, then $W_p \gg W_n$. For simplicity, we neglect W_n and assume that
the entire barrier potential V_B appears across the uncovered acceptor ions.
The relationship between potential and charge density is given by Poisson's
equation,

$$\frac{d^2V}{dx^2} = \frac{eN_A}{\epsilon} \qquad (6\text{-}45)$$

where ϵ is the permittivity of the semiconductor. If ϵ_r is the (relative) dielectric constant and ϵ_o is the permittivity of free space (Appendix B), then $\epsilon = \epsilon_r \epsilon_o$.
The electric lines of flux start on the positive donor ions and terminate on the
negative acceptor ions. Hence there are no flux lines to the left of the boundary $x = 0$ in Fig. 6-12, and $\mathcal{E} = -dV/dx = 0$ at $x = 0$. Also, since the zero
of potential is arbitrary, we choose $V = 0$ at $x = 0$. Integrating Eq. (6-45)

subject to these boundary conditions yields

$$V = \frac{eN_A x^2}{2\epsilon} \tag{6-46}$$

At $x = W_p \approx W$, $V = V_B$, the barrier height. Thus

$$V_B = \frac{eN_A}{2\epsilon} W^2 \tag{6-47}$$

If we now reserve the symbol V for the *applied* bias, then $V_B = V_o - V$, where V is a negative number for an applied *reverse* bias and V_o is the contact potential (Fig. 6-1d). This equation confirms our qualitative conclusion that the thickness of the depletion layer increases with applied reverse voltage. We now see that W varies as $V_B^{\frac{1}{2}}$.

If A is the area of the junction, the charge in the distance W is

$$Q = eN_A W A$$

The transition capacitance C_T, given by Eq. (6-42), is

$$C_T = \left| \frac{dQ}{dV} \right| = eN_A A \left| \frac{dW}{dV} \right| \tag{6-48}$$

From Eq. (6-47), $|dW/dV| = \epsilon/eN_A W$, and hence

$$C_T = \frac{\epsilon A}{W} \tag{6-49}$$

It is interesting to note that this formula is exactly the expression which is obtained for a parallel-plate capacitor of area A (square meters) and plate separation W (meters) containing a material of permittivity ϵ. If the concentration N_D is not neglected, the above results are modified only slightly. In Eq. (6-47) W represents the total space-charge width, and $1/N_A$ is replaced by $1/N_A + 1/N_D$. Equation (6-49) remains valid.

A Grown Junction A second form of junction, called a *grown junction*, is obtained by drawing a single crystal from a melt of germanium whose type is changed during the drawing process by adding first p-type and then n-type impurities. For such a grown junction the charge density varies gradually (almost linearly), as indicated in Fig. 6-13. If an analysis similar to that

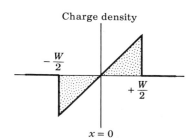

Fig. 6-13 The charge-density variation at a grown p-n junction.

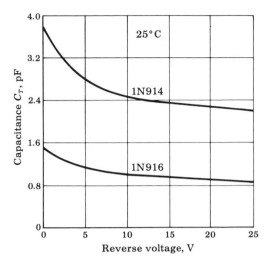

Fig. 6-14　Typical barrier-capacitance variation, with reverse voltage, of silicon diodes 1N914 and 1N916.　(Courtesy of Fairchild Semiconductor Corporation.)

given above is carried out for such a junction, Eq. (6-49) is found to be valid where W equals the total width of the space-charge layer.　However, it now turns out that W varies as $V_B^{\frac{1}{3}}$ instead of $V_B^{\frac{1}{2}}$.

Varactor Diodes　We observe from the above equations that the barrier capacitance is not a constant but varies with applied voltage.　The larger the reverse voltage, the larger is the space-charge width W, and hence the smaller the capacitance C_T.　The variation is illustrated for two typical diodes in Fig. 6-14　Similarly, for an increase in forward bias (V positive), W decreases and C_T increases.

The voltage-variable capacitance of a p-n junction biased in the reverse direction is useful in a number of circuits.　One of these applications is voltage tuning of an LC resonant circuit.　Other applications include self-balancing bridge circuits and special types of amplifiers, called *parametric amplifiers*.

Diodes made especially for the above applications which are based on the voltage-variable capacitance are called *varactors*, *varicaps*, or *voltacaps*. A circuit model for a varactor diode under reverse bias is shown in Fig. 6-15.

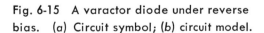

(*a*)

Fig. 6-15　A varactor diode under reverse bias.　(*a*) Circuit symbol; (*b*) circuit model.

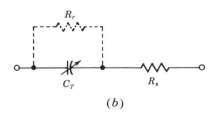

(*b*)

The resistance R_s represents the body (ohmic) series resistance of the diode. Typical values of C_T and R_s are 20 pF and 8.5 Ω, respectively, at a reverse bias of 4 V. The reverse diode resistance R_r shunting C_T is large (>1 M), and hence is usually neglected.

In circuits intended for use with fast waveforms or at high frequencies, it is required that the transition capacitance be as small as possible, for the following reason: A diode is driven to the reverse-biased condition when it is desired to prevent the transmission of a signal. However, if the barrier capacitance C_T is large enough, the current which is to be restrained by the low conductance of the reverse-biased diode will flow through the capacitor (Fig. 6-15b).

6-10   DIFFUSION CAPACITANCE

For a forward bias a capacitance which is much larger than that considered in the preceding section comes into play. The origin of this capacitance is now discussed. If the bias is in the forward direction, the potential barrier at the junction is lowered and holes from the p side enter the n side. Similarly, electrons from the n side move into the p side. This process of *minority-carrier injection* is discussed in Sec. 6-5, where we see that the excess hole density falls off exponentially with distance, as indicated in Fig. 6-6. The shaded area under this curve is proportional to the injected charge. As explained in Sec. 6-9, it is convenient to introduce an incremental capacitance, defined as the rate of change of injected charge with applied voltage. This capacitance C_D is called the *diffusion,* or *storage, capacitance.*

Derivation of Expressions for C_D We now make a quantitative study of the diffusion capacitance C_D. For simplicity of discussion we assume that one side of the diode, say, the p material, is so heavily doped in comparison with the n side that the current I is carried across the junction entirely by holes moving from the p to the n side, or $I = I_{pn}(0)$. The excess minority charge Q will then exist only on the n side, and is given by the shaded area of Fig. 6-6 multiplied by the diode cross section A and the electronic charge e. Hence

$$Q = \int_0^\infty AeP_n(0)\epsilon^{-x/L_p}\,dx = AeL_pP_n(0) \tag{6-50}$$

and

$$C_D = \frac{dQ}{dV} = AeL_p\frac{dP_n(0)}{dV} \tag{6-51}$$

The hole current I is given by $I_{pn}(x)$ in Eq. (6-19), with $x = 0$, or

$$I = \frac{AeD_pP_n(0)}{L_p} \tag{6-52}$$

and

$$\frac{dP_n(0)}{dV} = \frac{L_p}{AeD_p}\frac{dI}{dV} = \frac{L_p}{AeD_p}g \tag{6-53}$$

where $g \equiv dI/dV$ is the diode conductance given in Eq. (6-40). Combining Eqs. (6-51) and (6-53) yields

$$C_D = \frac{L_p^2 g}{D_p} \tag{6-54}$$

Since from Eq. (5-51) the mean lifetime for holes $\tau_p = \tau$ is given by

$$\tau = \frac{L_p^2}{D_p} \tag{6-55}$$

then

$$C_D = \tau g \tag{6-56}$$

From Eq. (6-41), $g = I/\eta V_T$, and hence

$$C_D = \frac{\tau I}{\eta V_T} \tag{6-57}$$

We see that the *diffusion capacitance is proportional to the current I.* In the derivation above we have assumed that the diode current I is due to holes only. If this assumption is not satisfied, Eq. (6-56) gives the diffusion capacitance C_{D_p} due to holes only, and a similar expression can be obtained for the diffusion capacitance C_{n_n} due to electrons. The total diffusion capacitance can then be obtained as the sum of C_{D_p} and C_{D_n} (Prob. 6-30).

For a reverse bias g is very small and C_D may be neglected compared with C_T. For a forward current, on the other hand, C_D is usually much larger than C_T. For example, for germanium ($\eta = 1$) at $I = 26$ mA, $g = 1$ mho, and $C_D = \tau$. If, say, $\tau = 20$ μsec, then $C_D = 20$ μF, a value which is about a million times larger than the transition capacitance.

Despite the large value of C_D, the time constant rC_D (which is of importance in circuit applications) may not be excessive because the dynamic forward resistance $r = 1/g$ is small. From Eq. (6-56),

$$rC_D = \tau \tag{6-58}$$

Hence the diode time constant equals the mean lifetime of minority carriers, which lies in range of nanoseconds to hundreds of microseconds. The importance of τ in circuit applications is considered in the following section.

Charge-control Description of a Diode   From Eqs. (6-50), (6-52), and (6-55),

$$I = Q\frac{D_p}{L_p^2} = \frac{Q}{\tau} \tag{6-59}$$

This very important equation states that the diode current (which consists of holes crossing the junction from the p to the n side) is proportional to the stored charge Q of excess minority carriers.   The factor of proportionality is the reciprocal of the decay time constant (the mean lifetime τ) of the minority carriers.   Thus, in the steady state, *the current I supplies minority carriers at the rate at which these carriers are disappearing because of the process of recombination.*

The charge-control characterization of a diode describes the device in terms of the current I and the stored charge Q, whereas the equivalent-circuit characterization uses the current I and the junction voltage V.   One immediately apparent advantage of this charge-control description is that the exponential relationship between I and V is replaced by the linear dependence I on Q.   The charge Q also makes a simple parameter, the sign of which determines whether the diode is forward- or reverse-biased.   The diode is forward-biased if Q is positive and reverse-biased if Q is negative.

6-11 p-n DIODE SWITCHING TIMES

When a diode is driven from the reversed condition to the forward state or in the opposite direction, the diode response is accompanied by a transient, and an interval of time elapses before the diode recovers to its steady state.   The forward recovery time t_{fr} is the time difference between the 10 percent point of the diode voltage and the time when this voltage reaches and remains within 10 percent of its final value.   It turns out[5] that t_{fr} does not usually constitute a serious practical problem, and hence we here consider only the more important situation of reverse recovery.

Diode Reverse Recovery Time   When an external voltage forward-biases a p-n junction, the steady-state density of minority carriers is as shown in Fig. 6-16a (compare with Fig. 6-6).   The number of minority carriers is very

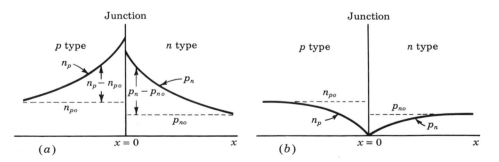

Fig. 6-16   Minority-carrier density distribution as a function of the distance x from a junction.   (a) A forward-biased junction; (b) a reverse-biased junction. The injected, or excess, hole (electron) density is $p_n - p_{no}$ ($n_p - n_{po}$).

large.   These minority carriers have, in each case, been supplied from the other side of the junction, where, being majority carriers, they are in plentiful supply.

When an external voltage reverse-biases the junction, the steady-state density of minority carriers is as shown in Fig. 6-16b.   Far from the junction the minority carriers are equal to their thermal-equilibrium values p_{no} and n_{po}, as is also the situation in Fig. 6-16a.   As the minority carriers approach the junction they are rapidly swept across, and the density of minority carriers diminishes to zero at this junction.   The current which flows, the reverse saturation current I_o, is small because the density of thermally generated minority carriers is very small.

If the external voltage is suddenly reversed in a diode circuit which has been carrying current in the forward direction, the diode current will not immediately fall to its steady-state reverse-voltage value.   For the current cannot attain its steady-state value until the minority-carrier distribution, which at the moment of voltage reversal had the form in Fig. 6-16a, reduces to the distribution in Fig. 6-16b.   Until such time as the *injected*, or *excess*, *minority-carrier density* $p_n - p_{no}$ (or $n_p - n_{po}$) has dropped nominally to zero, the diode will continue to conduct easily, and the current will be determined by the external resistance in the diode circuit.

Storage and Transition Times   The sequence of events which accompanies the reverse biasing of a conducting diode is indicated in Fig. 6-17. We consider that the voltage in Fig. 6-17b is applied to the diode-resistor circuit in Fig. 6-17a.   For a long time, and up to the time t_1, the voltage $v_i = V_F$ has been in the direction to forward-bias the diode.   The resistance R_L is assumed large enough so that the drop across R_L is large in comparison with the drop across the diode.   Then the current is $i \approx V_F/R_L = I_F$.   At the time $t = t_1$ the input voltage reverses abruptly to the value $v = -V_R$. For the reasons described above, the current does not drop to zero, but instead reverses and remains at the value $i \approx -V_R/R_L \equiv -I_R$ until the time $t = t_2$. At $t = t_2$, as is seen in Fig. 6-17c, the injected minority-carrier density at $x = 0$ has reached its equilibrium state.   If the diode ohmic resistance is R_d, then at the time t_1 the diode voltage falls slightly [by $(I_F + I_R)R_d$] but does not reverse.   At $t = t_2$, when the excess minority carriers in the immediate neighborhood of the junction have been swept back across the junction, the diode voltage begins to reverse and the magnitude of the diode current begins to decrease.   The interval t_1 to t_2, for the stored-minority charge to become zero, is called the *storage time* t_s.

The time which elapses between t_2 and the time when the diode has nominally recovered is called the *transition time* t_t.   This recovery interval will be completed when the minority carriers which are at some distance from the junction have diffused to the junction and crossed it and when, in addition, the junction transition capacitance across the reverse-biased junction has charged through R_L to the voltage $-V_R$.

Manufacturers normally specify the reverse recovery time of a diode t_{rr}

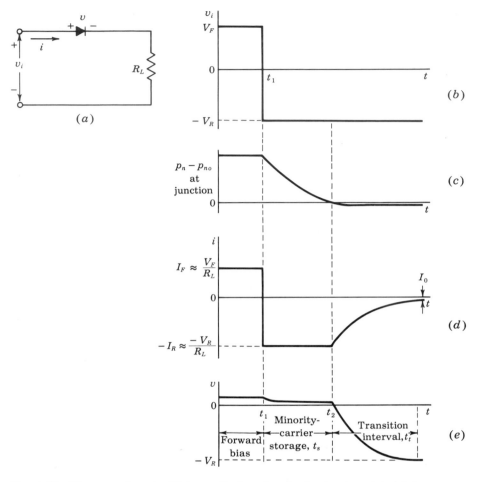

Fig. 6-17 The waveform in (b) is applied to the diode circuit in (a); (c) the excess carrier density at the junction; (d) the diode current; (e) the diode voltage.

in a typical operating condition in terms of the current waveform of Fig. 6-17d. The time t_{rr} is the interval from the current reversal at $t = t_1$ until the diode has recovered to a specified extent in terms either of the diode current or of the diode resistance. If the specified value of R_L is larger than several hundred ohms, ordinarily the manufacturers will specify the capacitance C_L shunting R_L in the measuring circuit which is used to determine t_{rr}. Thus we find, for the Fairchild 1N3071, that with $I_F = 30$ mA and $I_R = 30$ mA, the time required for the reverse current to fall to 1.0 mA is 50 nsec. Again we find, for the same diode, that with $I_F = 30$ mA, $-V_R = -35$ V, $R_L = 2$ K, and $C_L = 10$ pF ($-I_R = -35/2 = -17.5$ mA), the time required for the diode to recover to the extent that its resistance becomes 400 K is $t_{rr} = 400$ nsec.

Commercial switching-type diodes are available with times t_{rr} in the range from less than a nanosecond up to as high as 1 μsec in diodes intended for switching large currents.

6-12   BREAKDOWN DIODES[6]

The reverse-voltage characteristic of a semiconductor diode, including the breakdown region, is redrawn in Fig. 6-18a.   Diodes which are designed with adequate power dissipation capabilities to operate in the breakdown region may be employed as voltage-reference or constant-voltage devices.   Such diodes are known as *avalanche, breakdown,* or *Zener diodes.*   They are used characteristically in the manner indicated in Fig. 6-18b.   The source V and resistor R are selected so that, initially, the diode is operating in the break-down region.   Here the diode voltage, which is also the voltage across the load R_L, is V_Z, as in Fig. 6-18a, and the diode current is I_Z.   The diode will now regulate the load voltage against variations in load current and against variations in supply voltage V because, in the breakdown region, large changes in diode current produce only small changes in diode voltage.   Moreover, as load current or supply voltage changes, the diode current will accommodate itself to these changes to maintain a nearly constant load voltage.   The diode will continue to regulate until the circuit operation requires the diode current to fall to I_{ZK}, in the neighborhood of the knee of the diode volt-ampere curve.   The upper limit on diode current is determined by the power-dissipation rating of the diode.

Two mechanisms of diode breakdown for increasing reverse voltage are recognized.   In one mechanism, the thermally generated electrons and holes acquire sufficient energy from the applied potential to produce new carriers by removing valence electrons from their bonds.   These new carriers, in turn, produce additional carriers again through the process of disrupting bonds.

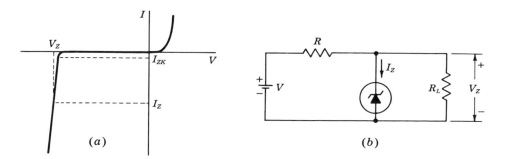

Fig. 6-18   (a) The volt-ampere characteristic of an avalanche, or Zener, diode.
(b) A circuit in which such a diode is used to regulate the voltage across R_L
against changes due to variations in load current and supply voltage.

This cumulative process is referred to as *avalanche multiplication*.   It results in the flow of large reverse currents, and the diode finds itself in the region of *avalanche breakdown*.   Even if the initially available carriers do not acquire sufficient energy to disrupt bonds, it is possible to initiate breakdown through a direct rupture of the bonds because of the existence of the strong electric field.   Under these circumstances the breakdown is referred to as *Zener break-down*.   This Zener effect is now known to play an important role only in diodes with breakdown voltages below about 6 V.   Nevertheless, the term *Zener* is commonly used for the *avalanche*, or *breakdown*, *diode* even at higher voltages.   Silicon diodes operated in avalanche breakdown are available with maintaining voltages from several volts to several hundred volts and with power ratings up to 50 W.

Temperature Characteristics   A matter of interest in connection with Zener diodes, as with semiconductor devices generally, is their temperature sensitivity.   The temperature dependence of the reference voltage, which is indicated in Fig. 6-19a and b, is typical of what may be expected generally. In Fig. 6-19a the temperature coefficient of the reference voltage is plotted as a function of the operating current through the diode for various different diodes whose reference voltage at 5 mA is specified.   The temperature coefficient is given as percentage change in reference voltage per centigrade degree

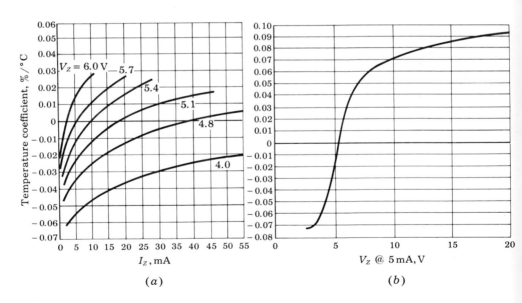

(a)   (b)

Fig. 6-19 Temperature coefficients for a number of Zener diodes having different operating voltages (a) as a function of operating current, (b) as a function of operating voltage.   The voltage V_Z is measured at $I_Z = 5$ mA (from 25 to 100°C). (Courtesy of Pacific Semiconductors, Inc.)

change in diode temperature. In Fig. 6-19*b* has been plotted the temperature coefficient at a fixed diode current of 5 mA as a function of Zener voltage.
The data which are used to plot this curve are taken from a series of different
diodes of different Zener voltages but of fixed dissipation rating. From the
curves in Fig. 6-19*a* and *b* we note that the temperature coefficients may be
positive or negative and will normally be in the range ± 0.1 percent/°C. Note
that, if the reference voltage is above 6 V, where the physical mechanism
involved is avalanche multiplication, the temperature coefficient is positive.
However, below 6 V, where true Zener breakdown is involved, the temperature coefficient is negative.

A qualitative explanation of the sign (positive or negative) of the temperature coefficient of V_Z is now given. A junction having a narrow depletion-
layer width and hence high field intensity ($\sim 10^6$ V/cm even at low voltages)
will break down by the Zener mechanism. An increase in temperature
increases the energies of the valence electrons, and hence makes it easier for
these electrons to escape from the covalent bonds. Less applied voltage is
therefore required to pull these electrons from their positions in the crystal
lattice and convert them into conduction electrons. Thus the Zener breakdown voltage decreases with temperature.

A junction with a broad depletion layer and therefore a low field intensity
will break down by the avalanche mechanism. In this case we rely on intrinsic
carriers to collide with valence electrons and create avalanche multiplication.
As the temperature increases, the vibrational displacement of atoms in the
crystal grows. This vibration increases the probability of collisions with the
lattice atoms of the intrinsic particles as they cross the depletion width. The
intrinsic holes and electrons thus have less of an opportunity to gain sufficient
energy between collisions to start the avalanche process. Therefore the value
of the avalanche voltage must increase with increased temperature.

Dynamic Resistance and Capacitance A matter of importance in connection with Zener diodes is the slope of the diode volt-ampere curve in the
operating range. If the reciprocal slope $\Delta V_Z/\Delta I_Z$, called the *dynamic resist-*
ance, is *r*, then a change ΔI_Z in the operating current of the diode produces a
change $\Delta V_Z = r \, \Delta I_Z$ in the operating voltage. Ideally, $r = 0$, corresponding
to a volt-ampere curve which, in the breakdown region, is precisely vertical.
The variation of *r* at various currents for a series of avalanche diodes of fixed
power-dissipation rating and various voltages is shown in Fig. 6-20. Note
the rather broad minimum which occurs in the range 6 to 10 V, and note that
at large V_Z and small I_Z, the dynamic resistance *r* may become quite large.
Thus we find that a TI 3051 (Texas Instruments Company) 200-V Zener diode
operating at 1.2 mA has an *r* of 1,500 Ω. Finally, we observe that, to the left
of the minimum, at low Zener voltages, the dynamic resistance rapidly becomes
quite large. Some manufacturers specify the minimum current I_{ZK} (Fig.
6-18*a*) below which the diode should not be used. Since this current is on
the knee of the curve, where the dynamic resistance is large, then for currents

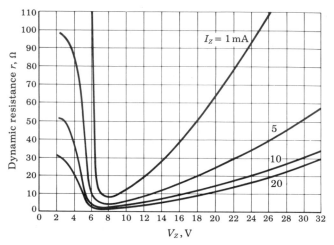

Fig. 6-20 The dynamic resistance at a number of currents for Zener diodes of different operating voltages at 25°C. The measurements are made with a 60-Hz current at 10 percent of the dc current. (Courtesy of Pacific Semiconductors, Inc.)

lower than I_{ZK} the regulation will be poor. Some diodes exhibit a very sharp knee even down into the microampere region.

The capacitance across a breakdown diode is the transition capacitance, and hence varies inversely as some power of the voltage. Since C_T is proportional to the cross-sectional area of the diode, high-power avalanche diodes have very large capacitances. Values of C_T from 10 to 10,000 pF are common.

Additional Reference Diodes   Zener diodes are available with voltages as low as about 2 V. Below this voltage it is customary, for reference and regulating purposes, to use diodes in the *forward* direction. As appears in Fig. 6-8, the volt-ampere characteristic of a forward-biased diode (sometimes called a *stabistor*) is not unlike the reverse characteristic, with the exception that, in the forward direction, the knee of the characteristic occurs at lower voltage. A number of forward-biased diodes may be operated in series to reach higher voltages. Such series combinations, packaged as single units, are available with voltages up to about 5 V, and may be preferred to reverse-biased Zener diodes, which at low voltages, as seen in Fig. 6-20, have very large values of dynamic resistance.

When it is important that a Zener diode operate with a low temperature coefficient, it may be feasible to operate an appropriate diode at a current where the temperature coefficient is at or near zero. Quite frequently, such operation is not convenient, particularly at higher voltages and when the diode must operate over a range of currents. Under these circumstances temperature-compensated avalanche diodes find application. Such diodes consist of a reverse-biased Zener diode with a positive temperature coefficient, combined in a single package with a forward-biased diode whose temperature coefficient is negative. As an example, the Transitron SV3176 silicon 8-V reference diode has a temperature coefficient of ± 0.001 percent/°C at 10 mA over the range -55 to $+100$°C. The dynamic resistance is only 15 Ω. The temperature coefficient remains below 0.002 percent/°C for currents in the range 8 to 12 mA. The voltage stability with time of some of these reference diodes is comparable with that of conventional standard cells.

When a high-voltage reference is required, it is usually advantageous (except of course with respect to economy) to use two or more diodes in series rather than a single diode. This combination will allow higher voltage, higher dissipation, lower temperature coefficient, and lower dynamic resistance.

6-13   THE TUNNEL DIODE

A p-n junction diode of the type discussed in Sec. 6-1 has an impurity concentration of about 1 part in 10^8. With this amount of doping, the width of the depletion layer, which constitutes a potential barrier at the junction, is of the order of 5 microns (5×10^{-4} cm). This potential barrier restrains the flow of carriers from the side of the junction where they constitute majority carriers to the side where they constitute minority carriers. If the concentration of impurity atoms is greatly increased, say, to 1 part in 10^3 (corresponding to a

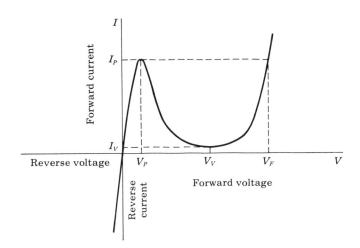

Fig. 6-21 Volt-ampere characteristic of a tunnel diode.

density in excess of 10^{19} cm^{-3}), the device characteristics are completely changed. This new diode was announced in 1958 by Esaki,[7] who also gave the correct theoretical explanation for its volt-ampere characteristic, depicted in Fig. 6-21.

The Tunneling Phenomenon   The width of the junction barrier varies inversely as the square root of impurity concentration [Eq. (6-47)] and therefore is reduced from 5 microns to less than 100 Å (10^{-6} cm). This thickness is only about one-fiftieth the wavelength of visible light. Classically, a particle must have an energy at least equal to the height of a potential-energy barrier if it is to move from one side of the barrier to the other. However, for barriers as thin as those estimated above in the Esaki diode, the Schrödinger equation indicates that there is a large probability that an electron will penetrate *through* the barrier. This quantum-mechanical behavior is referred to as *tunneling*, and hence these high-impurity-density *p-n* junction devices are called tunnel *diodes*. This same tunneling effect is responsible for high-field emission of electrons from a cold metal and for radioactive emissions.

We explain the tunneling effect by considering the following one-dimensional problem: An electron of total energy W (joules) moves in region 1, where the potential energy may be taken as zero, $U = 0$. At $x = 0$, there is a potential-energy barrier of height $U_o > W$, and as indicated in Fig. 6-22a, the potential energy remains constant in region 2 for $x > 0$.

Region 1   The Schrödinger equation (2-14),

$$\frac{d^2\psi}{dx^2} + \frac{8\pi^2 m}{h^2} W\psi = 0 \tag{6-60}$$

has a solution of the form $\psi = C\epsilon^{\pm j(8\pi^2 mW/h^2)^{\frac{1}{2}}x}$, where C is a constant. The electronic wave function $\phi = \epsilon^{j\omega t}\psi$ represents a traveling wave. In Sec. 2-8 the product of ψ and its complex conjugate ψ^* is interpreted as giving the probability of finding an electron between x and $x + dx$ (in a one-dimensional space). Since $\psi\psi^* = |\psi|^2 = C^2 = $ const, the electron has an equal probability of being found anywhere in region 1. In other words, the electron is free to move in a region of zero potential energy.

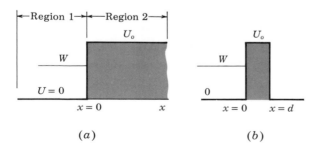

(a)   (b)

Fig. 6-22 (a) A potential-energy step of height U_o. The electronic energy is $W < U_o$. (b) A potential-energy hill of height U_o and depth d may be penetrated by the electron provided that d is small enough.

Region 2   The Schrödinger equation for $x > 0$ is

$$\frac{d^2\psi}{dx^2} - \frac{8\pi^2 m}{h^2}(U_o - W)\psi = 0 \tag{6-61}$$

Since $U_o > W$, this equation has a solution of the form

$$\psi = A\epsilon^{-[(8\pi^2 m/h^2)(U_o - W)]^{\frac{1}{2}}x} = A\epsilon^{-x/2d_o} \tag{6-62}$$

where A is a constant and

$$d_o = \frac{1}{2}\left[\frac{h^2}{8\pi^2 m(U_o - W)}\right]^{\frac{1}{2}} = \frac{h}{4\pi}\left[\frac{1}{2m(U_o - W)}\right]^{\frac{1}{2}} \tag{6-63}$$

The solution of Eq. (6-61) is actually of the form $\psi = A\epsilon^{-x/2d_o} + B\epsilon^{x/2d_o}$. However, $B = 0$, since it is required that ψ be finite everywhere in region 2. The probability of finding the electron between x and $x + dx$ in region 2 is

$$\psi\psi^* = A^2\epsilon^{-x/d_o} \tag{6-64}$$

From Eq. (6-64) we see that an electron can penetrate a potential-energy barrier and that this probability decreases exponentially with distance into the barrier region.   If, as in Fig. 6-22b, the potential-energy hill has a finite thickness d, then there is a nonzero probability $A^2\epsilon^{-d/d_o}$ that the electron will penetrate (tunnel) through the barrier.   If the depth of the hill d is very much larger than d_o, then the probability that the electron will tunnel through the barrier is virtually zero, in agreement with classical concepts (Sec. 3-2). A calculation of d_o for $U_o - W = 1.60 \times 10^{-20}$ J (corresponding to 0.1 eV) yields $d_o \approx 3$ Å.   For impurity densities in excess of those indicated above (10^{19} cm^{-3}), the barrier depth d approaches d_o, and $A^2\epsilon^{-d/d_o}$ becomes large enough to represent an appreciable number of electrons which have tunneled through the hill.

Energy-band Structure of a Highly Doped p-n Diode   The condition that d be of the same order of magnitude as d_o is a necessary but not a sufficient condition for tunneling.   It is also required that occupied energy states exist on the side from which the electron tunnels and that allowed empty states exist on the other side (into which the electron penetrates) at the same energy level.   Hence we must now consider the energy-band picture when the impurity concentration is very high.   In Fig. 6-4, drawn for the lightly doped p-n diode, the Fermi level E_F lies inside the forbidden energy gap.   We shall now demonstrate that, for a diode which is doped heavily enough to make tunneling possible, E_F lies outside the forbidden band.

From Eq. (6-6),

$$E_F = E_C - kT \ln \frac{N_C}{N_D}$$

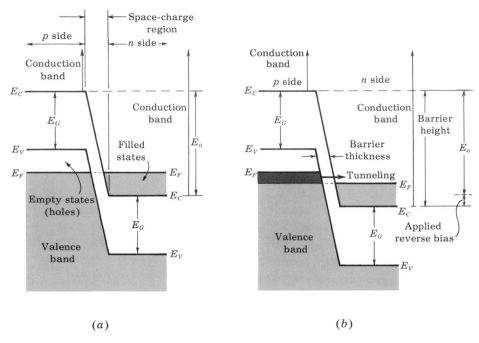

Fig. 6-23 Energy bands in a heavily doped p-n diode (a) under open-circuited conditions and (b) with an applied reverse bias. (These diagrams are strictly valid only at $0°$K, but are closely approximated at room temperature, as can be seen from Fig. 3-10.)

For a lightly doped semiconductor, $N_D < N_C$, so that $\ln (N_C/N_D)$ is a positive number. Hence $E_F < E_C$, and the Fermi level lies inside the forbidden band, as indicated in Fig. 6-4. Since $N_C \approx 10^{19}$ cm^{-3}, then, for donor concentrations in excess of this amount ($N_D > 10^{19}$ cm^{-3}, corresponding to a doping in excess of 1 part in 10^3), $\ln (N_C/N_D)$ is negative. Hence $E_F > E_C$, and the Fermi level in the n-type material lies in the conduction band. By similar reasoning we conclude that, for a heavily doped p region, $N_A > N_V$, and the Fermi level lies in the valence band [Eq. (6-7)]. A comparison of Eqs. (6-5) and (6-8) indicates that $E_o > E_G$, so that the contact difference of potential energy E_o now exceeds the forbidden-energy-gap voltage E_G. Hence, under open-circuit conditions, the band structure of a heavily doped p-n junction must be as pictured in Fig. 6-23a. The Fermi level E_F in the p side is at the same energy as the Fermi level E_F in the n side. Note that there are no filled states on one side of the junction which are at the same energy as empty allowed states on the other side. Hence there can be no flow of charge in either direction across the junction, and the current is zero, an obviously correct conclusion for an open-circuited diode.

The Volt-Ampere Characteristic   With the aid of the energy-band picture
of Fig. 6-23 and the concept of quantum-mechanical tunneling, the tunnel-
diode characteristic of Fig. 6-21 may be explained.   Let us consider that the
p material is grounded and that a voltage applied across the diode shifts the
n side with respect to the p side.   For example, if a reverse-bias voltage is
applied, we know from Sec. 6-2 that the height of the barrier is increased
above the open-circuit value E_o.   Hence the n-side levels must shift downward with respect to the p-side levels, as indicated in Fig. 6-23b.   We now
observe that there are some energy states (the heavily shaded region) in the
valence band of the p side which lie at the same level as allowed empty states
in the conduction band of the n side.   Hence these electrons will tunnel from
the p to the n side, giving rise to a reverse diode current.   As the magnitude

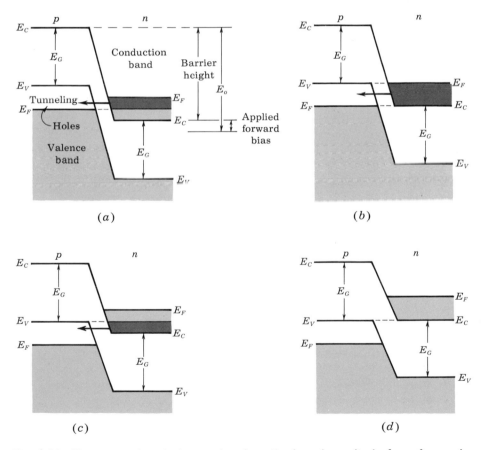

Fig. 6-24   The energy-band pictures in a heavily doped p-n diode for a forward
bias.   As the bias is increased, the band structure changes progressively from
(a) to (d).

of the reverse bias increases, the heavily shaded area grows in size, causing the reverse current to increase, as shown by section 1 of Fig. 6-25.

Consider now that a forward bias is applied to the diode so that the potential barrier is decreased below E_o. Hence the n-side levels must shift upward with respect to those on the p side, and the energy-band picture for this situation is indicated in Fig. 6-24a. It is now evident that there are occupied states in the conduction band of the n material (the heavily shaded levels) which are at the same energy as allowed empty states (holes) in the valence band of the p side. Hence electrons will tunnel from the n to the p material, giving rise to the forward current of section 2 in Fig. 6-25.

As the forward bias is increased further, the condition shown in Fig. 6-24b is reached. Now the maximum number of electrons can leave occupied states on the right side of the junction, and tunnel through the barrier to empty states on the left side, giving rise to the peak current I_P in Fig. 6-25. If still more forward bias is applied, the situation in Fig. 6-24c is obtained, and the tunneling current decreases, giving rise to section 3 in Fig. 6-25. Finally, at an even larger forward bias, the band structure of Fig. 6-24d is valid. Since now there are no empty *allowed* states on one side of the junction at the same energy as occupied states on the other side, the tunneling current must drop to zero.

In addition to the quantum-mechanical current described above, the regular p-n junction injection current is also being collected. This current is given by Eq. (6-31) and is indicated by the dashed section 4 of Fig. 6-25. The curve in Fig. 6-25b is the sum of the solid and dashed curves of Fig. 6-25a, and this resultant is the tunnel-diode characteristic of Fig. 6-21.

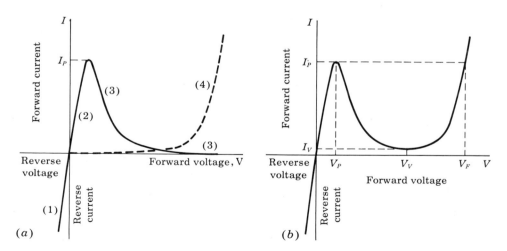

Fig. 6-25 (a) The tunneling current is shown solid. The injection current is the dashed curve. The sum of these two gives the tunnel-diode volt-ampere characteristic of Fig. 6-21, which is reproduced in (b) for convenience.

6-14   CHARACTERISTICS OF A TUNNEL DIODE[8]

From Fig. 6-21 we see that the tunnel diode is an excellent conductor in the reverse direction (the p side of the junction negative with respect to the n side). Also, for small forward voltages (up to 50 mV for Ge), the resistance remains small (of the order of 5 Ω).   At the *peak current* I_P corresponding to the voltage V_P, the slope dI/dV of the characteristic is zero.   If V is increased beyond V_P, then the current decreases.   As a consequence, the dynamic conductance $g = dI/dV$ is negative.   The tunnel diode exhibits a *negative-resistance characteristic* between the peak current I_P and the minimum value I_V, called the *valley current*.   At the *valley voltage* V_V at which $I = I_V$, the conductance is again zero, and beyond this point the resistance becomes and remains positive. At the so-called *peak forward voltage* V_F the current again reaches the value I_P. For larger voltages the current increases beyond this value.

For currents whose values are between I_V and I_P, the curve is triple-valued, because each current can be obtained at three different applied voltages.   It is this multivalued feature which makes the tunnel diode useful in pulse and digital circuitry.[9]

The standard circuit symbol for a tunnel diode is given in Fig. 6-26a. The small-signal model for operation in the negative-resistance region is indicated in Fig. 6-26b.   The negative resistance $-R_n$ has a minimum at the point of inflection between I_P and I_V.   The series resistance R_s is ohmic resistance.   The series inductance L_s depends upon the lead length and the geometry of the diode package.   The junction capacitance C depends upon the bias, and is usually measured at the valley point.   Typical values for these parameters for a tunnel diode of peak current value $I_P = 10$ mA are $-R_n = -30\ \Omega$, $R_s = 1\ \Omega$, $L_s = 5$ nH, and $C = 20$ pF.

One interest in the tunnel diode is its application as a very high speed switch.   Since tunneling takes place at the speed of light, the transient response is limited only by total shunt capacitance (junction plus stray wiring capacitance) and peak driving current.   Switching times of the order of a nanosecond are reasonable, and times as low as 50 psec have been obtained. A second application[8] of the tunnel diode is as a high-frequency (microwave) oscillator.

The most common commercially available tunnel diodes are made from germanium or gallium arsenide.   It is difficult to manufacture a silicon tunnel diode with a high ratio of peak-to-valley current I_P/I_V.   Table 6-1 summarizes the important static characteristics of these devices.   The voltage values in this table are determined principally by the particular semiconductor used and are almost independent of the current rating.   Note that gallium arsenide

Fig. 6-26   (a) Symbol for a tunnel diode; (b) small-signal model in the negative-resistance region.

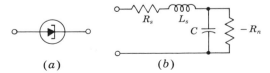

(a)   (b)

TABLE 6-1   Typical tunnel-diode
parameters

	Ge	GaAs	Si
I_P/I_V..........	8	15	3.5
V_P, V..........	0.055	0.15	0.065
V_V, V..........	0.35	0.50	0.42
V_F, V..........	0.50	1.10	0.70

has the highest ratio I_P/I_V and the largest voltage swing $V_F - V_P \approx 1.0$ V as against 0.45 V for germanium.

The peak current I_P is determined by the impurity concentration (the resistivity) and the junction area.   A spread of 20 percent in the value of I_P for a given tunnel-diode type is normal, but tighter-tolerance diodes are also available.   For computer applications, devices with I_P in the range of 1 to 100 mA are most common.   However, it is possible to obtain diodes whose I_P is as small as 100 μA or as large as 100 A.

The peak point (V_P, I_P), which is in the tunneling region, is not a very sensitive function of temperature.   Commercial diodes are available[8] for which I_P and V_P vary by only about 10 percent over the range -50 to $+150°$C. The temperature coefficient of I_P may be positive or negative, depending upon the impurity concentration and the operating temperature, but the temperature coefficient of V_P is always negative.   The valley point V_V, which is affected by injection current, is quite temperature-sensitive.   The value of I_V increases rapidly with temperature, and at 150°C may be two or three times its value at $-50°$C.   The voltages V_V and V_F have negative temperature coefficients of about 1.0 mV/°C, a value only about half that found for the shift in voltage with temperature of a *p-n* junction diode or transistor.   These values apply equally well to Ge or GaAs diodes.   Gallium arsenide devices show a marked reduction of the peak current if operated at high current levels in the forward injection region.   However, it is found empirically[8] that negligible degradation results if, at room temperature, the average operating current I is kept small enough to satisfy the condition $I/C \leq 0.5$ mA/pF, where C is the junction capacitance.   Tunnel diodes are found to be several orders of magnitude less sensitive to nuclear radiation than are transistors.

The advantages of the tunnel diode are low cost, low noise, simplicity, high speed, environmental immunity, and low power.   The disadvantages of the diode are its low output-voltage swing and the fact that it is a two-terminal device.   Because of the latter feature, there is no isolation between input and output, and this leads to serious circuit-design difficulties.   Hence a transistor (an essentially unilateral device) is usually preferred for frequencies below about 1 GHz (a kilomegacycle per second) or for switching times longer than several nanoseconds.   The tunnel diode and transistor may be combined advantageously.[9]

REFERENCES

1. Gray, P. E., D. DeWitt, A. R. Boothroyd, and J. F. Gibbons: "Physical Electronics and Circuit Models of Transistors," vol. 2, Semiconductor Electronics Education Committee, John Wiley & Sons, Inc., New York, 1964.
   Shockley, W.: The Theory of *p-n* Junctions in Semiconductor and *p-n* Junction Transistors, *Bell System Tech. J.*, vol. 28, pp. 435–489, July, 1949.
   Middlebrook, R. D.: "An Introduction to Junction Transistor Theory," pp. 115–130, John Wiley & Sons, Inc., New York, 1957.

2. Middlebrook, R. D.: "An Introduction to Junction Transistor Theory," pp. 93–112, John Wiley & Sons, Inc., New York, 1957.

3. Phillips, A. B.: "Transistor Engineering," pp. 129–133, McGraw-Hill Book Company, New York, 1962.

4. Moll, J.: "Physics of Semiconductors," pp. 117–121, McGraw-Hill Book Company, New York, 1964.
   Sah, C. T., R. N. Noyce, and W. Shockley: Carrier-generation and Recombination in P-N Junctions and P-N Junction Characteristics, *Proc. IRE*, vol. 45, pp. 1228–1243, September, 1957.

5. Millman, J., and H. Taub: "Pulse, Digital, and Switching Waveforms," pp. 745–749, McGraw-Hill Book Company, New York, 1965.

6. Corning, J. J.: "Transistor Circuit Analysis and Design," pp. 40–42, Prentice-Hall, Inc., Englewood Cliffs, N.J., 1965.

7. Esaki, L.: New Phenomenon in Narrow Ge *p-n* Junctions, *Phys. Rev.*, vol. 109, p. 603, 1958.
   Nanavati, R. P.: "Introduction to Semiconductor Electronics," chap. 12, McGraw-Hill Book Company, New York, 1963.

8. "Tunnel Diode Manual, TD-30," Radio Corporation of America, Semiconductor and Materials Division, Somerville, N.J., 1963.
   "Tunnel Diode Manual," General Electric Company, Semiconductor Products Dept., Liverpool, N.Y., 1961.

9. Ref. 5, chap. 13.

7/VACUUM-TUBE CHARACTERISTICS

The triode was invented in 1906 by De Forest,[1] who inserted a third electrode, called the *grid*, into a vacuum diode. He discovered that current in the triode could be controlled by adjusting the grid potential with respect to the cathode. This device was found to be capable of amplifying small-signal voltages, a discovery of such great practical importance that it made possible the electronics industry.

In this chapter we study the volt-ampere characteristics of triodes, tetrodes, and pentodes and define certain parameters which are useful in describing these curves. We carry through the analysis of a simple circuit containing a triode and show that such a circuit is indeed an amplifier.

7-1   THE ELECTROSTATIC FIELD OF A TRIODE

Suppose that the mechanical structure of a vacuum diode is altered by inserting an electrode in the form of a wire grid structure between the cathode and the anode, thus converting the tube into a triode. A schematic arrangement of the electrodes in a triode having cylindrical symmetry is shown in Fig. 7-1.

A study of the potential variation within a triode is very instructive. For simplicity, consider a plane cathode and a parallel anode, each of infinite extent. The grid is assumed to consist of parallel equidistant wires lying in a plane parallel to the cathode. The diameter of the wires is small compared with the distance between wires. Such an arrangement is shown in Fig. 7-2. If we assume that the cathode is so cold that it emits no electrons, the potential at any point in the tube satisfies Laplace's equation, with boundary conditions determined by the applied electrode voltages. The results of such a

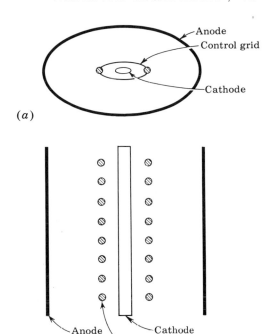

(a)

Fig. 7-1   Schematic arrangement
of the electrodes in a triode.   (a)
Top view; (b) side view.   (The
constructional details are similar
to those indicated in Fig. 7-13.)

(b)

calculation are shown in Fig. 7-3, where equipotential surfaces are indicated
for various values of grid voltage.   Since the electrodes are assumed to be of
infinite extent, it is only necessary to plot the equipotentials over a distance
corresponding to the spacing between grid wires.   Each picture is to be
imagined repeated indefinitely to the right and left.

It should be noted, in particular, that the grid structure does not produce
an equipotential plane at the position of the grid.   If it did, there could never
be plate current for *any* value of negative grid voltage because the electrons
would find themselves in a retarding field as soon as they left the cathode.
(We assume, for the moment, that the cathode is heated but that the electrons leave with zero initial velocity.)   Because of the influence of the positive
plate potential, it is possible for an electron to find a path between grid wires

Fig. 7-2   A plane-electrode triode, showing
the paths for the potential profiles given in
Fig. 7-4.

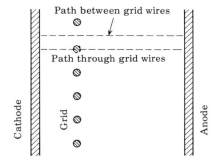

such that it does not collide with a potential-energy barrier (provided that the grid is not too highly negative). Thus the potential variation between cathode and anode depends upon the path. The potential-vs.-distance curves (called *profile presentations*) corresponding to Fig. 7-3 are given in Fig. 7-4 for the two extreme conditions, a path midway between grid wires (upper curve) and a path directly through the grid wires (lower curve).

If an electron finds itself in a retarding field regardless of what part of the cathode it comes from, it certainly cannot reach the anode. This situation is pictured in (*a*) of Figs. 7-3 and 7-4 and corresponds to conditions beyond cutoff. If we assume that all electrons leave the cathode with zero velocity, they cannot enter the shaded area in Fig. 7-3 because they encounter there a retarding field. In (*b*) are shown the conditions just at cutoff, where the electric field intensity at the cathode is nowhere positive. Actually, cutoff is obtained at a grid voltage slightly less than this value, so that the field at the cathode is somewhat negative and hence repels all the emitted electrons. It should be clear from a study of these figures that the current distribution is not constant along paths at different distances from the grid wires. If the grid is made sufficiently negative, cutoff will occur throughout the entire region. This con-

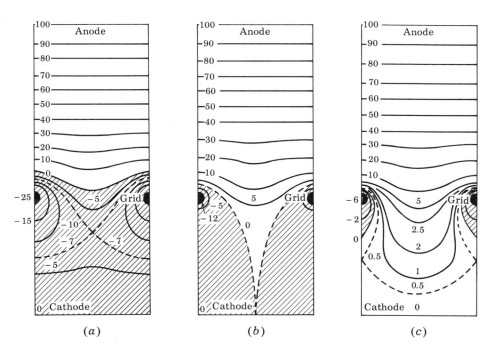

$$(a) \qquad\qquad (b) \qquad\qquad (c)$$

Fig. 7-3 Equipotential contours in volts in the plane-electrode triode. (a) Grid beyond cutoff potential ($V_G = -25$ V); (b) grid at cutoff potential ($V_G = -12$ V); (c) grid negative at one-half cutoff value ($V_G = -6$ V). (From K. R. Spangenberg, "Vacuum Tubes," McGraw-Hill Book Company, New York, 1948.)

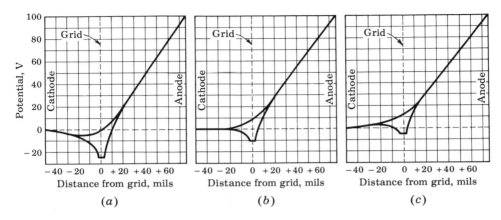

Fig. 7-4 Potential profiles of a plane-electrode triode.   (a) Grid at twice the cutoff value of potential; (b) grid at the cutoff value of potential; (c) grid negative at one-half the cutoff value of potential.   (From K. R. Spangenberg, "Vacuum Tubes," McGraw-Hill Book Company, New York, 1948.)

dition prevails for all grid voltages more negative than that indicated in (b). If the grid voltage is made more positive than this cutoff value, then, as shown in (c), current will flow only in the region midway between the grid wires, because any electrons starting out toward a grid will be repelled.   This situation corresponds to the usual operating conditions of a triode voltage amplifier.

It should be emphasized that these diagrams represent space-charge-free conditions.   In Chap. 4 it is shown that under space-charge conditions the electric field intensity at the cathode is reduced to zero.   Hence, for a hot cathode, the potential curve of Fig. 7-4c must be modified somewhat and, in particular, must have zero slope at the cathode.

7-2   THE ELECTRODE CURRENTS

From the qualitative discussion already given, it follows that the plate current should depend upon the space-charge-free cathode field intensity.   This electrostatic field, in turn, is a linear function of the grid and plate potentials. Since the grid is much closer to the cathode than the plate, a given change in potential of the grid has a much greater effect on the field intensity at the cathode than does the same change in potential of the anode.   For example, if the plate voltage is changed slightly in Fig. 7-4, it will affect the slope of the potential curve at the cathode very little.   If the grid voltage is altered the same amount, the slope will change by a very much larger amount.   In view of this discussion and the known three-halves-power law for diodes (Sec. 4-4), it is anticipated that the plate current i_P may be represented approximately by the equation[2]

$$i_P = G\left(v_G + \frac{v_P}{\mu}\right)^n \tag{7-1}$$

where v_P = plate potential

$\quad\quad v_G$ = grid potential

$\quad\quad \mu$ = a measure of relative effectiveness of grid and plate potentials
The parameter μ is known as the *amplification factor*, and is substantially constant and independent of current. The exponent n is approximately equal to $\frac{3}{2}$. The constant G is called the *perveance*. The validity of Eq. (7-1) has been verified experimentally for many triodes.

Grid Current Ideally, the grid electrode should control the plate current without drawing any grid current i_G. In practice, it is found that if the grid is made positive with respect to the cathode, electrons will be attracted to it. For many triodes this positive-grid current increases in the range of 0.5 to 4 mA for each volt increase in positive-grid voltage. Such an increment corresponds to an effective *static grid resistance* $r_G \equiv v_G/i_G$ of 250 Ω to 2 K. Positive-grid triodes are available for power-amplifier applications. Also, in many pulse and switching circuits[3] the grid is driven positive during a portion of the waveform (Fig. D-3).

Because the electrons from the cathode are emitted with nonzero initial velocities, some of them will be collected when the grid is zero or even somewhat negative with respect to the cathode. Typically, I_G = 0.5 mA at V_G = 0 and I_G = 10 μA at V_G = −0.5 V. As the magnitude of the negative-grid voltage is increased, the grid current decreases further, then goes to zero, and may reverse in sign.[4] This negative-grid current consists mainly of four components.

First, we have gas current, consisting of positive ions (carbon dioxide, carbon monoxide, hydrogen, etc.) collected by the negative grid. The positive-ion grid current is proportional to both the pressure in the tube and plate current. When the grid voltage becomes sufficiently negative, the plate current is zero (cutoff) and no ionization takes place. Second, electrons leave the grid (and hence negative-grid current flows) because of photoelectric emission from the grid. Third, the grid is usually operating at a temperature between 600 and 700°K, and therefore grid thermionic emission takes place. Finally, we have a component of grid current due to leakage between the grid and the other electrodes. Ordinarily, the glass stem used to support the leads and the mica pieces used to space the tube parts have a high resistance. However, sublimed materials from the cathode form films on the stem and mica surfaces which act to decrease the resistance. When the grid is negative, leakage currents develop, consisting of a flow of electrons from the grid to the cathode and plate. The negative-grid current due to all sources seldom exceeds a small fraction of a microampere. Unless otherwise stated, we neglect the grid current (positive or negative) for all negative values of grid voltage.

7-3   COMMERCIAL TRIODES

In Sec. 4-2 the construction of commercially available cathodes is described. Practical anodes are discussed in Sec. 4-8.

Grids   Conventional grids for vacuum tubes consist of supporting side rods on which are wound fine lateral wires. The wire size, the number of turns per inch, the grid-to-cathode spacing, and the dissipation capability of the grid structure determine the individual tube characteristics.[2,5] An improved grid structure, called the *strap frame grid*,[6] consists of a rigid self-supporting rectangular frame that permits the use of very small lateral wire (0.3 mil = 0.0003 in. in diameter) and thus makes possible the use of a large number of lateral wires per inch. This type of construction also permits close grid-to-cathode spacing which results in a tube with a large value of transconductance (Sec. 7-5).

The Nuvistor   Another type of grid structure is employed in the manufacture of the *nuvistor-type* vacuum tube shown in Fig. 7-5. This tube utilizes an all-ceramic and metal construction with cantilever-supported cylindrical electrode structure. The cylindrical-tube elements are supported by conical bases, which, in turn, rest on strong supporting pillars. This type of construction is mechanically rigid and of low mass, and is well suited to withstand shock and vibration.

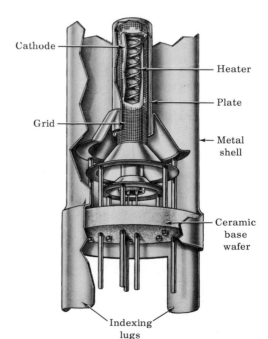

Fig. 7-5 Nuvistor triode. (Courtesy of Radio Corporation of America.)

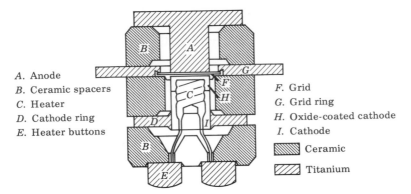

A. Anode
B. Ceramic spacers
C. Heater
D. Cathode ring
E. Heater buttons

F. Grid
G. Grid ring
H. Oxide-coated cathode
I. Cathode

[hatched] Ceramic
[hatched] Titanium

Fig. 7-6 Construction of a ceramic planar triode. (Courtesy of General Electric Co.)

Planar Ceramic Tube A type of electron tube construction that is extremely resistant to shock and vibration is indicated in Fig. 7-6. The close grid-to-cathode spacing (about 1.3 mils when the tube is hot) and the fine grid structure result in large values of transconductance. Noise and microphonics, as well as the danger of grid-to-cathode shorts due to loose grid wires, are minimized by a specially designed, tensioned wire grid structure. The small size of the elements and the close spacing of the electrodes result in a tube which is useful at frequencies in the gigahertz region.

7-4   TRIODE CHARACTERISTICS

The plate current depends upon the plate potential and the grid potential, and may be expressed mathematically by the functional relationship

$$i_P = f(v_P, v_G) \tag{7-2}$$

read "i_P is some function f of v_P and v_G." This relationship is sometimes written $i_P = i_P(v_P, v_G)$, the quantities in the parentheses designating the variables upon which the function f (or i_P) depends. If it is assumed that the grid current is zero, then under space-charge-limited conditions the approximate explicit form of this function is that expressed by Eq. (7-1). By plotting i_P versus v_P and v_G on a three-dimensional system of axes, a space diagram is obtained. The traces of this surface on the three coordinate planes (and on planes parallel to these) give three families of characteristic curves which are easy to visualize.

Figure 7-7a shows a family of curves known as the *plate characteristics*, since they give the variation of the plate current with the plate potential for various values of grid potential, $v_G = V_{G1}, V_{G2}$, etc. The effect of making the grid more negative is to shift the curves to the right without changing the

Fig. 7-7 (a) Plate and (b)
transfer characteristic
curves of a triode.
$V_{G1} > V_{G2} > V_{G3} > V_{G4}$;
$V_{P1} > V_{P2} > V_{P3}$.

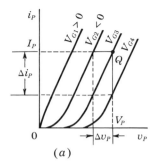
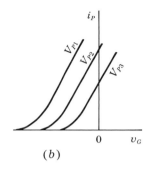

(a)   (b)

slopes appreciably. If the grid potential is made the independent variable
and if the plate voltage is held constant as a parameter, $v_P = V_{P1}, V_{P2}$, etc.,
the family of curves known as the *mutual*, or *transfer*, characteristics, illustrated in Fig. 7-7b, is obtained. The effect of making the plate potential less
positive is to shift the curves to the right, the slopes again remaining substantially unchanged. These conditions are readily evident if it is remembered that the sets of curves in these diagrams are plots of Eq. (7-1) with
either v_G or v_P maintained constant as a parameter. The simultaneous variation of both the plate and the grid potentials so that the plate current remains
constant, $i_P = I_{P1}, I_{P2}$, etc., gives rise to a third group of curves, known as
the *constant-current* characteristics (Prob. 7-1).

The most important family of characteristics is the plate family, and these
are supplied in convenient form in data books provided by the tube manufacturers. The plate characteristics for several representative tubes are reproduced in Appendix D. These curves are average values, and the characteristics for a specific tube may differ appreciably from these published values.
The Military Specifications for Electron Tubes, MIL-E-1, give the limits of
variability which may be expected in a given tube type.

The volt-ampere characteristics vary with heater temperature and with
aging of the tube. As with a diode, so for a multielement tube, the temperature effect is found experimentally to be equivalent to a 0.1-V shift in cathode
voltage (relative to the other electrodes) for each 10 percent change in heater
voltage.

7-5   TRIODE PARAMETERS

In the analysis of networks using tubes as circuit elements (Chap. 8), it is
found necessary to make use of the slopes of the characteristic curves of Fig.
7-7. Hence it is convenient to introduce special symbols and names for these
quantities. This is now done.

Amplification Factor This factor, designated by the symbol μ, is defined
as the ratio of the change in plate voltage to the change in grid voltage for a

constant plate current. Mathematically, μ is given by the relation

$$\mu = -\left(\frac{\partial v_P}{\partial v_G}\right)_{I_P} \tag{7-3}$$

The subscript I_P denotes that the plate current remains constant in performing the indicated partial differentiation. In order that μ be a positive number, the minus sign is necessary because an increasing plate voltage will require a decreasing grid potential if the current is to remain unchanged. The reciprocal of the amplification factor is called the *durchgriff*, or the *penetration factor*.

Plate Resistance The quantity $(\partial v_P/\partial i_P)_{v_G}$, which expresses the ratio of an increment of plate potential to the corresponding increment of plate current when the grid potential is kept constant, has units of resistance, and is known as the *plate resistance* of the tube, designated by the symbol r_p. We note that the plate resistance is the reciprocal of the slope of the plate characteristics of Fig. 7-7a. It should be recalled that the dynamic plate resistance of a diode was defined in a similar manner. The reciprocal of the plate resistance is called the *plate conductance, $g_p \equiv 1/r_p$.*

Transconductance The quantity $(\partial i_P/\partial v_G)_{V_P}$, which gives the ratio of an increment of plate current to the corresponding increment in grid potential for constant plate potential, has the units of conductance. This quantity is known as the *plate-grid transconductance*, and represents the change of current in the plate circuit for unit change in potential of the grid. The transconductance is frequently referred to as the *mutual conductance*, and is designated by the symbol g_m. The quantity g_m is the slope of the mutual characteristic curves of Fig. 7-7b.

Summary The triode coefficients, or parameters, which are characteristic of the tube are

$$\left(\frac{\partial v_P}{\partial i_P}\right)_{V_G} \equiv r_p \qquad \text{plate resistance}$$

$$\left(\frac{\partial i_P}{\partial v_G}\right)_{V_P} \equiv g_m \qquad \text{mutual conductance} \tag{7-4}$$

$$-\left(\frac{\partial v_P}{\partial v_G}\right)_{I_P} \equiv \mu \qquad \text{amplification factor}$$

Since there is only one equation, (7-2), relating the three quantities i_P, v_P, and v_G, the three partial derivatives cannot be independent. The interrelationship may be shown to be (Sec. 8-4)

$$\mu = r_p g_m \tag{7-5}$$

Parameter Values For a 6CG7 tube, the parameters μ, r_p, and g_m as a function of plate current (for three particular values of plate voltage) are

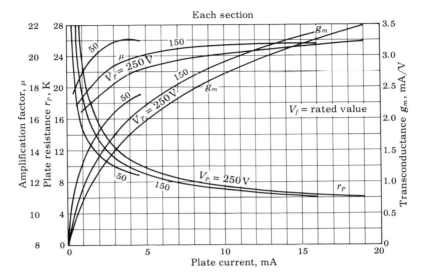

Fig. 7-8 The parameters μ, r_p, and g_m for a 6CG7 triode as a function of plate current for three values of plate voltage. (Courtesy of General Electric Co.)

shown in Fig. 7-8. Note that the plate resistance varies over rather wide limits. It is very high at zero plate current and varies approximately inversely as the one-third power of the plate current (Prob. 7-3). The transconductance increases with plate current from zero at zero plate current and varies directly as the one-third power of the plate current. The amplification factor is observed to remain reasonably constant over a wide range of currents, although it falls off rapidly at the low currents.

The usual order of magnitudes of the tube parameters for conventional triodes are approximately as follows:

μ: from 2.5 to 100
r_p: from 0.5 to 100 K
g_m: from 0.5 to 10 mA/V, or millimhos

Special tubes with extremely small grid-to-cathode spacing d_{gk} may have even larger values of transconductance. For example, the Western Electric type 416B triode with $d_{gk} = 0.018$ mm has the following parameters: $g_m = 60$ mA/V, $\mu = 300$, and $r_p = 5$ K.

Among the most commonly used triodes are those listed in Table 7-1. These contain two triode units in one envelope, and each section has, at the recommended operating point, the parameters given in the table. Since the plate current is given in milliamperes and the potentials in volts, it is convenient to express the plate resistance in kilohms and the transconductance in

TABLE 7-1   Some triode parameters

Triode type	μ	r_p, K	g_m, mA/V
6CG7............	20	7.7	2.6
12AT7..........	55	5.5	10
12AU7..........	17	7.7	2.2
12AX7..........	100	62	1.6
5965............	47	7.2	6.5

millimhos.   Note that the product of milliamperes and kilohms is volts and that the reciprocal of kilohms is millimhos or milliamperes per volt (mA/V).

Approximate values of r_p, μ, and g_m may be obtained directly from the plate characteristics.   Thus, referring to the definitions in Eqs. (7-4) and to Fig. 7-7a, we have, at the operating point Q,

$$r_p = \frac{\Delta v_P}{\Delta i_P}\bigg|_{V_{G_3}} = \text{reciprocal of slope of characteristic}$$

$$g_m = \frac{\Delta i_P}{\Delta v_G}\bigg|_{V_P} = \frac{|\Delta i_P|}{V_{G3} - V_{G4}}$$

$$\mu = -\frac{\Delta v_P}{\Delta v_G}\bigg|_{I_P} = \frac{|\Delta v_P|}{V_{G2} - V_{G3}}$$

If r_p were constant, the slope of the plate characteristics would everywhere be constant; in other words, these curves would be parallel lines.   If μ were constant, the horizontal spacing of the plate characteristics would be constant.   This statement assumes that the characteristics are drawn with equal increments in grid voltage (as they always are).   If r_p and μ are constant, so also is $g_m = \mu/r_p$.   Hence an important conclusion can be drawn: *If over a portion of the i_P-v_P plane the characteristics can be approximated by parallel lines which are equidistant for equal increments in grid voltage, the parameters μ, r_p, and g_m can be considered constant over this region.*   It is shown in the next chapter that if the tube operates under this condition (tube parameters sensibly constant), the behavior of the tube as a circuit element can be obtained analytically.

7-6   SCREEN–GRID TUBES OR TETRODES

In Chap. 8 it is shown that the capacitive coupling between the plate and grid of a triode may very seriously limit the use of the tube at high frequencies. In order to minimize this capacitance the screen-grid tube[2,5,7] was introduced commercially about 1928.   In these tubes a fourth electrode is interposed between the grid and the anode of the triode of Fig. 7-1.   This new electrode is similar in structure to the control grid, and is known as the *screen grid*, the *shield grid*, or *grid* 2, in order to distinguish it from the grid of the triode. Because of its design and disposition, the screen grid affords very complete electrostatic shielding between the plate and the grid. This shielding is such that the grid-plate capacitance is divided by a factor of about 1,000 or more. However, the screen mesh is sufficiently coarse so that it does not interfere appreciably with the flow of electrons.

Because of the shielding action of the plate by the screen grid, the electric field produced in the neighborhood of the cathode by the anode potential is practically zero. Since the total cathode or space current is determined almost wholly by the field near the cathode surface, the plate exerts little effect on the total space charge drawn from the cathode. The plate in a triode performs two distinct functions, that of controlling the total space current and that of collecting the plate current. In a tetrode, the plate only serves to collect those electrons which succeed in passing through the screen.

Volt-Ampere Characteristics We have already noted that the total space current remains essentially constant with variations in plate voltage provided that the control-grid and screen-grid potentials are held constant. Hence that portion of the space current which is not collected by the plate must be collected by the screen; i.e., the two currents are complementary. Where the plate current is large, the screen current must be small, and vice versa. These features can be noted in Fig. 7-9.

Although the plate voltage does not affect the total space current very markedly (a slight dip does occur in the curve of total space current at the lower plate potentials), it does determine the division of the space current between the plate and the screen. At zero plate potential, none of the electrons has sufficient energy to reach the anode, if it is assumed that the electrons are liberated with zero initial velocities. Hence the plate current should be zero. As the plate voltage is increased, one should expect a rapid rise in plate current and a corresponding fall in the screen current. When the plate potential is very much larger than the screen potential, the plate current should approach the space current, and the screen current should approach zero. This asymptotic behavior is noted in Fig. 7-9.

Fig. 7-9 The currents in a tetrode. The screen potential is 100 V, and the grid potential is −2 V.

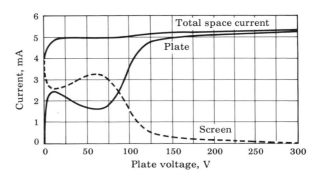

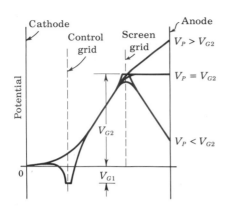

Fig. 7-10 The approximate potential profiles in an idealized tetrode for several values of plate voltage. Two curves are shown for each plate voltage. One is for a path between grid and screen wires, and the other is for a path through the wires.

Negative-resistance Region An inspection of Fig. 7-9 indicates that the plate current rises very rapidly for the first few volts, but it is then followed by a rather anomalous behavior in the region of plate potentials from a few volts to potentials somewhat lower than the screen voltage. The plate current is seen to decrease with increasing values of plate potential. That is, the tube possesses a *negative plate resistance* in this region.

The general character of the curves of Fig. 7-9 may be described on the basis of the approximate potential-distribution diagram of Fig. 7-10. This diagram should be compared with Fig. 7-4, which shows the potential profiles in a triode. The control-grid and the screen-grid voltages are held at fixed values, and the plate voltage V_P may be adjusted from zero to a value considerably in excess of the screen voltage.

The kinks, or folds, that appear in the curves of Fig. 7-9 in the region where the plate potential is lower than the screen potential are caused by the liberation of secondary electrons from the plate by the impact of the primary electrons with the plate. These secondary electrons are attracted to the screen. The screen current is increased, whereas the plate current is decreased. The number of secondary electrons liberated by this electron bombardment depends upon many factors, and may even exceed the total number of primary electrons that strike the plate and thus result in an effective negative plate current.

In the region where the plate potential is higher than the potential of the screen, the secondary electrons that are liberated from the plate by the impact of the primary electrons are drawn back to the plate. In addition, some secondary electrons may also be liberated from the screen by the impact of the primary electrons on it. These secondary electrons from the screen are attracted to the plate, with the result that the plate current is slightly higher than it would be in the absence of secondary emission from the screen. Furthermore, the plate current continues to increase with increasing plate potentials because the collection of these secondary electrons is more complete. At the same time, the screen current tends toward zero.

Parameter Values In a tetrode circuit application the screen potential is almost always held at a fixed value. Hence the tetrode small-signal parameters r_p, g_m, and μ are defined as in Eqs. (7-4) for the triode, with the added constraint that the partial derivatives are taken at constant screen voltage.

The construction and spacing of the grid and cathode are essentially the same in a tetrode as in a triode.   Hence the control of the electron stream by the grid is nearly alike for both tube types.   Consequently, the order of magnitude of g_m is the same for a tetrode as for a triode.   Since changes in plate voltage have very little effect upon the plate current, it follows that the plate resistance of a tetrode must be very high.   Correspondingly, the amplification factor of the screen-grid tube must also be large.   This statement follows from the fact that μ measures the relative effectiveness of changes in plate and grid voltage in producing equal plate-current increments.

In summary, the tetrode is characterized by the following features: a plate-grid capacitance which is only a few thousandths of that of a triode, a plate-grid transconductance which is roughly the same as that of a triode, and an amplification factor and plate resistance which are about ten times that of a triode.

7-7   PENTODES[2]

Although the insertion of the screen grid between the control grid and the plate serves to isolate the plate circuit from the grid circuit, nevertheless the folds in the plate characteristic arising from the effects of secondary emission limit the range of operation of the tube.   This limitation results from the fact that, if the plate-voltage swing is made too large, the instantaneous plate potential may extend into the region of rapidly falling plate current, which will cause a marked distortion in the output.

The negative-resistance portion of the plate characteristic curves of the tetrode may be removed or suppressed by inserting a coarse grid structure between the screen grid and the plate.   Tubes equipped with this extra suppressor grid are known as *pentodes*, and were first introduced commercially in 1929.   The suppressor grid must be maintained at a lower potential than the instantaneous potential reached by the plate.   It is usually connected directly to the cathode, either internally in the tube or externally.   Because the potential of the screen is considerably above that of the suppressor grid, a retarding force prevents the secondary electrons liberated from the screen from flowing to the plate.   On the other hand, the secondary electrons emitted from the plate are constrained, by the retarding field between the suppressor grid and the plate, to return to the plate.   However, the electrons from the cathode that pass through the screen are not kept from reaching the plate by the presence of the suppressor grid, although their velocities may be affected thereby.

Volt-Ampere Characteristics   The plate, screen, and total current curves as a function of the plate voltage are shown in Fig. 7-11 for a pentode.   These should be compared with the corresponding tetrode curves of Fig. 7-9.   Note that the kinks resulting from the effects of secondary emission are entirely

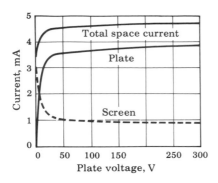

Fig. 7-11 The currents in a pentode. The suppressor is at zero voltage, the screen at 100 V, and the grid at −2 V.

missing in the pentode. Furthermore, the screen current no longer falls asymptotically to zero, but approaches a constant value for large plate voltages. This value is determined principally by the amount of space current that is intercepted by the screen-grid wires. An examination of the characteristics of a number of the more important voltage pentodes indicates that the screen current is ordinarily from 0.2 to 0.4 of the plate current at the recommended operating point. The total space current is seen to remain practically constant over the entire range of plate voltage, except for the very

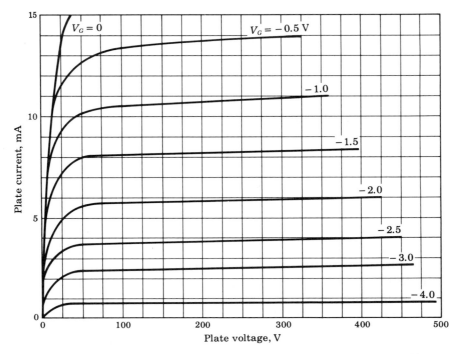

Fig. 7-12 The plate characteristics of a 6AU6 pentode with $V_{G2} = 150$ V and $V_{G3} = 0$ V. (Courtesy of General Electric Co.)

low values of potential. The plate characteristics of a typical pentode are given in Fig. 7-12.

Parameter Values The plate resistance r_p, plate-grid transconductance g_m, and amplification factor μ of a pentode are defined exactly as for a triode (but with the suppressor and screen grid held constant) by Eqs. (7-4). Typical values lie in the range from $r_p = 0.1$ to 2 M, $g_m = 0.5$ to 10 mA/V, and $\mu = 100$ to 10,000. Since the shape and disposition of the control grid and cathode are the same for triode and pentode, these tubes have comparable values of g_m. The highest transconductance available is about 50 mA/V, and is obtained with a frame-grid pentode (for example, Amperex type 7788) whose grid-to-cathode spacing is extremely small (0.05 mm). The values of r_p and μ may be 100 times as great in the pentode as in the triode.

The most important pentode parameter is the grid-plate transconductance. Since g_m is not a constant but depends sensitively upon the operating point, a manufacturer usually supplies curves of g_m as a function of grid voltage, with screen voltage as a parameter.

Applications The pentode has displaced the tetrode (except the beam power tube discussed in Sec. 7-8) in all applications. The tetrode was discussed above for historical reasons and because an understanding of this tube is necessary before the pentode can be appreciated. The pentode, rather than the triode, is used in radio-frequency voltage amplifiers because the former virtually eliminates feedback from the plate to the grid. The pentode is used as a video amplifier because a triode at these high frequencies has a very large input admittance which acts as a heavy load on the preceding stage. The pentode has also found extensive application as an audio-frequency power-output tube. Finally, the pentode has been used as a constant-current device because the plate current is essentially constant, independent of the plate potential.

7-8   BEAM POWER TUBES

The ideal power-tube plate characteristic has a constant current for all values of plate voltage; it is capable of delivering large amounts of power in the plate circuit with negligible loss to the other electrodes; and it generates small distortion. These desirable properties are approached in the beam power tube,[2,8] a sketch of which is given in Fig. 7-13.

One feature of the design of this tube is that each spiral turn of the screen is aligned with a spiral turn of the control grid. This serves to keep the screen current small. The screen current in such tubes ranges from 0.05 to 0.08 of the plate current, which is considerably below the range 0.2 to 0.4 for voltage pentodes. Other features are the flattened cathode, the beam-forming side plates (maintained at zero potential), and a relatively large spacing

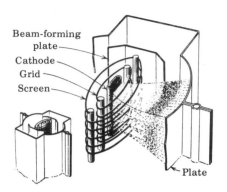

Fig. 7-13 Schematic view of the shapes and arrangements of the electrodes in a beam power tube. (Courtesy of Radio Corporation of America.)

between the screen and the plate. As a result of these design characteristics, the electrons flow between the grid wires toward the plate in dense sheets or beams, as indicated schematically in Fig. 7-13.

The region between the screen and the plate possesses features which are somewhat analogous to those existing in the space-charge-limited diode. That is, a flow of electrons exists between two electrodes between which a difference of potential exists. There is one significant difference, however. Whereas the electrons leave the cathode of a diode with almost zero initial velocities, the electrons that pass through the screen wires in the beam tube do so with a velocity corresponding essentially to the screen potential. As described in Sec. 4-5 in connection with the effects of initial velocities on the space-charge equations, the effect of the initial velocities of the electrons in the screen-plate region will appear as a potential minimum in this region (Fig. 4-3). This minimum is shown in the approximate potential profile in Fig. 7-14, which should be compared with the corresponding figure for the tetrode (Fig. 7-10). The potential minimum produced acts as a virtual suppressor grid, since any secondary electrons emitted from either the plate or the screen will encounter a potential-energy barrier. They will be compelled to return to the electrode

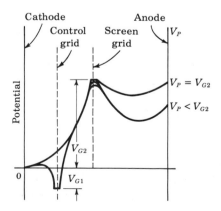

Fig. 7-14 Approximate potential profiles in an idealized beam power tube for two values of plate voltage. Two curves are shown for each plate voltage, one for a path between grid and screen wires, and the other for a path through the wires. Note the potential minimum in the region between the screen grid and the anode.

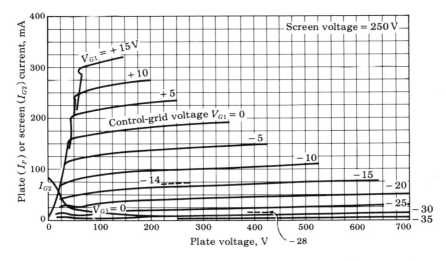

Fig. 7-15 The plate characteristics of a 6L6 beam tube with $V_{G2} = 250$ V.

(which is at a positive potential with respect to the potential minimum) from which they originate.

Variable Suppressor Action The actual potential distribution in the screen-plate region will depend upon the instantaneous plate potential and the plate current (a constant screen potential being assumed), and so is not constant. This variable suppressor action is quite different from that which arises in a simple pentode provided only with a mechanical grid structure for supplying the retarding field.

Thus, because of the beam formation, which serves to keep the screen current small, and because of the variable suppressor action, which serves to suppress secondary emission from the screen and from the plate, the ideal power-tube characteristic is closely approximated. A family of plate characteristics for the 6L6 is shown in Fig. 7-15. It should be noted that this tube is a tetrode when considered in terms of the number of active electrodes. At low currents, where the suppressor action of the beam is too small, the characteristic "kinks" of a tetrode are noticeable.

7-9   THE TRIODE AS A CIRCUIT ELEMENT

Even if the tube characteristics are very nonlinear, we can determine the behavior of the triode in a circuit by a graphical method. This procedure is essentially the same as that used (Sec. 4-9) in treating the diode as a circuit element, except that the diode has two active electrodes and one characteristic curve, whereas the triode has three active elements and a family of curves. The three terminals are marked P (plate), K (cathode), and G (grid). A

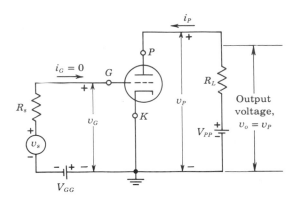

Fig. 7-16 The basic circuit of a triode used as an amplifier.

grounded-cathode circuit in which the triode acts as an amplifier is shown in Fig. 7-16. Before proceeding with an analysis of this circuit, it is necessary to explain the meanings of the symbols and the terminology to be used in this and subsequent analyses.

The input circuit of this amplifier refers to all elements of the circuit that are connected between the grid and cathode terminals of the tube. Similarly, the output, or plate, circuit usually refers to the elements that are connected between the plate and cathode terminals. In the circuit illustrated, the output circuit contains a dc supply voltage in series with a load resistor R_L. The input circuit consists of a dc supply voltage in series with the input voltage. The input signal may have any waveshape whatsoever, but it is usually chosen, for convenience in analysis, to be a sinusoidally varying voltage.

Notation Because a variety of potentials and currents, both dc and ac, are involved simultaneously in a vacuum-tube circuit, it is necessary that a precise method of labeling be established if confusion is to be avoided. Our notation for vacuum-tube symbols is adopted from the IEEE standards[9] for semiconductor symbols, and may be summarized as follows:

1. Instantaneous values of quantities which vary with time are represented by lowercase letters (i for current, v for voltage, and p for power).
2. Maximum, average (dc), and effective, or root-mean-square (rms), values are represented by the uppercase letter of the proper symbol (I, V, or P).
3. Average (dc) values and instantaneous total values are indicated by the uppercase subscript of the proper electrode symbol (G for grid, P for plate, and K for cathode).
4. Varying component values are indicated by the lowercase subscript of the proper electrode symbol.
5. If necessary to distinguish between maximum, average, and rms values, maximum and average values may be distinguished by the additional subscript m and avg, respectively.

TABLE 7-2   Triode symbols

	Grid voltage with respect to cathode	Plate voltage with respect to cathode	Current in direction toward plate through the load
Instantaneous total value............	v_G	v_P	i_P
Quiescent value....................	V_G	V_P	I_P
Instantaneous value of varying component....................	v_g	v_p	i_p
Effective value of varying component..	V_g	V_p	I_p
Amplitude of varying component......	V_{gm}	V_{pm}	I_{pm}
Supply voltage....................	V_{GG}†	V_{PP}†	

† These are positive numbers, giving the *magnitude* of the voltages.

6. Conventional current flow into an electrode from the external circuit is positive.

7. A single subscript is used if the reference electrode is clearly understood. If there is any possibility of ambiguity, the conventional double-subscript notation should be used. For example, v_{pk} = instantaneous value of varying component of voltage drop from plate to cathode, and is positive if the plate is positive with respect to the cathode. If the cathode is grounded and all voltages are understood to be measured with respect to ground, the symbol v_{pk} may be shortened to v_p. The ground symbol is N. For example, v_{PN} = instantaneous value of total voltage from plate to ground.

8. The *magnitude* of the supply voltage is indicated by repeating the electrode subscript.

Table 7-2 summarizes the notation introduced above. In the table are also listed some symbols not yet defined but which are used in later sections. This table should serve as a convenient reference until the reader is thoroughly familiar with the notation. For example, if the input-signal voltage is sinusoidal and of the form

$$v_s = V_{sm} \sin \omega t = \sqrt{2} \, V_s \sin \omega t$$

then the net instantaneous grid voltage in Fig. 7-16 is

$$v_G = -V_{GG} + v_s = -V_{GG} + V_{sm} \sin \omega t \tag{7-6}$$

7-10   GRAPHICAL ANALYSIS OF THE GROUNDED–CATHODE CIRCUIT

Assume for the moment that no grid signal is applied in Fig. 7-16, so that $v_s = 0$. It must not be supposed that there will be no plate current, although this might be true if the bias were very negative. In general, a definite direct

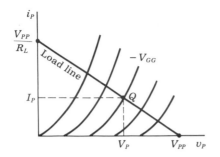

Fig. 7-17 The operating point Q is located at the intersection of the load line and the plate characteristic for the bias $v_G = -V_{GG}$.

current will exist when the input signal is zero. The value of this current may be found graphically in the same way as that used to determine the instantaneous plate current in the diode circuit of Fig. 4-7 for a given instantaneous input voltage.

Because of the presence of the load resistor R_L, the potential that exists between the plate and the cathode will depend upon both the magnitude of the supply voltage and the magnitude of the current in the load resistor. It follows from Fig. 7-16 that

$$v_P = V_{PP} - i_P R_L \tag{7-7}$$

This one equation is not sufficient to determine the current corresponding to any voltage V_{PP} because there are two unknown quantities in this expression, v_P and i_P. A second relation between these two variables is given by the plate characteristics of the triode. The straight line represented by Eq. (7-7) is plotted on the plate curves of Fig. 7-17. This line is obviously independent of the tube characteristics, for it depends only upon elements external to the tube itself. The intersection of this *load line* with the curve for $v_G = -V_{GG}$ is called the *operating point*, or the *quiescent point*, Q. The quiescent current in the external circuit is I_P, and the corresponding quiescent plate potential is V_P.

The simplest method of drawing the load line is to locate two points of this line and to connect these with a straightedge. One such point is the intersection with the horizontal axis, namely, $i_P = 0$ and $v_P = V_{PP}$. Another is the intersection with the vertical axis, namely, $v_P = 0$ and $i_P = V_{PP}/R_L$. These are illustrated in Fig. 7-17. Sometimes this latter point falls off the printed plate characteristics supplied by the manufacturer, the current V_{PP}/R_L being considerably greater than the rated tube current. In such a situation any value of current, say I', that is given on the plate characteristics is chosen, and the corresponding plate voltage is found from Eq. (7-7), namely, $V_{PP} - I'R_L$.

EXAMPLE (a) One section of a 6CG7 triode is operated at a bias of -8 V and a supply voltage of 360 V. If the load resistance is 12 K, what are the quiescent current and voltage values? (b) If the peak-to-peak signal voltage is 12 V, what is the peak-to-peak output swing?

Solution   *a.* The plate characteristics are given in Fig. D-2 (Appendix D).   One point on the load line is $i_P = 0$ and $v_P = 360$ V.   Corresponding to $v_P = 0$, $i_P = V_{PP}/R_L = 360/12 = 30$ mA, whereas the largest current in Fig. D-2 is 28 mA.   Hence a second point on the load line is found by choosing $i_P = 20$ mA = I', and then

$$v_P = V_{PP} - I'R_L = 360 - 20 \times 12 = 360 - 240 = 120 \text{ V}$$

The load line is now drawn through the pair (i_P, v_P) of points (0, 360) and (20, 120) on Fig. D-2.   This line is found to intersect the plate characteristic for $V_G = -8$ V at $I_P = 9.2$ mA and $V_P = 250$ V.   (The reader should check these values.)

   b. For a peak swing of 6 V, the extreme values of grid voltage are $-8 + 6 = -2$ V and $-8 - 6 = -14$ V.   The intersection of the load line with the curve for $V_G = -2$ V is $V_P = 170$ V, and with the characteristic $V_G = -14$ V is $V_P = 315$ V.   Hence the peak-to-peak plate swing is $315 - 170 = 145$ V.   The output swing is $\frac{145}{12} = 12.1$ times as great as the input signal.   This example illustrates that the tube has functioned as a voltage amplifier.

The *grid base* of a tube is defined as the grid-voltage swing required to take the tube from $V_G = 0$ to cutoff.   In the above example, since cutoff corresponding to $V_P = 360$ V is -22 V, the grid base = 22 V.   Note that the grid base depends upon the peak plate voltage.

   The foregoing method of finding the output current corresponding to a given input voltage is now discussed in more detail.   Suppose that the grid potential is given by Eq. (7-6).   The maximum and minimum values of v_G will be $-V_{GG} \pm V_{sm}$, which indicates that the grid swings about the point $-V_{GG}$.   Consequently, the plate current and the plate voltage will then swing about the values I_P and V_P, respectively.   The graphical construction show-

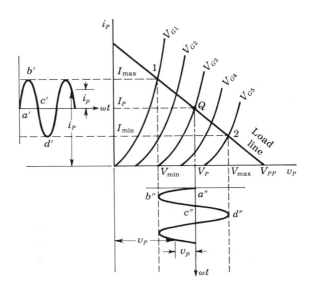

Fig. 7-18   The output current and voltage waveforms for a given input grid signal are determined from the plate characteristics and the load line.

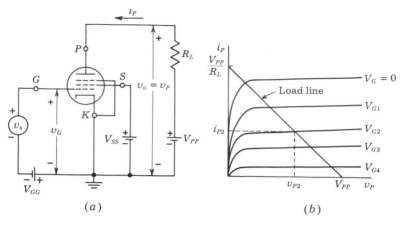

Fig. 7-19 (a) A pentode amplifier. (b) The graphical construction for obtaining i_{P2} and v_{P2} corresponding to V_{G2}.

ing these conditions is illustrated in Fig. 7-18. *For any given value of v_G, the corresponding values of i_P and v_P are located at the intersection of the load line and the i_P-v_P curve corresponding to this value of v_G.* This construction is valid *for any input waveform*, and is not restricted to sinusoidal voltages. The points a', b', c', etc., of the output-current waveform correspond, respectively, to the points a'', b'', c'', etc., of the output-voltage waveform.

A Pentode Circuit The simplest amplifier circuit using a pentode is indicated in Fig. 7-19a. The suppressor is tied to the cathode, and the screen is held at a fixed voltage V_{SS}. The input signal is applied to the grid, and the output is taken at the plate, just as in the triode amplifier. The load line [Eq. (7-7)] expresses Kirchhoff's voltage law (KVL) at the output port, and hence is independent of the device (diode, triode, pentode, etc.). This load line is drawn in Fig. 7-19b on the pentode plate characteristics corresponding to the given screen voltage V_{SS}. The graphical analysis is identical with that described for the triode. For example, corresponding to an instantaneous grid voltage $v_G = V_{G2}$, we find $i_P = i_{P2}$ and $v_P = v_{P2}$.

7-11 THE DYNAMIC TRANSFER CHARACTERISTIC

The static transfer characteristic of Fig. 7-7b gives the relationship between i_P and v_G with the plate voltage held constant. The dynamic transfer characteristic gives the relationship between i_P and v_G for a given plate supply voltage V_{PP} and a given load resistance R_L. This functional relationship is obtained from the plate characteristics and the load line by the graphical construction described in the preceding section. Thus the values of i_P and v_G at points 1,

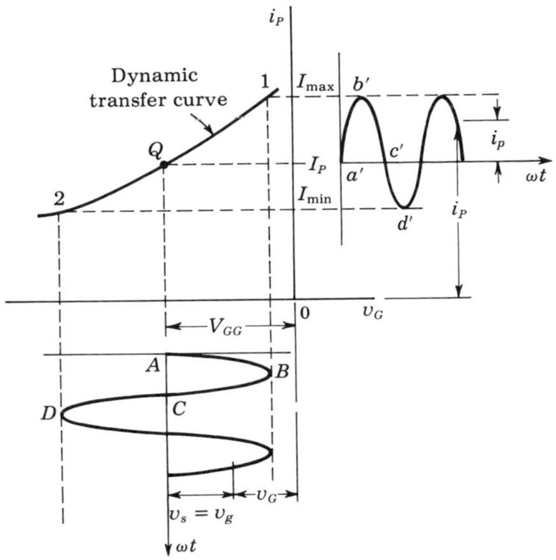

Fig. 7-20 The dynamic transfer characteristic is used to determine the output waveshape for a given input signal.

Q, and 2 in Fig. 7-20 are the same as those obtained at the corresponding points 1, Q, and 2 in Fig. 7-18. The dynamic characteristic will, in general, be curved, although often it may be approximated by a straight line.

The utility of the dynamic characteristic is that it allows the output waveform to be determined for any given input waveform. The construction should be clear from Fig. 7-20, where points a', b', c', etc., of the output current correspond to points A, B, C, etc., respectively, of the input grid-voltage signal $v_s = v_g$.

7-12   LOAD CURVE. DYNAMIC LOAD LINE

A graphical method of obtaining the operating characteristics of a triode with a resistance load is given in Sec. 7-10. It is there shown that the operating region in the i_P-v_P plane is a straight line, called the *load line*. However, if the load is reactive, the work curve is no longer a straight line, but attains the form of an ellipse. This result follows from the fact that if the plate voltage is sinusoidal, then (under conditions of linear operation) the plate current is also sinusoidal of the same frequency but shifted in phase with respect to the voltage. Hence the plate current and the plate voltage are given by

$$v_p = V_{pm} \sin \omega t \qquad \text{and} \qquad i_p = -I_{pm} \sin (\omega t + \theta) \qquad (7\text{-}8)$$

which are the parametric equations of an ellipse. If the angle θ is zero, the ratio of these equations yields

$$\frac{v_p}{i_p} = -\frac{V_{pm}}{I_{pm}} = -R_L$$

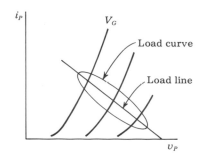

Fig. 7-21   The load line for a resistive load becomes a load curve (an ellipse, under linear operation) for a reactive load.

which represents the load line for a resistance load.   This load line, and also the elliptical work curve for a reactive load, are shown on the volt-ampere characteristics of Fig. 7-21.

The above analysis depends upon the tube parameters μ, r_p, and g_m being constant over the range of operation in the i_P-v_P plane.   If these parameters are not constant, the operating curve will no longer be an ellipse.   No simple analysis of the output of an amplifier with a reactive load exists under these conditions.

An RC-coupled Load   Consider the reactive load indicated in Fig. 7-22a. Here the output is taken, not across the plate-circuit resistor R_p, but rather across R_g, which is isolated from the plate of the tube by means of a capacitor C. Since a capacitor cannot pass direct current, no dc voltage appears across R_g. The ac signal voltage developed across R_g may then be applied to the input of another amplifier without affecting its bias voltage.   This method of connection between amplifier stages is called RC coupling, and is discussed in detail in Chap. 16.

Under dc conditions the capacitor C acts as an open circuit.   Hence the quiescent tube current and voltage are obtained as in Fig. 7-17 by drawing a *static* load line corresponding to the resistance R_p through the point $v_P = V_{PP}$, $i_P = 0$.   If we assume, as is often the case, that at the signal frequency the

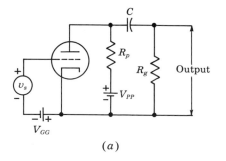

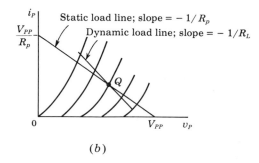

(a)   (b)

Fig. 7-22   (a) An RC-coupled circuit.   (b) Static and dynamic load lines for the RC-coupled circuit.

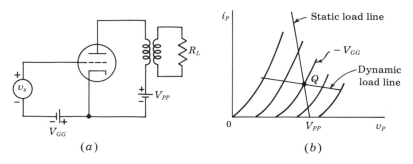

Fig. 7-23 (a) A transformer-coupled load. (b) Static and dynamic load lines for a transformer-coupled load.

reactance of C is negligible compared with R_g, then under signal conditions the effective load is again resistive. This *dynamic* load R_L represents the parallel resistance of R_p and R_g and has a value given by

$$R_L = R_p \| R_g = \frac{R_p R_g}{R_p + R_g} < R_p$$

The dynamic load line must be drawn with a slope equal to $-1/R_L$ through the quiescent point Q, as indicated in Fig. 7-22b.

A Transformer-coupled Load   For the RC-coupled circuit the ac load resistance is always smaller than the dc resistance. If the load is transformer-coupled to the plate, as indicated in Fig. 7-23a, the converse is true. The static load corresponds to the very small dc resistance of the transformer primary, and hence is almost a vertical line, as indicated in Fig. 7-23b. The dynamic load line corresponds to the much larger resistance R_L reflected into the plate circuit.

If the dynamic load resistance were infinite, the dynamic load line would be horizontal. Under these circumstances the output voltage would vary with signal voltage, but the output current would remain constant. Hence *a circuit with a very large effective load acts as a constant-current device.*

7-13   GRAPHICAL ANALYSIS OF A CIRCUIT WITH A CATHODE RESISTOR

Many practical circuits have a resistor R_k in series with the cathode in addition to (or in place of) the load resistor R_L in series with the plate. The resistor R_k is returned either to ground or to a negative supply $-V_{KK}$, as indicated in Fig. 7-24.

We consider now how to use the characteristic curves of a vacuum triode to determine such matters as range of output-voltage swing, proper bias volt-

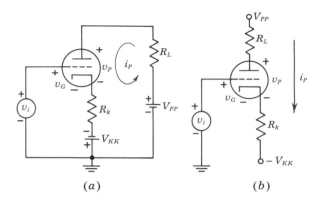

Fig. 7-24 (a) A tube with both a cathode and a load resistor. (b) An alternative representation of the same circuit.

(a)   (b)

age, and operating point for any arbitrary input voltage v_i. In Fig. 7-24, v_i, v_G, v_P, and i_P are, respectively, the *total* instantaneous input voltage, grid-to-cathode voltage, plate-to-cathode voltage, and plate current. Kirchhoff's voltage law (KVL) applied to the plate circuit yields

$$V_{PP} + V_{KK} = v_P + i_P(R_L + R_k) \tag{7-9}$$

Similarly, from the grid circuit, we obtain

$$v_i = v_G + i_P R_k - V_{KK} \tag{7-10}$$

Equation (7-9) is the equation of the load line corresponding to an effective voltage $V_{PP} + V_{KK}$ and a total resistance $R_L + R_k$. The procedure for constructing the dynamic characteristic (plate current vs. external input voltage) is, then, the following:

1. On the plate characteristics draw the load line corresponding to the given values of $V_{PP} + V_{KK}$ and $R_L + R_k$.
2. Note the current value corresponding to each point of intersection of the load line with the characteristic curves. In each case relabel the individual plate characteristics with an input voltage v_i equal to $v_G + i_P R_k - V_{KK}$ in accordance with Eq. (7-10). The procedure is illustrated in Fig. 7-25.
3. The required curve is now a plot of the plate current vs. the input voltage. For example, i_{p2} and v_{i2} are corresponding values on the graph.

When cutoff occurs, there is, of course, no drop across the cathode resistor. Consequently, the externally applied voltage required to attain cutoff is independent of the size of the cathode resistor. If the tube operates within its grid base, the potential of the cathode will be slightly (perhaps a few volts) positive with respect to the grid. Hence, *if the grid is grounded* ($v_i = 0$), *the cathode voltage is slightly positive with respect to ground, independent of the magnitudes of the supply voltages or the resistances as long as the tube is within its grid base.* As the input voltage v_i increases positively, the grid-to-cathode voltage must decrease slightly in magnitude in order to supply the increased

Fig. 7-25 Construction for obtaining the dynamic characteristic of a circuit with both a cathode and a load resistor, as in Fig. 7-24. The symbolism $v_{G1} \rightarrow v_{i1}$ means that v_{G1} is replaced by $v_{i1} = v_{G1} + i_{P1}R_k - V_{KK}$.

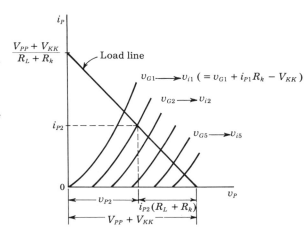

tube current demanded by this increased v_i.   Hence the cathode tries to follow the grid in potential.   If $R_L = 0$, it turns out (Sec. 7-14) that the change in cathode voltage is almost exactly equal to the change in grid voltage.   Hence such a circuit is called a *cathode follower*.   The grid voltage is sometimes driven highly (perhaps several hundreds of volts) positive *with respect to ground*.   The maximum input voltage is limited by grid current, which takes place approximately where the grid-to-cathode voltage is zero.

The Quiescent-point Calculation   It is often desirable to find the current corresponding to a specified fixed input voltage without drawing the entire dynamic characteristic as outlined above.   A very simple procedure is as follows:

1. On the plate characteristics draw the load line as in Fig. 7-25.
2. Corresponding to each value of v_G for which there is a plotted plate characteristic, calculate the current for the specified value of quiescent input voltage V.   In accordance with Eq. (7-10), this current is given by

$$i_P = \frac{V + V_{KK} - v_G}{R_k}$$

The corresponding values of i_p and v_G are plotted on the plate characteristics, as indicated by the dots in Fig. 7-26.   The locus of these points is called the *bias curve*.

3. The intersection Q of the bias curve and the load line gives the plate current I_P corresponding to the given input voltage V.

The foregoing outlined procedure is very easy to carry out.   It is not really necessary to use all values of v_G, but only two adjacent values which give currents above and below the load line, as indicated by points A and B in Fig. 7-26.   The intersection of the straight line connecting A and B with the load line gives the desired current.   In particular, it should be noted that,

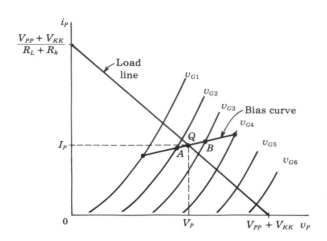

Fig. 7-26 The intersection of the load line and the bias curve gives the quiescent point.

if $V + V_{KK}$ is large compared with the range of values of v_G within the grid base, then i_P will be almost constant, and hence the curve connecting the dots in Fig. 7-26 will be approximately a horizontal straight line.

Self-bias　Often no negative supply is available, and *self-bias* is obtained from the quiescent voltage drop across R_k. For example, if the plate current and the grid-to-cathode voltage at the quiescent point are I_P and V_G, respectively, the proper bias is obtained by choosing $R_k = -V_G/I_P$. On the other hand, if a circuit with a definite R_k is specified, the quiescent point is obtained from the construction in Fig. 7-26. For the special case under consideration, $V = V_{KK} = 0$, and the bias curve is obtained from $i_P = -v_G/R_k$.

For a pentode, the screen current I_S also passes through the cathode resistance R_k. Hence, for proper self-bias, we must choose $R_k = -V_G/(I_P + I_S)$.

7-14　PRACTICAL CATHODE–FOLLOWER CIRCUITS

In order to see why it is sometimes advantageous to use a negative supply, consider the cathode-follower configuration of Fig. 7-27.

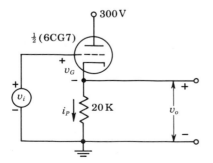

Fig. 7-27　An example of a cathode-follower circuit.

EXAMPLE Find the maximum positive and negative input voltages and the corresponding output voltages. Calculate the voltage amplification.

Solution From the characteristics (Fig. D-2) and the load line it is found that the current corresponding to $v_G = 0$ is $i_P = 10.4$ mA. Hence the maximum output voltage is $i_P R_k = 208$ V, and since $v_G = 0$, the maximum input voltage is also 208 V.

The cutoff voltage for the 6CG7 corresponding to 300 V is found to be -19 V. The cathode-follower input may swing from $+208$ to -19 V without drawing grid current or driving the tube beyond cutoff. The corresponding output swing is from $+208$ V to zero. Hence the amplification is $208/227 = 0.916$. A more general proof that the voltage gain of a cathode follower is approximately unity (but always less than unity) is given in Sec. 8-6.

In passing, we note that the corresponding input range for an amplifier using the same tube and the same supply voltage is only 0 to -19 V, which is far narrower than that of the cathode follower.

In the preceding example the input could swing 208 V in the positive direction before drawing grid current, but could go only 19 V in the negative direction before driving the tube to cutoff. If a more symmetrical operation is desired, the tube must be properly biased. One configuration is that indicated in Fig. 7-24, where the bottom of R_k is made negative with respect to ground, $R_L = 0$, and the output is taken from the cathode. Two other biasing arrangements, indicated in Fig. 7-28a and b, do not require the use of a negative supply. In (a) the grid is held V (volts) positive with respect to ground by the use of a voltage divider across the plate supply. In (b) self-bias is used, the self-biasing voltage appearing across R_1. That is, with no input signal, the grid-to-cathode voltage is the drop across R_1. The resistance R_1 is chosen so that the quiescent voltage across R_k is approximately one-half the peak-to-peak output swing. In the above example, where the total

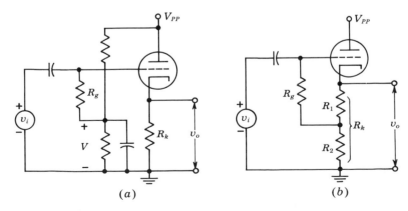

Fig. 7-28 Two biasing arrangements for a cathode-follower circuit.

output swing was ~200 V, the quiescent value is chosen as 100 V across the 20-K resistance. This corresponds to a quiescent plate current of 5 mA. From the plate characteristics of the 6CG7 and the 20-K load line, the grid-to-cathode voltage corresponding to 5 mA is -7 V. Hence R_1 must be chosen equal to $\frac{7}{5}$ K $= 1.4$ K.

REFERENCES

1. De Forest, L.: U.S. Patent 841,387, January, 1907.

2. Spangenberg, K. R.: "Vacuum Tubes," McGraw-Hill Book Company, New York, 1948.

3. Millman, J., and H. Taub: "Pulse, Digital, and Switching Waveforms," McGraw-Hill Book Company, New York, 1965.

4. Valley, G. E., Jr., and H. Wallman: "Vacuum Tube Amplifiers," p. 418, MIT Radiation Laboratory Series, vol. 18, McGraw-Hill Book Company, New York, 1948.
   Natapoff, M.: Some Physical Aspects of Electron-receiving-tube Operation, *Am. J. Phys.*, vol. 30, no. 9, pp. 621–626, September, 1962.

5. Gewartowski, J. W., and H. A. Watson: "Principles of Electron Tubes," chap. 5, D. Van Nostrand Company, Inc., Princeton, N.J., 1965.

6. Noiles, D., E. Campagna, and A. Overstrom: Performance of Frame Grid I-F Tubes, *Electron. Prod.*, December, 1964, p. F3.

7. Pidgeon, H. A.: Theory of Multi-electrode Vacuum Tube, *Bell System Tech. J.*, vol. 14, pp. 44–84, January, 1935.

8. Schade, O. H.: Beam Power Tubes, *Proc. IRE*, vol. 26, pp. 137–181, February, 1938.

9. IEEE Standard Letter Symbols for Semiconductor Devices, *IEEE Trans. Electron Devices*, vol. ED-11, no. 8, pp. 392–397, August, 1964.
   Reich, H. J.: Standard Symbols for Electron Devices, *Proc. IEEE*, vol. 51, no. 2, pp. 362–363, February, 1963.

8 / VACUUM-TUBE SMALL-SIGNAL MODELS AND APPLICATIONS

If the tube parameters r_p, g_m, and μ are reasonably constant in some region of operation, the tube behaves linearly over this range. Two linear equivalent circuits, one involving a voltage source and the other a current source, are derived in this chapter. Networks involving vacuum tubes are replaced by these linear representations and solved analytically (rather than graphically, as in the preceding chapter). The voltage gain and the input and output impedances are obtained for several amplifier configurations.

8-1   VARIATIONS FROM QUIESCENT VALUES

Suppose that in Fig. 7-16, v_s represents the output from a microphone and R_L is the effective resistance of a loudspeaker. There is no particular interest in the quiescent current, which is the current to the speaker when no one talks into the microphone. (Actually, the speaker would be transformer-coupled into the plate circuit, and the current in the secondary under quiescent conditions would be zero.) The principal interest is in the speaker output for a given microphone output. Thus the variations in current and voltage with respect to the quiescent values are most important.

If the load is a resistor and not a speaker and if the output from this resistor is taken through a coupling capacitor (as in Fig. 7-22a), then, under zero input conditions, the capacitor will charge up to the quiescent voltage V_P. The voltage across R_g is zero under these conditions. If a varying grid voltage is now added to the bias, the output will again represent voltage variations about the quiescent value.

It is evident that the significant quantities are the currents and voltages with respect to their quiescent values. To examine this

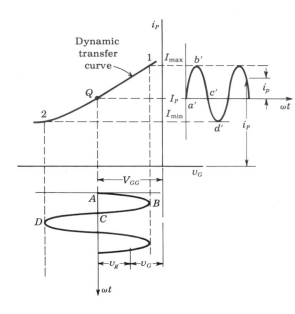

Fig. 8-1 The dynamic transfer characteristic is used to determine the output waveshape for a given input signal.

matter in some detail, refer to Figs. 7-18 and 7-20. For convenience, the latter is repeated in Fig. 8-1. We see that the output current, defined by the equation

$$i_p \equiv i_P - I_P \tag{8-1}$$

is simply the current variation about the quiescent-point current I_P. The output voltage v_p, which is similarly defined, represents the potential variations about the Q point. Consequently, if the input signal is a pure sinusoidal wave and if the tube characteristics are equidistant lines for equal intervals of v_G, i_p will also be a sinusoidal wave. If the characteristic curves are not equidistant lines over the range 1-2 for equal intervals of v_G, the waveform of i_p will differ from that of the input-signal waveform. Such a nonlinearity generates harmonics, since a nonsinusoidal periodic wave may be expressed as a Fourier series in which some of the higher-harmonic terms are appreciable. These considerations should be clear if reference is made to Figs. 7-18 and 8-1.

Corresponding to Eq. (8-1), the variables v_p and v_g are defined by the equations

$$v_p \equiv v_P - V_P \qquad v_g \equiv v_G - (-V_{GG}) = v_G + V_{GG} \tag{8-2}$$

If the symbol Δ is used to denote a change from the quiescent value, then

$$\Delta v_P \equiv v_p \qquad \Delta v_G \equiv v_g \qquad \Delta i_P \equiv i_p \tag{8-3}$$

8-2 VOLTAGE–SOURCE MODEL OF A TUBE

The graphical methods of the previous chapter are tedious to apply and often are very inaccurate. Certainly, if the input signal is very small, say, 0.1 V or less, values cannot be read from the plate characteristic curves with any degree of accuracy. But for such small input signals, the parameters μ, r_p, and g_m will remain substantially constant over the small operating range. Under these conditions it is possible to replace the graphical method by an analytical one. This is often called the *small-signal method*, but it is applicable even for large signals, provided only that the tube parameters are constant over the range of operation. The constancy of the parameters is judged by an inspection of the plate characteristics. If these are straight lines, equally spaced for equal intervals of grid bias over the operating range, the parameters are constant. Under these conditions it will be found that the tube may be replaced by a simple linear system. The resulting circuit may then be analyzed by the general methods of circuit analysis.

Thévenin's Theorem   The small-signal equivalent circuit between the plate and cathode terminals may be obtained from Thévenin's theorem. This theorem states that any *two-terminal linear network may be replaced by a generator equal to the open-circuit voltage between the terminals in series with the output impedance seen at this port.* The *output impedance* is that which appears between the output terminals when all independent energy sources are replaced by their internal impedances. From the definition of r_p given in Eqs. (7-4) as

$$r_p \equiv \left(\frac{\Delta v_P}{\Delta i_P} \right)_{V_G} = \frac{v_p}{i_p}$$

this dynamic plate resistance is the output resistance between the terminals P and K. The open-circuit voltage v_{pk} between P and K is $-\mu v_{gk}$. This result follows from the definition of μ given in Eqs (7-4) as

$$\mu \equiv -\left(\frac{\Delta v_P}{\Delta v_G} \right)_{I_P} = -\left. \frac{v_p}{v_g} \right|_{I_P} = -\left. \frac{v_{pk}}{v_{gk}} \right|_{I_P} \tag{8-4}$$

where use has been made of the definitions in Eqs. (8-3) and, for the sake of clarity, v_p (v_g) has been replaced by v_{pk} (v_{gk}) to represent the voltage drop from plate (grid) to cathode. The subscript I_P in Eq. (8-4) means that the plate current is constant, and hence that variations in plate current are zero. Since $i_p = 0$, the plate is open-circuited for signal voltages. Therefore the open-circuit plate voltage is $v_{pk} = -\mu v_{gk}$ for a signal voltage v_{gk}.

The Small-signal Voltage-source Equivalent Circuit   From Thévenin's theorem it follows that the tube may be replaced, viewed from its output terminals, by a generator $-\mu v_{gk}$ in series with a resistor r_p. This linear equivalent circuit is indicated in Fig. 8-2 for instantaneous voltages and currents. This diagram also includes a schematic of the tube itself in order to stress the correspondence between it and its equivalent representation.

A point of the utmost importance is that no dc quantities are indicated in Fig. 8-2 because the small-signal model of the tube applies only for signal voltages, that is, for changes about the Q point. Moreover, the equivalent tube-circuit representation is valid for any type of load, whether it be a pure

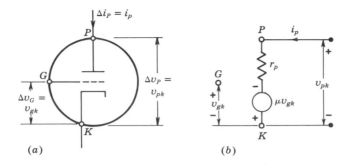

Fig. 8-2 (a) A tube triode (or pentode) and (b) its voltage-source model. The quantity v_{gk} is to be evaluated by traversing the circuit from G to K and adding all the voltage drops on the way.

resistance, an impedance, or another tube. This statement is true because the above derivation was accomplished without any regard to the external circuit in which the tube is incorporated. The only restriction is that the parameters μ, r_p, and g_m must remain substantially constant over the operating range.

If sinusoidally varying quantities are involved in the circuit—and this is usually assumed to be the case—the analysis proceeds most easily if the phasors (sinors) of elementary circuit theory are introduced. For this case of sinusoidal excitation, the tube is replaced by the equivalent circuit of Fig. 8-2b, with v_{gk}, v_{pk}, and i_p replaced by the phasors V_{gk}, V_{pk}, and I_p.

Since in a pentode the screen voltage is held constant, then with respect to variations from the quiescent point, the small-signal model of a triode is equally valid for a pentode (or a tetrode).

8-3   LINEAR ANALYSIS OF A TUBE CIRCUIT

Based on the foregoing discussion, a tube circuit may be replaced by an equivalent form which permits an analytic determination of its small-signal (ac) operation. The following simple rules should be adhered to in drawing the equivalent form of even relatively complicated amplifier circuits:

1. Draw the actual wiring diagram of the circuit neatly.
2. Mark the points G, P, and K on this circuit diagram. Locate these points as the start of the equivalent circuit. Maintain the same relative positions as in the original circuit.
3. Replace the tube by its linear model (Fig. 8-2b).
4. Transfer all circuit elements from the actual circuit to the equivalent circuit of the amplifier. Keep the relative positions of these elements intact.

Fig. 8-3 (a) The sche-matic diagram and (b) the equivalent circuit of a simple grounded-cathode amplifier.

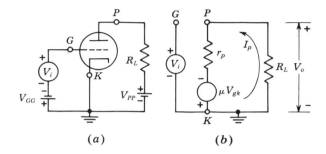

(a)   (b)

5. Replace each independent dc source by its internal resistance.   The ideal voltage source is replaced by a short circuit, and the ideal current source by an open circuit.

A point of special importance is that, regardless of the form of the input circuit, the fictitious generator that appears in the equivalent representation of the tube is *always* μV_{gk}, where V_{gk} is the signal voltage from grid to cathode.   The positive reference terminal of the generator is *always* at the cathode.

To illustrate the application of these rules, two examples are given below. The first is a single-mesh circuit, the results being given in terms of symbols rather than numerical values.   The second example is a two-mesh circuit, solved numerically.

EXAMPLE   Find the signal output current and voltage of the basic tube ampli-fier circuit illustrated in Fig. 8-3a.

Solution   According to the foregoing rules, the equivalent circuit is that of Fig. 8-3b.   Kirchhoff's voltage law (KVL), which requires that the sum of the voltage drops around the circuit equal zero, yields

$$I_p R_L + I_p r_p - \mu V_{gk} = 0$$

A glance at this circuit shows that the voltage drop from grid to cathode is V_i. Hence $V_{gk} = V_i$, and the output current I_p is

$$I_p = \frac{\mu V_i}{R_L + r_p}$$

The corresponding output-voltage drop from plate to cathode is

$$V_o = V_{pk} = -I_p R_L$$

The minus sign arises because the direction from P to K is opposite to the positive reference direction of the current I_p.

$$V_o = \frac{-\mu V_i R_L}{R_L + r_p}$$

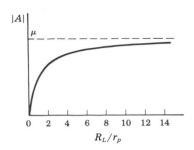

Fig. 8-4 The gain of the amplifier of Fig. 8-3 as a function of the load resistance. μ and r_p are assumed to be constant.

The *voltage gain*, or *voltage amplification*, A of the tube circuit is defined as the ratio of the output- to input-voltage drops. For the simple amplifier of Fig. 8-3a,

$$A \equiv \frac{V_o}{V_i} = -\mu \frac{R_L}{R_L + r_p} = -\mu \frac{1}{1 + r_p/R_L} \tag{8-5}$$

The minus sign signifies a phase shift of 180° between the output and the input voltages; as the input becomes more positive, the current increases and the output becomes more negative.

The magnitude of the gain increases with the load resistance and approaches a maximum value as R_L becomes much greater than r_p. The general form of this variation is illustrated in Fig. 8-4. We note that the *maximum possible gain is* μ, although this can be obtained only if $R_L = \infty$. Too large a value of R_L cannot be used, however, since, for a given quiescent current, this would require an impractically high power-supply voltage. Nevertheless, since $|A|$ increases rapidly at first and then approaches μ asymptotically, a gain approaching μ may be realized with a reasonable value of R_L. For $R_L = r_p$, then, $|A| = \mu/2$.

From Eq. (7-5), $g_m = \mu/r_p$. The total output resistance R' at the plate, taking the load into account, is R_L in parallel with r_p or $R' = r_p R_L/(R_L + r_p)$. Hence Eq. (8-5) may be put in the form

$$A = -g_m R' \tag{8-6}$$

a very compact and easily remembered expression: *the voltage gain of a tube is the product of the transconductance and the total impedance between the plate and cathode.* If the load Z_L is reactive, R' in Eq. (8-6) must be replaced by Z', where Z' represents the parallel combination of r_p and Z_L. If a pentode is under consideration, then usually $r_p \gg Z_L$. Hence $Z' \approx Z_L$, and

$$A \approx -g_m Z_L \tag{8-7}$$

EXAMPLE Draw the equivalent circuit and find the signal plate voltage for the circuit shown in Fig. 8-5a. The tube parameters are $\mu = 10$ and $r_p = 5$ K. The 1-kHz oscillator V has an rms output of 0.2 V.

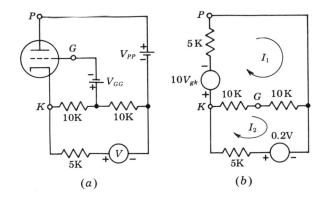

Fig. 8-5 (a) Illustrative example. (b) The small-signal equivalent circuit.

Solution Following the rules emphasized above, the small-signal equivalent circuit is indicated in Fig. 8-5b. In numerical problems we express currents in milliamperes and resistances in kilohms. (Note that the product of milliamperes and kilohms is volts.) The reference directions for the mesh directions are completely arbitrary and have been chosen clockwise. It is important to note that V_{gk} is *not* equal to the input voltage. It can be found by traversing the network from the grid to the cathode and adding all the voltage drops encountered. Any path from G to K may be chosen, but the most direct one is usually taken since it involves the least amount of labor. Thus

$$V_{gk} = 10(I_1 - I_2) \tag{8-8}$$

KVL around the two indicated meshes yields

$$10V_{gk} + 25I_1 - 20I_2 = 0 \tag{8-9}$$

$$-20I_1 + 25I_2 - 0.2 = 0 \tag{8-10}$$

If the expression for V_{gk} is substituted into (8-9), we obtain

$$100I_1 - 100I_2 + 25I_1 - 20I_2 = 0$$

or

$$I_2 = \tfrac{125}{120}I_1 = 1.042I_1$$

From this value of I_2 and Eq. (8-10) we obtain

$$I_1 = 0.0331 \text{ mA} \quad \text{and} \quad I_2 = 0.0345 \text{ mA}$$

Also,

$$V_{gk} = 10(I_1 - I_2) = 10(I_1 - 1.042I_1) = (-0.42)(0.0331) = -0.0138 \text{ mV}$$

The signal voltage drop from plate to cathode is, from mesh 1,

$$V_{pk} = -5I_1 - 10V_{gk} = -(5)(0.0331) + (10)(0.0138) = -0.028 \text{ mV}$$

Alternatively, from mesh 2,

$$V_{pk} = -0.2 + 5I_2 = -0.2 + (5)(0.0345) = -0.028 \text{ mV}$$

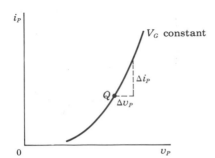

Fig. 8-6   If the grid voltage is constant, then
$\Delta i_P = (\text{slope})(\Delta v_P) = (\partial i_P/\partial v_P)_{V_g}\,\Delta v_P$.

8-4   TAYLOR'S SERIES DERIVATION OF THE EQUIVALENT CIRCUIT

It is instructive to obtain the equivalent circuit of a triode from a Taylor's series expansion of the current i_P about the quiescent point Q. This derivation will show the limitations of this equivalent circuit and will also supply the proof that $\mu = r_p g_m$.

If the grid voltage remains constant but the plate voltage changes by an amount Δv_P, then the change in current equals the rate of change of current with plate voltage times the change in plate voltage, or

$$\Delta i_P = \left(\frac{\partial i_P}{\partial v_P}\right)_{V_G}\Delta v_P$$

The subscript indicates the variable held constant in performing the partial differentiation. This relationship is illustrated in Fig. 8-6 and is seen to be strictly true only if the slope of the plate characteristic is constant for the assumed change in voltage. Similarly, if the plate voltage remains constant but the grid voltage changes by Δv_G, then the change in current is given by

$$\Delta i_P = \left(\frac{\partial i_P}{\partial v_G}\right)_{V_P}\Delta v_G$$

If both the grid and plate voltages are varied, the plate-current change is the sum of the two changes indicated above, or

$$\Delta i_P = \left(\frac{\partial i_P}{\partial v_P}\right)_{V_G}\Delta v_P + \left(\frac{\partial i_P}{\partial v_G}\right)_{V_P}\Delta v_G \tag{8-11}$$

As mentioned above, this expression is only approximate. It is, in fact, just the first two terms of the Taylor's series expansion of the function $i_P(v_P, v_G)$. In the general case,

$$\Delta i_P = \left(\frac{\partial i_P}{\partial v_P}\right)_{V_G}\Delta v_P + \left(\frac{\partial i_P}{\partial v_G}\right)_{V_P}\Delta v_G + \frac{1}{2}\left(\frac{\partial^2 i_P}{\partial v_P{}^2}\right)_{V_G}(\Delta v_P)^2$$
$$+ \frac{1}{2}\left(\frac{\partial^2 i_P}{\partial v_G{}^2}\right)_{V_P}(\Delta v_G)^2 + \frac{\partial^2 i_P}{\partial v_P\,\partial v_G}\Delta v_P\,\Delta v_G + \cdots \tag{8-12}$$

Consider the third term in this expansion. Since from Eqs. (7-4) the plate resistance is given by $1/r_p = (\partial i_P/\partial v_P)_{V_G}$, this term equals

$$\frac{1}{2}\left[\frac{\partial(1/r_p)}{\partial v_P}\right]_{V_G}(\Delta v_P)^2$$

Similarly, the fourth-, fifth-, and higher-order terms in Eq. (8-12) represent derivatives of r_p and g_m with respect to plate and grid voltages.

Small-signal Model   This method of analysis is based on the assumption that the tube parameters are sensibly constant over the operating range Δv_P and Δv_G.   Under these conditions a satisfactory representation of the variations in plate current about the quiescent point is given by Eq. (8-11).   This expression may be written in the following form, by virtue of Eqs. (7-4):

$$\Delta i_P = \frac{1}{r_p}\Delta v_P + g_m\,\Delta v_G \tag{8-13}$$

Using the notation of Eqs. (8-3), and remembering that $g_m = \mu/r_p$ (see below), Eq. (8-13) becomes

$$v_p = i_p r_p - \mu v_g \tag{8-14}$$

This expression shows that the varying voltage v_p with respect to the Q point is made up of two components: One is a generated emf which is μ times as large as the grid-to-cathode voltage variation v_g; the second is a signal voltage across the tube resistor r_p that results from the signal load current i_p through it.

The result of this discussion is the circuit model shown in Fig. 8-2.   It is seen from the diagram that the voltage drop v_{pk} from plate to cathode is equal to the voltage drop in the plate resistor less the generator voltage, or

$$v_{pk} - i_p r_p \qquad \mu v_{gk}$$

This is exactly Eq. (8-14), which verifies that Fig. 8-2 is the correct equivalent-circuit representation of the tube.

Relationship between μ, r_p, and g_m   It follows from Eq. (8-13) that, if the plate current is constant so that $\Delta i_P = 0$, then

$$-\frac{\Delta v_P}{\Delta v_G} = g_m r_p$$

But since the plate current has been taken to be constant, then $-\Delta v_P/\Delta v_G$ is by definition [Eq. (7-3)] the amplification factor.   Hence

$$\mu = g_m r_p \tag{8-15}$$

8-5   CURRENT–SOURCE MODEL OF A TUBE

Thévenin's equivalent circuit is used if a network is analyzed by the mesh method.   However, if a nodal analysis is made, Norton's equivalent circuit is more useful.

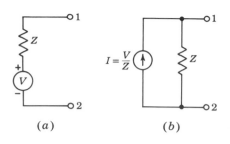

(a)   (b)

Fig. 8-7 As viewed from terminals 1 and 2, the Thévenin's circuit in (a) is equivalent to the Norton's circuit in (b).

Norton's Theorem *The equivalent circuit between two points in a network consists of the impedance Z, seen looking back between these two terminals, in parallel with a current generator whose value is the current I which flows when the terminals are short-circuited.* In other words, *a voltage source V in series with an impedance Z is equivalent to a current source V/Z in parallel with an impedance Z.* These equivalent circuits are indicated in Fig. 8-7a and b.

The Small-signal Current-source Equivalent Circuit From the voltage-source representation of a tube given in Fig. 8-2b we see that the short-circuit current has a magnitude $\mu v_{gk}/r_p = g_m v_{gk}$, where use is made of Eq. (8-15). The direction of the current is such that it will flow *through an external load* from cathode to plate. Hence the current-source equivalent circuit is as indicated in Fig. 8-8.

We shall now again solve the first example in Sec. 8-3, using the Norton's equivalent representation. For convenience, the circuit of Fig. 8-3 is repeated in Fig. 8-9a. Its current-source model in Fig. 8-9b is the same as that indicated in Fig. 8-8, but with the addition of the load resistor R_L in parallel with r_p. If $R' \equiv r_p R_L/(r_p + R_L)$ = the parallel combination of r_p and R_L, then the output voltage is

$$v_o = -iR' = -g_m v_i R'$$

The voltage amplification A is

$$A = \frac{v_o}{v_i} = -g_m R' \qquad\qquad (8\text{-}16)$$

which is identical with Eq. (8-6).

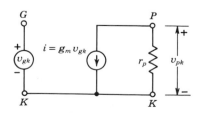

Fig. 8-8 The current-source model of a triode.

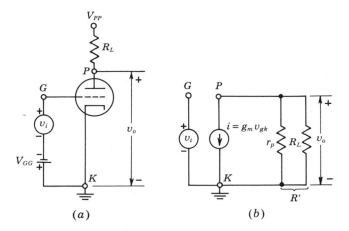

Fig. 8-9 (a) The common-cathode amplifier configuration and (b) its current-source equivalent circuit.

8-6   A GENERALIZED TUBE AMPLIFIER

The circuit (Fig. 8-9) considered in the preceding section has its cathode common to the input and output circuits, and hence is called the *common-cathode* (or *grounded-cathode*) amplifier.   This circuit is the one most frequently used, but two other configurations, the *grounded-grid* and the *grounded-plate* amplifiers, are also possible.

The Grounded-grid Amplifier   This circuit is shown in Fig. 8-10a. As far as signal voltages are concerned, the grid is at ground potential, which accounts for the name grounded-grid amplifier.   The input signal v is applied between cathode and ground, and R_s is the resistance of the signal source. The output v_o is taken across the plate-circuit resistor R_p.   Since the grid is

Fig. 8-10 (a) The grounded-grid amplifier and (b) the grounded-plate (cathode-follower) amplifier.

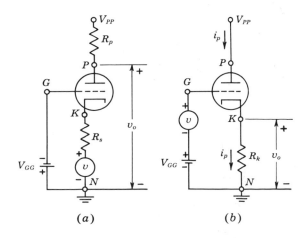

common to the input and the output circuits, this configuration is also called the *common-grid amplifier*.

The Grounded-plate Amplifier This circuit is indicated in Fig. 8-10b. The signal v is applied between grid and ground, and the output v_o is taken across a resistor R_k between cathode and ground. As far as signal (ac) voltages are concerned, the plate is at ground potential, which accounts for the name grounded-plate amplifier. For an increase in input-signal voltage v, the current i_p increases, and so does the output-signal voltage $v_o = i_pR_p$. Consequently, the polarity of the output signal is the same as that for the input signal. Furthermore, as verified for a particular circuit in Sec. 7-14 and as demonstrated in general in Sec. 8-8, the magnitudes of these voltages v_o and $v_i = v$ are almost the same (unity gain). Hence the cathode voltage follows the grid voltage closely, and this feature accounts for the name cathode follower given to the circuit.

The Generalized Circuit The analysis of the grounded-grid and the grounded-plate amplifiers is made by considering the generalized configuration indicated in Fig. 8-11a. This circuit contains three independent signal sources, v_i in series with the grid, v_k in series with the cathode, and v_a in series with the anode. For the grounded-grid amplifier $v_i = v_a = 0$, the signal voltage is v_k with a source resistance R_k, and the output is v_{o1} taken at the plate. For the cathode follower, $R_p = 0$, $v_k = v_a = 0$, the signal voltage is v_i, and the output is v_{o2} taken at the cathode. (The signal-source impedance is unimportant since it is in series with a grid which, we assume, draws negligible current.)

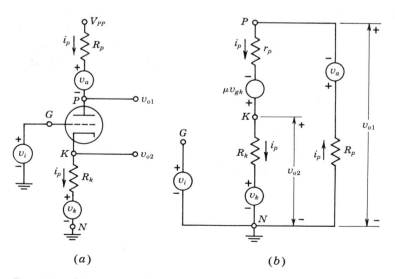

(*a*) (*b*)

Fig. 8-11 (*a*) A generalized amplifier configuration. (*b*) The small-signal equivalent circuit.

If the effect of the ripple voltage in the power supply V_{PP} is to be investigated, then v_a will be included in the circuit to represent these small voltage changes in V_{PP}.

Following the rules given in Sec. 8-3, we obtain the small-signal equivalent circuit of Fig. 8-11b, from which it follows that

$$v_{gk} = v_i - v_k - i_p R_k \qquad (8\text{-}17)$$

and

$$i_p = \frac{\mu v_{gk} - v_k - v_a}{r_p + R_k + R_p} \qquad (8\text{-}18)$$

Substituting from Eq. (8-17) in Eq. (8-18), we find

$$i_p = \frac{\mu v_i/(\mu + 1) - v_k - v_a/(\mu + 1)}{(r_p + R_p)/(\mu + 1) + R_k} \qquad (8\text{-}19)$$

The output voltages v_{o1} and v_{o2} are found as follows:

$$v_{o1} = -i_p R_p - v_a \qquad v_{o2} = i_p R_k + v_k \qquad (8\text{-}20)$$

Using the basic concepts enunciated in the following section, the physical significance of Eqs. (8-19) and (8-20) is given in Sec. 8-8.

8-7   THE THEVENIN'S EQUIVALENT OF ANY AMPLIFIER

If an active device (tube or transistor) in a circuit acts as amplifier, this configuration is characterized by three parameters, the input impedance Z_i, the output impedance Z_o, and the open-circuit voltage gain A_v. If these parameters are independent of the source impedance Z_s and the external load impedance Z_L, then the Thévenin's model of the amplifier is as shown in Fig. 8-12. The external source voltage V_s is applied in series with Z_s to the input terminals marked 1 and 2. The voltage across this input port is V_i. The output terminals are marked 3 and 4. Since the open-circuit voltage is the amplifier voltage gain A_v times the input voltage, the Thévenin's generator is $A_v V_i$, as indicated. Note that A_v is the unloaded voltage gain, i.e., the gain with no external load placed across the amplifier, and hence zero load current, $I_L = 0$. The loaded gain (the amplification with the load Z_L in place) is called A_V.

Fig. 8-12   The Thévenin equivalent circuit of an amplifier. When Z_L is connected to the output terminals, a current I_L flows in the load.

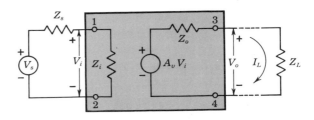

The output voltage is given by

$$V_o = A_v V_i - I_L Z_o \tag{8-21}$$

This equation may be used to define A_v and Z_o for a particular circuit. For example, if we find that the output voltage of an amplifier varies linearly with load current, as indicated in Eq. (8-21), the factor multiplying the input voltage V_i is the unloaded gain A_v and the factor multiplying the load current I_L is the output impedance Z_o, *provided that these factors A_v and Z_o are independent of the load Z_L.*

The following theorem offers an alternative method for finding Z_o.

Open-circuit Voltage–Short-circuit Current Theorems As corollaries to Thévenin's and Norton's theorems we have the following relationships: If V represents the open-circuit voltage, I the short-circuit current, and Z (Y) the impedance (admittance) between two terminals in a network, then

$$Z = \frac{V}{I} \qquad I = \frac{V}{Z} = VY \qquad V = IZ = \frac{I}{Y} \tag{8-22}$$

The first relationship states that "the impedance between two nodes equals the open-circuit voltage divided by the short-circuit current." This method is one of the simplest for finding the output impedance Z_o.

The last relationship of Eqs. (8-22) is often the quickest way to calculate the voltage between two points in a network. This equation states that "the voltage equals the short-circuit current divided by the admittance."

The Output Impedance A third method for obtaining Z_o is to set the source voltage V_s to zero and to drive the amplifier by an external voltage generator connected across terminals 3-4. Then the ratio of the voltage across 3-4 divided by the current delivered by the generator yields the output impedance Z_o. This same method may be used to find the input impedance if the above measurement is made at terminals 1-2 instead of 3-4.

8-8 LOOKING INTO THE PLATE OR CATHODE OF A TUBE

Let us now return to the generalized amplifier of Fig. 8-11a and find a Thévenin's equivalent circuit, first from plate to ground and then from cathode to ground.

The Output from the Plate The signal v_a and the resistor R_p are now considered external to the amplifier. Hence, for the moment, we set $v_a = 0$ and interpret R_p as the external load R_L. The load current i_L from plate to ground is the negative of the plate current i_p. Hence, with $R_L = R_p = 0$, we obtain the short-circuit load current I from Eq. (8-19):

$$I = \frac{-\dfrac{\mu v_i}{\mu + 1} + v_k}{\dfrac{r_p}{\mu + 1} + R_k} = \frac{-\mu v_i + (\mu + 1)v_k}{r_p + (\mu + 1)R_k} \tag{8-23}$$

The open-circuit voltage V is found as follows, using Eq. (8-19):

$$V = \lim_{R_p \to \infty} (-i_p R_p) = \lim_{R_p \to \infty} \frac{-\dfrac{\mu v_i}{\mu + 1} + v_k}{\dfrac{r_p + R_p}{\mu + 1} + R_k} R_p$$

$$= -\mu v_i + (\mu + 1)v_k \tag{8-24}$$

The open-circuit voltage gain A_v for the signal v_i is $-\mu$, and for the signal v_k is $+(\mu + 1)$.

The output impedance Z is given by Eqs. (8-22).   Thus

$$Z = \frac{V}{I} = r_p + (\mu + 1)R_k \tag{8-25}$$

The above results lead to the Thévenin's circuit of Fig. 8-13a.   We conclude that, *"looking into the plate" of an amplifier, we see (for small-signal operation) an equivalent circuit consisting of two generators in series, one of $-\mu$ times the grid signal voltage v_i, and the second $(\mu + 1)$ times the cathode-signal voltage v_k. These generators are in series with a resistance $r_p + (\mu + 1)R_k$.*   Note that the voltage v_k and the resistance R_k in the cathode circuit are both multiplied by the same factor, $\mu + 1$.

Since R_p and v_a were considered external to the amplifier, they have been drawn to the right of the output terminals P and N in Fig. 8-13a.

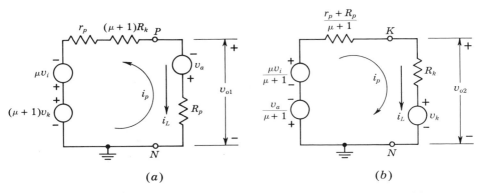

(a)   (b)

Fig. 8-13   The equivalent circuit for the generalized amplifier of Fig. 8-11 between (a) plate and ground, (b) cathode and ground.

The Output from the Cathode The signal v_k and the resistor R_k are considered external to the amplifier. Hence, for the moment, set $v_k = 0$ and interpret R_k as the external load R_L in Fig. 8-11a. The load current i_L from cathode to ground equals i_p. Hence, with $R_L = R_k = 0$, we obtain for the short-circuit load current I from Eq. (8-19)

$$I = \frac{\mu v_i - v_a}{r_p + R_p} \tag{8-26}$$

The open-circuit voltage V is given by

$$V = \lim_{R_k \to \infty} i_p R_k = \frac{\mu v_i - v_a}{\mu + 1} \tag{8-27}$$

The open-circuit voltage gain A_v for the signal v_i is $\mu/(\mu + 1)$, and for the signal v_a is $-1/(\mu + 1)$.

The output impedance is

$$Z = \frac{V}{I} = \frac{r_p + R_p}{\mu + 1} \tag{8-28}$$

The above results lead to the Thévenin's circuit of Fig. 8-13b. We conclude that, *"looking into the cathode" of an amplifier, we see (for small-signal operation) an equivalent circuit consisting of two generators in series, one of value $\mu/(\mu + 1)$ times the grid signal voltage v_i, and the second $1/(\mu + 1)$ times the plate signal voltage v_a. These generators are in series with a resistance $(r_p + R_p)/(\mu + 1)$.* Note that the voltage v_a and the resistance in the plate circuit are both divided by the same factor, $\mu + 1$.

The Grounded-grid Amplifier This configuration is obtained from the generalized circuit of Fig. 8-11 by setting $v_a = v_i = 0$. The equivalent circuit, obtained from Fig. 8-13a, is indicated in Fig. 8-14a. By inspection the gain is

$$A = \frac{v_o}{v_k} = \frac{(\mu + 1)R_p}{R_p + r_p + (\mu + 1)R_k} \tag{8-29}$$

Note that, since A is positive, there is no phase shift between output and input. If $R_k = 0$ and $\mu \gg 1$, then the gain has almost the same value as for

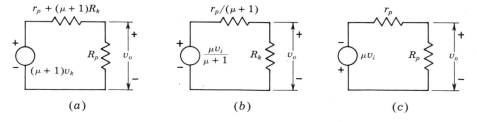

Fig. 8-14 The Thévenin circuits for the three basic amplifier configurations.

a common-cathode amplifier [Eq. (8-16)].   The voltage gain is greatly reduced unless R_k is kept small compared with $(R_p + r_p)/(\mu + 1)$, which is usually of the order of 1,000 Ω or less.

The output impedance of the grounded-grid amplifier will be much higher than the plate resistance if the source has appreciable resistance R_k or if an additional resistance is intentionally added in series with the cathode.   On the other hand, the input impedance is quite low (Prob. 8-24).   Hence a grounded-grid amplifier may be employed when a low input impedance and a high output impedance are desired.   Such applications are infrequent.   The grounded-grid amplifier is used as a tuned voltage amplifier at ultrahigh frequencies[1] because the grounded grid acts as a grounded electrostatic shield which prevents coupling between input and output circuits.

The Cathode Follower   This configuration is obtained from the generalized circuit of Fig. 8-11 by setting $v_k = v_a = 0$ and $R_p = 0$.   The equivalent circuit is indicated in Fig. 8-14b.   By inspection the gain is

$$A = \frac{v_o}{v_i} = \frac{\dfrac{\mu}{\mu + 1} R_k}{\dfrac{r_p}{\mu + 1} + R_k} = \frac{\mu R_k}{r_p + (\mu + 1)R_k} \approx \frac{g_m R_k}{1 + g_m R_k} \qquad \text{if } \mu \gg 1$$

$$(8\text{-}30)$$

Since A is positive, there is no phase shift between grid and cathode. Note that, since the denominator is always larger than the numerator, then A never exceeds unity.   However, if $(\mu + 1)R_k \gg r_p$, then

$$A \approx \frac{\mu}{\mu + 1} \qquad\qquad (8\text{-}31)$$

which approaches unity.   For example, for a type 6CG7 tube with $\mu = 20$, $A \approx 0.95$ (which is to be compared with the value $A = 0.91$ obtained graphically in Sec. 7-14).

The output impedance of the cathode follower is much smaller than the plate resistance.   For example, if $\mu \gg 1$, then

$$Z_o = \frac{r_p}{\mu + 1} \approx \frac{r_p}{\mu} = \frac{1}{g_m} \qquad\qquad (8\text{-}32)$$

For a g_m of 2 millimhos, the output impedance is only 500 Ω, and for a higher value of transconductance, Z_o is even less.   On the other hand, since the input signal is applied to the grid, the input impedance (for negative grid voltages where the grid current is negligible) is very high (ideally infinite).   A cathode follower is usually employed when a high input impedance and a low output impedance are desired.

The high input impedance of a cathode follower makes it ideal for applications where the loading on a signal source must be kept at a minimum. The low output impedance permits it to support a heavy capacitive load.

These features account for the many applications found for cathode followers. For example, the cathode follower is very often used as the input tube in oscilloscope amplifiers. It is also used where a signal must be transmitted through a short section of coaxial cable or shielded wire, with its attendant high shunt capacitance.

If the output from one circuit acts as the input to another circuit and the second circuit reacts back onto the first, a cathode follower may be used as a buffer stage to eliminate this reaction.

Because the cathode follower is a feedback amplifier (Sec. 17-5), it possesses great stability and linearity. Many electronic instruments take advantage of these desirable features of cathode followers. The high-frequency characteristics of the cathode follower are considered in Sec. 8-14.

The Grounded-cathode Amplifier The equivalent circuit for this configuration is given in Fig. 8-3b and repeated in Fig. 8-14c, for comparison with the grounded-grid and grounded-plate amplifiers. The grounded-cathode amplifier has a high input impedance, an output impedance equal to the plate resistance, and a voltage gain which may approach the μ of the tube (although an amplification of the order of $\mu/2$ is more common). There is a phase inversion between the plate and grid. This circuit is employed more often than the other two configurations.

8-9 CIRCUITS WITH A CATHODE RESISTOR[1]

Many practical networks involve the use of a resistor in the cathode circuit. Some of the most important of these "cathode-follower-type" circuits are described in this section.

The Split-load Phase Inverter This circuit appears in Fig. 8-15. A single input signal provides two output signals, v_{kn}, which is of the same polarity as the input, and v_{pn}, which is of opposite polarity. Further, if the

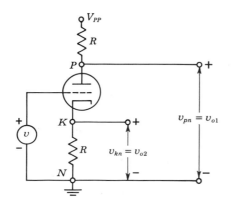

Fig. 8-15 The split-load phase inverter.

plate and cathode resistors are identical, the magnitudes of the two signals must be the same, since the currents in the plate and cathode resistors are equal. The amplification $|A| \equiv |v_{kn}/v| = |v_{pn}/v|$ may be written directly by comparison with either of the equivalent circuits of Fig. 8-13 (with $v_k = v_a = 0$) as

$$|A| = \frac{\mu R}{r_p + (\mu + 2)R} \approx \frac{g_m R}{1 + g_m R} \tag{8-33}$$

The exact result differs from that given for the cathode follower [Eq. (8-30)] only in the appearance of a factor $\mu + 2$ in place of the factor $\mu + 1$. The gain may be made to approach 1 if $g_m R \gg 1$. The ratio of the plate-to-cathode signal to the input signal may then approach 2. The output impedances at the plate and at the cathode are different, the plate impedance being higher than the cathode impedance.

If the capacitance from the plate to ground is greater than that from cathode to ground, it is possible to equalize the frequency response of the two outputs by adding capacitance across the cathode resistor. A phase inverter, also called a *paraphase amplifier*, is used to convert an input voltage v, one terminal of which is grounded, into two symmetrical output voltages ($v_{o1} = -v_{o2}$).

The Cathode-coupled Phase Inverter   This circuit, shown in Fig. 8-16a, serves the same purpose as the split-load phase inverter but additionally provides some gain and equal output impedances. The two signals v_{o1} and v_{o2} are of opposite polarity and are nominally of equal amplitude. The equivalent circuit of Fig. 8-13b may again be used to advantage to analyze the operation of the cathode-coupled phase inverter. We replace each tube by its

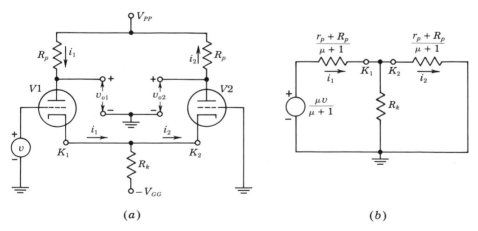

(a)   (b)

Fig. 8-16   (a) The cathode-coupled phase inverter and (b) its equivalent circuit from cathode to ground.

equivalent circuit *as seen from the cathode.* The resulting circuit is shown in Fig. 8-16b. The *signal* currents flowing, respectively, out of the cathode of $V1$ and into the cathode of $V2$ are i_1 and i_2. The output signals are $v_{o1} = -i_1R_p$ and $v_{o2} = i_2R_p$.

The output signals will be of equal magnitude if $i_1 = i_2$. This requirement will be satisfied nominally if $R_k \gg (r_p + R_p)/(\mu + 1)$. Typically, if, say, $r_p = R_p = 10$ K and $\mu + 1 = 20$ as for a 12AU7 tube, $(r_p + R_p)/(\mu + 1) = 1$ K and R_k should be selected to be about 10 K if an unbalance of no more than about 10 percent is desired (Prob. 8-19). It is possible to obtain balanced outputs by choosing unequal values for the two plate load resistors.

By applying Kirchhoff's voltage law to the outside loop of Fig. 8-16b, we find for the plate-to-plate gain

$$A \equiv \frac{v_{o2} - v_{o1}}{v} = \frac{(i_1 + i_2)R_p}{v} = \frac{\mu R_p}{r_p + R_p} \tag{8-34}$$

which is the same gain that would be provided by a single-tube grounded-cathode amplifier with plate resistor R_p.

If each tube carries a quiescent current of, say, 5 mA, the quiescent drop across R_k is 100 V. We may require for convenience that the quiescent grid voltages be at ground potential. In the linear range of operation the grid-to-cathode voltage of a tube is usually only of the order of several volts. The voltage at the cathodes is therefore also required to be in the neighborhood of ground potential. These requirements with respect to quiescent operating voltages may be satisfied by returning the cathode resistor, as in Fig. 8-16a, to an appropriately large negative voltage (in this example, $V_{GG} = 100$ V).

The Difference Amplifier Suppose that we have two signals, v_1 and v_2, each measured with respect to ground. It is desired to generate a third signal, also to be referred to ground, which signal is to be proportional to the voltage difference $v_1 - v_2$. One such application would occur if it were required to convert the symmetrical signals, which appear at the plates of a paraphase amplifier, back to an unsymmetrical signal. If the voltage v in Fig. 8-16a is v_1 and if v_2 is applied between grid and ground of $V2$ (in place of the short circuit), this circuit is a difference amplifier. If $(\mu + 1)R_k \gg r_p$, then it turns out that v_{o1} and v_{o2} are each proportional to $v_1 - v_2$. The transistorized version of the difference amplifier is discussed in detail in Sec. 12-12.

An Amplifier with a Constant-current Source The cathode follower, paraphase amplifier, and difference amplifier all operate with improved performance as the cathode resistance becomes larger. A large cathode resistance, however, results in a large dc voltage drop due to the quiescent tube current. Hence a device which has a small static resistance but a very large dynamic resistance may be used to advantage in the cathode circuit to replace a large ordinary resistance. An arrangement of this type is shown in the difference amplifier of Fig. 8-17. Referring to Fig. 8-13a, it appears that the

Fig. 8-17   Tube $V3$ acts as a very high dynamic resistance of value $r_p + (\mu + 1)R_k$ in the cathode circuit of tubes $V1$ and $V2$.   The voltage divider R is used to balance the outputs from the two plates.

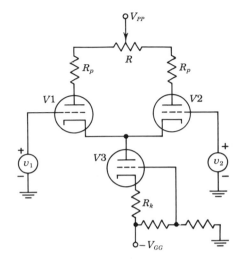

impedance seen looking into the plate of the tube $V3$ in the cathode circuit is $r_p + (1 + \mu)R_k \approx \mu R_k$ if R_k is large.   Under typical circumstances, $-V_{GG}$ might be -300 V, $R_k = 500$ K, and the cathode tube a 12AX7 with $\mu = 100$ and $r_p = 100$ K.   The effective cathode impedance of the difference amplifier would then be about 50 M.   In the circuit of Fig. 8-17, high-μ low-current tubes would be appropriate.   Suppose, then, that the individual tubes carried only 0.1 mA of current.   The total cathode current is 0.2 mA, and if an ordinary 50-M resistor were used, a negative supply voltage of 10,000 V would be required.   This voltage is, of course, impractically high, which demonstrates the advantage of tube $V3$ over an ordinary 50-M resistor in this application.

   A large dynamic resistance is plotted as a horizontal load line (Sec. 7-12) and corresponds to a constant current.   Hence the difference amplifier of Fig. 8-17 is said to be fed from a constant-current source.

8-10   A CASCODE AMPLIFIER

This circuit, consisting of two triodes in series (the same current in each), is indicated in Fig. 8-18.   That this circuit behaves like a pentode can be seen as follows: The load for $V1$ is the effective impedance looking into the cathode of $V2$; namely, $R_p \equiv (R + r_p)/(\mu + 1)$.   For large values of μ this may be very small, and to a first approximation can be considered as a short circuit for signal voltage.   Hence the plate potential of $V1$ is constant.   The definition of the transconductance is

$$g_m \equiv \left(\frac{\Delta i_P}{\Delta v_G}\right)_{V_P}$$

Hence the signal current is $\Delta i_P = g_m \, \Delta v_G = g_m v_1$, where v_1 is the signal-input

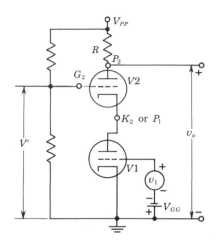

Fig. 8-18 The cascode amplifier.

voltage. The gain is $A = -R \, \Delta i_P/v_1 = -g_m R$, which is the expression for the gain of a pentode [Eq. (8-7) with $Z_L = R$].

Another point of view is the following: The plate dc voltage V_{P1} of $V1$ is determined by the grid-to-ground voltage V' of $V2$. Actually,

$$V_{P1} = V' - V_{G2}$$

where V_{G2} is the drop from grid to cathode of $V2$ and is a negative number. The value of V_{G2} may vary between zero and the cutoff voltage, but this is small compared with the value of V' (which may be one or several hundred volts). Hence V_{P1} is essentially constant, and the dc tube current is also constant since it is determined by V_{P1} and the bias V_{GG}. Hence a curve of dc plate current vs. dc voltage from the plate of $V2$ to ground resembles the constant-current characteristic of a pentode. From this discussion it is clear that V' takes the place of the screen voltage in a pentode. The cascode amplifier has the advantages over the pentode that no screen current need be supplied and it has the low noise of a triode.

The exact expression for the amplification is found by replacing $V2$ by an impedance $(R + r_p)/(\mu + 1)$ and $V1$ by a generator μv_1 in series with an impedance r_p. The result is

$$A_1 = \frac{-(\mu)(\mu + 1)R}{R + (\mu + 2)r_p} \tag{8-35}$$

If $(\mu + 2)r_p \gg R$ and if $\mu \gg 1$, this is approximately

$$A_1 \approx \frac{-\mu R}{r_p} = -g_m R$$

which is the result obtained by the qualitative arguments given above.

It is possible to apply an ac signal voltage V_2 (in addition to the bias voltage V') to the grid of $V2$. Under these circumstances $V1$ acts as an impedance of magnitude r_p in the cathode of $V2$. The voltage gain for this signal V_2 is

$$A_2 = \frac{-\mu R}{R + (\mu + 2)r_p} \tag{8-36}$$

If sinusoidal signals V_1 and V_2 are applied simultaneously to both inputs, then, by the principle of superposition, the output V_o will be

$$V_o = A_1 V_1 + A_2 V_2$$

The quiescent operating current in a cascode amplifier is found by the method of successive approximations. The method converges very rapidly, and is best illustrated by a numerical example.

EXAMPLE Find the quiescent current in the cascode amplifier of Fig. 8-18 if $R = 20$ K, $V_{PP} = 300$ V, $V' = 125$ V, and $V_{GG} = 4$ V. The tube is a 6CG7, whose plate characteristics are given in Appendix D (Fig. D-2).

Solution If $V2$ is not to draw grid current, then K_2 must be at a higher potential than G_2. However, it cannot be at too high a potential, or $V2$ will be cut off. Let us take as a first approximation $V_{G2} = -5$ V, and hence $V_{P1} = 125 + 5 = 130$ V. Corresponding to this value of V_{P1} and to $V_{G1} = -4$ V, the plate current I_P is found from the 6CG7 characteristics to be 4.2 mA. Hence $V_{P2} = V_{PP} - I_P R - V_{P1} = 300 - (4.2)(20) - 130 = 86$ V. For $V_{P2} = 86$ V and $I_{P2} = 4.2$ mA, we find that $V_{G2} \approx -2$ V.

The second approximation is $V_{P1} = 125 + 2 = 127$ V. Corresponding to this value of V_{P1} and to $V_{G1} = -4$ V, we find that $I_P = 4.0$ mA. Hence $V_{P2} = 300 - (4.0)(20) - 130 = 90$ V. Corresponding to this V_{P2} and to $I_{P2} = 4.0$ mA, we find $V_{G2} \approx -2.1$ V.

The third approximation to V_{p1} is $125 + 2.1 = 127.1$ V, which is close enough to the previous value of 127 V so as not to affect the value of the current appreciably. Hence $I_P = 4.0$ mA.

8-11   INTERELECTRODE CAPACITANCES IN A TRIODE[2]

We assumed in the foregoing discussions that with a negative bias the input current was negligible and that changes in the plate circuit were not reflected into the grid circuit. These assumptions are not strictly true, as is now shown.

The grid, plate, and cathode elements are conductors separated by a dielectric (a vacuum), and hence, by elementary electrostatics, there exist capacitances between pairs of electrodes. Clearly, the input current in a grounded-cathode amplifier cannot be zero because the source must supply current to the grid-cathode and the grid-plate capacitances. Furthermore, the input and output circuits are no longer isolated, but there is coupling

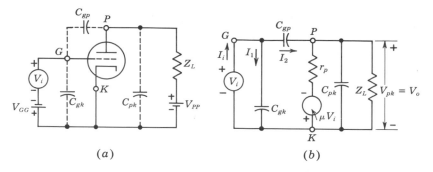

Fig. 8-19 The schematic and equivalent circuits of a grounded-cathode amplifier, taking into account the interelectrode capacitances.

between them through the grid-plate capacitance. Although these capacitances are small, usually less than 10 pF, yet, at the upper audio frequencies and above, they produce appreciable loading of the input source and also cause output-to-input feedback. They must therefore be taken into account.

A more complete circuit and its equivalent circuit, which includes the interelectrode capacitances, are given in Fig. 8-19. In this circuit C_{gp} represents the capacitance between the grid and the plate, C_{gk} is the capacitance between the grid and the cathode, and C_{pk} is the capacitance between the plate and the cathode. The inclusion of these tube capacitances (shown dashed in the schematic diagram and explicitly in the equivalent amplifier circuit of Fig. 8-19b) yields results that are more precise than those resulting from the analysis of the simple circuit of Fig. 8-3. It will be noted that the same procedure outlined in Sec. 8-3 has been followed in order to obtain the equivalent circuit of the amplifier. It is evident that $V_{gk} = V_i$, and so μV_i has been written for the emf of the Thévenin's generator in the equivalent circuit of Fig. 8-19b.

The Voltage Gain The output voltage between terminals P and K is easily found with the aid of the theorem of Sec. 8-5, namely, $V_o = IZ$, where I is the short-circuit current and Z is the impedance seen between the terminals. To find Z, the generators V_i and μV_i in Fig. 8-19b are (imagined) short-circuited, and we note that Z is the parallel combination of the impedances corresponding to Z_L, C_{pk}, r_p, and C_{gp}. Hence

$$Y \equiv \frac{1}{Z} = Y_L + Y_{pk} + g_p + Y_{gp} \tag{8-37}$$

where $Y_L = 1/Z_L$ = admittance corresponding to Z_L
$\quad Y_{pk} = j\omega C_{pk}$ = admittance corresponding to C_{pk}
$\quad g_p = 1/r_p$ = admittance corresponding to r_p
$\quad Y_{gp} = j\omega C_{gp}$ = admittance corresponding to C_{gp}

The current in the direction from P to K in a zero-resistance wire connecting the output terminals is $-\mu V_i/r_p = -g_m V_i$ due to the generator μV_i and is $V_i Y_{gp}$ due to the signal V_i. Hence the total short-circuit current is

$$I = -g_m V_i + V_i Y_{gp} \tag{8-38}$$

The amplification A with the load Z_L in place is given by

$$A = \frac{V_o}{V_i} = \frac{IZ}{V_i} = \frac{I}{V_i Y}$$

or, from Eqs. (8-37) and (8-38),

$$A = \frac{-g_m + Y_{gp}}{Y_L + Y_{pk} + g_p + Y_{gp}} \tag{8-39}$$

It is interesting to see that Eq. (8-39) reduces to the expression already developed for the case where the interelectrode capacitances are neglected. Under these conditions, $Y_{pk} = Y_{gp} = 0$, and Eq. (8-39) reduces to

$$A = \frac{-g_m}{g_p + Y_L} = \frac{-g_m}{1/r_p + 1/Z_L} = -g_m Z'_L \tag{8-40}$$

where Z'_L is $r_p \| Z_L$. This equation is identical with Eq. (8-6).

It is a simple matter to show that the error made in the calculation of the gain is very small when the interelectrode capacitances are neglected for frequencies covering the entire audio-frequency range. These interelectrode capacitances are seldom as large as 15 pf, which corresponds to an admittance of only about 2 micromhos at 20 kHz. Since the transconductance g_m of a triode is generally several millimhos, Y_{gp} may be neglected in comparison with g_m. Furthermore, if g_p is greater than 20 micromhos ($r_p < 50$ K), the terms $Y_{gp} + Y_{pk}$ may be neglected in comparison with $g_p + Y_L$. Under these conditions the gain is that given by the simple expression (8-40).

Since the interelectrode capacitances have a relatively minor effect on the audio gain of an amplifier, why is it important to make note of them? The answer is to be found in the input impedance of the tube (the loading of the tube on the input circuit) and in the feedback between output and input circuits. Also, if the amplifier is to be used beyond the audio range, say, as a video (television or radar) amplifier, the capacitances may seriously affect the gain and the exact expression, Eq. (8-39), must be used. These effects are now examined.

8-12   INPUT ADMITTANCE OF A TRIODE

An inspection of Fig. 8-19 reveals that the grid circuit is no longer isolated from the plate circuit. The input signal must supply a current I_i. In order to calculate this current, it is observed from the diagram that

$$I_1 = V_i Y_{gk}$$

and

$$I_2 = V_{gp} Y_{gp} = (V_i + V_{kp}) Y_{gp}$$

Since $V_{kp} = -V_{pk} = -AV_i$, then the total input current is

$$I_i = I_1 + I_2 = [Y_{gk} + (1 - A)Y_{gp}]V_i \tag{8-41}$$

From Eq. (8-41), the input admittance is given by

$$Y_i = \frac{I_i}{V_i} = Y_{gk} + (1 - A)Y_{gp} \tag{8-42}$$

This expression clearly indicates that, for the triode to possess a negligible input admittance over a wide range of frequencies, the grid-cathode and the grid-plate capacitances must be negligible.

Input Capacitance (Miller Effect)   Consider a triode with a plate-circuit resistance R_p.   From the preceding section it follows that within the audio-frequency range, the gain is given by the simple expression $A = -g_m R'_p$, where R'_p is $r_p \| R_p$.   In this case Eq. (8-42) becomes

$$Y_i = j\omega[C_{gk} + (1 + g_m R'_p)C_{gp}] \tag{8-43}$$

Thus the input admittance is that arising from the presence of a capacitance from the grid to the cathode of magnitude C_i, where

$$C_i = C_{gk} + (1 + g_m R'_p)C_{gp} \tag{8-44}$$

This increase in input capacitance C_i over the capacitance from grid to cathode C_{gk} is known as the *Miller effect*.   The maximum possible value of this expression is $C_{gk} + (1 + \mu)C_{gp}$, which, for large values of μ, may be considerably larger than any of the interelectrode capacitances.

This input capacitance is important in the operation of cascaded amplifiers.   In such a system the output from one tube is used as the input to a second tube.   Hence the input impedance of the second stage acts as a shunt across the output of the first stage and R_p is shunted by the capacitance C_i. Since the reactance of a capacitor decreases with increasing frequencies, the resultant output impedance of the first stage will be correspondingly low for the high frequencies.   This will result in a decreasing gain at the higher frequencies.

EXAMPLE   A triode has a plate-circuit resistance of 100 K and operates at 20 kHz.   Calculate the gain of this tube as a single stage and then as the first tube in a cascaded amplifier consisting of two identical stages.   The tube parameters are $g_m = 1.6$ millimhos, $r_p = 44$ K, $\mu = 70$, $C_{gk} = 3.0$ pF, $C_{pk} = 3.8$ pF, and $C_{gp} = 2.8$ pF.

Solution

$$Y_{gk} = j\omega C_{gk} = j2\pi \times 2 \times 10^4 \times 3.0 \times 10^{-12} = j3.76 \times 10^{-7} \text{ mho}$$

$$Y_{pk} = j\omega C_{pk} = j4.77 \times 10^{-7} \text{ mho}$$

$$Y_{gp} = j\omega C_{gp} = j3.52 \times 10^{-7} \text{ mho}$$

$$g_p = \frac{1}{r_p} = 2.27 \times 10^{-5} \text{ mho}$$

$$Y_p = \frac{1}{R_p} = 10^{-5} \text{ mho}$$

$$g_m = 1.60 \times 10^{-3} \text{ mho}$$

The gain of a one-stage amplifier is given by Eq. (8-39):

$$A = \frac{-g_m + Y_{gp}}{g_p + Y_p + Y_{pk} + Y_{gp}} = \frac{-1.60 \times 10^{-3} + j3.52 \times 10^{-7}}{3.27 \times 10^{-5} + j8.29 \times 10^{-7}}$$

It is seen that the j terms (arising from the interelectrode capacitances) are negligible in comparison with the real terms. If these are neglected, then $A = -48.8$. This value can be checked by using Eq. (8-5), which neglects interelectrode capacitances. Thus

$$A = \frac{-\mu R_L}{R_L + r_p} = \frac{-70 \times 100}{100 + 44} = -48.6$$

Since the gain is a real number, the input impedance consists of a capacitor whose value is given by Eq. (8-11):

$$C_i = C_{gk} + (1 + g_m R_p')C_{gp} = 3.0 + (1 + 49)(2.8) = 143 \text{ pF}$$

Consider now a two-stage amplifier, each stage consisting of a tube operating as above. The gain of the second stage is that just calculated. However, in calculating the gain of the first stage, it must be remembered that *the input impedance of the second stage acts as a shunt on the output of the first stage.* Thus the plate load now consists of a 100-K resistance in parallel with 143 pF. To this must be added the capacitance from plate to cathode of the first stage since this is also in shunt with the plate load. Furthermore, any stray capacitances due to wiring should be taken into account. For example, for every 1 pF capacitance between the leads going to the plate and grid of the second stage, 50 pF is effectively added across the load resistor of the first tube! This clearly indicates the importance of making connections with very short direct leads in high-frequency amplifiers. Let it be assumed that the input capacitance, taking into account the various factors just discussed, is 200 pF (probably a conservative figure). Then the load admittance is

$$Y_L = \frac{1}{R_p} + j\omega C_i = 10^{-5} + j2\pi \times 2 \times 10^4 \times 200 \times 10^{-12}$$

$$= 10^{-5} + j2.52 \times 10^{-5} \text{ mho}$$

The gain is given by Eq. (8-40):

$$A = \frac{-g_m}{g_p + Y_L} = \frac{-1.6 \times 10^{-3}}{2.27 \times 10^{-5} + 10^{-5} + j2.52 \times 10^{-5}}$$

$$= -30.7 + j23.7 = 38.8\underline{/143.3°}$$

Thus the effect of the capacitances has been to reduce the magnitude of the amplification from 48.8 to 38.8 and to change the phase angle between the output and input from 180 to 143.3°.

If the frequency were higher, the gain would be reduced still further. For example, this circuit would be useless as a video amplifier, say, to a few megahertz, since the gain would then be less than unity. This variation of gain with frequency is called *frequency distortion*. Cascaded amplifiers and frequency distortion are discussed in detail in Chap. 16.

Negative Input Resistance   If the plate circuit of the amplifier includes an impedance instead of a pure resistance, then A is a complex number in general and the input admittance will consist of two terms, a resistive and a reactive term. Let A be written in the general form

$$A = A_1 + jA_2 \tag{8-45}$$

Then Eq. (8-42) becomes

$$Y_i = \omega C_{gp}A_2 + j\omega[C_{gk} + (1 - A_1)C_{gp}] \tag{8-46}$$

The expression indicates that the equivalent grid input circuit comprises a resistance R_i in parallel with a capacitance C_i. For such a parallel circuit,

$$Y_i = \frac{1}{R_i} + j\omega C_i \tag{8-47}$$

Comparing Eqs. (8-46) and (8-47), we have

$$R_i = \frac{1}{\omega C_{gp}A_2} \qquad C_i = C_{gk} + (1 - A_1)C_{gp} \tag{8-48}$$

Since no restrictions have been placed on the system, it is possible for the term A_2 to be negative and the effective input resistance to be negative. It is interesting to note that an effective negative input resistance is possible only when the load is inductive, with the inductance in a definite range.[3]

The presence of a negative resistance in a circuit can mean only that some power is being generated rather than being absorbed. Physically, this means that power is being fed back from the output circuit into the grid circuit through the coupling provided by the grid-plate capacitance. If this feedback feature reaches an extreme stage, the system will lose its entire utility as an amplifier, becoming in fact a self-excited amplifier, or oscillator.

8-13   INTERELECTRODE CAPACITANCES
IN A MULTIELECTRODE TUBE[2]

The wiring diagram of a tetrode is given in Fig. 8-20a, and the equivalent circuit taking interelectrode capacitances into account is indicated in Fig. 8-20b.

In drawing the equivalent circuit, the rules given in Sec. 8-3 have been appropriately extended and employed. Thus, in addition to the points K, G, and P, the screen terminal S is also marked. The circuit elements of the original circuit are included in their appropriate positions between these four points, except that all dc potentials are omitted and the tube itself is replaced by an equivalent current generator $g_m V_i$, having an internal resistance r_p, between the points K and P. The capacitances between all pairs of the four electrodes are included, the double subscript denoting the pair of electrodes under consideration.

Since the screen supply must be short-circuited in the equivalent circuit, this puts the screen at ground potential in so far as signal variations about the Q point are concerned. Usually, the screen potential is obtained from the plate supply through a screen dropping resistor. In this case a capacitor is connected from the screen to cathode. This capacitance is chosen sufficiently large so that the screen potential remains constant even though the screen current may vary. In this case, too, the screen is at signal ground potential. Thus, as indicated in the figure, this effectively shorts out C_{ks} and puts C_{gk} and C_{gs} in parallel. Let this parallel combination be denoted C_1. The capacity C_{ps} now appears from plate to ground and is effectively in parallel with C_{pk}. Let this parallel combination be denoted C_2. From the discussion of the shielding action of the screen grid in Sec. 7-6, the capacitance between the plate and the control grid C_{gp} has been reduced to a very small value. If this capacitance is assumed to be negligible, Fig. 8-20b may be redrawn more simply, as shown in Fig. 8-21, where

$$C_1 = C_{gk} + C_{gs} \qquad C_2 = C_{ps} + C_{pk} \tag{8-49}$$

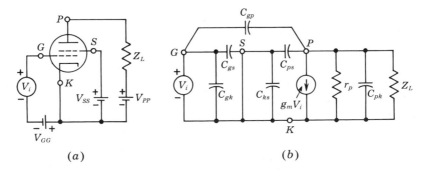

(a) $\qquad\qquad\qquad\qquad\qquad$ (b)

Fig. 8-20   The schematic and equivalent circuits of a tetrode connected as an amplifier.

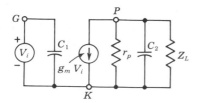

Fig. 8-21 The ideal equivalent circuit of a tetrode. The grid-plate capacitance has been assumed equal to zero.

Because of the shielding action of the screen, little error will be made if C_{pk} is neglected in comparison with C_{ps}, so that $C_2 = C_{ps}$, to a good approximation. This capacitance acts as a shunt across the plate-circuit impedance. The input admittance of the tube is seen to be simply

$$Y_i = j\omega C_1 \tag{8-50}$$

A significant difference is seen to exist between the ideal equivalent circuit of the tetrode and the complete equivalent circuit of the triode, given in Fig. 8-19. The idealization made here consists in the assumption that the grid-plate capacitance is zero rather than a very small fraction of a picofarad. The circuit of Fig. 8-21 clearly shows that under this condition the plate circuit has been isolated from the grid circuit.

It should be pointed out, however, that the mere substitution of a tetrode for a triode will not, in general, effect any marked difference in the amplifier response. This statement follows because the wiring and stray capacitances between circuit elements external to the tube may provide the capacitances that the tube itself seeks to eliminate. It is necessary, therefore, that the elements of the circuit be carefully arranged in order to permit short interconnecting leads and generally neat wiring so as to reduce wiring capacitances. It is only if the capacitance between the grid and anode circuits external to the tube is small that the inherent possibilities of the tetrode can be utilized.

Pentode When used as a voltage amplifier, the pentode is connected in a circuit exactly like a tetrode (Fig. 8-20), with the addition that the suppressor grid is connected to the cathode. Then, from an equivalent circuit analogous to that in Fig. 8-20b, it follows that the equivalent circuit of a pentode is also given by Fig. 8-21. In this diagram

$$C_1 = C_{gk} + C_{gs} \qquad C_2 = C_{pk} + C_{ps} + C_{p3} \tag{8-51}$$

where C_{p3} is the capacitance between the plate and grid 3 (the suppressor). When the input and output capacitances of a tube are listed by the manufacturer, reference is being made to C_1 and C_2, respectively.

8-14   THE CATHODE FOLLOWER AT HIGH FREQUENCIES

Our previous discussion of cathode followers neglected the influence of the tube capacitances. These capacitances are now taken into account.

Voltage Gain   The grounded-plate configuration of a triode, including all capacitances, is given in Fig. 8-22a, and its linear equivalent circuit, in Fig. 8-22b.   The capacitance from cathode to ground is C_{kn} and includes the capacitance from cathode to heater if, as usual, the heater is grounded.   The output voltage V_o can be found as in Sec. 8-11 from the product of the short-circuit current and the impedance between terminals K and N.   We now find for the voltage gain $A \equiv V_o/V_i$

$$A = \frac{g_m + Y_{gk}}{Y_k + g_p + g_m + Y_T} \tag{8-52}$$

where

$$Y_k \equiv \frac{1}{R_k} \qquad Y_T \equiv j\omega C_T \qquad C_T \equiv C_{gk} + C_{pk} + C_{kn}$$

Equation (8-52) may be written in the form

$$A = \frac{(g_m + j\omega C_{gk})R_k}{1 + [(\mu + 1)/r_p + j\omega C_T]R_k} \tag{8-53}$$

Assuming $\mu + 1 \approx \mu$ and $g_m R_k \gg 1$,

$$A \approx \frac{g_m + j\omega C_{gk}}{g_m + j\omega C_T} \tag{8-54}$$

The term $j\omega C_{gk}$ in the numerator represents the effect of the coupling from input to output through C_{gk}.   If the cathode follower is driving a capacitive load C_L, the expression for A need but be modified by adding C_L to C_T.

Usually, C_T is much larger than C_{gk}, and hence the decrease in gain with frequency is due principally to $C_T + C_L$.   The frequency f_2 at which the magnitude of the amplification has dropped 3 dB to 0.707 of its low-frequency value is, under these circumstances, given by the condition $\omega(C_T + C_L) = g_m$. Typically, if the total capacitance is, say, 50 pF and $g_m = 3$ millimhos, as for a half section of a 12AU7, then $f_2 \approx 9.5$ MHz.   This calculation shows that a cathode follower may be useful well into the video range.

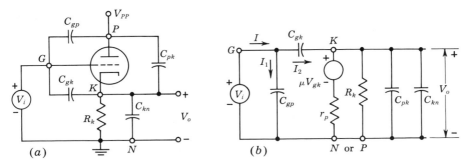

Fig. 8-22   (a) The cathode follower, with interelectrode capacitances taken into account, and (b) its equivalent circuit.

Input Admittance   An important advantage of the cathode follower over a conventional triode amplifier is that the capacitive impedance seen looking into the grid of the cathode follower is appreciably larger than the capacitive impedance looking into the amplifier.   We now calculate the input admittance from Fig. 8-22b.   The current $I_1 = V_i(j\omega C_{gp})$ and

$$I_2 = (V_i - V_o)j\omega C_{gk} = V_i(1 - A)(j\omega C_{gk})$$

where A is the amplifier gain.   Hence the input admittance

$$Y_i \equiv \frac{I}{V_i} = \frac{I_1 + I_2}{V_i}$$

is given by

$$Y_i = j\omega C_{gp} + j\omega C_{gk}(1 - A) \tag{8-55}$$

In general, Y_i contains a resistive as well as a capacitive component.   If the frequency is low enough so that A may be considered a real number, the input impedance consists of a capacitance C_i, and hence $Y_i = j\omega C_i$.   From Eq. (8-55) the input capacitance is given by

$$C_i(\text{cathode follower}) = C_{gp} + C_{gk}(1 - A) \tag{8-56}$$

On the other hand, for a grounded-cathode amplifier, we have, from Eq. (8-44),

$$C_i(\text{amplifier}) = C_{gk} + C_{gp}(1 - A) \tag{8-57}$$

A numerical comparison is interesting.   Consider a half section of a 12AU7, first as a cathode follower of nominal gain, say, equal to 0.8, and then as an amplifier of nominal gain, say, $A = -10$.   The capacitances are $C_{gp} = 1.5$ pF, $C_{gk} = 1.6$ pF.   At a frequency at which the capacitances do not yet have a marked effect on the gain, we have

$$C_i(\text{cathode follower}) = 1.5 + 0.2 \times 1.6 = 1.8 \text{ pF}$$

$$C_i(\text{amplifier}) = 1.6 + 11 \times 1.5 = 18 \text{ pF}$$

The input capacitance of the amplifier is ten times that of the cathode follower.
A fairer comparison may be made between the cathode follower and a conventional amplifier of equivalent gain.   In this case

$$C_i(\text{amplifier}) = 1.6 + 1.8 \times 1.5 = 4.3 \text{ pF}$$

which is still more than twice that for the cathode follower.

Output Admittance   The output impedance, or more conveniently, the output admittance Y_o of a cathode follower, taking interelectrode capacitances into account, is obtained by adding to the low-frequency admittance $g_m + g_p$ [Eq. (8-32)] the admittance of the total shunting capacitance C_T.   Thus

$$Y_o = g_m + g_p + Y_T \tag{8-58}$$

This result may be justified directly by applying a signal V to the output terminals and computing the current which flows through V with the grid grounded (and R_k considered as an external load). Since $g_m = \mu g_p$ and assuming $\mu \gg 1$, we may neglect g_p compared with g_m and consider that the output admittance is unaffected by the capacitance until Y_T becomes large enough to be comparable with g_m. The calculation made above in connection with the frequency response of the cathode follower indicates that the output impedance does not acquire an appreciable reactive component until the frequency exceeds several megahertz.

REFERENCES

1. Valley, G. E., Jr., and H. Wallman: "Vacuum Tube Amplifiers," MIT Radiation Laboratory Series, vol. 18, chap. 11, McGraw-Hill Book Company, New York, 1948.

2. Gewartowski, J. W., and H. A. Watson: "Principles of Electron Tubes," D. Van Nostrand Company, Inc., Princeton, N.J., 1965.

3. Millman, J., and S. Seely: "Electronics," 1st ed., p. 536, McGraw-Hill Book Company, New York, 1941.

9/ TRANSISTOR CHARACTERISTICS

The volt-ampere characteristics of a semiconductor triode, called a transistor, are described qualitatively and also derived theoretically. Simple circuits are studied, and it is demonstrated that the transistor is capable of producing amplification. A quantitative study of the transistor as an amplifier is left for Chap. 11.

9-1   THE JUNCTION TRANSISTOR[1]

A junction transistor consists of a silicon (or germanium) crystal in which a layer of n-type silicon is sandwiched between two layers of p-type silicon. Alternatively, a transistor may consist of a layer of p-type between two layers of n-type material. In the former case the transistor is referred to as a p-n-p transistor, and in the latter case, as an n-p-n transistor. The semiconductor sandwich is extremely small, and is hermetically sealed against moisture inside a metal or plastic case. Manufacturing techniques and constructional details for several transistor types are described in Sec. 9-4.

The two types of transistor are represented in Fig. 9-1a. The representations employed when transistors are used as circuit elements are shown in Fig. 9-1b. The three portions of a transistor are known as *emitter, base,* and *collector.* The arrow on the emitter lead specifies the direction of current flow when the emitter-base junction is biased in the forward direction. In *both* cases, however, the emitter, base, and collector currents, I_E, I_B, and I_C, respectively, are assumed positive when the currents flow *into* the transistor. The symbols V_{EB}, V_{CB}, and V_{CE} are the emitter-base, collector-base, and collector-emitter voltages, respectively. (More specifically, V_{EB} represents the voltage *drop* from emitter to base.)

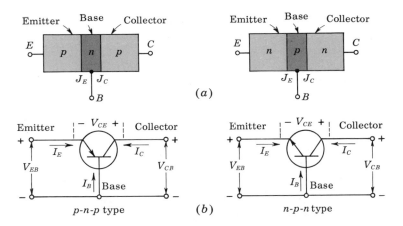

Fig. 9-1 (a) A p-n-p and an n-p-n transistor. The emitter (collector) junction is J_E (J_C). (b) Circuit representation of the two transistor types.

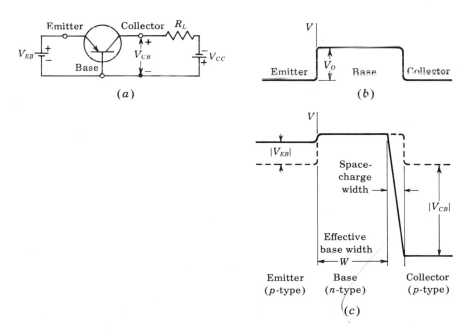

Fig. 9-2 (a) A p-n-p transistor with biasing voltages. (b) The potential barriers at the junction of the unbiased transistor. (c) The potential variation through the transistor under biased conditions. As the reverse-bias collector junction voltage $|V_{CB}|$ is increased, the effective base width W decreases.

The Potential Distribution through a Transistor We may now begin to appreciate the essential features of a transistor as an active circuit element by considering the situation depicted in Fig. 9-2a. Here a p-n-p transistor is shown with voltage sources which serve to bias the emitter-base junction in the forward direction and the collector-base junction in the reverse direction. The variation of potential through an unbiased (open-circuited) transistor is shown in Fig. 9-2b. The potential variation through the biased transistor is indicated in Fig. 9-2c. The dashed curve applies to the case before the application of external biasing voltages, and the solid curve to the case after the biasing voltages are applied. In the absence of applied voltage, the potential barriers at the junctions adjust themselves to the height V_o—given in Eq. (6-13) (a few tenths of a volt)—required so that no current flows across each junction. (Since the transistor may be looked upon as a p-n junction diode in series with an n-p diode, much of the theory developed in Chap. 6 for the junction diode is used in order to explain the characteristics of a transistor.) If now external potentials are applied, these voltages appear essentially across the junctions. Hence the forward biasing of the emitter-base junction lowers the emitter-base potential barrier by $|V_{EB}|$, whereas the reverse biasing of the collector-base junction increases the collector-base potential barrier by $|V_{CB}|$. The lowering of the emitter-base barrier permits the emitter current to increase, and holes are injected into the base region. The potential is constant across the base region (except for the small ohmic drop), and the injected holes diffuse across the n-type material to the collector-base junction. The holes which reach this junction fall down the potential barrier, and are therefore *collected* by the collector.

9-2   TRANSISTOR CURRENT COMPONENTS

In Fig. 9-3 we show the various current components which flow across the forward-biased emitter junction and the reverse-biased collector junction. The emitter current I_E consists of hole current I_{pE} (holes crossing from emitter into base) and electron current I_{nE} (electrons crossing from base into the emitter). The ratio of hole to electron currents, I_{pE}/I_{nE}, crossing the emitter junction is proportional to the ratio of the conductivity of the p material to that of the n material (Prob. 9-1). In a commercial transistor the doping of the emitter is made much larger than the doping of the base. This feature ensures (in a p-n-p transistor) that the emitter current consists almost entirely of holes. Such a situation is desired since the current which results from electrons crossing the emitter junction from base to emitter does not contribute carriers which can reach the collector.

Not all the holes crossing the emitter junction J_E reach the collector junction J_C because some of them combine with the electrons in the n-type base. If I_{pC} is the hole current at J_C, there must be a bulk recombination current $I_{pE} - I_{pC}$ leaving the base, as indicated in Fig. 9-3 (actually, electrons

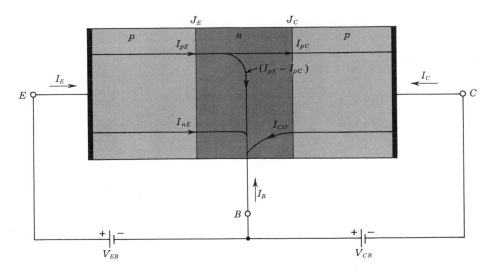

Fig. 9-3 Transistor current components for a forward-biased emitter junction and a reversed-biased collector junction.

enter the base region through the base lead to supply those charges which have been lost by recombination with the holes injected into the base across J_E).

If the emitter were open-circuited so that $I_E = 0$, then I_{pC} would be zero. Under these circumstances, the base and collector would act as a reverse-biased diode, and the collector current I_C would equal the reverse saturation current I_{CO}. If $I_E \neq 0$, then, from Fig. 9-3, we note that

$$I_C = I_{CO} - I_{pC} \tag{9-1}$$

For a p-n-p transistor, I_{CO} consists of holes moving across J_C from left to right (base to collector) and electrons crossing J_C in the opposite direction. Since the assumed reference direction for I_{CO} in Fig. 9-3 is from right to left, then for a p-n-p transistor, I_{CO} is negative. For an n-p-n transistor, I_{CO} is positive.

We now define various parameters which relate the current components discussed above.

Emitter Efficiency γ The emitter, or injection, efficiency γ is defined as

$$\gamma \equiv \frac{\text{current of injected carriers at } J_E}{\text{total emitter current}}$$

In the case of a p-n-p transistor we have

$$\gamma = \frac{I_{pE}}{I_{pE} + I_{nE}} = \frac{I_{pE}}{I_E} \tag{9-2}$$

where I_{pE} is the injected hole diffusion current at emitter junction and I_{nE} is the injected electron diffusion current at emitter junction.

Transport Factor β^*   The transport factor β^* is defined as

$$\beta^* \equiv \frac{\text{injected carrier current reaching } J_C}{\text{injected carrier current at } J_E}$$

In the case of a *p-n-p* transistor we have

$$\beta^* = \frac{I_{pC}}{I_{pE}} \tag{9-3}$$

Large-signal Current Gain α   We define the ratio of the negative of the collector-current increment to the emitter-current change from zero (cutoff) to I_E as the *large-signal current gain* of a common-base transistor, or

$$\alpha \equiv -\frac{I_C - I_{co}}{I_E} \tag{9-4}$$

Since I_C and I_E have opposite signs, then α, as defined, is always positive. Typical numerical values of α lie in the range of 0.90 to 0.995.

From Eqs. (9-1) and (9-4),

$$\alpha = \frac{I_{pC}}{I_E} = \frac{I_{pC}}{I_{pE}} \frac{I_{pE}}{I_E} \tag{9-5}$$

Using Eqs. (9-2) and (9-3),

$$\alpha = \beta^* \gamma \tag{9-6}$$

The transistor alpha is the product of the transport factor and the emitter efficiency.   This statement assumes that the *collector multiplication ratio*[2] α^* is unity. α^* is the ratio of the total current crossing J_C to the hole current (for a *p-n-p* transistor) arriving at the junction.   For most transistors, $\alpha^* = 1$.

The parameter α is extremely important in transistor theory, and we examine it in more detail in Sec. 9-6.   It should be pointed out that α is not a constant, but varies with emitter current I_E, collector voltage V_{CB}, and temperature.

From our discussion of transistor currents we see that if the transistor is in its *active region* (that is, if the emitter is forward-biased and the collector is reverse-biased), the collector current is given by Eq. (9-4), or

$$I_C = -\alpha I_E + I_{co} \tag{9-7}$$

In the active region the collector current is essentially independent of collector voltage and depends only upon the emitter current.   Suppose now that we seek to generalize Eq. (9-7) so that it may apply not only when the collector junction is substantially reverse-biased, but also for any voltage across J_C.   To achieve this generalization we need but replace I_{co} by the current in a *p-n* diode (that consisting of the base and collector regions). This current is given by the volt-ampere relationship of Eq. (6-31), with I_o

replaced by $-I_{CO}$ and V by V_C, where the symbol V_C represents the drop across J_C from the p to the n side. The complete expression for I_C for any V_C and I_E is

$$I_C = -\alpha I_E + I_{CO}(1 - \epsilon^{V_C/V_T}) \tag{9-8}$$

Note that if V_C is negative and has a magnitude large compared with V_T, Eq. (9-8) reduces to Eq. (9-7). The physical interpretation of Eq. (9-8) is that the p-n junction diode current crossing the collector junction is augmented by the fraction α of the current I_E flowing in the emitter. This relationship is derived in Sec. 9-6.

9-3   THE TRANSISTOR AS AN AMPLIFIER

A load resistor R_L is in series with the collector supply voltage V_{CC} of Fig. 9-2a. A small voltage change ΔV_i between emitter and base causes a relatively large emitter-current change ΔI_E. We define by the symbol α' that fraction of this current change which is collected and passes through R_L. The change in output voltage across the load resistor $\Delta V_o = \alpha' R_L \Delta I_E$ may be many times the change in input voltage ΔV_i. Under these circumstances, the voltage amplification $A \equiv \Delta V_o/\Delta V_i$ will be greater than unity, and the transistor acts as an amplifier. If the dynamic resistance of the emitter junction is r'_e, then $\Delta V_i = r'_e \Delta I_E$, and

$$A = \frac{\alpha' R_L \Delta I_E}{r'_e \Delta I_E} = \frac{\alpha' R_L}{r'_e} \tag{9-9}$$

From Eq. (6-41), $r'_e = 26/I_E$, where I_E is the quiescent emitter current in milliamperes. For example, if $r'_e = 40\ \Omega$, $\alpha' = -1$, and $R_L = 3,000\ \Omega$, $A = -75$. This calculation is oversimplified, but in essence it is correct and gives a physical explanation of why the transistor acts as an amplifier. The transistor provides power gain as well as voltage or current amplification. From the foregoing explanation it is clear that current in the low-resistance input circuit is transferred to the high-resistance output circuit. The word "transistor," which originated as a contraction of "transfer resistor," is based upon the above physical picture of the device.

The Parameter α' The parameter α' introduced above is defined as the ratio of the change in the collector current to the change in the emitter current at constant collector-to-base voltage and is called the *small-signal forward short-circuit current transfer ratio, or gain.* More specifically,

$$\alpha' \equiv \frac{\Delta I_C}{\Delta I_E}\bigg|_{V_{CB}} \tag{9-10}$$

On the assumption that α is independent of I_E, then from Eq. (9-7) it follows that $\alpha' = -\alpha$.

9-4   TRANSISTOR CONSTRUCTION

Five basic techniques have been developed for the manufacture of diodes, transistors, and other semiconductor devices. Consequently, such devices may be classified[3,4] into one of the following types: grown, alloy, electro-chemical, diffusion, or epitaxial.

Grown Type The n-p-n grown-junction transistor is illustrated in Fig. 9-4a. It is made by drawing a single crystal from a melt of silicon or germanium whose impurity concentration is changed during the crystal-drawing operation by adding n- or p-type atoms as required.

Alloy Type This technique, also called the *fused* construction, is illustrated in Fig. 9-4b for a p-n-p transistor. The center (base) section is a thin wafer of n-type material. Two small dots of indium are attached to opposite sides of the wafer, and the whole structure is raised for a short time to a high temperature, above the melting point of indium but below that of germanium. The indium dissolves the germanium beneath it and forms a saturation solution. On cooling, the germanium in contact with the base material recrystallizes with enough indium concentration to change it from n type to p type. The collector is made larger than the emitter, so that the collector subtends a large angle as viewed from the emitter. Because of this geometrical arrangement, very little emitter current follows a diffusion path which carries it to the base rather than to the collector.

Electrochemically Etched Type This technique consists in etching depressions on opposite sides of a semiconductor wafer in order to reduce the

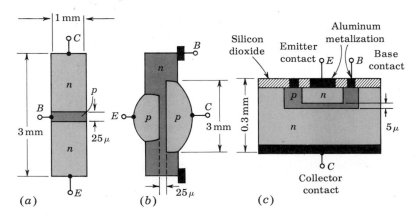

Fig. 9-4 Construction of transistors. (a) Grown, (b) alloy, and (c) diffused, or epitaxial, planar types. (The dimensions are approximate, and the figures are not drawn to scale. The base width is given in microns, where 1 $\mu = 10^{-6}$ m $= 10^{-3}$ mm.)

thickness of this base section.   The emitter and collector junctions are then formed by electroplating a suitable metal into the depression areas.   This type of device, also referred to as a *surface-barrier transistor*, is no longer of commercial importance.

Diffusion Type   This technique consists in subjecting a semiconductor wafer to gaseous diffusions of both n- and p-type impurities to form both the emitter and the collector junctions.   A *planar* silicon transistor of the diffusion type is illustrated in Fig. 9-4c.   In this process (described in greater detail in Chap. 15 on integrated-circuit techniques), the base-collector junction area is determined by a diffusion mask which is photoetched just prior to the base diffusion.   The emitter is then diffused on the base, and a final layer of silicon oxide is thermally grown over the entire surface.   Because of the passivating action of this oxide layer, most surface problems are avoided and very low leakage currents result.   There is also an improvement in the current gain at low currents and in the noise figure.

Epitaxial Type   The epitaxial technique (Sec. 15-2) consists in growing a very thin, high-purity, single-crystal layer of silicon or germanium on a heavily doped substrate of the same material.   This augmented crystal forms the collector on which the base and emitter may be diffused (Fig. 15-11b).

The foregoing techniques may be combined to form a large number of methods for constructing transistors.   For example, there are *diffused-alloy* types, *grown-diffused* devices, *alloy-emitter–epitaxial-base* transistors, etc.   The special features of transistors of importance at high frequencies are discussed in Chap. 13.   The volt-ampere characteristics at low frequencies of all types of junction transistors are essentially the same, and the discussion to follow applies to them all.

Finally, because of its historical significance, let us mention the first type of transistor to be invented.   This device consists of two sharply pointed tungsten wires pressed against a semiconductor wafer.   However, the reliability and reproducibility of such point-contact transistors are very poor, and as a result these transistors are no longer of practical importance.

9-5   DETAILED STUDY OF THE CURRENTS IN A TRANSISTOR

This analysis follows in many respects that given in Sec. 6-5 for the current components in a junction diode.   From Eq. (6-14) we see that the net current crossing a junction equals the sum of the electron current I_{np} in the p side and the hole current I_{pn} in the n side, evaluated at the junction ($x = 0$).   For a p-n-p transistor (Fig. 9-1a) electrons are injected from the base region across the emitter junction into a p region which is large compared with the diffusion length.   This is precisely the condition that exists in a junction diode, and hence the expression for I_{np} calculated previously is also valid for the transistor. From Eq. (6-25) we find that at the junction

$$I_{np}(0) = \frac{AeD_n n_{Eo}}{L_E} (\epsilon^{V_E/V_T} - 1) \tag{9-11}$$

where in Eq. (6-25) we have replaced V by V_E; we have changed n_{po} to n_{EO} because there are now two p regions and the emitter (E) is under consideration; we have changed L_n to L_E in order to refer to the diffusion length of the minority carriers in the emitter. A summary of the symbols used follows:

$$A = \text{cross section of transistor, m}^2$$
$$e = \text{magnitude of electronic charge, C}$$
$$D_n\ (D_p) = \text{diffusion constant for electrons (holes), m}^2/\text{sec}$$
$$n_{Eo}\ (n_{Co}) = \text{thermal-equilibrium electron concentration in the } p\text{-type material of the emitter (collector), m}^{-3}$$
$$L_E\ (L_C)\ (L_B) = \text{diffusion length for minority carriers in the emitter (collector) (base), m}$$
$$V_E\ (V_C) = \text{voltage drop across emitter (collector) junction; positive for a forward bias, i.e., for the } p \text{ side positive with respect to the } n \text{ side}$$
$$V_T = \text{volt equivalent of temperature [Eq. (6-34)]}$$
$$p_n = \text{hole concentration in the } n\text{-type material, m}^{-3}$$
$$p_{no} = \text{thermal-equilibrium value of } p_n$$
$$W = \text{base width, m}$$
$$I_{pn}\ (I_{np}) = \text{hole (electron) current in } n\ (p) \text{ material}$$

The Hole Current in the n-type Base Region The value of I_{pn} is not that found in Sec. 6-5 for a diode because, in the transistor, the hole current exists in a base region of small width, whereas in a diode, the n region extends over a distance large compared with L_n. The diffusion current is given, as usual, by Eq. (6-18); namely,

$$I_{pn} = -AeD_p \frac{dp_n}{dx} \tag{9-12}$$

where p_n is found from the continuity equation. From Eq. (5-50),

$$p_n - p_{no} = K_1 \epsilon^{-x/L_B} + K_2 \epsilon^{+x/L_B} \tag{9-13}$$

where K_1 and K_2 are constants to be determined by the boundary conditions. The situation at each junction is exactly as for the diode junction, and the boundary condition is that given by Eq. (6-22), or

$$p_n = p_{no}\epsilon^{V_E/V_T} \qquad \text{at } x = 0$$

and

$$p_n = p_{no}\epsilon^{V_C/V_T} \qquad \text{at } x = W$$

$$\tag{9-14}$$

The exact solution is not difficult to find (Prob. 9-3). Usually, however, the base width W is small compared with L_B, and we can simplify the solution by introducing this inequality. Since $0 \leq x \leq W$, we shall assume that $x/L_B \ll 1$, and then the exponentials in Eq. (9-13) can be expanded into a power series. If only the first two terms are retained, this equation has the form

$$p_n - p_{no} = K_3 + K_4 x \qquad (9\text{-}15)$$

where K_3 and K_4 are new (and, as yet, undetermined) constants. To this approximation, p_n is a linear function of distance in the base. Then, from Eqs. (9-12) and (9-15),

$$I_{pn} = -AeD_p K_4 = \text{const} \qquad (9\text{-}16)$$

This result—that the minority-carrier current is a constant throughout the base region—is readily understood because we have assumed that $W \ll L_B$. Under these circumstances, little recombination can take place within the base, and hence the hole current entering the base at the emitter junction leaves the base at the collector junction unattenuated. This means that the transport factor β^* is unity. Substituting the boundary conditions (9-14) in (9-15), we easily solve for K_4 and then find

$$I_{pn}(0) = -\frac{AeD_p p_{no}}{W}[(\epsilon^{V_C/V_T} - 1) - (\epsilon^{V_E/V_T} - 1)] \qquad (9\text{-}17)$$

The Ebers-Moll Equations From Fig. 9-3 we have for the emitter current

$$I_E = I_{pE} + I_{nE} = I_{pn}(0) + I_{np}(0) \qquad (9\text{-}18)$$

Using Eqs. (9-11), (9-17), and (9-18), we find

$$I_E = a_{11}(\epsilon^{V_E/V_T} - 1) + a_{12}(\epsilon^{V_C/V_T} - 1) \qquad (9\text{-}19)$$

where

$$a_{11} = Ae\left(\frac{D_p p_{no}}{W} + \frac{D_n n_{Eo}}{L_E}\right) \qquad a_{12} = -\frac{AeD_p p_{no}}{W} \qquad (9\text{-}20)$$

In a similar manner we can obtain

$$I_C = a_{21}(\epsilon^{V_E/V_T} - 1) + a_{22}(\epsilon^{V_C/V_T} - 1) \qquad (9\text{-}21)$$

where we can show (Prob. 9-2) that

$$a_{21} = -\frac{AeD_p p_{no}}{W} \qquad a_{22} = Ae\left(\frac{D_p p_{no}}{W} + \frac{D_n n_{Co}}{L_C}\right) \qquad (9\text{-}22)$$

We note that $a_{12} = a_{21}$. This result may be shown[5] to be valid for a transistor possessing any geometry. Equations (9-19) and (9-21) are valid for any positive or negative value of V_E or V_C, and they are known as the *Ebers-Moll equations*.

9-6   THE TRANSISTOR ALPHA

If V_E is eliminated from Eqs. (9-19) and (9-21), the result is

$$I_C = \frac{a_{21}}{a_{11}} I_E + \left(a_{22} - \frac{a_{21}a_{12}}{a_{11}} \right) (\epsilon^{V_C/V_T} - 1) \tag{9-23}$$

This equation has the same form as Eq. (9-8). Hence we have, by comparison,

$$\alpha \equiv - \frac{a_{21}}{a_{11}} \tag{9-24}$$

$$I_{CO} \equiv \frac{a_{21}a_{12}}{a_{11}} - a_{22} \tag{9-25}$$

Using Eqs. (9-20) and (9-22), we obtain

$$\alpha = \frac{1}{1 + D_n n_{Eo} W/L_E D_p p_{no}} \tag{9-26}$$

Making use of Eq. (5-2) for the conductivity, Eq. (5-33) for the diffusion constant, and Eq. (5-19) for the concentration, Eq. (9-26) reduces to

$$\alpha = \frac{1}{1 + W\sigma_B/L_E\sigma_E} \tag{9-27}$$

where σ_B (σ_E) is the conductivity of the base (emitter). We see that, in order to keep α close to unity, σ_E/σ_B should be large and W/L_E should be kept small.

The analysis of the preceding section is based upon the assumption that $W/L_B \ll 1$. If this restriction is removed, the solution given in Prob. 9-3 is obtained. We then find (Prob. 9-5) that

$$\gamma = \frac{1}{1 + (D_n L_B n_{Eo}/D_p L_E p_{no}) \tanh (W/L_B)} \tag{9-28}$$

and

$$\beta^* = \operatorname{sech} \frac{W}{L_B} \tag{9-29}$$

If $W \ll L_B$, the hyperbolic secant and the hyperbolic tangent can be expanded in powers of W/L_B, and the first approximations are (Prob. 9-6)

$$\gamma \approx \frac{1}{1 + W\sigma_B/L_E\sigma_E} \approx 1 - \frac{W\sigma_B}{L_E\sigma_E} \tag{9-30}$$

$$\beta^* \approx 1 - \frac{1}{2} \left(\frac{W}{L_B} \right)^2 \tag{9-31}$$

and

$$\alpha = \beta^*\gamma \approx 1 - \frac{1}{2} \left(\frac{W}{L_B} \right)^2 - \frac{W\sigma_B}{L_E\sigma_E} \tag{9-32}$$

As the magnitude of the reverse-bias collector voltage increases, the space-charge width at the collector increases (Fig. 9-2) and the effective base width W

decreases. Hence Eq. (9-32) indicates that α increases as the collector junction becomes more reverse-biased.

The emitter efficiency and hence also α is a function of emitter current. Equation (9-30) indicates that γ decreases at high currents where σ_B increases because of the additional charges injected into the base. (This effect is called *conductivity modulation*.) Also, it is found that γ decreases at very low values of I_E. This effect is due to the recombination of charge carriers in the transition region at the emitter junction.[6] At low injection currents this barrier recombination current is a large fraction of the total current and hence γ must be reduced.[7] Since silicon has many recombination centers in the space-charge layer, then $\gamma \rightarrow 0$ (and $\alpha \rightarrow 0$) as $I_E \rightarrow 0$. On the other hand, $\alpha \approx 0.9$ for germanium at $I_E = 0$ because germanium can be produced relatively free of recombination centers.

The collector reverse saturation current can be determined using Eqs. (9-25), (9-20), and (9-22).

9-7   THE COMMON–BASE CONFIGURATION

If the voltages across the two junctions are known, the three transistor currents can be uniquely determined using Eqs. (9-19) and (9-21). Many different families of characteristic curves can be drawn, depending upon which two parameters are chosen as the independent variables. In the case of the transistor, it turns out to be most useful to select the input current and output voltage as the independent variables. The output current and input voltage are expressed graphically in terms of these independent variables. In Fig. 9-2a, a p-n-p transistor is shown in a *grounded-base* configuration. This circuit is also referred to as a *common-base*, or CB, configuration, since the base is common to the input and output circuits. For a p-n-p transistor the largest current components are due to holes. Since holes flow from the emitter to the collector and down toward ground out of the base terminal, then, referring to the polarity conventions of Fig. 9-1, we see that I_E is positive, I_C is negative, and I_B is negative. For a forward-biased emitter junction, V_{EB} is positive, and for a reverse-biased collector junction, V_{CB} is negative. For an n-p-n transistor all current and voltage polarities are the negative of those for a p-n-p transistor. We may completely describe the transistor of Fig. 9-1a or b by the following two relations, which give the input voltage V_{EB} and output current I_C in terms of the output voltage V_{CB} and input current I_E:

$$V_{EB} = \phi_1(V_{CB}, I_E) \tag{9-33}$$

$$I_C = \phi_2(V_{CB}, I_E) \tag{9-34}$$

(This equation is read, "I_C is some function ϕ_2 of V_{CB} and I_E.")

The relation of Eq. (9-34) is given in Fig. 9-5 for a typical p-n-p germanium transistor and is a plot of collector current I_C versus collector-to-base

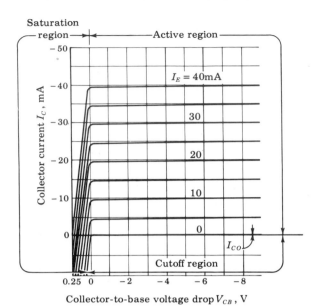

Fig. 9-5 Typical common-base output characteristics of a p-n-p transistor. The cutoff, active, and saturation regions are indicated. Note the expanded voltage scale in the saturation region.

voltage drop V_{CB}, with emitter current I_E as a parameter. The curves of Fig. 9-5 are known as the *output*, or *collector*, *static characteristics*. The relation of Eq. (9-33) is given in Fig. 9-6 for the same transistor, and is a plot of emitter-to-base voltage V_{EB} versus emitter current I_E, with collector-to-base voltage V_{CB} as a parameter. This set of curves is referred to as the *input*, or *emitter*, *static characteristics*. We digress now in order to discuss a phenomenon known as the *Early effect*,[8] which is used to account for the shapes of the transistor characteristics.

The Early Effect An increase in magnitude of collector voltage increases the space-charge width at the output junction diode as indicated by Eq. (6-47). From Fig. 9-2 we see that such action causes the effective base width W to decrease, a phenomenon known as the *Early effect*. This decrease in W has

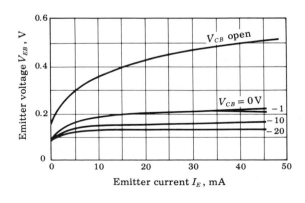

Fig. 9-6 Common-base input characteristics of a typical p-n-p germanium junction transistor.

two consequences: First, there is less chance for recombination within the base region. Hence the transport factor β^*, and also α, increase with an increase in the magnitude of the collector junction voltage. Second, the charge gradient is increased within the base, and consequently, the current of minority carriers injected across the emitter junction increases.

The Input Characteristics A qualitative understanding of the form of the input and output characteristics is not difficult if we consider the fact that the transistor consists of two diodes placed in series "back to back" (with the two cathodes connected together). In the active region the input diode (emitter-to-base) is biased in the forward direction. The input characteristics of Fig. 9-6 represent simply the forward characteristic of the emitter-to-base diode for various collector voltages. A noteworthy feature of the input characteristics is that there exists a *cutin, offset,* or *threshold,* voltage V_γ, below which the emitter current is very small. In general, V_γ is approximately 0.1 V for germanium transistors (Fig. 9-6) and 0.5 V for silicon.

The shape of the input characteristics can be understood if we consider the fact that an increase in magnitude of collector voltage will, by the Early effect, cause the emitter current to increase, with V_{EB} held constant. Thus the curves shift downward as $|V_{CB}|$ increases, as noted in Fig. 9-6.

The curve with the collector open represents the characteristic of the forward-biased emitter diode. When the collector is shorted to the base, the emitter current increases for a given V_{EB} since the collector now removes minority carriers from the base, and hence the base can attract more holes from the emitter. This means that the curve with $V_{CB} = 0$ is shifted downward from the collector characteristic marked "V_{CB} open."

The Output Characteristics Note, as in Fig. 9-5, that it is customary to plot along the abscissa and to the right that polarity of V_{CB} which reverse-biases the collector junction even if this polarity is negative. The collector-to-base diode is normally biased in the reverse direction. If $I_E = 0$, the collector current is $I_C = I_{CO}$. For other values of I_E, the output-diode reverse current is augmented by the fraction of the input-diode forward current which reaches the collector. Note also that I_{CO} is negative for a *p-n-p* transistor and positive for an *n-p-n* transistor.

Active Region In this region *the collector junction is biased in the reverse direction and the emitter junction in the forward direction.* Consider first that the emitter current is zero. Then the collector current is small and equals the reverse saturation current I_{CO} (microamperes for germanium and nanoamperes for silicon) of the collector junction considered as a diode. Suppose now that a forward emitter current I_E is caused to flow in the emitter circuit. Then a fraction $-\alpha I_E$ of this current will reach the collector, and I_E is therefore given by Eq. (9-7). In the active region, the collector current is essentially independent of collector voltage and depends only upon the emitter current.

However, because of the Early effect, we note in Fig. 9-5 that there actually is a small (perhaps 0.5 percent) increase in $|I_C|$ with $|V_{CB}|$. Because α is less than, but almost equal to, unity, the magnitude of the collector current is (slightly) less than that of the emitter current.

Saturation Region The region to the left of the ordinate, $V_{CB} = 0$, and above the $I_E = 0$ characteristics, in which *both emitter and collector junctions are forward-biased*, is called the *saturation* region. We say that "bottoming" has taken place because the voltage has fallen near the bottom of the characteristic where $V_{CB} \approx 0$. Actually, V_{CB} is slightly positive (for a p-n-p transistor) in this region, and this forward biasing of the collector accounts for the large change in collector current with small changes in collector voltage. For a forward bias, I_C increases exponentially with voltage according to the diode relationship [Eq. (9-21)]. A forward bias means that the collector p material is made positive with respect to the base n side, and hence that hole current flows from the p side across the collector junction to the n material. This hole flow corresponds to a positive change in collector current. Hence the collector current increases rapidly, and as indicated in Fig. 9-5, I_C may even become positive if the forward bias is sufficiently large.

Cutoff Region The characteristic for $I_E = 0$ passes through the origin, but is otherwise similar to the other characteristics. This characteristic is not coincident with the voltage axis, though the separation is difficult to show because I_{CO} is only a few nanoamperes or microamperes. The region below and to the right of the $I_E = 0$ characteristic, for which the *emitter and collector junctions are both reverse-biased*, is referred to as the *cutoff* region. The temperature characteristics of I_{CO} are discussed in Sec. 9-9.

9-8   THE COMMON–EMITTER CONFIGURATION

Most transistor circuits have the emitter, rather than the base, as the terminal common to both input and output. Such a *common-emitter* CE, or *grounded-emitter*, configuration is indicated in Fig. 9-7. In the common-emitter, as in the common-base, configuration, the input current and the output voltage

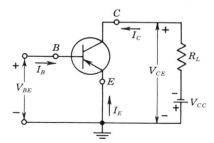

Fig. 9-7 A transistor common-emitter configuration. The symbol V_{CC} is a positive number representing the magnitude of the supply voltage.

are taken as the independent variables, whereas the input voltage and output current are the dependent variables. We may write

$$V_{BE} = f_1(V_{CE}, I_B) \tag{9-35}$$

$$I_C = f_2(V_{CE}, I_B) \tag{9-36}$$

Equation (9-35) describes the family of input characteristic curves, and Eq. (9-36) describes the family of output characteristic curves. Typical output and input characteristic curves for a p-n-p junction germanium transistor are given in Figs. 9-8 and 9-9, respectively. In Fig. 9-8 the abscissa is the collector-to-emitter voltage V_{CE}, the ordinate is the collector current I_C, and the curves are given for various values of base current I_B. For a fixed value of I_B, the collector current is not a very sensitive value of V_{CE}. However, the slopes of the curves of Fig. 9-8 are larger than in the common-base characteristics of Fig. 9-5. Observe also that the base current is much smaller than the emitter current.

The locus of all points at which the collector dissipation is 150 mW is indicated in Fig. 9-8 by a solid line $P_C = 150$ mW. This curve is the hyperbola $P_C = V_{CB}I_C \approx V_{CE}I_C =$ constant. To the right of this curve the rated collector dissipation is exceeded. In Fig. 9-8 we have selected $R_L = 500\ \Omega$ and a supply $V_{CC} = 10$ V and have superimposed the corresponding load line on the output characteristics. The method of constructing a load line is identical with that explained in Sec. 4-9 in connection with a diode.

The Input Characteristics In Fig. 9-9 the abscissa is the base current I_B, the ordinate is the base-to-emitter voltage V_{BE}, and the curves are given for various values of collector-to-emitter voltage V_{CE}. We observe that, with the collector shorted to the emitter and the emitter forward-biased, the input characteristic is essentially that of a forward-biased diode. If V_{BE} becomes zero,

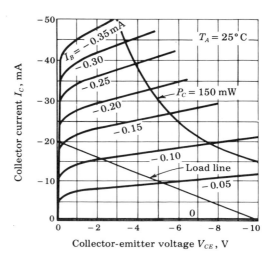

Fig. 9-8 Typical common-emitter output characteristics of a p-n-p germanium junction transistor. A load line corresponding to $V_{CC} = 10$ V and $R_L = 500\ \Omega$ is superimposed. (Courtesy of Texas Instruments, Inc.)

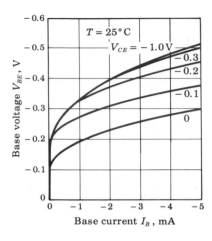

Fig. 9-9 Typical common-emitter input characteristics of the p-n-p germanium junction transistor of Fig. 9-8.

then I_B will be zero, since under these conditions both emitter and collector junctions will be short-circuited.   For any other value of V_{CE}, the base current for $V_{BE} = 0$ is not actually zero but is too small (Sec. 9-15) to be observed in Fig. 9-9.   In general, increasing $|V_{CE}|$ with constant V_{BE} causes a decrease in base width W (the Early effect) and results in a decreasing recombination base current.   These considerations account for the shape of input characteristics shown in Fig. 9-9.

The input characteristics for silicon transistors are similar in form to those in Fig. 9-9.   The only notable difference in the case of silicon is that the curves break away from zero current in the range 0.5 to 0.6 V, rather than in the range 0.1 to 0.2 V as for germanium.

The Output Characteristics   This family of curves may be divided into three regions, just as was done for the CB configuration.   The first of these, the *active region*, is discussed here, and the *cutoff* and *saturation regions* are considered in the next two sections.

In the active region *the collector junction is reverse-biased and the emitter junction is forward-biased.*   In Fig. 9-8 the active region is the area to the right of the ordinate $V_{CE} = $ a few tenths of a volt and above $I_B = 0$.   In this region the transistor output current responds most sensitively to an input signal.   If the transistor is to be used as an amplifying device without appreciable distortion, it must be restricted to operate in this region.

The common-emitter characteristics in the active region are readily understood qualitatively on the basis of our earlier discussion of the common-base configuration.   The base current is

$$I_B = -(I_C + I_E) \tag{9-37}$$

Combining this equation with Eq. (9-7), we find

$$I_C = \frac{I_{CO}}{1 - \alpha} + \frac{\alpha I_B}{1 - \alpha} \tag{9-38}$$

Equation (9-7) is based on the assumption that V_{CB} is fixed. However, if V_{CB} is larger than several volts, the voltage across the collector junction is much larger than that across the emitter junction, and we may consider $V_{CE} \approx V_{CB}$. Hence Eq. (9-38) is valid for values of V_{CE} in excess of a few volts.

If α were truly constant, then, according to Eq. (9-38), I_C would be independent of V_{CE} and the curves of Fig. 9-8 would be horizontal. Assume that, because of the Early effect, α increases by only one-half of 1 percent, from 0.98 to 0.985, as $|V_{CE}|$ increases from a few volts to 10 V. Then the value of $\alpha/(1 - \alpha)$ increases from $0.98/(1 - 0.98) = 49$ to $0.985/(1 - 0.985) = 66$, or about 34 percent. This numerical example illustrates that a very small change (0.5 percent) in α is reflected in a very large change (34 percent) in the value of $\alpha/(1 - \alpha)$. It should also be clear that a slight change in α has a large effect on the common-emitter curves, and hence that common-emitter characteristics are normally subject to a wide variation even among transistors of a given type. This variability is caused by the fact that I_B is the difference between large and nearly equal currents, I_E and I_C.

9-9   THE CE CUTOFF REGION

We might be inclined to think that cutoff in Fig. 9-8 occurs at the intersection of the load line with the current $I_B = 0$; however, we now find that appreciable collector current may exist under these conditions. The common-base characteristics are described to a good approximation even to the point of cutoff by Eq. (9-7), repeated here for convenience:

$$I_C = -\alpha I_E + I_{CO} \tag{9-39}$$

From Fig. 9-7, if $I_B = 0$, then $I_E = -I_C$. Combining with Eq. (9-39), we have

$$I_C = -I_E = \frac{I_{CO}}{1 - \alpha} \equiv I_{CEO} \tag{9-40}$$

The actual collector current with collector junction reverse-biased and base open-circuited is designated by the symbol I_{CEO}. Since, even in the neighborhood of cutoff, α may be as large as 0.9 for germanium, then $I_C \approx 10 I_{CO}$ at zero base current. Accordingly, in order to cut off the transistor, it is not enough to reduce I_B to zero. Instead, it is necessary to reverse-bias the emitter junction slightly. We shall define cutoff as the condition where the collector current is equal to the reverse saturation current I_{CO} and the emitter current is zero. In Sec. 9-15 we show that a reverse-biasing voltage of the order of 0.1 V established across the emitter junction will ordinarily be adequate to cut off a germanium transistor. In silicon, at collector currents of the order of I_{CO}, it is found[6,7] that α is very nearly zero because of recombination in the emitter-junction transition region. Hence, even with $I_B = 0$, we find, from Eq. (9-40), that $I_C = I_{CO} = -I_E$, so that the transistor is still very close to cutoff. We verify in Sec. 9-15 that, in silicon, cutoff occurs at $V_{BE} \approx 0$ V, corresponding to a base short-circuited to the emitter. *In summary, cutoff means that $I_E = 0$, $I_C = I_{CO}$, $I_B = -I_C = -I_{CO}$, and V_{BE} is a reverse voltage whose magnitude is of the order of* 0.1 V *for germanium and* 0 V *for a silicon transistor.*

The Reverse Collector Saturation Current I_{CBO}   The collector current in a physical transistor (a real, nonidealized, or commercial device) when the emitter current is zero is designated by the symbol I_{CBO}. Two factors cooperate to make $|I_{CBO}|$ larger than $|I_{CO}|$. First, there exists a leakage current which flows, not through the junction, but around it and across the surfaces. The leakage current is proportional to the voltage across the junction. The second reason why $|I_{CBO}|$ exceeds $|I_{CO}|$ is that new carriers may be generated by collision in the collector-junction transition region, leading to avalanche multiplication of current and eventual breakdown. But even before breakdown is approached, this *multiplication* component of current may attain considerable proportions.

At 25°C, I_{CBO} for a germanium transistor whose power dissipation is in the range of some hundreds of milliwatts is of the order of microamperes. Under similar conditions a silicon transistor has an I_{CBO} in the range of nanoamperes. The temperature sensitivity of I_{CBO} in silicon is approximately the same as that of germanium. Specifically, it is found[9] that the temperature coefficient of I_{CBO} is 8 percent/°C for germanium and 6 percent/°C for silicon. Using 7 percent as an average value and since $(1.07)^{10} \approx 2$, we see that I_{CBO} approximately doubles for every 10°C increase in temperature for both Ge and Si. However, because of the lower absolute value of I_{CBO} in silicon, these transistors may be used up to about 200°C, whereas germanium transistors are limited to about 100°C.

In addition to the variability of reverse saturation current with temperature, there is also a wide variability of reverse current among samples of a given transistor type. For example, the specification sheet for a Texas Instrument type 2N337 grown diffused silicon switching transistor indicates that this type number includes units with values of I_{CBO} extending over the tremendous range from 0.2 nA to 0.3 µA. Accordingly, any particular transistor may have an I_{CBO} which differs very considerably from the average characteristic for the type.

Circuit Considerations at Cutoff   Because of temperature effects, avalanche multiplication, and the wide variability encountered from sample to sample of a particular transistor type, even silicon may have values of I_{CBO} of the order of many tens of microamperes. Consider the circuit configuration of Fig. 9-10, where V_{BB} represents a biasing voltage intended to keep the transistor cut off. We consider that the transistor is just at the point of cutoff, with $I_E = 0$, so that $I_B = -I_{CBO}$. If we require that at cutoff $V_{BE} \approx -0.1$ V,

Fig. 9-10 Reverse biasing of the
emitter junction to maintain the
transistor in cutoff in the presence
of the reverse saturation current
I_{CBO} through R_B.

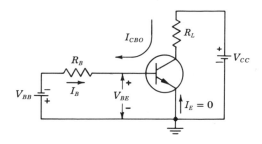

then the condition of cutoff requires that

$$V_{BE} = -V_{BB} + R_B I_{CBO} \leq -0.1 \text{ V} \tag{9-41}$$

As an extreme example consider that R_B is, say, as large as 100 K and that
we want to allow for the contingency that I_{CBO} may become as large as 100 μA.
Then V_{BB} must be at least 10.1 V.   When I_{CBO} is small, the magnitude of the
voltage across the base-emitter junction will be 10.1 V.   Hence we must use
a transistor whose maximum allowable reverse base-to-emitter junction voltage before breakdown exceeds 10 V.   It is with this contingency in mind that
a manufacturer supplies a rating for the reverse *breakdown voltage* between
emitter and base, represented by the symbol BV_{EBO}.   The subscript O indicates that BV_{EBO} is measured under the condition that the collector current is
zero.   Breakdown voltages BV_{EBO} may be as high as some tens of volts or as
low as 0.5 V.   If $BV_{EBO} = 1$ V, then V_{BB} must be chosen to have a maximum
value of 1 V.   For $V_{BB} = 1$ V and for $I_{CBO} = 0.1$ mA maximum, R_B cannot
exceed 9 K.   For example, if $R_B = 8$ K, then

$$-V_{BB} + I_{CBO}R_B = -1 + 0.8 = -0.2 \text{ V}$$

so that the transistor is indeed cut off.

9-10   THE CE SATURATION REGION

A load line has been superimposed on Fig. 9-8 corresponding to a load resistor
$R_L = 500$ Ω and a supply voltage of 10 V.   The saturation region may be
defined as the one where the collector junction (as well as the emitter junction)
is forward-biased.   In this region bottoming occurs, $|V_{CE}|$ drops to a few tenths
of a volt, and the collector current is approximately independent of base current, for given values of V_{CC} and R_L.   Hence we may consider that the onset
of saturation takes place at the knee of the transistor curves in Fig. 9-8.   Saturation occurs for the given load line at a base current of -0.17 mA, and at this
point the collector voltage is too small to be read in Fig. 9-8.   In saturation,
the collector current is nominally V_{CC}/R_L, and since R_L is small, it may well
be necessary to keep V_{CC} correspondingly small in order to stay within the
limitations imposed by the transistor on maximum current and dissipation.

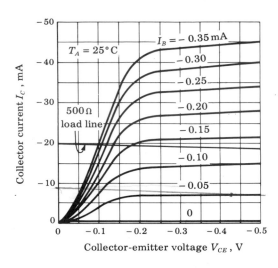

Fig. 9-11   Saturation-region common-emitter characteristics of the type 2N404 germanium transistor. A load line corresponding to $V_{CC} = 10$ V and $R_L = 500\,\Omega$ is superimposed.   (Courtesy of Texas Instruments, Inc.)

We are not able to read the collector-to-emitter saturation voltage, $V_{CE}(\text{sat})$, with any precision from the plots of Fig. 9-8. We refer instead to the characteristics shown in Fig. 9-11. In these characteristics the 0- to -0.5-V region of Fig. 9-8 has been expanded, and we have superimposed the same load line as before, corresponding to $R_L = 500\ \Omega$. We observe from Figs. 9-8 and 9-11 that V_{CE} and I_C no longer respond appreciably to base current I_B, after the base current has attained the value -0.15 mA. At this current the transistor enters saturation. For $I_B = -0.15$ mA, $|V_{CE}| \approx 175$ mV. At $I_B = -0.35$ mA, $|V_{CE}|$ has dropped to $|V_{CE}| \approx 100$ mV. Larger magnitudes of I_B will, of course, decrease $|V_{CE}|$ slightly further.

Saturation Resistance   For a transistor operating in the saturation region, a quantity of interest is the ratio $V_{CE}(\text{sat})/I_C$. This parameter is called the *common-emitter saturation resistance*, variously abbreviated R_{CS}, R_{CES}, or $R_{CE}(\text{sat})$. To specify R_{CS} properly, we must indicate the operating point at which it was determined. For example, from Fig. 9-11, we find that, at $I_C = -20$ mA and $I_B = -0.35$ mA, $R_{CS} \approx -0.1/(-20 \times 10^{-3}) = 5\ \Omega$. The usefulness of R_{CS} stems from the fact, as appears in Fig. 9-11, that to the left of the knee each of the plots, for fixed I_B, may be approximated, at least roughly, by a straight line.

Saturation Voltages   Manufacturers specify saturation values of input and output voltages in a number of different ways, in addition to supplying characteristic curves such as Figs. 9-9 and 9-11. For example, they may specify R_{CS} for several values of I_B or they may supply curves of $V_{CE}(\text{sat})$ and $V_{BE}(\text{sat})$ as functions of I_B and I_C.[10]

The saturation voltage $V_{CE}(\text{sat})$ depends not only on the operating point, but also on the semiconductor material (germanium or silicon) and on the type of transistor construction. Alloy-junction and epitaxial transistors give the lowest values for $V_{CE}(\text{sat})$ (corresponding to about 1 Ω saturation resistance), whereas grown-junction transistors yield the highest. Germanium transistors have lower values for $V_{CE}(\text{sat})$ than silicon. For example, an alloy-junction Ge transistor may have, with adequate base currents, values for $V_{CE}(\text{sat})$ as low as tens of millivolts at collector currents which are some tens of milliamperes. Similarly, epitaxial silicon transistors may yield saturation voltages as low as 0.2 V with collector currents as high as an ampere. On the other hand, grown-junction germanium transistors have saturation voltages which are several tenths of a volt, and silicon transistors of this type may have saturation voltages as high as several volts.

Typical values of the temperature coefficient of the saturation voltages are ~ -2.5 mV/$^\circ$C for $V_{BE}(\text{sat})$ and approximately one-tenth of this value for $V_{CE}(\text{sat})$ for either germanium or silicon. The temperature coefficient for $V_{BE}(\text{sat})$ is that of a forward-biased diode [Eq. (6-39)]. In saturation the transistor consists of two forward-biased diodes back-to-back in series opposing. Hence, it is to be anticipated that the temperature-induced voltage change in one junction will be canceled by the change in the other junction. We do indeed find[10] such to be the case for $V_{CE}(\text{sat})$.

The DC Current Gain h_{FE} A transistor parameter of interest is the ratio I_C/I_B, where I_C is the collector current and I_B is the base current. This quantity is designated by β_{dc} or h_{FE}, and is known as the *dc beta*, the *dc forward current transfer ratio*, or the *dc current gain*.

In the saturation region, the parameter h_{FE} is a useful number and one which is usually supplied by the manufacturer when a switching transistor is involved. We know $|I_C|$, which is given approximately by V_{CC}/R_L, and a knowledge of h_{FE} tells us how much input base current (I_C/h_{FE}) will be needed to saturate the transistor. For the type 2N404, the variation of h_{FE} with collector current at a low value of V_{CE} is as given in Fig. 9-12. Note the

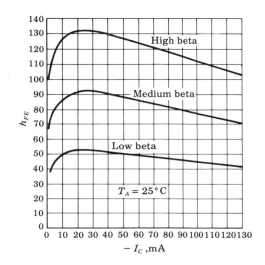

Fig. 9-12 Plots of dc current gain h_{FE} (at $V_{CE} = -0.25$ V) versus collector current for three samples of the type 2N404 germanium transistor. (Courtesy of General Electric Company.)

wide spread (a ratio of 3:1) in the value which may be obtained for h_{FE} even for a transistor of a particular type. Commercially available transistors have values of h_{FE} that cover the range from 10 to 150 at collector currents as small as 5 mA and as large as 30 A.

Tests for Saturation   It is often important to know whether or not a transistor is in saturation. We have already given two methods for making such a determination. These may be summarized as follows:

1. *If I_C and I_B can be determined independently from the circuit under consideration, the transistor is in saturation if $|I_B| \geq |I_C|/h_{FE}$.*
2. *If V_{CB} is determined from the circuit configuration and if this quantity is positive for a p-n-p transistor (or negative for an n-p-n), the transistor is in saturation.*   Of course, the emitter junction must be simultaneously forward-biased, but then we should not be testing for saturation if this condition were not satisfied.

9-11   LARGE–SIGNAL, DC, AND SMALL–SIGNAL CE VALUES OF CURRENT GAIN

If we define β by

$$\beta \equiv \frac{\alpha}{1 - \alpha} \tag{9-42}$$

and replace I_{co} by I_{CBO}, then Eq. (9-38) becomes

$$I_C = (1 + \beta)I_{CBO} + \beta I_B \tag{9-43}$$

From Eq. (9-43) we have

$$\beta = \frac{I_C - I_{CBO}}{I_B - (-I_{CBO})} \tag{9-44}$$

In Sec. 9-9 we define *cutoff* to mean that $I_E = 0$, $I_C = I_{CBO}$, and $I_B = -I_{CBO}$. Consequently, Eq. (9-44) gives the ratio of the collector-current increment to the base-current change from cutoff to I_B, and hence β *represents the large-signal current gain of a common-emitter transistor.*   This parameter is of primary importance in connection with the biasing and stability of transistor circuits as discussed in Chap. 10.

In Sec. 9-10 we define the dc current gain by

$$\beta_{dc} \equiv \frac{I_C}{I_B} \equiv h_{FE} \tag{9-45}$$

In that section it is noted that h_{FE} is most useful in connection with determining whether or not a transistor is in saturation. In general, the base current (and hence the collector current) is large compared with I_{CBO}. Under these conditions the large-signal and the dc betas are approximately equal; then $h_{FE} \approx \beta$.

The small-signal CE forward short-circuit current gain β' is defined as the ratio of a collector-current increment ΔI_C for a small base-current change ΔI_B (at a given quiescent operating point, at a fixed collector-to-emitter voltage V_{CE}), or

$$\beta' \equiv \frac{\partial I_C}{\partial I_B}\bigg|_{V_{CE}} \tag{9-46}$$

If β is independent of current, we see from Eq. (9-43) that $\beta' = \beta \approx h_{FE}$. However, Fig. 9-12 indicates that β is a function of current, and from Eq. (9-43),

$$\beta' = \beta + (I_{CBO} + I_B) \frac{\partial \beta}{\partial I_B} \tag{9-47}$$

The small-signal CE forward gain β' is used in the analysis of amplifier circuits and is designated by h_{fe} in Chap. 11. Using $\beta' = h_{fe}$ and $\beta = h_{FE}$, Eq. (9-47) becomes

$$h_{fe} = \frac{h_{FE}}{1 - (I_{CBO} + I_B) \dfrac{\partial h_{FE}}{\partial I_C}} \tag{9-48}$$

Since h_{FE} versus I_C given in Fig. 9-12 shows a maximum, then h_{fe} is larger than h_{FE} for small currents (to the left of the maximum) and $h_{fe} < h_{FE}$ for currents larger than that corresponding to the maximum. It should be emphasized that Eq. (9-48) is valid in the active region only. From Fig. 9-11 we see that $h_{fe} \rightarrow 0$ in the saturation region because $\Delta I_C \rightarrow 0$ for a small increment ΔI_B.

9-12   THE COMMON–COLLECTOR CONFIGURATION

Another transistor-circuit configuration, shown in Fig. 9-13, is known as the common-collector configuration. The circuit is basically the same as the circuit of Fig. 9-7, with the exception that the load resistor is in the emitter circuit rather than in the collector circuit. If we continue to specify the operation of the circuit in terms of the currents which flow, the operation for the

Fig. 9-13 The transistor common-collector configuration.

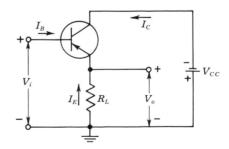

common-collector is much the same as for the common-emitter configuration. When the base current is I_{CO}, the emitter current will be zero, and no current will flow in the load. As the transistor is brought out of this back-biased condition by increasing the magnitude of the base current, the transistor will pass through the active region and eventually reach saturation. In this condition all the supply voltage, except for a very small drop across the transistor, will appear across the load.

9-13   GRAPHICAL ANALYSIS OF THE CE CONFIGURATION

It is our purpose in this section to analyze graphically the operation of the circuit of Fig. 9-14. In Fig. 9-15a the output characteristics of a p-n-p germanium transistor and in Fig. 9-15b the corresponding input characteristics are indicated. We have selected the CE configuration because, as we see in Chap. 11, it is the most generally useful configuration.

In Fig. 9-15a we have drawn a load line for a 250-Ω load with $V_{CC} = 15$ V. If the input base-current signal is symmetric, the quiescent point Q is usually selected at about the center of the load line, as shown in Fig. 9-15a. We postpone until Chap. 10 our discussion on biasing of transistors.

Notation   At this point it is important to make a few remarks on transistor symbols. The convention used to designate transistor voltages and currents is the same as that introduced for vacuum tubes in Sec. 7-9. Specifically, instantaneous values of quantities which vary with time are represented by lowercase letters (i for current, v for voltage, and p for power). Maximum, average (dc), and effective, or root-mean-square (rms), values are represented by the uppercase letter of the proper symbol (I, V, or P). Average (dc) values and instantaneous total values are indicated by the uppercase subscript of the proper electrode symbol (B for base, C for collector, E for emitter). Varying components from some quiescent value are indicated by the lowercase subscript of the proper electrode symbol. A single subscript is used if the reference electrode is clearly understood. If there is any possi-

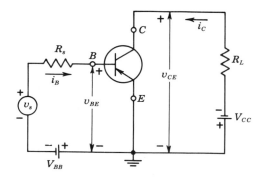

Fig. 9-14   The CE transistor configuration.

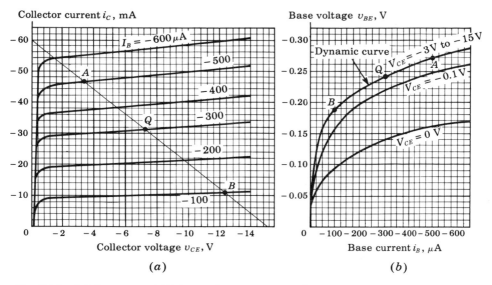

Fig. 9-15 (a) Output and (b) input characteristics of a $p\text{-}n\text{-}p$ germanium transistor.

bility of ambiguity, the conventional double-subscript notation should be used. For example, in Figs. 9-16a to d and 9-14, we show collector and base currents and voltages in the common-emitter transistor configuration, employing the notation just described. The collector and emitter current and voltage component variations from the corresponding quiescent values are

$$i_c = i_C - I_C = \Delta i_C \qquad v_c = v_C - V_C = \Delta v_C$$
$$i_b = i_B - I_B = \Delta i_B \qquad v_b = v_B - V_B = \Delta v_B$$

The *magnitude* of the supply voltage is indicated by repeating the electrode subscript. This notation is summarized in Table 9-1.

TABLE 9-1   Notation

	Base (collector) voltage with respect to emitter	Base (collector) current toward electrode from external circuit
Instantaneous total value....................	v_B (v_C)	i_B (i_C)
Quiescent value............................	V_B (V_C)	I_B (I_C)
Instantaneous value of varying component......	v_b (v_c)	i_b (i_c)
Effective value of varying component (phasor, if a sinusoid)................................	V_b (V_c)	I_b (I_c)
Supply voltage (magnitude)...................	V_{BB} (V_{CC})	

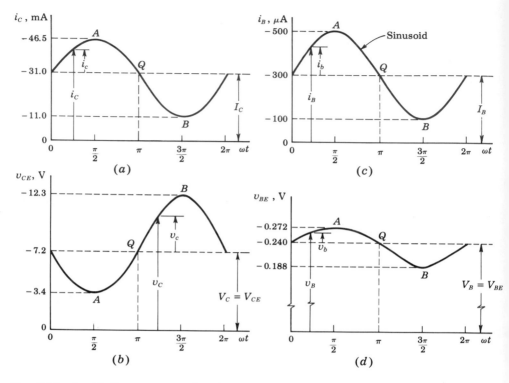

Fig. 9-16 (a, b) Collector and (c, d) base current and voltage waveforms.

The Waveforms Assume a 200-μA peak sinusoidally varying base current around the quiescent point Q, where $I_B = -300$ μA. Then the extreme points of the base waveform are A and B, where $i_B = -500$ μA and -100 μA, respectively. These points are located on the load line in Fig. 9-15a. We find i_C and v_{CE}, corresponding to any given value of i_B, at the intersection of the load line and the collector characteristics corresponding to this value of i_B. For example, at point A, $i_B = -500$ μA, $i_C = -46.5$ mA, and $v_{CE} = -3.4$ V. The waveforms i_C and v_{CE} are plotted in Fig. 9-16a and b, respectively. We observe that the collector current and collector voltage waveforms are not the same as the base-current waveform (the sinusoid of Fig. 9-16c) because the collector characteristics in the neighborhood of the load line in Fig. 9-15a are not parallel lines equally spaced for equal increments in base current. This change in waveform is known as *output nonlinear distortion*.

The base-to-emitter voltage v_{BE} for any combination of base current and collector-to-emitter voltage can be obtained from the input characteristic curves. In Fig. 9-15b we show the *dynamic operating curve* drawn for the combinations of base current and collector voltage found along A-Q-B of the load line of Fig. 9-15a. The waveform v_{BE} can be obtained from the dynamic operating curve of Fig. 9-15b by reading the voltage v_{BE} corresponding to a given base current i_B. We now observe that, since the dynamic curve is not a straight line, the waveform of v_b (Fig. 9-16d) will not, in general, be the same as the waveform of i_b. This change in waveform is known as *input nonlinear distortion*. In some cases it is more reasonable to assume that v_b in Fig. 9-16d is sinusoidal, and then i_b will be distorted. The above condition will be true if the sinusoidal voltage source v_s driving the transistor has a small output resistance R_s in comparison with the input resistance R_i of the transistor, so that the transistor input-voltage waveform is essentially the same as the source waveform. However, if $R_s \gg R_i$, the variation in i_B is given by $i_b \approx v_s/R_s$, and hence the base-current waveform is also sinusoidal.

From Fig. 9-15b we see that *for a large sinusoidal base voltage v_b* around the point Q the base-current swing $|i_b|$ is smaller to the left of Q than to the right of Q. This input distortion tends to cancel the output distortion because, in Fig. 9-15a, the collector-current swing $|i_c|$ for a given base-current swing is larger over the section BQ than over QA. Hence, if the amplifier is biased so that Q is near the center of the i_C-v_{CE} plane, there will be less distortion if the excitation is a sinusoidal base voltage than if it is a sinusoidal base current.

It should be noted here that the dynamic load curve can be approximated by a straight line over a sufficiently small line segment, and hence, if the input signal is small, there will be negligible input distortion under any conditions of operation (current-source or voltage-source driver).

9-14   ANALYTICAL EXPRESSIONS FOR TRANSISTOR CHARACTERISTICS

The dependence of the currents in a transistor upon the junction voltages, or vice versa, may be obtained by starting with Eq. (9-8), repeated here for convenience:

$$I_C = -\alpha_N I_E - I_{CO}(\epsilon^{V_C/V_T} - 1) \tag{9-49}$$

We have added the subscript N to α in order to indicate that we are using the transistor in the *normal* manner. We must recognize, however, that there is no essential reason which constrains us from using a transistor in an *inverted* fashion, that is, interchanging the roles of the emitter junction and the collector junction. From a practical point of view, such an arrangement might not be as effective as the *normal* mode of operation, but this matter does not concern us now. With this inverted mode of operation in mind, we may now write, in correspondence with Eq. (9-49),

$$I_E = -\alpha_I I_C - I_{EO}(\epsilon^{V_E/V_T} - 1) \tag{9-50}$$

Here α_I is the *inverted* common-base current gain, just as α_N in Eq. (9-49) is the current gain in *normal* operation. I_{EO} is the emitter-junction reverse saturation current, and V_E is the voltage drop from p side to n side at the emitter junction and is positive for a forward-biased emitter. In the literature,

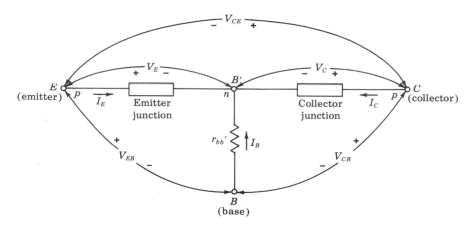

Fig. 9-17 Defining the voltages and currents used in the Ebers-Moll equations. For either a *p-n-p* or an *n-p-n* transistor, a positive value of current means that positive charge flows into the junction and a positive V_E (V_C) means that the emitter (collector) junction is forward-biased (the *p* side positive with respect to the *n* side).

α_R (*reversed* alpha) and α_F (*forward* alpha) are sometimes used in place of α_I and α_N, respectively.

The Base-spreading Resistance $r_{bb'}$ The symbol V_C represents the drop across the collector junction and is positive if the junction is forward-biased. The reference directions for currents and voltages are indicated in Fig. 9-17. Since V_{CB} represents the voltage drop from collector-to-base terminals, then V_{CB} differs from V_C by the ohmic drops in the base and the collector materials. Recalling that the base region is very thin (Fig. 9-4), we see that the current which enters the base region across the junction area must flow through a long narrow path to reach the base terminal. The cross-sectional area for current flow in the collector (or emitter) is very much larger than in the base. Hence, usually, the ohmic drop in the base alone is of importance. This dc ohmic base resistance $r_{bb'}$ is called the *base-spreading resistance*, and is indicated in Fig. 9-17. The difference between V_{CB} and V_C is due to the ohmic drop across the body resistances of the transistor, particularly the base-spreading resistance $r_{bb'}$.

The Ebers-Moll Model Equations (9-49) and (9-50) have a simple interpretation in terms of a circuit known as the *Ebers-Moll model*.[5] This model is shown in Fig. 9-18 for a *p-n-p* transistor. We see that it involves two ideal diodes placed back to back with reverse saturation currents $-I_{EO}$ and $-I_{CO}$ and two dependent current-controlled current sources shunting the ideal diodes. For a *p-n-p* transistor, both I_{CO} and I_{EO} are negative, so that $-I_{CO}$

and $-I_{EO}$ are positive values, giving the magnitudes of the reverse saturation currents of the diodes. The current sources account for the minority-carrier transport across the base. An application of KCL to the collector node of Fig. 9-18 gives

$$I_C = -\alpha_N I_E + I = -\alpha_N I_E + I_o(\epsilon^{V_C/V_T} - 1)$$

where the diode current I is given by Eq. (6-26). Since I_o is the magnitude of the reverse saturation, then $I_o = -I_{CO}$. Substituting this value of I_o into the preceding equation for I_C yields Eq. (9-49).

This model is valid for both forward and reverse static voltages applied across the transistor junctions. It should be noted that we have omitted the base-spreading resistance from Fig. 9-17 and have neglected the difference between I_{CBO} and I_{CO}.

Observe from Fig. 9-18 that the dependent current sources can be eliminated from this figure provided $\alpha_N = \alpha_I = 0$. For example, by making the base width much larger than the diffusion length of minority carriers in the base, all minority carriers will recombine in the base and none will survive to reach the collector. For this case the transport factor β^*, and hence also α, will be zero. Under these conditions, transistor action ceases, and we simply have two diodes placed back to back. This discussion shows why it is impossible to construct a transistor by simply connecting two separate (isolated) diodes back to back.

Currents as Functions of Voltages We may use Eqs. (9-49) and (9-50) to solve explicitly for the transistor currents in terms of the junction voltages as defined in Fig. 9-17, with the result that

$$I_E = \frac{\alpha_I I_{CO}}{1 - \alpha_N \alpha_I} (\epsilon^{V_C/V_T} - 1) - \frac{I_{EO}}{1 - \alpha_N \alpha_I} (\epsilon^{V_E/V_T} - 1) \qquad (9\text{-}51)$$

$$I_C = \frac{\alpha_N I_{EO}}{1 - \alpha_N \alpha_I} (\epsilon^{V_E/V_T} - 1) - \frac{I_{CO}}{1 - \alpha_N \alpha_I} (\epsilon^{V_C/V_T} - 1) \qquad (9\text{-}52)$$

These two equations were first presented by Ebers and Moll,[5] and are identical with Eqs. (9-19) and (9-21), derived from physical principles in Sec. 9-5. In

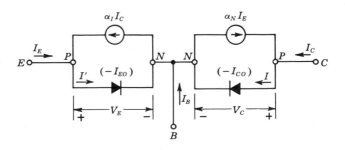

Fig. 9-18 The Ebers-Moll model for a *p-n-p* transistor.

that section it is verified that the coefficients

$$a_{12} \equiv \frac{\alpha_I I_{CO}}{1 - \alpha_N \alpha_I} \quad \text{and} \quad a_{21} \equiv \frac{\alpha_N I_{EO}}{1 - \alpha_N \alpha_I}$$

are equal. Hence the parameters α_N, α_I, I_{CO}, and I_{EO} are not independent, but are related by the condition

$$\alpha_I I_{CO} = \alpha_N I_{EO} \tag{9-53}$$

Manufacturer's data sheets often provide information about α_N, I_{CO}, and I_{EO}, so that α_I may be determined. For many transistors I_{EO} lies in the range $0.5I_{CO}$ to I_{CO}.

Since the sum of the three currents must be zero, the base current is given by

$$I_B = -(I_E + I_C) \tag{9-54}$$

Voltages as Functions of Currents We may solve explicitly for the junction voltages in terms of the currents from Eqs. (9-51) and (9-52), with the result that

$$V_E = V_T \ln \left(1 - \frac{I_E + \alpha_I I_C}{I_{EO}} \right) \tag{9-55}$$

$$V_C = V_T \ln \left(1 - \frac{I_C + \alpha_N I_E}{I_{CO}} \right) \tag{9-56}$$

We now derive the analytic expression for the common-emitter characteristics of Fig. 9-8. The abscissa in this figure is the collector-to-emitter voltage $V_{CE} = V_E - V_C$ for an *n-p-n* transistor and is $V_{CE} = V_C - V_E$ for a *p-n-p* transistor (remember that V_C and V_E are positive at the *p* side of the junction). Hence the common-emitter characteristics are found by subtracting Eqs. (9-55) and (9-56) and by eliminating I_E by the use of Eq. (9-54). The resulting equation can be simplified provided that the following inequalities are valid: $I_B \gg I_{EO}$ and $I_B \gg I_{CO}/\alpha_N$. After some manipulations and by the use of Eqs. (9-42) and (9-53), we obtain (except for very small values of I_B)

$$V_{CE} = \pm V_T \ln \frac{\dfrac{1}{\alpha_I} + \dfrac{1}{\beta_I} \dfrac{I_C}{I_B}}{1 - \dfrac{1}{\beta} \dfrac{I_C}{I_B}} \tag{9-57}$$

where

$$\beta_I \equiv \frac{\alpha_I}{1 - \alpha_I} \quad \text{and} \quad \beta_N \equiv \beta \equiv \frac{\alpha}{1 - \alpha}$$

Note that the $+$ sign in Eq. (9-57) is used for an *n-p-n* transistor, and the $-$ sign for a *p-n-p* device. For a *p-n-p* germanium-type transistor, at $I_C = 0$, $V_{CE} = -V_T \ln (1/\alpha_I)$, so that the *common-emitter characteristics do not pass through the origin*. For $\alpha_I = 0.78$ and $V_T = 0.026$ V, we have $V_{CE} \approx -6$ mV

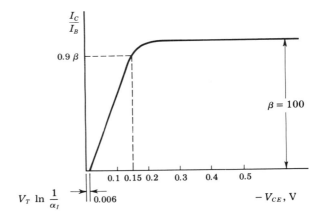

Fig. 9-19 The common-emitter output character-istic for a p-n-p transistor as obtained analytically.

at room temperature. This voltage is so small that the curves of Fig. 9-8 look as if they pass through the origin, but they are actually displaced to the right by a few millivolts.

If I_C is increased, then V_{CE} rises only slightly until I_C/I_B approaches β. For example, even for $I_C/I_B = 0.9\beta = 90$ (for $\beta = 100$),

$$V_{CE} = -0.026 \ln \frac{1/0.78 + 90/3.5}{1 - 0.9} \approx -0.15 \text{ V}$$

This voltage can barely be detected at the scale to which Fig. 9-8 is drawn, and hence near the origin it appears as if the curves rise vertically. However, note that Fig. 9-11 confirms that a voltage of the order of 0.2 V is required for I_C to reach 0.9 of its maximum value.

The maximum value of I_C/I_B is β, and as this value of I_C/I_B is approached, $V_{CE} \rightarrow -\infty$. Hence, as I_C/I_B increases from 0.9β to β, $|V_{CE}|$ increases from 0.15 V to infinity. A plot of the theoretical common-emitter characteristic is indicated in Fig. 9-19. We see that, at a fixed value of V_{CE}, the ratio I_C/I_B is a constant. Hence, for equal increments in I_B, we should obtain equal increments in I_C at a given V_{CE}. This conclusion is fairly well satisfied by the curves in Fig. 9-8. However, the $I_B = 0$ curve seems to be inconsistent since, for a constant I_C/I_B, this curve should coincide with the $I_C = 0$ axis. This discrepancy is due to the approximation made in deriving Eq. (9-57), which is not valid for $I_B = 0$.

The theoretical curve of Fig. 9-19 is much flatter than the curves of Fig. 9-8 because we have implicitly assumed that α_N is truly constant. As already pointed out, a very slight increase of α_N with V_{CE} can account for the slopes of the common-emitter characteristic.

9-15   ANALYSIS OF CUTOFF AND SATURATION REGIONS

Let us now apply the equations of the preceding section to find the dc currents and voltages in the grounded-emitter transistor.

The Cutoff Region If we define *cutoff* as we did in Sec. 9-9 to mean zero emitter current and reverse saturation current in the collector, what emitter-junction voltage is required for cutoff? Equation (9-55) with $I_E = 0$ and $I_C = I_{CO}$ becomes

$$V_E = V_T \ln \left(1 - \frac{\alpha_I I_{CO}}{I_{EO}} \right) = V_T \ln \left(1 - \alpha_N \right) \tag{9-58}$$

where use was made of Eq. (9-53). At 25°C, $V_T = 26$ mV, and for $\alpha_N = 0.98$, $V_E = -100$ mV. Near cutoff we may expect that α_N may be smaller than the nominal value of 0.98. With $\alpha_N = 0.9$ for germanium, we find that $V_E = -60$ mV. For silicon near cutoff, $\alpha_N \approx 0$, and from Eq. (9-58), $V_E \approx V_T \ln 1 = 0$ V. The voltage V_E is the drop from the p to the n side of the emitter junction. To find the voltage which must be applied between base and emitter terminals, we must in principle take account of the drop across the base-spreading resistance $r_{bb'}$ in Fig. 9-17. If $r_{bb'} = 100$ Ω and $I_{CO} = 2$ μA, then $I_{CO}r_{bb'} = 0.2$ mV, which is negligible. Since the emitter current is zero, the potential V_E is called *the floating emitter potential*.

The foregoing analysis indicates that a reverse bias of approximately 0.1 V (0 V) will cut off a germanium (silicon) transistor. It is interesting to determine what currents will flow if a larger reverse input voltage is applied. Assuming that both V_E and V_C are negative and much larger than V_T, so that the exponentials may be neglected in comparison with unity, Eqs. (9-49) and (9-50) become

$$I_C = -\alpha_N I_E + I_{CO} \qquad I_E = -\alpha_I I_C + I_{EO} \tag{9-59}$$

Solving these equations and using Eq. (9-53), we obtain

$$I_C = \frac{I_{CO}(1 - \alpha_I)}{1 - \alpha_N \alpha_I} \qquad I_E = \frac{I_{EO}(1 - \alpha_N)}{1 - \alpha_N \alpha_I} \tag{9-60}$$

Since (for Ge) $\alpha_N \approx 1$, $I_C \approx I_{CO}$ and $I_E \approx 0$. Using $\alpha_N = 0.9$ and $\alpha_I = 0.5$, then $I_C = I_{CO}(0.50/0.55) = 0.91 I_{CO}$ and $I_E = I_{EO}(0.10/0.55) = 0.18 I_{EO}$ and represents a very small *reverse* current. Using $\alpha_I \approx 0$ and $\alpha_N \approx 0$ (for Si), we have that $I_C \approx I_{CO}$ and $I_E \approx I_{EO}$. Hence, increasing the magnitude of the reverse base-to-emitter bias beyond cutoff has very little effect (Fig. 9-20) on the very small transistor currents.

Short-circuited Base Suppose that, instead of reverse-biasing the emitter junction, we simply short the base to the emitter terminal. The currents which now flow are found by setting $V_E = 0$ and by neglecting exp (V_C/V_T) in the Ebers-Moll equations. The results are

$$I_C = \frac{I_{CO}}{1 - \alpha_N \alpha_I} \equiv I_{CES} \qquad \text{and} \qquad I_E = -\alpha_I I_{CES} \tag{9-61}$$

where I_{CES} represents the collector current in the common-emitter configuration with a short-circuited base. If (for Ge) $\alpha_N = 0.9$ and $\alpha_I = 0.5$, then I_{CES} is about $1.8 I_{CO}$ and $I_E = -0.91 I_{CO}$. If (for Si) $\alpha_N \approx 0$ and $\alpha_I \approx 0$, then

$I_{CES} \approx I_{CO}$ and $I_E \approx 0$.   Hence, even with a short-circuited emitter junction, the transistor is virtually at cutoff (Fig. 9-20).

Open-circuited Base   If instead of a shorted base we allow the base to "float," so that $I_B = 0$, the cutoff condition is not reached.   The collector current under this condition is called I_{CEO}, and is given by

$$I_{CEO} = \frac{I_{CO}}{1 - \alpha_N} \tag{9-62}$$

It is interesting to find the emitter-junction voltage under this condition of a floating base.   From Eq. (9-55), with $I_E = -I_C$, and using Eq. (9-53),

$$V_E = V_T \ln \left[1 + \frac{\alpha_N(1 - \alpha_I)}{\alpha_I(1 - \alpha_N)} \right] \tag{9-63}$$

For $\alpha_N = 0.9$ and $\alpha_I = 0.5$ (for Ge), we find $V_E = +60$ mV.   For $\alpha_N \approx 2\alpha_I \approx 0$ (for Si), we have $V_E \approx V_T \ln 3 = +28$ mV.   Hence an open-circuited base represents a slight *forward* bias.

The Cutin Voltage   The volt-ampere characteristic between base and emitter at constant collector-to-emitter voltage is not unlike the volt-ampere characteristic of a simple junction diode.   When the emitter junction is reverse-biased, the base current is very small, being of the order of nano-amperes or microamperes for silicon and germanium, respectively.   When the emitter junction is forward-biased, again, as in the simple diode, no appreciable base current flows until the emitter junction has been forward-biased to the extent where $|V_{BE}| \geq |V_\gamma|$, where V_γ is called the *cutin voltage*.   Since the collector current is nominally proportional to the base current, no appreciable collector current will flow until an appreciable base current flows.   Therefore a plot of collector current against base-to-emitter voltage will exhibit a cutin voltage, just as does the simple diode.   Such plots for Ge and Si transistors are shown in Fig. 9-20a and b.

In principle, a transistor is in its active region whenever the base-to-emitter voltage is on the forward-biasing side of the cutoff voltage, which occurs at a reverse voltage of 0.1 V for germanium and 0 V for silicon.   In effect, however, a transistor enters its active region when $V_{BE} > V_\gamma$.

We may estimate the cutin voltage V_γ in a typical case in the following manner: Assume that we are using a transistor as a switch, so that when the switch is ON it will carry a current of 20 mA.   We may then consider that the cutin point has been reached when, say, the collector current equals 1 percent of the maximum current or a collector current $I_C = 0.2$ mA.   Hence V_γ is the value of V_E given in Eq. (9-55), with $I_E = -(I_C + I_B) \approx -I_C = -0.2$ mA. Assume a germanium transistor with $\alpha_I = 0.5$ and $I_{EO} = 1 \, \mu$A.   Since at room temperature $V_T = 0.026$ V, we obtain from Eq. (9-55)

$$V_\gamma = (0.026)(2.30) \log \left[1 + \frac{0.2 \times 10^{-3}(1 - 0.5)}{10^{-6}} \right] = 0.12 \text{ V}$$

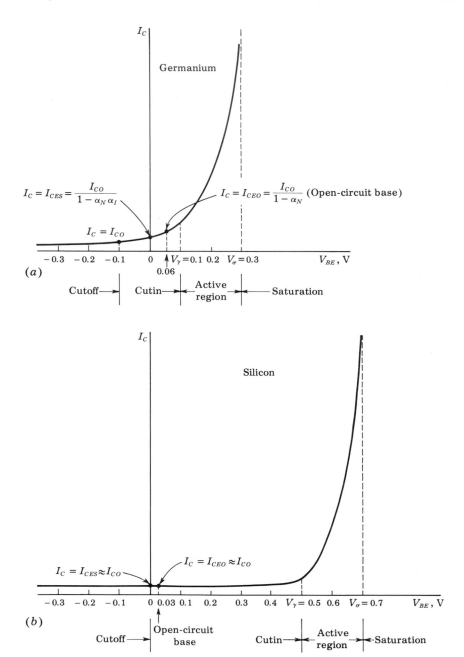

Fig. 9-20 Plots of collector current against base-to-emitter voltage for (a) germanium and (b) silicon transistors. (I_C is not drawn to scale.)

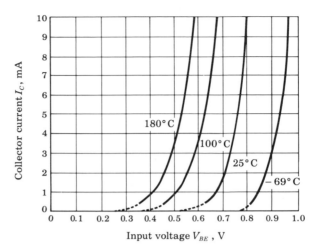

Fig. 9-21   Plot of collector current against base-to-emitter voltage for various temperatures for the type 2N337 silicon transistor. (Courtesy of Transitron Electronic Corporation.)

If the switch had been called upon to carry 2 mA rather than 20 mA, a cutin voltage of 0.06 V would have been obtained.   For a silicon transistor with $\alpha_I = 0.5$ and $I_{EO} = 1$ nA and operating at 20 mA (2 mA) we obtain from Eq. (9-55) that $V_\gamma = 0.6$ V (0.3 V).   Hence, in Fig. 9-20 the following reasonable values for the cutin voltages V_γ are indicated: 0.1 V for germanium and 0.5 V for silicon.

Figure 9-21 shows plots, for several temperatures, of the collector current as a function of the base-to-emitter voltage at constant collector-to-emitter voltage for a typical silicon transistor.   We see that a value for V_γ of the order of 0.5 V at room temperature is entirely reasonable.   The temperature dependence results from the temperature coefficient of the emitter-junction diode.   Therefore the lateral shift of the plots with change in temperature and the change with temperature of the cutin voltage V_γ are approximately -2.5 mV/°C [Eq. (6-39)].

The Saturation Region   Let us consider the 2N404 p-n-p germanium transistor operated with $I_C = -20$ mA, $I_B = -0.35$, and $I_E = +20.35$ mA. Assume the following reasonable values: $I_{CO} = -2.0$ µA, $I_{EO} = -1.0$ µA, and $\alpha_N = 0.99$.   From Eq. (9-53), $\alpha_I = 0.50$.   From Eqs. (9-55) and (9-56), we calculate that, at room temperature,

$$V_E = (0.026)(2.30) \log \left[1 - \frac{20.35 - (0.50)(20)}{-10^{-3}} \right] = 0.24 \text{ V}$$

and

$$V_C = (0.026)(2.30) \log \left[1 - \frac{-20 + 0.99(20.35)}{-(2)(10^{-3})} \right] = 0.11 \text{ V}$$

For a p-n-p transistor,

$$V_{CE} = V_C - V_E = 0.11 - 0.24 \approx -0.13 \text{ V}$$

Taking the voltage drop across $r_{bb'}$ ($\sim$100 Ω) into account (Fig. 9-17),

$$V_{CB} = V_C - I_B r_{bb'} = 0.11 + 0.035 \approx 0.15 \text{ V}$$

and

$$V_{BE} = I_B r_{bb'} - V_E = -0.035 - 0.24 \approx -0.28 \text{ V}$$

Note that the base-spreading resistance does not enter into the calculation of the collector-to-emitter voltage. For a diffused-junction transistor the voltage drop resulting from the collector-spreading resistance may be significant for saturation currents. If so, this ohmic drop can no longer be neglected, as we have done above. For example, if the collector resistance is 5 Ω, then with a collector current of 20 mA, the ohmic drop is 0.10 V, and $|V_{CE}|$ increases from 0.13 to 0.23 V.

9-16   TYPICAL TRANSISTOR–JUNCTION VOLTAGE VALUES

Quite often, in making a transistor-circuit calculation, we are beset by a complication when we seek to determine the transistor currents. These currents are influenced by the transistor-junction voltages. However, to determine these junction voltages, we should first have to know the very currents we seek to determine. A commonly employed and very effective procedure to overcome this problem arises from the recognition that certain of the transistor-junction voltages are ordinarily small in comparison with externally impressed voltages, the junction voltages being in the range of only tenths of volts. We may therefore start the calculation by making the first-order approximation that these junction voltages are all zero. On this basis we calculate a first-order approximation of the current. These first-order currents are now used to determine the junction voltages either from transistor characteristics or from the Ebers-Moll equations. The junction voltages so calculated are used to determine a second-order approximation of the currents, etc. As a matter of practice, it ordinarily turns out that not many orders are called for, since the successive approximations converge to a limit very rapidly. Furthermore, a precise calculation is not justifiable because of the variability from sample to sample of transistors of a given type.

The required number of successive approximations may be reduced, or more importantly, the need to make successive approximations may usually be eliminated completely by recognizing that for many low- and medium-power transistors, over a wide range of operating conditions, certain transistor-junction voltages lie in a rather narrow range, and may be approximated by the entries in Table 9-2. This table lists the collector-to-emitter saturation voltage [V_{CE}(sat)], the base-to-emitter saturation voltage [V_{BE}(sat) $\equiv V_\sigma$], the base-to-emitter voltage in the active region [V_{BE}(active)], at cutin [V_{BE}(cutin) $\equiv V_\gamma$], and at cutoff [V_{BE}(cutoff)]. The entries in the table are appropriate for an n-p-n transistor. For a p-n-p transistor the signs of all entries should be reversed. Observe that the total range of V_{BE} between cutin and saturation is rather small, being only 0.2 V.   The voltage $V_{BE}(\text{active})$ has been located somewhat arbitrarily, but nonetheless reasonably, at the mid-point of the active region in Fig. 9-20.

Of course, particular cases will depart from the estimates of Table 9-2. But it is unlikely that the larger of the numbers will be found in error by more than about 0.1 V or that the smaller entries will be wrong by more than about 0.05 V.   In any event, starting a calculation with the values of Table 9-2 may well make further approximations unnecessary.

TABLE 9-2   Typical n-p-n transistor-junction voltages at 25°C†

	$V_{CE}(\text{sat})$	$V_{BE}(\text{sat}) \equiv V_\sigma$	$V_{BE}(\text{active})$	$V_{BE}(\text{cutin}) \equiv V_\gamma$	$V_{BE}(\text{cutoff})$
Si	0.3	0.7	0.6	0.5	0.0
Ge	0.1	0.3	0.2	0.1	-0.1

† The temperature variation of these voltages is discussed in Sec. 9-15.

Finally, it should be noted that the values in Table 9-2 apply to the intrinsic junctions.   The base terminal-to-emitter voltage includes the drop across the base-spreading resistance $r_{bb'}$.   Ordinarily, the drop $r_{bb'}I_B$ is small enough to be neglected.   If, however, the transistor is driven very deeply into saturation, the base current I_B may not be negligible, but we must take

$$V_{BE} - V_\sigma + I_B r_{bb'}$$

9-17   TRANSISTOR SWITCHING TIMES

When a transistor is used as a switch, it is usually made to operate alternately in the cutoff condition and in saturation.   In the preceding sections we have computed the transistor currents and voltages in the cutoff and saturation states.   We now turn our attention to the behavior of the transistor as it makes a transition from one state to the other.   We consider the transistor circuit shown in Fig. 9-22a, driven by the pulse waveform shown in Fig. 9-22b. This waveform makes transitions between the voltage levels V_2 and V_1.   At V_2 the transistor is at cutoff, and at V_1 the transistor is in saturation.   The input waveform v_i is applied between base and emitter through a resistor R_s, which may be included explicitly in the circuit or may represent the output impedance of the source furnishing the waveform.

The response of the collector current i_C to the input waveform, together with its time relationship to that waveform, is shown in Fig. 9-22c.   The current does not immediately respond to the input signal.   Instead, there is a delay, and the time that elapses during this delay, together with the time required for the current to rise to 10 percent of its maximum (saturation)

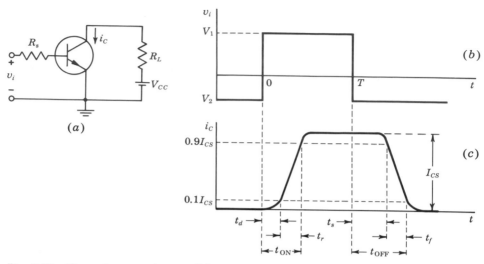

Fig. 9-22 The pulse waveform in (b) drives the transistor in (a) from cutoff to saturation and back again. (c) The collector-current response to the driving input pulse.

value $I_{CS} \approx V_{CC}/R_L$, is called the *delay time* t_d. The current waveform has a nonzero *rise time* t_r, which is the time required for the current to rise from 10 to 90 percent of I_{CS}. The total *turn-on* time t_{ON} is the sum of the delay and rise time, $t_{ON} \equiv t_d + t_r$. When the input signal returns to its initial state at $t = T$, the current again fails to respond immediately. The interval which elapses between the transition of the input waveform and the time when i_C has dropped to 90 percent of I_{CS} is called the *storage time* t_s. The storage interval is followed by the *fall time* t_f, which is the time required for i_C to fall from 90 to 10 percent of I_{CS}. The *turnoff time* t_{OFF} is defined as the sum of the storage and fall times, $t_{OFF} \equiv t_s + t_f$. We shall consider now the physical reasons for the existence of each of these times. The actual calculation of the time intervals (t_d, t_r, t_s, and t_f) is complex, and the reader is referred to Ref. 11. Numerical values of delay time, rise time, storage time, and fall time for the Texas Instruments *n-p-n* epitaxial planar silicon transistor 2N3830 under specified conditions can be as low as $t_d = 10$ nsec, $t_r = 50$ nsec, $t_s = 40$ nsec, and $t_f = 30$ nsec.

The Delay Time Three factors contribute to the delay time: First, when the driving signal is applied to the transistor input, a nonzero time is required to charge up the emitter-junction transition capacitance so that the transistor may be brought from cutoff to the active region. Second, even when the transistor has been brought to the point where minority carriers have begun to cross the emitter junction into the base, a time interval is required before these carriers can cross the base region to the collector junction and be recorded as collector current. Finally, some time is required for the collector current to rise to 10 percent of its maximum.

Rise Time and Fall Time The rise time and the fall time are due to the fact that, if a base-current step is used to saturate the transistor or return it from saturation to cutoff, the transistor collector current must traverse the active region. The collector current increases or decreases along an exponential curve whose time constant τ_r can be shown[11] to be given by $\tau_r = h_{FE}(C_c R_c + 1/\omega_T)$, where C_c is the collector transition capacitance and ω_T is the radian frequency at which the current gain is unity (Sec. 13-7).

Storage Time The failure of the transistor to respond to the trailing edge of the driving pulse for the time interval t_s (indicated in Fig. 9-22c) results from the fact that a transistor in saturation has a saturation charge of excess minority carriers stored in the base. The transistor cannot respond until this saturation excess charge has been removed. The stored charge density in the base is indicated in Fig. 9-23 under various operating conditions.

The concentration of minority carriers in the base region decreases linearly from $p_{no}\epsilon^{V_E/V_T}$ at $x = 0$ to $p_{no}\epsilon^{V_C/V_T}$ at $x = W$, as indicated in Fig. 9-24b. In the cutoff region, both V_E and V_C are negative, and p_n is almost zero everywhere. In the active region, V_E is positive and V_C negative, so that p_n is large at $x = 0$ and almost zero at $x = W$. Finally, in the saturation region, where V_E and V_C are both positive, p_n is large everywhere, and hence a large amount of minority-carrier charge is stored in the base. These densities are pictured in Fig. 9-23.

Consider that the transistor is in its saturation region and that at $t = T$ an input step is used to turn the transistor off, as in Fig. 9-22. Since the turnoff process cannot begin until the abnormal carrier density (the heavily shaded area of Fig. 9-23) has been removed, a relatively long storage delay time t_s may elapse before the transistor responds to the turnoff signal at the input. In an extreme case this storage-time delay may be two or three times

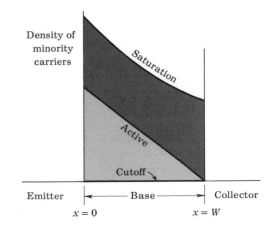

Fig. 9-23 Minority-carrier concentration in the base for cutoff, active, and saturation conditions of operation.

Density of minority carriers

Saturation

Active

Cutoff

Emitter | Base | Collector

$x = 0$ $x = W$

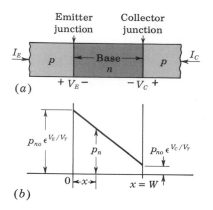

Fig. 9-24 The minority-carrier density in the base region.

the rise or fall time through the active region.   In any event, it is clear that, when transistor switches are to be used in an application where speed is at a premium, it is advantageous to restrain the transistor from entering the saturation region.

9-18   MAXIMUM VOLTAGE RATING[10]

Even if the rated dissipation of a transistor is not exceeded, there is an upper limit to the maximum allowable collector-junction voltage since, at high voltages, there is the possibility of voltage breakdown in the transistor.   Two types of breakdown are possible, *avalanche breakdown*, discussed in Sec. 6-12, and *reach-through*, discussed below.

Avalanche Multiplication   The maximum reverse-biasing voltage which may be applied before breakdown between the collector and base terminals of the transistor, under the condition that the emitter lead be open-circuited, is represented by the symbol BV_{CBO}.   This breakdown voltage is a characteristic of the transistor alone.   Breakdown may occur because of avalanche multiplication of the current I_{CO} that crosses the collector junction.   As a result of this multiplication, the current becomes MI_{CO}, in which M is the factor by which the original current I_{CO} is multiplied by the avalanche effect.   (We neglect leakage current, which does not flow through the junction and is therefore not subject to avalanche multiplication.)   At a high enough voltage, namely, BV_{CBO}, the multiplication factor M becomes nominally infinite, and the region of breakdown is then attained.   Here the current rises abruptly, and large changes in current accompany small changes in applied voltage.

The avalanche multiplication factor depends on the voltage V_{CB} between collector and base.   We shall consider that

$$M \equiv \frac{1}{1 - (V_{CB}/BV_{CBO})^n} \qquad (9\text{-}64)$$

Equation (9-64) is employed because it is a simple expression which gives a good empirical fit to the breakdown characteristics of many transistor types.

The parameter n is found to be in the range of about 2 to 10, and controls the sharpness of the onset of breakdown.

If a current I_E is caused to flow across the emitter junction, then, neglecting the avalanche effect, a fraction αI_E, where α is the common-base current gain, reaches the collector junction. Taking multiplication into account, I_C has the magnitude $M\alpha I_E$. Consequently, it appears that, in the presence of avalanche multiplication, the transistor behaves as though its common-base current gain were $M\alpha$.

An analysis[10] of avalanche breakdown for the CE configuration indicates that the collector-to-emitter breakdown voltage *with open-circuited base*, designated BV_{CEO}, is

$$BV_{CEO} = BV_{CBO} \sqrt[n]{\frac{1}{h_{FE}}} \tag{9-65}$$

For an *n-p-n* germanium transistor, a reasonable value for n, determined experimentally, is $n = 6$. If we now take $h_{FE} = 50$, we find that

$$BV_{CEO} = 0.52 BV_{CBO}$$

so that if $BV_{CBO} = 40$ V, BV_{CEO} is about half as much, or about 20 V. Idealized common-emitter characteristics extended into the breakdown region are shown in Fig. 9-25. If the base is not open-circuited, these breakdown characteristics are modified, the shapes of the curves being determined by the base-circuit connections. In other words, the maximum allowable collector-to-emitter voltage depends not only upon the transistor, but also upon the circuit in which it is used.

Reach-through   The second mechanism by which a transistor's usefulness may be terminated as the collector voltage is increased is called *punch-through*, or *reach-through*, and results from the increased width of the collector-junction transition region with increased collector-junction voltage (the Early effect).

The transition region at a junction is the region of uncovered charges on both sides of the junction at the positions occupied by the impurity atoms. As the voltage applied across the junction increases, the transition region penetrates deeper into the collector and base. Because neutrality of charge must be maintained, the number of uncovered charges on each side remains

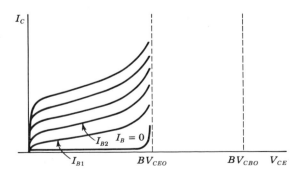

Fig. 9-25 Idealized common-emitter characteristics extended into the breakdown region.

equal. Since the doping of the base is ordinarily substantially smaller than that of the collector, the penetration of the transition region into the base is larger than into the collector (Fig. 9-2c). Since the base is very thin, it is possible that, at moderate voltages, the transition region will have spread completely across the base to reach the emitter junction. At this point normal transistor action ceases, since emitter and collector are effectively shorted.

Punch-through differs from avalanche breakdown in that it takes place at a fixed voltage between collector and base, and is not dependent on circuit configuration. In a particular transistor, the voltage limit is determined by punch-through or breakdown, whichever occurs at the lower voltage.

REFERENCES

1. Shockley, W.: The Theory of p-n Junctions in Semiconductors and p-n Junction Transistors, *Bell System Tech. J.*, vol. 28, pp. 435–489, July, 1949.
   Middlebrook, R. D.: "An Introduction to Junction Transistor Theory," pp. 115–130, John Wiley & Sons, Inc., New York, 1957.
   Terman, F. E.: "Electronic and Radio Engineering," 4th ed., pp. 747–760, McGraw-Hill Book Company, New York, 1955.
   Moll, J. L.: "Junction Transistor Electronics," *Proc. IRE*, vol. 43, pp. 1807–1819, December, 1955.

2. Phillips, A. B.: "Transistor Engineering," pp. 157–159, McGraw-Hill Book Company, New York, 1962.

3. Ref. 2, chap. 1.

4. Texas Instruments, Inc.: J. Miller (ed.), "Transistor Circuit Design," chap. 1, McGraw-Hill Book Company, New York, 1963.

5. Ebers, J. J., and J. L. Moll: Large-signal Behavior of Junction Transistors, *Proc. IRE*, vol. 42, pp. 1761–1772, December, 1954.

6. Sah, C. T., R. N. Noyce, and W. Shockley: Carrier-generation and Recombination in p-n Junctions and p-n Junction Characteristics, *Proc. IRE*, vol. 45, pp. 1228–1243, September, 1957.
   Pritchard, R. L.: Advances in the Understanding of the P-N Junction Triode, *Proc. IRE*, vol. 46, pp. 1130–1141, June, 1958.

7. Ref. 2, pp. 236–237.

8. Early, J. M.: Effects of Space-charge Layer Widening in Junction Transistors, *Proc. IRE*, vol. 40, pp. 1401–1406, November, 1952.

9. Millman, J., and H. Taub: "Pulse, Digital, and Switching Waveforms," p. 196, McGraw-Hill Book Company, New York, 1965.

10. Ref. 9, chap. 6.

11. Ref. 9, chap. 20.
    "Transistor Manual," 7th ed., pp. 149–169, General Electric Co., Syracuse, N.Y., 1964.

10/TRANSISTOR BIASING AND THERMAL STABILIZATION

This chapter presents methods for establishing the quiescent operating point of a transistor amplifier in the active region of the characteristics. The operating point shifts with changes in temperature T because the transistor parameters (β, I_{CO}, etc.) are functions of T. A criterion is established for comparing the stability of different biasing circuits. Compensation techniques are also presented for quiescent-point stabilization.

10-1   THE OPERATING POINT

From our discussion of transistor characteristics in Secs. 9-8 to 9-10, it is clear that the transistor functions most linearly when it is constrained to operate in its active region. To establish an operating point in this region it is necessary to provide appropriate direct potentials and currents, using external sources. Once an operating point Q is established, such as the one shown in Fig. 9-15a, time-varying excursions of the input signal (base current, for example) should cause an output signal (collector voltage or collector current) of the same waveform. If the output signal is not a faithful reproduction of the input signal, for example, if it is clipped on one side, the operating point is unsatisfactory and should be relocated on the collector characteristics. The question now naturally arises as to how to choose the operating point. In Fig. 10-1 we show a common-emitter circuit (the capacitors have negligible reactance at the lowest frequency of operation of this circuit). Figure 10-2 gives the output characteristics of the transistor used in Fig. 10-1. Note that even if we are free to choose R_c, R_L, R_b, and V_{CC}, we may not operate the transistor everywhere in the active region because the various transistor ratings limit the range of useful

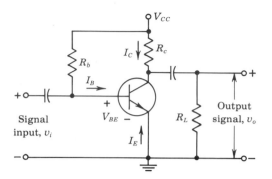

Fig. 10-1   The fixed-bias circuit.

operation.   These ratings (listed in the manufacturer's specification sheets) are maximum collector dissipation $P_C(\text{max})$, maximum collector voltage $V_C(\text{max})$, maximum collector current $I_C(\text{max})$, and maximum emitter-to-base voltage $V_{EB}(\text{max})$.   Figure 10-2 shows three of these bounds on typical collector characteristics.

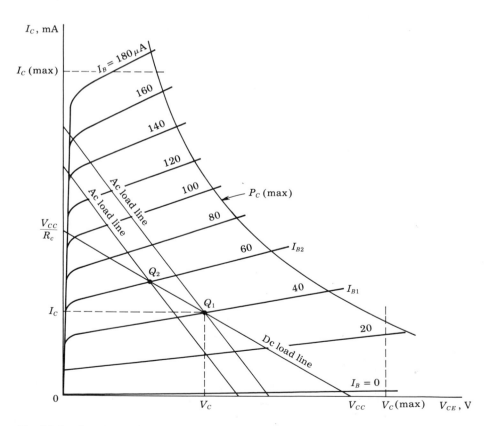

Fig. 10-2   Common-emitter collector characteristics; ac and dc load lines.

The DC and AC Load Lines   Let us suppose that we can select R_c so that the dc load line is as drawn in Fig. 10-2. If $R_L = \infty$ and if the input signal (base current) is large and symmetrical, we must locate the operating point Q_1 at the center of the load line. In this way the collector voltage and current may vary approximately symmetrically around the quiescent values V_C and I_C, respectively. If $R_L \neq \infty$, however, an ac load line (Sec. 7-12) corresponding to a load of $R'_L = R_L \| R_c$ must be drawn through the operating point Q_1. This ac load line is indicated in Fig. 10-2, where we observe that the input signal may swing a maximum of approximately 40 μA around Q_1 because, if the base current decreases by more than 40 μA, the transistor is driven off.

If a larger input swing is available, then in order to avoid cutoff during a part of the cycle, the quiescent point must be located at a higher current. For example, by simple trial and error we locate Q_2 *on the dc load line* such that a line with a slope corresponding to the ac resistance R'_L and drawn through Q_2 gives as large an output as possible without too much distortion. In Fig. 10-2 the choice of Q_2 allows an input peak current swing of about 60 μA.

The Fixed-bias Circuit   The point Q_2 can be established by noting the required current I_{B2} in Fig. 10-2 and choosing the resistance R_b in Fig. 10-1 so that the base current is equal to I_{B2}. Therefore

$$I_B = \frac{V_{CC} - V_{BE}}{R_b} = I_{B2} \tag{10-1}$$

The voltage V_{BE} across the forward-biased emitter junction is (Table 9-2, page 257) approximately 0.2 V for a germanium transistor and 0.6 V for a silicon transistor in the active region. Since V_{CC} is usually much larger than V_{BE}, we have

$$I_B \approx \frac{V_{CC}}{R_b} \tag{10-2}$$

The current I_B is constant, and the network of Fig. 10-1 is called the *fixed-bias circuit*. In summary, we see that the selection of an operating point Q depends upon a number of factors. Among these factors are the ac and dc loads on the stage, the available power supply, the maximum transistor ratings, the peak signal excursions to be handled by the stage, and the tolerable distortion.

10-2   BIAS STABILITY

In the preceding section we examined the problem of selecting an operating point Q on the load line of the transistor. We now consider some of the problems of maintaining the operating point stable.

Let us refer to the biasing circuit of Fig. 10-1. In this circuit the base

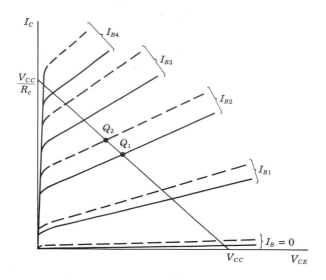

Fig. 10-3 Graphs showing the collector characteristics for two transistors of the same type. The dashed characteristics are for a transistor whose β is much larger than that of the transistor represented by the solid curves.

current I_B is kept constant since $I_B \approx V_{CC}/R_b$. Let us assume that the transistor of Fig. 10-1 is replaced by another of the same type. In spite of the tremendous strides that have been made in the technology of the manufacture of semiconductor devices, transistors of a particular type still come out of production with a wide spread in the values of some parameters. For example, Fig. 9-12 shows a range of $h_{FE} \approx \beta$ of about 3 to 1. To provide information about this variability, a transistor data sheet, in tabulating parameter values, often provides columns headed minimum, typical, and maximum.

In Sec. 9-8 we see that the spacing of the output characteristics will increase or decrease (for equal changes in I_B) as β increases or decreases. In Fig. 10-3 we have assumed that β is greater for the replacement transistor of Fig. 10-1, and since I_B is maintained constant at I_{B2} by the external biasing circuit, it follows that the operating point will move to Q_2. This new operating point may be completely unsatisfactory. Specifically, it is possible for the transistor to find itself in the saturation region. We now conclude that maintaining I_B constant will not provide operating-point stability as β changes. On the contrary, I_B should be allowed to change so as to maintain I_C and V_{CE} constant as β changes.

Thermal Instability A second very important cause for bias instability is a variation in temperature. In Sec. 9-9 we note that the reverse saturation current I_{CO}† changes greatly with temperature. Specifically, I_{CO} doubles for every 10°C rise in temperature. This fact may cause considerable practical difficulty in using a transistor as a circuit element. For example, the collector current I_C causes the collector-junction temperature to rise, which in turn increases I_{CO}. As a result of this growth of I_{CO}, I_C will increase [Eq. (9-43)], which may further increase the junction temperature, and consequently I_{CO}.

† Throughout this chapter I_{CBO} is abbreviated I_{CO} (Sec. 9-9).

It is possible for this succession of events to become cumulative, so that the ratings of the transistor are exceeded and the device burns out.

Even if the drastic state of affairs described above does not take place, it is possible for a transistor which was biased in the active region to find itself in the saturation region as a result of this operating-point instability (Sec. 10-10). To see how this may happen, we note that if $I_B = 0$, then, from Eq. (9-38), $I_C = I_{CO}/(1 - \alpha)$. As the temperature increases, I_{CO} increases, and even if we assume that α remains constant (actually it also increases), it is clear that the $I_B = 0$ line in the CE output characteristics will move upward. The characteristics for other values of I_B will also move upward by the same amount (provided that β remains constant), and consequently the operating point will move if I_B is forced to remain constant. In Fig. 10-4 we show the output characteristics of the 2N708 transistor at temperatures of $+25$ and $+100°C$. This transistor, used in the circuit of Fig. 10-1 with $V_{CC} = 10$ V, $R_c = 250$ Ω, $R_b = 24$ K, operates at Q with $I_B = (10 - 0.6)/24 \approx 0.4$ mA. Hence it would find itself almost in saturation at a temperature of $+100°C$ even though it would be biased in the middle of its active region at $+25°C$.

The Stability Factor S From our discussion so far we see that in biasing a transistor in the active region we should strive to maintain the operating point stable by keeping I_C and V_{CE} constant. The techniques normally used to do so may be classified in two categories: (1) *stabilization techniques* and (2) *compensation techniques*. Stabilization techniques refer to the use of resistive biasing circuits which allow I_B to vary so as to keep I_C relatively constant with variations in I_{CO}, β, and V_{BE}. Compensation techniques refer to the use of temperature-sensitive devices such as diodes, transistors, thermistors, etc.,

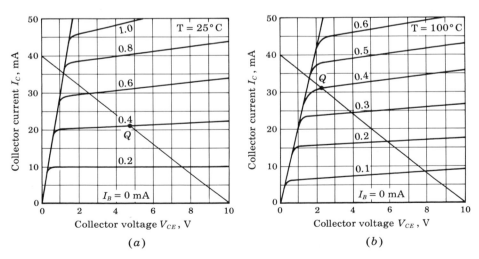

Fig. 10-4   Diffused silicon planar 2N708 *n-p-n* transistor output CE characteristics for (a) 25°C and (b) 100°C. (Courtesy of Fairchild Semiconductor.)

which provide compensating voltages and currents to maintain the operating point constant. A number of stabilization and compensation circuits are presented in the sections that follow. In order to compare these biasing circuits we define a *stability factor* S as the rate of change of collector current with respect to the reverse saturation current, keeping β and V_{BE} constant, or

$$S = \frac{\partial I_C}{\partial I_{CO}} \approx \frac{\Delta I_C}{\Delta I_{CO}} \tag{10-3}$$

The larger the value of S, the more likely the circuit is to exhibit thermal instability.† S as defined here cannot be smaller than unity. Other stability factors may also be defined, for example, $\partial I_C/\partial\beta$ and $\partial I_C/\partial V_{BE}$. As we show in Sec. 10-5, however, bias circuits which provide stabilization of I_C with respect to I_{CO} will also perform satisfactorily for transistors which have large variations of β and V_{BE} with temperature. In the active region the basic relationship between I_C and I_B is given by Eq. (9-43), repeated here for convenience:

$$I_C = (1 + \beta)I_{CO} + \beta I_B \tag{10-4}$$

If we differentiate Eq. (10-4) with respect to I_C and consider β constant with I_C, we obtain

$$1 = \frac{1 + \beta}{S} + \beta\frac{dI_B}{dI_C} \tag{10-5}$$

or

$$S = \frac{1 + \beta}{1 - \beta(dI_B/dI_C)} \tag{10-6}$$

In order to calculate the factor S for any biasing arrangement, it is only necessary to find the relationship between I_B and I_C and to use Eq. (10-6). For the fixed-bias circuit of Fig. 10-1, I_B is independent of I_C [Eq. (10-2)]. Hence the stability factor S of the fixed-bias circuit is

$$S = \beta + 1 \tag{10-7}$$

For $\beta = 50$, $S = 51$, which means that I_C increases 51 times as fast as I_{CO}. Such a large value of S makes thermal runaway a definite possibility with this circuit. In the following sections bias-stabilization techniques are presented which reduce the value of S, and hence make I_C more independent of I_{CO}.

10-3   COLLECTOR–TO–BASE BIAS

An improvement in stability is obtained if the resistor R_b in Fig. 10-1 is returned to the collector junction rather than to the battery terminal. Such

---

† In this sense, S should more properly be called an instability factor.

a connection is indicated in Fig. 10-5a.   The physical reason that this circuit is an improvement over that in Fig. 10-1 is not difficult to find.   If I_C tends to increase (either because of a rise in temperature or because the transistor has been replaced by another of larger β), then V_{CE} decreases.   Hence I_B also decreases; and as a consequence of this lowered bias current, the collector current is not allowed to increase as much as it would have if fixed bias had been used.

We now calculate the stability factor S.   From KVL applied to the circuit of Fig. 10-5a,

$$-V_{CC} + (I_B + I_C)R_c + I_B R_b + V_{BE} = 0 \tag{10-8}$$

or

$$I_B = \frac{V_{CC} - I_C R_c - V_{BE}}{R_c + R_b} \tag{10-9}$$

Since V_{BE} is almost independent of collector current ($V_{BE} = 0.6$ V for Si and 0.2 V for Ge), then from Eq. (10-9) we obtain

$$\frac{dI_B}{dI_C} = -\frac{R_c}{R_c + R_b} \tag{10-10}$$

Substituting Eq. (10-10) in Eq. (10-6), we obtain

$$S = \frac{\beta + 1}{1 + \beta R_c/(R_c + R_b)} \tag{10-11}$$

This value is smaller than $\beta + 1$, which is obtained for the fixed-bias circuit, and hence an improvement in stability is obtained.

Stabilization with Changes in β It is important to determine how well the circuit of Fig. 10-5 will stabilize the operating point against variations in β.

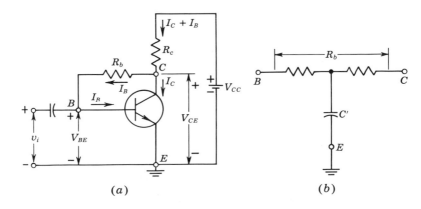

Fig. 10-5   (a) A collector-to-base bias circuit.   (b) A method of avoiding ac degeneration.

From Eqs. (10-4) and (10-8) we obtain, after some manipulation, and with $\beta \gg 1$,

$$I_C \approx \frac{\beta[V_{CC} - V_{BE} + (R_c + R_b)I_{CO}]}{\beta R_c + R_b} \tag{10-12}$$

To make I_C insensitive to β we must have

$$\beta R_c \gg R_b \tag{10-13}$$

The inequality of Eq. (10-13) cannot be realized in all practical circuits. However, note that even if R_c is so small that $R_c = R_b/\beta$, the sensitivity to variations in β is half what it would be if fixed bias (I_B constant) were used.

EXAMPLE The transistor in Fig. 10-5 is a silicon-type 2N708 with $\beta = 50$, $V_{CC} = 10$ V, and $R_c = 250$ Ω. It is desired that the quiescent point be approximately at the middle of the load line. Find R_b and calculate S. The output characteristics are shown in Fig. 10-4.

Solution Since we may neglect I_b compared with I_c in R_c, we may draw a load line corresponding to 10 V and 250 Ω. From the load line shown in Fig. 10-4, we choose the operating point at $I_B = 0.4$ mA, $I_C = 21$ mA, and $V_{CE} = 4.6$ V (at a temperature of $+25°C$). From Fig. 10-5 we have

$$R_b = \frac{V_{CE} - V_{BE}}{I_B} = \frac{4.6 - 0.6}{0.4} = 10 \text{ K}$$

The stability factor S can now be calculated using Eq. (10-11), or

$$S = \frac{51}{1 + 50 \times 0.25/10.25} = 23$$

which is about half the value found for the circuit of Fig. 10-1. We should note here that the numerical values of R_c and R_b of this example do not satisfy Eq. (10-13) since $\beta R_c = 12.5$ K whereas $R_b = 10$ K. We should then expect I_C to vary with variations in β, but to a smaller extent than if fixed bias were used.

Analysis of the Collector-to-Base Bias Circuit If the component values are specified, the quiescent point is found as follows: Corresponding to each value of I_B given on the collector curves, the collector voltage

$$V_{CE} = I_B R_b + V_{BE}$$

is calculated. The locus of these corresponding points V_{CE} and I_B plotted on the common-emitter characteristics is called the *bias curve*. The intersection of the load line and the bias curve gives the quiescent point. Alternatively, if the collector characteristics can be represented analytically by Eq. (10-4), I_C is found directly from Eq. (10-12).

A Method for Decreasing Signal-gain Feedback The increased stability of the circuit in Fig. 10-5a over that in Fig. 10-1 is due to the *feedback* from the output (collector) terminal to the input (base) terminal via R_b.   Feedback amplifiers are studied in detail in Chap. 17.   The ac voltage gain of such an amplifier is less than it would be if there were no feedback.   Thus, if the signal voltage causes an increase in the base current, i_C tends to increase, v_{CE} decreases, and the component of base current coming from R_b decreases.   Hence the net change in base current is less than it would have been if R_b were connected to a fixed potential rather than to the collector terminal.   This signal-gain degeneration may be avoided by splitting R_b into two parts and connecting the junction of these resistors to ground through a capacitor C', as indicated in Fig. 10-5b.   At the frequencies under consideration, the reactance of C' must be negligible.

Note that if the output impedance of the signal source is small compared with the input resistance of the transistor, then the capacitance C' is not needed, because any feedback current in R_b is bypassed to ground through the signal impedance and does not contribute to the base current.

10-4   SELF–BIAS, OR EMITTER BIAS

If the load resistance R_c is very small, as, for example, in a transformer-coupled circuit, then from Eq. (10-11) we see that there is no improvement in stabilization in the collector-to-base bias circuit over the fixed-bias circuit. A circuit which can be used even if there is zero dc resistance in series with the collector terminal is the self-biasing configuration of Fig. 10-6a.   The current in the resistance R_e in the emitter lead causes a voltage drop which is in the direction to reverse-bias the emitter junction.   Since this junction must be forward-biased, the base voltage is obtained from the supply through the R_1R_2 network.   Note that if $R_b \equiv R_1\|R_2 \to 0$, then the base-to-ground voltage V_{BN} is independent of I_{CO}.   Under these circumstances we may verify

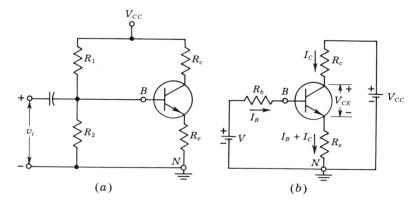

Fig. 10-6   (a) A self-biasing circuit.   (b) Simplification of the base circuit in (a) by the use of Thévenin's theorem.

[Eq. (10-17)] that $S = \partial I_C / \partial I_{CO} \rightarrow 1$. For best stability R_1 and R_2 must be kept as small as possible.

The physical reason for an improvement in stability with $R_b \neq 0$ is the following: If I_C tends to increase, say, because I_{CO} has risen as a result of an elevated temperature, the current in R_e increases. As a consequence of the increase in voltage drop across R_e, the base current is decreased. Hence I_C will increase less than it would have had there been no self-biasing resistor R_e.

The Stabilization Factor S We now find the analytical expression for the stabilization factor S. Since such a calculation is made under dc or no-signal conditions, the network of Fig. 10-6a contains three independent loops. If the circuit to the left between the base B and ground N terminals in Fig. 10-6a is replaced by its Thévenin equivalent, the two-mesh circuit of Fig. 10-6b is obtained, where

$$V \equiv \frac{R_2 V_{CC}}{R_2 + R_1} \qquad R_b \equiv \frac{R_2 R_1}{R_2 + R_1} \tag{10-14}$$

Obviously, R_b is the effective resistance seen looking back from the base terminal. Kirchhoff's voltage law around the base circuit yields

$$V = I_B R_b + V_{BE} + (I_B + I_C) R_e \tag{10-15}$$

If we consider V_{BE} to be independent of I_C, we can differentiate Eq. (10-15) to obtain

$$\frac{dI_B}{dI_C} = -\frac{R_e}{R_e + R_b} \tag{10-16}$$

Substituting Eq. (10-16) in Eq. (10-6) results in

$$S = \frac{1 + \beta}{1 + \beta R_e / (R_e + R_b)} = (1 + \beta) \frac{1 + R_b / R_e}{1 + \beta + R_b / R_e} \tag{10-17}$$

Note that S varies between 1 for small R_b / R_e and $1 + \beta$ for $R_b / R_e \rightarrow \infty$. Equation (10-17) is plotted in Fig. 10-7 for various values of β. It can be seen that, for a fixed R_b / R_e, S increases with increasing β. (Therefore stability decreases with increasing β.) Also note that S is essentially independent of β for small S.

The smaller the value of R_b, the better the stabilization. We have already noted that even if R_b approaches zero, the value of S cannot be reduced below unity. Hence I_C always increases more than I_{CO}. As R_b is reduced while the Q point is held fixed, the current drawn in the $R_1 R_2$ network from the supply V_{CC} increases. Also, if R_e is increased while R_b is held constant, then to operate at the same quiescent currents, the magnitude of V_{CC} must be increased. In either case a loss of power (decreased efficiency) is the disadvantage which accompanies the improvement in stability.

In order to avoid the loss of ac (signal) gain because of the feedback caused by R_e (Sec. 12-7), this resistance is often bypassed by a large capacitance

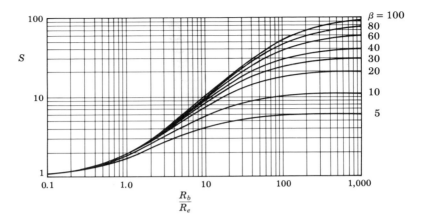

Fig. 10-7 Stability factor S [Eq. (10-17)] versus R_b/R_e for the self-bias circuit of Fig. 10-6b, with β as a parameter. (Courtesy of L. P. Hunter, "Handbook of Semiconductor Electronics," McGraw-Hill Book Company, New York, 1962.)

($>10\ \mu\text{F}$), so that its reactance at the frequencies under consideration is very small.

EXAMPLE Assume that a silicon transistor with $\beta = 50$, $V_{BE} = 0.6$ V, $V_{CC} = 22.5$ V, and $R_c = 5.6$ K is used in Fig. 10-6a. It is desired to establish a Q point at $V_{CE} = 12$ V, $I_C = 1.5$ mA, and a stability factor $S \le 3$. Find R_e, R_1, and R_2.

Solution The current in R_e is $I_C + I_B \approx I_C$. Hence, from the collector circuit of Fig. 10-6b, we have

$$R_e + R_c = \frac{V_{CC} - V_{CE}}{I_C} = \frac{22.5 - 12}{1.5} = 7.0 \text{ K}$$

or

$$R_e = 7.0 - 5.6 = 1.4 \text{ K}$$

From Eq. (10-17) we can solve for R_b/R_e:

$$3 = 51 \frac{1 + R_b/R_e}{51 + R_b/R_e}$$

We find $R_b/R_e = 2.12$ and $R_b = 2.12 \times 1.4 = 2.96$ K. If $R_b < 2.96$ K, then $S < 3$.

The base current I_B is given by

$$I_B \approx \frac{I_C}{\beta} = \frac{1.5}{50} \text{ mA} = 30 \ \mu\text{A}$$

We can solve for R_1 and R_2 from Eqs. (10-14). We find

$$R_1 = R_b \frac{V_{CC}}{V} \qquad R_2 = \frac{R_1 V}{V_{CC} - V} \tag{10-18}$$

From Eqs. (10-15) and (10-18) we obtain

$$V = (0.030)(2.96) + 0.6 + (0.030 + 1.5)(1.4) = 2.83 \text{ V}$$

$$R_1 = \frac{2.96 \times 22.5}{2.83} = 23.6 \text{ K}$$

$$R_2 = \frac{23.6 \times 2.83}{22.5 - 2.83} = 3.38 \text{ K}$$

Analysis of the Self-bias Circuit If the circuit component values in Fig. 10-6a are specified, the quiescent point is found as follows: Kirchhoff's voltage law around the collector circuit yields

$$-V_{CC} + I_C(R_c + R_e) + I_B R_e + V_{CE} = 0 \tag{10-19}$$

If the drop in R_e due to I_B is neglected compared with that due to I_C, then this relationship between I_C and V_{CE} is a straight line whose slope corresponds to $R_c + R_e$ and whose intercept at $I_C = 0$ is $V_{CE} = V_{CC}$. This load line is drawn on the collector characteristics. If I_C from Eq. (10-19) is substituted in Eq. (10-15), a relationship between I_B and V_{CE} results. Corresponding to each value of I_B given on the collector curves, V_{CE} is calculated and the bias curve is plotted. The intersection of the load line and the bias curve gives the quiescent point.

EXAMPLE A silicon transistor whose common-emitter output characteristics are shown in Fig. 10-8b is used in the circuit of Fig. 10-6a, with $V_{CC} = 22.5$ V, $R_c = 5.6$ K, $R_e = 1$ K, $R_2 = 10$ K, and $R_1 = 90$ K. For this transistor, $\beta = 55$. (*a*) Find the Q point. (*b*) Calculate S.

Solution *a.* From Eqs. (10-14) we have

$$V = \frac{10 \times 22.5}{100} = 2.25 \text{ V} \qquad R_b = \frac{10 \times 90}{100} = 9.0 \text{ K}$$

The equivalent circuit is shown in Fig. 10-8a. The load line corresponding to a total resistance of 6.6 K and a supply of 22.5 V is drawn on the collector characteristics of Fig. 10-8b. Kirchhoff's voltage law applied to the collector and base circuits, respectively, yields (with $V_{BE} = 0.6$)

$$-22.5 + 6.6 I_C + I_B + V_{CE} = 0 \tag{10-20}$$

$$0.6 - 2.25 + I_C + 10.0 I_B = 0 \tag{10-21}$$

Eliminating I_C from these two equations, we find

$$V_{CE} = 65.0 I_B + 11.6$$

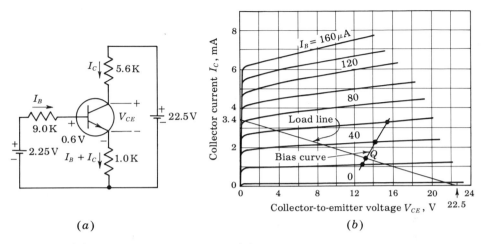

Fig. 10-8 (a) An illustrative example. (b) The intersection of the load line and the bias curve determines the Q point.

Values of V_{CE} corresponding to $I_R = 20$, 40, and 60 μA are obtained from this equation and are plotted in Fig. 10-8b.   We see that the intersection of the bias curve and the load line occurs at $V_{CE} = 13.3$ V, $I_C = 1.4$ mA, and from the bias-curve equation, $I_B = 26\ \mu$A.

In many cases transistor characteristics are not available but β is known. Then the calculation of the Q point may be carried out as follows: In the active region and for base currents large compared with the reverse saturation current ($I_B \gg I_{co}$), it follows from Eq. (10-4) that

$$I_C = \beta I_B \qquad\qquad (10\text{-}22)$$

This equation can now be used in place of the collector characteristics.   Since $\beta = 55$ for the transistor used in this example, substituting $I_B = I_C/55$ in Eq. (10-21) for the base circuit yields

$$-1.65 + I_C + \tfrac{10}{55}I_C = 0$$

or

$$I_C = 1.40 \text{ mA} \qquad \text{and} \qquad I_B = \frac{I_C}{55} = \frac{1.40}{55}\text{ mA} = 25.5\ \mu\text{A}$$

These values are very close to those found from the characteristics.

The collector-to-emitter voltage can be found from Eq. (10-20) and the known values of I_B and I_C:

$$-22.5 + 6.6 \times 1.40 + 0.026 + V_{CE} = 0$$

or

$$V_{CE} = 13.2 \text{ V}$$

b. From Eq. (10-17),

$$S = 56\left(\frac{1+9}{56+9}\right) = 8.61$$

This value is about one-sixth of the stabilization factor for the fixed-bias circuit, which indicates that a great improvement in stability can result if self-bias is used.

In the collector-to-base bias circuit the value of R_b is determined from the desired quiescent base current, and no control is exercised over the stabilization factor S. However, in the self-bias circuit, I_B and S may be specified independently because these requirements can be satisfied by the proper choice of R_e and R_b. For this reason, and because generally lower values of S are obtained with the self-bias arrangement, this circuit is more popular than that of Fig. 10-5a.

For the sake of simplicity the resistor R_2 is sometimes omitted from Fig. 10-6a. In such a circuit R_1 is determined by I_B but S cannot be specified as a design parameter. The value of S is calculated from Eq. (10-17), with R_b replaced by R_1.

10-5 STABILIZATION AGAINST VARIATIONS IN V_{BE} AND β FOR THE SELF–BIAS CIRCUIT

In the preceding sections we examine in detail a number of bias circuits which provide stabilization of I_C against variations in I_{CO}. There remain to be considered two other sources of instability in I_C, those due to the variation of V_{BE} and β with temperature and with manufacturing tolerances in the production of transistors. We shall neglect the effect of the change of V_{CE} with temperature, because this variation is very small (Sec. 9-10) and because we assume that the transistor operates in the active region, where I_C is approximately independent of V_{CE}. However, the variation of V_{BE} with temperature has a very important effect on bias stability. For a silicon transistor, V_{BE} is about 0.6 V at room temperature, and for a germanium transistor, it is about 0.2 V. As the temperature increases, $|V_{BE}|$ decreases at the rate of 2.5 mV/°C for both germanium and silicon transistors (Sec. 9-10).

The Transfer Characteristic The output current I_C is plotted in Fig. 10-9 as a function of input voltage for the germanium transistor, type 2N1631. This transfer characteristic for a silicon transistor is given in Fig. 9-21. Each curve shifts to the left at the rate of 2.5 mV/°C (at constant I_C) for increasing temperature. We now examine in detail the effect of the shift in transfer characteristics and the variation of β and I_{CO} with temperature. If Eq. (10-15), obtained by applying KVL around the base circuit of the self-bias circuit of Fig. 10-6b, is combined with Eq. (10-4), which represents the collector characteristics in the active region, the result is

$$V_{BE} = V + (R_b + R_e)\frac{\beta + 1}{\beta} I_{CO} - \frac{R_b + R_e(1 + \beta)}{\beta} I_C \qquad (10\text{-}23)$$

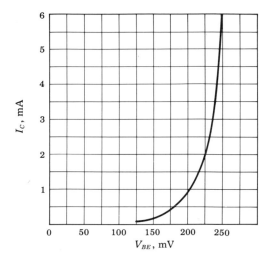

Fig. 10-9 Transfer characteristic for the 2N1631 germanium p-n-p alloy-type transistor at $V_{CE} = -9$ V and $T_A = 25°C$. (Courtesy of Radio Corp. of America.)

Equation (10-23) represents a load line in the I_C-V_{BE} plane, and is indicated in Fig. 10-10. The intercept on the V_{BE} axis is $V + V'$, where

$$V' = (R_b + R_e)\frac{\beta + 1}{\beta} I_{CO} \approx (R_b + R_e)I_{CO} \tag{10-24}$$

since $\beta \gg 1$. If at $T = T_1$ (T_2), $I_C = I_{CO1}$ (I_{CO2}) and $\beta = \beta_1$ (β_2), then $V'_1 \approx (R_b + R_e)I_{CO1}$ and $V'_2 \approx (R_b + R_e)I_{CO2}$. Hence the intercept of the load line on the V_{BE} axis is a function of temperature because I_{CO} increases with T. The slope of the load line is

$$\sigma = \frac{-\beta}{R_b + R_e(1 + \beta)}$$

and hence $|\sigma|$ increases with T because β increases with T. The transfer characteristic for $T = T_2 > T_1$ shifts to the left of the corresponding curve for

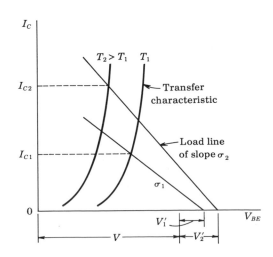

Fig. 10-10 Illustrating that the collector current varies with temperature T because V_{BE}, I_{CO}, and β change with T.

$T = T_1$ because V_{BE} (at constant I_C) varies with T as indicated above. The intersection of the load line with the transfer characteristic gives the collector current I_C. We see that $I_{C2} > I_{C1}$ because I_{CO}, β, and V_{BE} all vary with temperature.

The Stability Factor S'   The variation of I_C with V_{BE} is given by the stability factor S', defined by

$$S' \equiv \frac{\partial I_C}{\partial V_{BE}} \tag{10-25}$$

where both I_{CO} and β are considered constant. From Eq. (10-23) we find

$$S' = \frac{-\beta}{R_b + R_e(1 + \beta)} = -\frac{S}{R_b + R_e}\frac{\beta}{\beta + 1} \tag{10-26}$$

where we made use of Eq. (10-17). We now see from Eq. (10-26) that as we reduce S toward unity, we minimize the change of I_C with respect to both V_{BE} and I_{CO}.

The Stability Factor S''   The variation of I_C with respect to β is given by the stability factor S'', defined by

$$S'' \equiv \frac{\partial I_C}{\partial \beta} \tag{10-27}$$

where both I_{CO} and V_{BE} are considered constant. From Eq. (10-23),

$$I_C = \frac{\beta(V + V' - V_{BE})}{R_b + R_e(1 + \beta)} \tag{10-28}$$

where, from Eq. (10-24), V' may be taken to be independent of β. We obtain, after differentiation and some algebraic manipulation,

$$S'' = \frac{\partial I_C}{\partial \beta} = \frac{I_C S}{\beta(1 + \beta)} \tag{10-29}$$

A difficulty arises in the use of S'' which is not present with S and S'. The change in collector current due to a change in β is

$$\Delta I_C = S'' \Delta\beta = \frac{I_C S}{\beta(1 + \beta)} \Delta\beta \tag{10-30}$$

where $\Delta\beta = \beta_2 - \beta_1$ may represent a large change in β. Hence it is not clear whether to use β_1, β_2, or perhaps some average value of β in the expressions for S'' and S. This difficulty is avoided if S'' is obtained by taking finite differences rather than by evaluating a derivative. Thus

$$S'' = \frac{I_{C2} - I_{C1}}{\beta_2 - \beta_1} = \frac{\Delta I_C}{\Delta\beta} \tag{10-31}$$

From Eq. (10-28), we have

$$\frac{I_{C2}}{I_{C1}} = \frac{\beta_2 R_b + R_e(1 + \beta_1)}{\beta_1 R_b + R_e(1 + \beta_2)} \tag{10-32}$$

Subtracting unity from both sides of Eq. (10-32) yields

$$\frac{I_{C2}}{I_{C1}} - 1 = \left(\frac{\beta_2}{\beta_1} - 1\right)\frac{R_b + R_e}{R_b + R_e(1 + \beta_2)} \tag{10-33}$$

or

$$S'' = \frac{\Delta I_C}{\Delta \beta} = \frac{I_{C1}S_2}{\beta_1(1 + \beta_2)} \tag{10-34}$$

where S_2 is the value of the stabilizing factor S when $\beta = \beta_2$ as given by Eq. (10-17). Note that this equation reduces to Eq. (10-29) as $\Delta\beta = \beta_2 - \beta_1 \to 0$. It is clear from Eq. (10-29) that minimizing S also minimizes S''. This means that the ratio R_b/R_e must be small. From Eq. (10-26) it is seen that, in order to keep S' small, a large R_b or R_e is required. Hence, in all cases, it is desirable to use as large an emitter resistance R_e as practical, and a compromise will usually be necessary for the selection of R_b.

In the examples given previously, illustrating how to design a bias network, the stability factor S was arbitrarily chosen. Equation (10-34) is of prime importance because it allows us to determine the maximum value of S allowed for a given spread of β. This variation in β may be due to any cause, such as a temperature change, a transistor replacement, etc.

EXAMPLE Transistor type 2N335, used in the circuit of Fig. 10-6a, may have any value of β between 36 and 90 at a temperature of 25°C, and the leakage current I_{CO} has negligible effect on I_C at room temperature. Find R_e, R_1, and R_2 subject to the following specifications: $R_c = 4$ K, $V_{CC} = 20$ V; the nominal bias point is to be at $V_{CE} = 10$ V, $I_C = 2$ mA; and I_C should be in the range 1.75 to 2.25 mA as β varies from 36 to 90.

Solution From the collector circuit (with $I_C \gg I_B$),

$$R_c + R_e = \frac{V_{CC} - V_{CE}}{I_C} = \frac{20 - 10}{2} = 5 \text{ K}$$

Hence $R_e = 5 - 4 = 1$ K.

From Eq. (10-34) we can solve for S_2. Hence, with $\Delta I_C = 0.5$ mA, $I_{C1} = 1.75$ mA, $\beta_1 = 36$, $\beta_2 = 90$, and $\Delta\beta = 54$, we obtain

$$\frac{0.5}{54} = \frac{1.75}{36}\frac{S_2}{1 + 90}$$

or

$$S_2 = 17.3$$

Substituting $S_2 = 17.3$, $R_e = 1$ K, and $\beta_2 = 90$ in Eq. (10-17) yields

$$(17.3)(91 + R_b) = 91(1 + R_b)$$

or

$$R_b = 20.1 \text{ K}$$

From Eq. (10-23), with $I_C = 1.75$ mA, $\beta = 36$, $R_b = 20.1$ K, $R_e = 1$ K, $V_{BE} = 0.6$ V, and $I_{CO} = 0$, we obtain

$$V = V_{BE} + \frac{R_b + R_e(1 + \beta)}{\beta} I_C = 0.6 + \left(\frac{20.1 + 37}{36}\right)(1.75) = 3.38 \text{ V}$$

From Eqs. (10-18),

$$R_1 = R_b \frac{V_{CC}}{V} = 20.1 \times \frac{20}{3.38} = 119 \text{ K}$$

$$R_2 = \frac{R_1 V}{V_{CC} - V} = \frac{119 \times 3.38}{20 - 3.38} = 24.2 \text{ K}$$

10-6   GENERAL REMARKS ON COLLECTOR–CURRENT STABILITY[1]

Stability factors were defined in the preceding sections, which considered the change in collector current with respect to I_{CO}, V_{BE}, and β. These stability factors are repeated here for convenience:

$$S = \frac{\Delta I_C}{\Delta I_{CO}} \qquad S' = \frac{\Delta I_C}{\Delta V_{BE}} \qquad S'' = \frac{\Delta I_C}{\Delta \beta} \tag{10-35}$$

Each differential quotient (partial derivative) is calculated with all other parameters maintained constant.

If we desire to obtain the total change in collector current over a specified temperature range, we can do so by expressing this change as the sum of the individual changes due to the three stability factors. Specifically, by taking the total differential of $I_C = f(I_{CO}, V_{BE}, \beta)$, we obtain

$$\Delta I_C = \frac{\partial I_C}{\partial I_{CO}} \Delta I_{CO} + \frac{\partial I_C}{\partial V_{BE}} \Delta V_{BE} + \frac{\partial I_C}{\partial \beta} \Delta \beta$$

$$= S \Delta I_{CO} + S' \Delta V_{BE} + S'' \Delta \beta \tag{10-36}$$

If ΔI_C is known, the corresponding change in V_{CE} can be obtained from the dc load line.

We now examine in detail the order of magnitude of the terms of Eq. (10-36) for both silicon and germanium transistors over their entire range of temperature operation as specified by transistor manufacturers. This range usually is -65 to $+75°C$ for germanium transistors and -65 to $+175°C$ for silicon transistors.

Tables 10-1 and 10-2 show typical parameters of silicon and germanium

TABLE 10-1   Typical silicon transistor parameters

T, °C	−65	+25	+175
I_{CO}, nA	1.95×10^{-3}	1.0	33,000
β	25	55	100
V_{BE}, V	0.78	0.60	0.225

TABLE 10-2   Typical germanium transistor parameters

T, °C	−65	+25	+75
I_{CO}, μA	1.95×10^{-3}	1.0	32
β	20	55	90
V_{BE}, V	0.38	0.20	0.10

transistors, each having the same β (55) at room temperature. For Si, I_{CO} is much smaller than for Ge. Note that I_{CO} doubles approximately every 10°C and $|V_{BE}|$ decreases by approximately 2.5 mV/°C.

EXAMPLE For the self-bias circuit of Fig. 10-6a, $R_e = 4.7$ K, $R_b = 7.75$ K, and $R_b/R_e = 1.65$. The collector supply voltage and R_e are adjusted to establish a collector current of 1.5 mA.

    a. Determine the variation of I_C in the temperature range of −65 to +175°C when the silicon transistor of Table 10-1 is used.

    b. Repeat (*a*) for the range −65 to +75°C when the germanium transistor of Table 10-2 is used.

Solution   *a.* Since R_e, R_b, and β are known, the stability factor S can be determined at +25°C from Eq. (10-17):

$$S(25°\mathrm{C}) = \frac{(1 + \beta)(1 + R_b/R_e)}{1 + \beta + R_b/R_e} = \frac{(56)(2.65)}{56 + 1.65} = 2.57$$

Similarly, S' at +25°C can be determined from Eq. (10-26):

$$S'(25°\mathrm{C}) = \frac{-S}{R_b + R_e}\frac{\beta}{1 + \beta} = -\left(\frac{2.57}{12.45}\right)\left(\frac{55}{56}\right) = -0.203 \text{ mA/V}$$

The values of S and S' are valid for either a silicon or a germanium transistor operating in the circuit of Fig. 10-6a. Since the stability factor S'' contains both β_1 and β_2, it must be determined individually for each transistor at each new temperature, using Eq. (10-34). Hence, for the silicon transistor at +175°C, we have, using Eq. (10-17),

$$S_2(+175°\mathrm{C}) = (1 + \beta_2)\frac{1 + R_b/R_e}{1 + \beta_2 + R_b/R_e} = \frac{(101)(2.65)}{101 + 1.65} = 2.61$$

Then

$$S''(+175°C) = \frac{I_{C_1}S_2}{\beta_1(1 + \beta_2)} = \frac{(1.5)(2.62)}{(55)(101)} = 0.71 \times 10^{-3} \text{ mA}$$

Similarly,

$$S_2(-65°C) = \frac{(26)(2.65)}{26 + 1.65} = 2.49$$

$$S''(-65°C) = \frac{(1.5)(2.49)}{(55)(26)} = 2.61 \times 10^{-3} \text{ mA}$$

We are now in a position to calculate the change in I_C, using Eq. (10-36) and Table 10-1.

$$\Delta I_C(+175°C) = S\, \Delta I_{CO} + S'\, \Delta V_{BE} + S''\, \Delta \beta$$

$$= (2.57)(33 \times 10^{-3}) + (-0.203)(-0.375) + (0.71 \times 10^{-3})(45)$$

$$= 0.085 + 0.077 + 0.032 = 0.194 \text{ mA}$$

and at $-65°C$,

$$\Delta I_C(-65°C) = (2.57)(-10^{-6}) - (0.203)(0.18) + (2.61 \times 10^{-3})(-30)$$

$$= 0 - 0.036 - 0.078 = -0.114 \text{ mA}$$

Therefore, for the silicon transistor, the collector current will be approximately 1.69 mA at $+175°C$ and 1.39 mA at $-65°C$.

b. To calculate the change in collector current using the germanium transistor, we must compute S'' at $+75$ and $-65°C$.

$$S_2(+75°C) = \frac{(91)(2.65)}{91 + 1.65} = 2.60$$

$$S''(+75°C) = \frac{I_{C_1}S_2}{\beta_1(1 + \beta_2)} = \frac{(1.5)(2.60)}{(55)(91)} = 0.78 \times 10^{-3} \text{ mA}$$

Similarly,

$$S_2(-65°C) = \frac{(21)(2.65)}{21 + 1.65} = 2.45$$

$$S''(-65°C) = \frac{(1.5)(2.45)}{(55)(21)} = 3.18 \times 10^{-3} \text{ mA}$$

Hence the change in collector current is

$$\Delta I_C(+75°C) = (2.57)(31 \times 10^{-3}) + (-0.203)(-0.10) + (0.78 \times 10^{-3})(35)$$

$$= 0.080 + 0.020 + 0.027 = 0.127 \text{ mA}$$

and at $-65°C$,

$$\Delta I_C(-65°C) = (2.57)(-10^{-3}) + (+0.203)(0.18) + (3.18 \times 10^{-3})(-35)$$

$$= -0.002 - 0.036 - 0.111 = -0.149 \text{ mA}$$

Therefore, for the germanium transistor, the collector current will be approximately 1.63 mA at $+75°C$ and 1.35 mA at $-65°C$.

Practical Considerations   The foregoing example illustrates the superiority of silicon over germanium transistors because, approximately, the same change in collector current is obtained for a much higher temperature change in the silicon transistor.   In the above example, with $S = 2.57$, the current change at the extremes of temperature is only about 10 percent.   Hence this circuit could be used at temperatures in excess of 75°C for germanium and 175°C for silicon.   If S is larger, the current instability is greater.   For example, in Prob. 10-19, we find for $R_e = 1$ K and $S = 7.70$ that the collector current varies about 30 percent at -65°C and $+75$°C (Ge) or $+175$°C (Si). These numerical values illustrate why a germanium transistor is seldom used above 75°C, and a silicon device above 175°C.   The importance of keeping S small is clear.

The change in collector current that can be tolerated in any specific application depends on design requirements, such as peak signal voltage required across R_c.   We should also point out that the tolerance in bias resistors and supply voltages must be taken into account, in addition to the variation of β, I_{CO}, and V_{BE}.

Our discussion of stability and the results obtained are independent of R_c, and hence they remain valid for $R_c = 0$.   If the output is taken across R_e, such a circuit is called *an emitter follower* (discussed in detail in Sec. 12-8). If we have a direct-coupled emitter follower *driven from an ideal voltage source*, then $R_b = 0$ and S is at its lowest possible value, namely, $S = 1$.   It is clear that a circuit with $R_b = 0$ can be used to a higher temperature than a similar circuit with $R_b \neq 0$.

In the above example the increase in collector current from 25 to 75°C for a germanium transistor is 0.08 mA due to I_{CO} and 0.02 mA due to V_{BE}. Hence, for Ge, the effect of I_{CO} has the dominant influence on the collector current.   On the other hand, the increase in I_C for a silicon transistor over the range from 25 to 175°C due to I_{CO} is approximately the same as that due to V_{BE}.   However, if the temperature range is restricted somewhat, say, from 25 to 145°C, then $\Delta I_C = 0.01$ mA due to I_{CO} and $\Delta I_C = 0.06$ mA due to V_{BE}.   These numbers are computed as follows: If T_{max} is reduced from 175 to 145°C, or by 30°, then I_{CO} is divided by $2^{\Delta T/10} = 2^3 = 8$.   Hence $S \Delta I_{CO} = 0.085/8 \approx 0.01$ mA.   Also, ΔV_{BE} is increased by $(30)(2.5) = 75$ mV, or ΔV_{BE} goes from -0.375 to -0.30 V and $S' \Delta V_{BE} = (-0.2)(-0.30) = 0.06$ mA.   Hence, for Si, the effect of V_{BE} has the dominant influence on the collector current.

10-7   BIAS COMPENSATION[1]

The collector-to-base bias circuit of Fig. 10-5a and the self-bias circuit of Fig. 10-6a are used to limit the variation in the operating collector current I_C caused by variations in I_{CO}, V_{BE}, and β.   These circuits are examples of feedback amplifiers, which are studied in Chap. 17, where it is found that a

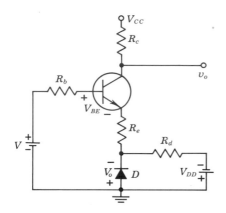

Fig. 10-11 Stabilization by means of self-bias and diode-compensation techniques.

consequence of feedback is to reduce drastically the amplification of the signal. If this loss in signal gain is intolerable in a particular application, it is often possible to use compensating techniques to reduce the drift of the operating point. Very often both stabilization and compensation techniques are used to provide maximum bias and thermal stabilization.

Diode Compensation for V_{BE} A circuit utilizing the self-bias stabilization technique and diode compensation is shown in Fig. 10-11. The diode is kept biased in the forward direction by the source V_{DD} and resistance R_d. If the diode is of the same material and type as the transistor, the voltage V_o across the diode will have the same temperature coefficient (-2.5 mV/°C) as the base-to-emitter voltage V_{BE}. If we write KVL around the base circuit of Fig. 10-11, then Eq. (10-28) becomes

$$I_C = \frac{\beta[V - (V_{BE} - V_o)] + (R_b + R_e)(\beta + 1)I_{CO}}{R_b + R_e(1 + \beta)} \qquad (10\text{-}37)$$

Since V_{BE} tracks V_o with respect to temperature, it is clear from Eq. (10-37) that I_C will be insensitive to variations in V_{BE}. In practice, the compensation of V_{BE} as explained above is not exact, but it is sufficiently effective to take care of a great part of transistor drift due to variations in V_{BE}.

Diode Compensation for I_{CO} We demonstrate in Sec. 10-6 that changes of V_{BE} with temperature contribute significantly to changes in collector current of silicon transistors. On the other hand, for germanium transistors, changes in I_{CO} with temperature play the more important role in collector-current stability. The diode compensation circuit shown in Fig. 10-12 offers stabilization against variations in I_{CO}, and is therefore useful for stabilizing germanium transistors.

If the diode and the transistor are of the same type and material, the reverse saturation current I_o of the diode will increase with temperature at

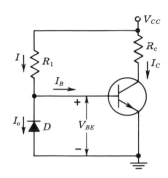

Fig. 10-12　Diode compensation for a germanium transistor.

the same rate as the transistor collector saturation current I_{CO}. From Fig. 10-12 we have

$$I = \frac{V_{CC} - V_{BE}}{R_1} \approx \frac{V_{CC}}{R_1} = \text{const}$$

Since the diode is reverse-biased by an amount $V_{BE} \approx 0.2$ V for germanium devices, it follows that the current through D is I_o. The base current is $I_B = I - I_o$. Substituting this expression for I_B in Eq. (10-4), we obtain

$$I_C = \beta I - \beta I_o + (1 + \beta)I_{CO} \tag{10-38}$$

We see from Eq. (10-38) that if $\beta \gg 1$ and if I_o of D and I_{CO} of Q track each other over the desired temperature range, then I_C remains essentially constant.

10-8　BIASING CIRCUITS FOR LINEAR INTEGRATED CIRCUITS[2]

In Chap. 15 we study the fabrication techniques employed to construct integrated circuits. These circuits consist of transistors, diodes, resistors, and capacitors, *all made with silicon and silicon oxides* in one piece of crystal or chip. One of the most basic problems encountered in linear integrated circuits is bias stabilization of a common-emitter amplifier. The self-bias circuit of Fig. 10-6a is impractical because the bypass capacitor required across R_e is much too large (usually in excess of 10 μF) to be fabricated with present-day integrated-circuit technology. This technology offers specific advantages, which are exploited in the biasing circuits of Fig. 10-13a and b. The special features are (1) close matching of active and passive devices over a wide temperature range; (2) excellent thermal coupling, since the whole circuit is fabricated on a very tiny chip of crystal material (approximately 90 mils square); and (3) the active components made with this technology are no more expensive than the passive components. Hence transistors or diodes can be used economically in place of resistors.

　　The biasing technique shown in Fig. 10-13a uses transistor $Q1$ connected as a diode across the base-to-emitter junction of transistor $Q2$, whose collector

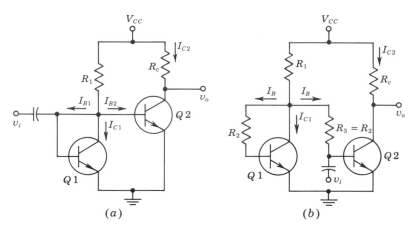

Fig. 10-13 Biasing techniques for linear integrated circuits.

current is to be temperature-stabilized.   The collector current of $Q1$ is given by

$$I_{C1} = \frac{V_{CC} - V_{BE}}{R_1} - I_{B1} - I_{B2} \qquad (10\text{-}39)$$

For $V_{BE} \ll V_{CC}$ and $(I_{B1} + I_{B2}) \ll I_{C1}$, Eq. (10-39) becomes

$$I_{C1} \approx \frac{V_{CC}}{R_1} = \text{const} \qquad (10\text{-}40)$$

If transistors $Q1$ and $Q2$ are identical and have the same V_{BE}, their collector currents will be equal.   Hence $I_{C2} = I_{C1} = \text{const}$.   Even if the two transistors are not identical, experiments[2] have shown that this biasing scheme gives collector-current matching between the biasing and operating transistors typically better than 5 percent and is stable over a wide temperature range.

The circuit of Fig. 10-13a is modified as indicated in Fig. 10-13b so that the transistors are driven by equal base currents rather than the same base voltage.   Since the collector current in the active region varies linearly with I_B, but exponentially with V_{BE}, improved matching of collector currents results.   The resistors R_2 and R_3 are fabricated in an identical manner, so that $R_3 = R_2$.   Since the two bases are driven from a common voltage node through equal resistances, then $I_{B1} = I_{B2} \equiv I_B$, and the collector currents are well matched for identically constructed transistors.

From Fig. 10-13b, the collector current of $Q1$ is given by

$$I_{C1} = \frac{V_{CC} - V_{BE}}{R_1} - \left(2 + \frac{R_2}{R_1}\right) I_B \qquad (10\text{-}41)$$

Under the assumptions that $V_{BE} \ll V_{CC}$, and $(2 + R_2/R_1)I_B \ll V_{CC}/R_1$, Eq. (10-41) becomes

$$I_{C1} = I_{C2} = \frac{V_{CC}}{R_1}$$

If $R_c = \frac{1}{2}R_1$, then $V_{CE} = V_{CC} - I_{c2}R_c \approx V_{CC}/2$, which means that the amplifier will be biased at one-half the supply voltage V_{CC}, independent of the supply voltage as well as temperature, and dependent only on the matching of components within the integrated circuit. An evaluation of the effects of mismatch in this circuit on bias stability is given in Ref. 2.

10-9 THERMISTOR AND SENSISTOR COMPENSATION[1]

There is a method of transistor compensation which involves the use of temperature-sensitive resistive elements rather than diodes or transistors. The *thermistor* (Sec. 5-2) has a negative temperature coefficient, its resistance decreasing exponentially with increasing T. The circuit of Fig. 10-14 uses a thermistor R_T to minimize the increase in collector current due to changes in I_{CO}, V_{BE}, or β with T. As T rises, R_T decreases, and the current fed through R_T into R_e increases. Since the voltage drop across R_e is in the direction to reverse-bias the transistor, the temperature sensitivity of R_T acts so as to tend to compensate the increase in I_C due to T.

An alternative configuration using thermistor compensation is to move R_T from its position in Fig. 10-14 and place it across R_2. As T increases, the drop across R_T decreases, and hence the forward-biasing base voltage is reduced. This behavior will tend to offset the increase in collector current with temperature.

Instead of a thermistor, it is possible to use a temperature-sensitive resistor with a positive temperature coefficient such as a metal, or the *sensistor* (manufactured by Texas Instruments). The sensistor has a temperature coefficient of resistance which is $+0.7$ percent/°C (over the range from -60 to $+150$°C). A heavily doped semiconductor can exhibit a positive temperature coefficient of resistance, for under these conditions the material acquires metallic properties and the resistance increases because of the decrease of carrier mobility with temperature. In the circuit of Fig. 10-14 (with R_T

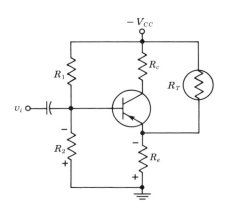

Fig. 10-14 Thermistor compensation of the increase in I_C with T.

removed), temperature compensation may be obtained by placing a sensistor either in parallel with R_1 or in parallel with (or in place of) R_e. Why?

In practice it is often necessary to use silicon resistors and carbon resistors in series or parallel combinations to form the proper shaping network.[3] The characteristics required to eliminate the temperature effects can be determined experimentally as follows: A variable resistance is substituted for the shaping network and is adjusted to maintain constant collector current as the operating temperature changes. The resistance vs. temperature can then be plotted to indicate the required characteristics of the shaping network. The problem now is reduced to that of synthesizing a network with this measured temperature characteristic by using thermistors or sensistors padded with temperature-insensitive resistors.

10-10   THERMAL RUNAWAY

The maximum average power P_D(max) which a transistor can dissipate depends upon the transistor construction and may lie in the range from a few milliwatts to 200 W. This maximum power is limited by the temperature that the collector-to-base junction can withstand. For silicon transistors this temperature is in the range 150 to 225°C, and for germanium it is between 60 and 100°C. The junction temperature may rise either because the ambient temperature rises or because of self-heating. The maximum power dissipation is usually specified for the transistor enclosure (case) or ambient temperature of 25°C. The problem of self-heating, which is mentioned in Sec. 10-2, results from the power dissipated at the collector junction. As a consequence of the junction power dissipation, the junction temperature rises, and this in turn increases the collector current, with a subsequent increase in power dissipation. If this phenomenon, referred to as *thermal runaway*, continues, it may result in permanently damaging the transistor.

Thermal Resistance It is found experimentally that the steady-state temperature rise at the collector junction is proportional to the power dissipated at the junction, or

$$\Delta T = T_j - T_A = \Theta P_D \tag{10-42}$$

where T_j and T_A are the junction and ambient temperatures, respectively, in degrees centigrade, and P_D is the power in watts dissipated at the collector junction. The constant of proportionality Θ is called the *thermal resistance*. Its value depends on the size of the transistor, on convection or radiation to the surroundings, on forced-air cooling (if used), and on the thermal connection of the device to a metal chassis or to a heat sink. Typical values for various transistor designs vary from 0.2°C/W for a high-power transistor with an efficient heat sink to 1000°C/W for a low-power transistor in free air.

The maximum collector power P_C allowed for safe operation is specified

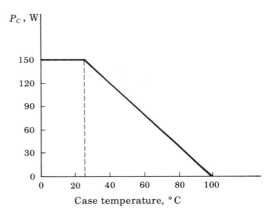

Fig. 10-15 Power-temperature derating curve for a germanium power transistor.

at 25°C.   For ambient temperatures above this value, P_C must be decreased, and at the extreme temperature at which the transistor may operate, P_C is reduced to zero.   A typical power-temperature derating curve, supplied in a manufacturer's specification sheet, is indicated in Fig. 10-15.

Operating-point Considerations   The effects of self-heating may be appreciated by referring to Fig. 10-16, which shows three constant-power hyperbolas and a dc load line tangent to one of them.   It can be shown (Prob. 10-26) that the point of tangency C bisects the load line AB.   Consider that the quiescent point is above the point of tangency, say at Q_1.   If now the collector current increases, the result is a *lower* collector dissipation because Q_1 moves along the load line in the direction away from the 300 W toward the 100-W parabola.   The opposite is true if the quiescent point is below the point of tangency, such as at Q_2.   We can conclude that if V_{CE} is less than $V_{CC}/2$, the quiescent point lies in a safe region, where an increase in collector current results in a decreased dissipation.   If, on the other hand, the operating

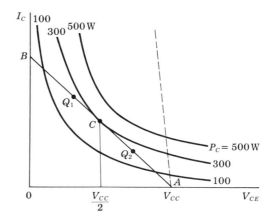

Fig. 10-16 Concerning transistor self-heating. The dashed load line corresponds to a very small dc resistance.

point is located so that $V_{CE} > V_{CC}/2$, the self-heating results in even more collector dissipation, and the effect is cumulative.

It is not always possible to select an operating point which satisfies the restriction $V_{CE} < \frac{1}{2}V_{CC}$. For example, if the load R_L is transformer-coupled to the collector, as in Fig. 10-17, then R_c represents the small primary dc resistance, and hence the load line is almost vertical, as indicated by the dashed line in Fig. 10-16. Clearly V_{CE} can be less than $\frac{1}{2}V_{CC}$ only for excessively large collector currents. Hence thermal runaway can easily occur with a transformer-coupled load or with a power amplifier which has small collector and emitter resistances. For such circuits it is particularly important to take precautions to keep the stability factors (discussed in the preceding sections) so small as to maintain essentially constant collector current.

The Condition for Thermal Stability We now obtain the restrictions to be met if thermal runaway is to be avoided. The required condition is that the rate at which heat is released at the collector junction must not exceed the rate at which the heat can be dissipated; that is,

$$\frac{\partial P_C}{\partial T_j} < \frac{\partial P_D}{\partial T_j} \tag{10-43}$$

If we differentiate Eq. (10-42) with respect to T_j and substitute in Eq. (10-43), we obtain

$$\frac{\partial P_C}{\partial T_j} < \frac{1}{\Theta} \tag{10-44}$$

This condition must be satisfied to prevent thermal runaway. By suitable circuit design it is possible to ensure that the transistor cannot run away below a specified ambient temperature or even under any conditions. Such an analysis is made in the next section.

10-11   THERMAL STABILITY

Let us refer to Fig. 10-6a and assume that the transistor is biased in the active region. The power generated at the collector junction with no signal is

$$P_C = I_C V_{CB} \approx I_C V_{CE} \tag{10-45}$$

If we assume that the quiescent collector and emitter currents are essentially equal, Eq. (10-45) becomes

$$P_C = I_C V_{CC} - I_C{}^2(R_e + R_c) \tag{10-46}$$

Equation (10-44), the condition to avoid thermal runaway, can be rewritten as follows:

$$\frac{\partial P_C}{\partial I_C}\frac{\partial I_C}{\partial T_j} < \frac{1}{\Theta} \tag{10-47}$$

The first partial derivative of Eq. (10-47) can be obtained from Eq. (10-46):

$$\frac{\partial P_C}{\partial I_C} = V_{CC} - 2I_C(R_e + R_c) \tag{10-48}$$

The second partial derivative in Eq. (10-47) gives the rate at which collector current increases with temperature. From our discussion in this chapter we know that junction temperature affects collector current by affecting I_{CO}, V_{BE}, and β. Hence we have, from Eq. (10-36),

$$\frac{\partial I_C}{\partial T_j} = S\frac{\partial I_{CO}}{\partial T_j} + S'\frac{\partial V_{BE}}{\partial T_j} + S''\frac{\partial \beta}{\partial T_j} \tag{10-49}$$

Since for any given transistor the derivatives in Eq. (10-49) are known, the designer is required to satisfy Eq. (10-47) by the proper selection of S, S', S'', and Θ. In some practical problems the effect of I_{CO} dominates, and we present an analysis of the thermal-runaway problem for this case. From Eqs. (10-47) and (10-49),

$$\frac{\partial P_C}{\partial I_C}\left(S\frac{\partial I_{CO}}{\partial T_j}\right) < \frac{1}{\Theta} \tag{10-50}$$

In Sec. 6-7 it is noted that the reverse saturation current for either silicon or germanium increases about 7 percent/°C, or

$$\frac{\partial I_{CO}}{\partial T_j} = 0.07 I_{CO} \tag{10-51}$$

Substituting Eqs. (10-48) and (10-51) in Eq. (10-50) results in

$$[V_{CC} - 2I_C(R_e + R_c)](S)(0.07I_{CO}) < \frac{1}{\Theta} \tag{10-52}$$

Equation (10-52) remains valid for a *p-n-p* transistor provided that I_C (and I_{CO}) are understood to represent the magnitude of the current. Remembering that Θ, S, and I_{CO} are positive, we see that the inequality (10-52) is always satisfied provided that the quantity in the brackets is negative, or provided that

$$I_C > \frac{V_{CC}}{2(R_e + R_c)} \tag{10-53}$$

Since $V_{CE} = V_{CC} - I_C(R_e + R_c)$, then Eq. (10-53) implies that $V_{CE} < V_{CC}/2$, and this checks with our previous conclusion from Fig. 10-16. If the inequality of Eq. (10-53) is not satisfied and $V_{CE} > V_{CC}/2$, then from Eq. (10-48) we see that $\partial P_C/\partial I_C$ is positive, and the designer must ensure that Eq. (10-50) will be satisfied, or else thermal runaway will occur.

EXAMPLE Find the value of Θ required for the transistor of the example on page 274 in order for the circuit to be thermally stable. Assume that $I_{CO} = 1$ nA at 25°C.

Solution   Since $V_{CC}/2 = 11.25$ V and $V_{CE} = 13.3$ V, the circuit is not inherently stable, because $V_{CE} > \frac{1}{2}V_{CC}$. Substituting in Eq. (10-52), we obtain

$$[22.5 - 2 \times 1.4 \times (5.6 + 1.0)](8.61)(0.07 \times 10^{-9}) < \frac{1}{\Theta}$$

$$4.0 \times 8.61 \times 0.07 \times 10^{-9} < \frac{1}{\Theta}$$

or

$$\Theta < 4.1 \times 10^8 \text{ °C/W}$$

The upper bound on the value of Θ is so high that no transistor can violate it, and therefore this circuit will always be safe from thermal runaway.

This example illustrates that amplifier circuits operated at low current and designed with low values of stability factor ($S < 10$) are very rarely susceptible to thermal runaway. In contrast, power amplifiers operate at high power levels. In addition, in such circuits R_e is a small resistance for power efficiency, and this results in a high stability factor S. As a result, thermal runaway in power stages is a major consideration, and the designer must guard against it.

EXAMPLE   Figure 10-17 shows a power amplifier using a *p-n-p* germanium transistor with $\beta = 100$ and $I_{CO} = -5$ mA. The quiescent collector current is $I_C = -1$ A. Find (*a*) the value of resistor R_b; (*b*) the largest value of Θ that can result in a thermally stable circuit.

Solution   *a.* The collector current is given by Eq. (10-4), or

$$I_C = \beta I_B + (1 + \beta)I_{CO} \approx \beta(I_B + I_{CO})$$

and

$$I_B = -\frac{1 - 5 \times 10^{-3} \times 100}{100} \text{ A} = -5 \text{ mA}$$

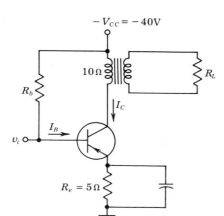

Fig. 10-17   Power amplifier with a transformer-coupled load.

If we neglect V_{BE}, we have

$$5 \times 10^{-3} R_b = 40 - 5 \qquad \text{or} \qquad R_b = 7,000 \ \Omega$$

b. Since $|V_{CE}| = 40 - 15 = 25 > \frac{1}{2}|V_{CC}| = 20$ V, the circuit of Fig. 10-17 is not inherently stable. The stability factor S is obtained from Eq. (10-17).

$$S = 101 \frac{1 + 7,000/5}{101 + 7,000/5} = 94.3$$

Substituting in Eq. (10-52), we obtain

$$(40 - 2 \times 1 \times 15)(94.3)(0.07 \times 5 \times 10^{-3}) < \frac{1}{\Theta}$$

or

$$\Theta < 3.03°\text{C/W}$$

REFERENCES

1. Hunter, L. P.: "Handbook of Semiconductor Electronics," McGraw-Hill Book Company, New York, 1962.
   "Transistor Manual," 7th ed., General Electric Co., Syracuse, N.Y., 1964.
   "Motorola Power Transistor Handbook," Phoenix, Ariz., 1961.

2. Widlar, R. I.: Some Circuit Design Techniques for Linear Integrated Circuits, *IEEE Trans. Circuit Theory*, vol. CT-12, no. 4, pp. 586–590, December, 1965.

3. Konjian, E., and J. S. Schaffner: Shaping of the Characteristics of Temperature-sensitive Elements, *Commun. and Electron.*, vol. 14, pp. 396–400, September, 1954.

11 / SMALL-SIGNAL LOW-FREQUENCY TRANSISTOR MODELS

In Chap. 9 we are primarily interested in the static characteristics of a transistor. In the active region the transistor operates with reasonable linearity, and we now inquire into small-signal linear models which represent the operation of the transistor in this active region. The parameters introduced in the models presented here are interpreted in terms of the external volt-ampere characteristics of the transistor. Methods for measuring these parameters are also given. Finally, a detailed study of the transistor amplifier in its various configurations is made.

11-1 TWO-PORT DEVICES AND THE HYBRID MODEL

The terminal behavior of a large class of two-port devices is specified by two voltages and two currents. The box in Fig. 11-1 represents such a two-port network. We may select two of the four quantities as the independent variables and express the remaining two in terms of the chosen independent variables. It should be noted that, in general, we are not free to select the independent variables arbitrarily. For example, if the two-port device is an ideal transformer, we cannot pick the two voltages v_1 and v_2 as the independent variables because their ratio is a constant equal to the transformer turns ratio. If the current i_1 and the voltage v_2 are independent and if the two-port is linear, we may write

$$v_1 = h_{11}i_1 + h_{12}v_2 \tag{11-1}$$

$$i_2 = h_{21}i_1 + h_{22}v_2 \tag{11-2}$$

The quantities h_{11}, h_{12}, h_{21}, and h_{22} are called the h, or *hybrid*, *parameters* because they are not all alike dimensionally. Let us assume that there

294

Fig. 11-1   A two-port network.

are no reactive elements within the two-port network.   Then, from Eqs. (11-1) and (11-2), the h parameters are defined as follows:

$$h_{11} \equiv \frac{v_1}{i_1}\bigg|_{v_2 = 0} = \text{ input resistance with output short-circuited (ohms).}$$

$$h_{12} \equiv \frac{v_1}{v_2}\bigg|_{i_1 = 0} = \text{ fraction of output voltage at input with input open-}$$
circuited, or more simply, reverse-open-circuit voltage amplification (dimensionless).

$$h_{21} \equiv \frac{i_2}{i_1}\bigg|_{v_2 = 0} = \text{ negative of current transfer ratio (or current gain)}$$
with output short-circuited.   (Note that the current into a load across the output port would be the negative of i_2.)   This parameter is usually referred to, simply, as the *short-circuit current gain* (dimensionless).

$$h_{22} \equiv \frac{i_2}{v_2}\bigg|_{i_1 = 0} = \text{ output conductance with input open-circuited (mhos).}$$

Notation   The following convenient alternative subscript notation is recommended by the IEEE Standards:[1]

$i = 11 =$ input $o = 22 =$ output

$f = 21 =$ forward transfer $r = 12 =$ reverse transfer

In the case of transistors, another subscript (b, e, or c) is added to designate the type of configuration.   For example,

$h_{ib} = h_{11b} =$ input resistance in common-base configuration

$h_{fe} = h_{21e} =$ short-circuit forward current gain in common-emitter circuit

Since the device described by Eqs. (11-1) and (11-2) is assumed to include no reactive elements, the four parameters h_{11}, h_{12}, h_{21}, and h_{22} are real numbers, and the voltages and currents v_1, v_2, and i_1, i_2 are functions of time.   However, if reactive elements had been included in the device, the excitation would be considered to be sinusoidal, the h parameters would in general be functions of frequency, and the voltages and currents would be represented by phasors V_1, V_2, and I_1, I_2.

The Model   We may now use the four h parameters to construct a mathematical model of the device of Fig. 11-1.   The hybrid circuit for any

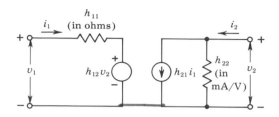

Fig. 11-2 **Fig. 11-2** The hybrid model for the two-port network of Fig. 11-1. The parameters h_{12} and h_{21} are dimensionless.

device characterized by Eqs. (11-1) and (11-2) is indicated in Fig. 11-2. We can verify that the model of Fig. 11-2 satisfies Eqs. (11-1) and (11-2) by writing Kirchhoff's voltage and current laws for the input and output ports, respectively.

11-2　TRANSISTOR HYBRID MODEL

The basic assumption in arriving at a transistor linear model or equivalent circuit is the same as that used in the case of a vacuum tube: the variations about the quiescent point are assumed small, so that the transistor parameters can be considered constant over the signal excursion.

Many transistor models have been proposed, each one having its particular advantages and disadvantages. The transistor model presented in this chapter, and exploited in the next chapter, is given in terms of the h parameters, which are *real numbers* at audio frequencies, are easy to measure, can also be obtained from the transistor static characteristic curves, and are particularly convenient to use in circuit analysis and design. Furthermore, a set of h parameters is specified for many transistors by the manufacturers.

To see how we can derive a hybrid model for a transistor, let us consider the common-emitter connection shown in Fig. 11-3. The variables i_B, i_C, v_B, and v_C represent total instantaneous currents and voltages. From our discussion in Chap. 9 of transistor voltages and currents, we see that we may select the current i_B and voltage v_C as independent variables. Since v_B is some function f_1 of i_B and v_C and since i_C is another function f_2 of i_B and v_C,

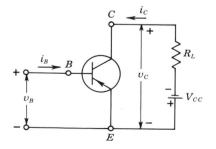

Fig. 11-3 A simple common-emitter connection.

we may write

$$v_B = f_1(i_B, v_C) \tag{11-3}$$

$$i_C = f_2(i_B, v_C) \tag{11-4}$$

Making a Taylor's series expansion of Eqs. (11-3) and (11-4) around the quiescent point I_B, V_C, similar to that of Eq. (8-12), and neglecting higher-order terms, we obtain

$$\Delta v_B = \left.\frac{\partial f_1}{\partial i_B}\right|_{V_C} \Delta i_B + \left.\frac{\partial f_1}{\partial v_C}\right|_{I_B} \Delta v_C \tag{11-5}$$

$$\Delta i_C = \left.\frac{\partial f_2}{\partial i_B}\right|_{V_C} \Delta i_B + \left.\frac{\partial f_2}{\partial v_C}\right|_{I_B} \Delta v_C \tag{11-6}$$

The partial derivatives are taken, keeping the collector voltage or the base current constant, as indicated by the subscript attached to the derivative.

The quantities Δv_B, Δv_C, Δi_B, and Δi_C represent the small-signal (incremental) base and collector voltages and currents. According to the notation in Table 9-1, we represent them with the symbols v_b, v_c, i_b, and i_c. We may now write Eqs. (11-5) and (11-6) in the following form:

$$v_b = h_{ie}i_b + h_{re}v_c \tag{11-7}$$

$$i_c = h_{fe}i_b + h_{oe}v_c \tag{11-8}$$

where

$$h_{ie} \equiv \frac{\partial f_1}{\partial i_B} = \left.\frac{\partial v_B}{\partial i_B}\right|_{V_C} \qquad h_{re} \equiv \frac{\partial f_1}{\partial v_C} = \left.\frac{\partial v_B}{\partial v_C}\right|_{I_B} \tag{11-9}$$

and

$$h_{fe} \equiv \frac{\partial f_2}{\partial i_B} = \left.\frac{\partial i_C}{\partial i_B}\right|_{V_C} \qquad h_{oe} \equiv \frac{\partial f_2}{\partial v_C} = \left.\frac{\partial i_C}{\partial v_C}\right|_{I_B} \tag{11-10}$$

The partial derivatives of Eqs. (11-9) and (11-10) define the h parameters for the common-emitter connection. In the next section we show that the above partial derivatives can be obtained from the transistor characteristic curves and that they are real numbers. We now observe that Eqs. (11-7) and (11-8) are of exactly the same form as Eqs. (11-1) and (11-2). Hence the model of Fig. 11-2 can be used to represent a transistor.

The Three Transistor Configurations   The common-emitter (CE), common-collector (CC), and common-base (CB) configurations, their hybrid models, and the terminel v-i equations are summarized in Table 11-1. We should note here that, for any one of the three different transistor connections, the input and output voltages have a common terminal. Moreover, we note from Kirchhoff's current law that

$$i_b + i_e + i_c = 0 \tag{11-11}$$

TABLE 11-1   Transistor configurations and their hybrid models

Circuit schematic	Hybrid model	v-i equations

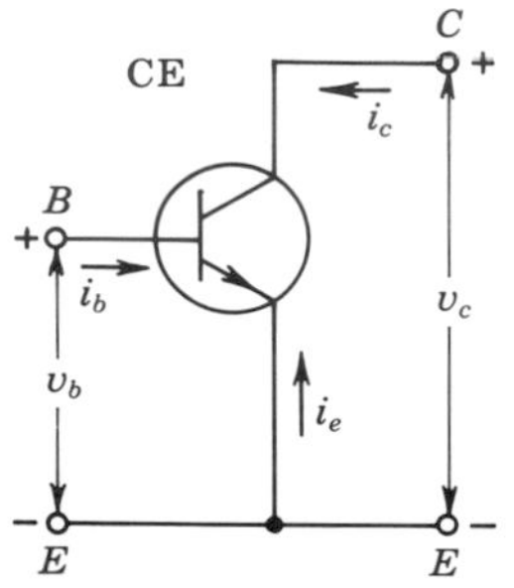

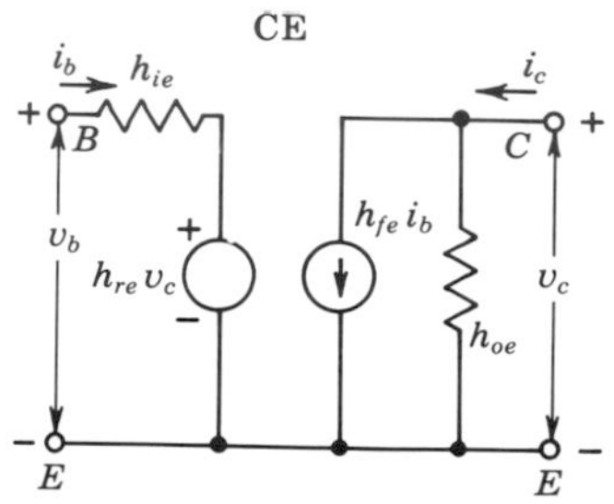

CE

$$v_b = h_{ie}i_b + h_{re}v_c$$
$$i_c = h_{fe}i_b + h_{oe}v_c$$

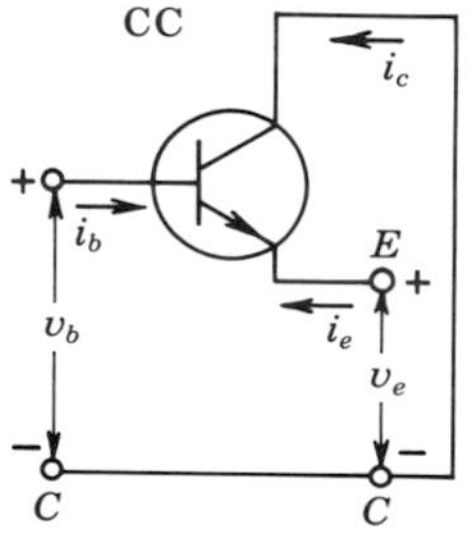

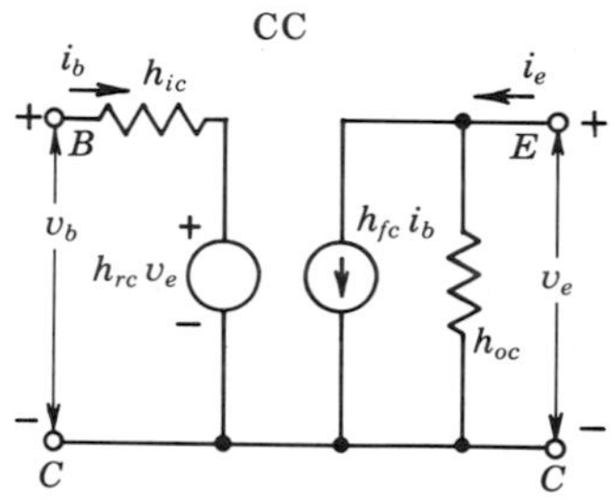

CC

$$v_b = h_{ic}i_b + h_{rc}v_e$$
$$i_e = h_{fc}i_b + h_{oc}v_e$$

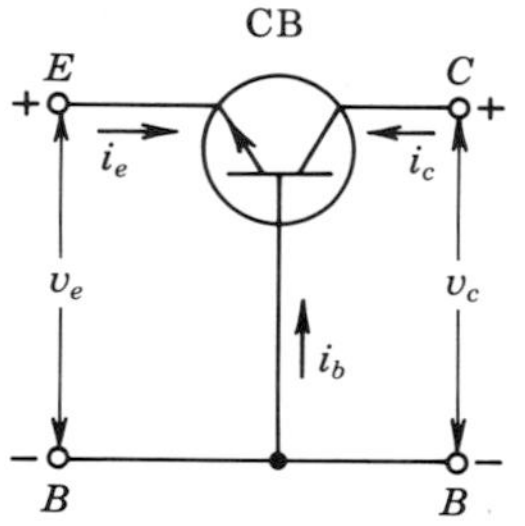

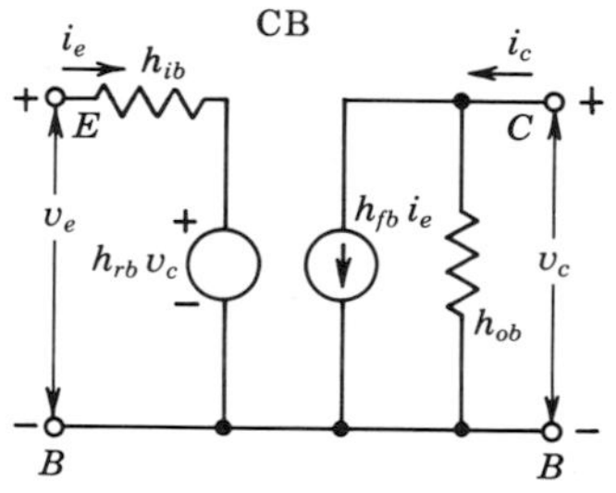

CB

$$v_e = h_{ib}i_e + h_{rb}v_c$$
$$i_c = h_{fb}i_e + h_{ob}v_c$$

The circuits and equations in Table 11-1 are valid for either an n-p-n or p-n-p transistor and are independent of the type of load or method of biasing.

11-3   DETERMINATION OF THE h PARAMETERS FROM THE CHARACTERISTICS[2]

Equations (11-3) and (11-4) give the form of the functional relationships for the common-emitter connection of total instantaneous collector current and base voltage in terms of two variables, namely, base current and collector voltage. Such functional relationships are represented in Chap. 9 by families of characteristic curves. Two families of curves are usually specified for transistors. The *output characteristic curves* depict the relationship between output current and voltage, with input current as the parameter. Figures 9-5 and 9-8 show typical output characteristic curves for the common-base and common-emitter transistor configurations. The *input characteristics* depict the relationship between input voltage and current with output voltage as the parameter. Typical input characteristic curves for the common-base and common-emitter transistor connections are shown in Figs. 9-6 and 9-9. If the input and output characteristics of a particular connection are given, the *h* parameters can be determined graphically.

The Parameter h_{fe} For a common-emitter connection the characteristics are shown in Fig. 11-4. From the definition of h_{fe} given in Eq. (11-10) and from Fig. 11-4a, we have

$$h_{fe} = \frac{\partial i_C}{\partial i_B} \approx \frac{\Delta i_C}{\Delta i_B}\bigg|_{Vc} = \frac{i_{C2} - i_{C1}}{i_{B2} - i_{B1}} \qquad (11\text{-}12)$$

The current increments are taken around the quiescent point Q, which corresponds to the base current $i_B = I_B$ and to the collector voltage $v_{CE} = V_C$ (a vertical line in Fig. 11-4a).

The parameter h_{fe} is the most important small-signal parameter of the transistor. This common-emitter current transfer ratio, or CE alpha, is also written α_e, or β', and called the *small-signal beta* of the transistor. The relationship between $\beta' = h_{fe}$ and the *large-signal beta*, $\beta \approx h_{FE}$, is given in Eq. (9-47).

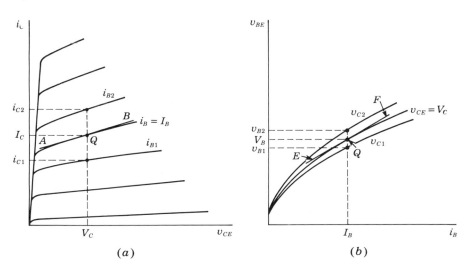

Fig. 11-4 Characteristic curves of a common-emitter transistor. (a) CE output characteristics—determination of h_{fe} and h_{oe}; (b) CE input characteristics—determination of h_{ie} and h_{re}.

The Parameter h_{oe}   From Eq. (11-10),

$$h_{oe} = \frac{\partial i_C}{\partial v_C} \approx \frac{\Delta i_C}{\Delta v_C}\bigg|_{I_B} \tag{11-13}$$

The value of h_{oe} at the quiescent point Q is given by the slope of the output characteristic curve at that point. This slope can be evaluated by drawing the line AB in Fig. 11-4a tangent to the characteristic curve at the point Q.

The Parameter h_{ie}   From Eq. (11-9),

$$h_{ie} = \frac{\partial v_B}{\partial i_B} \approx \frac{\Delta v_B}{\Delta i_B}\bigg|_{V_C} \tag{11-14}$$

Hence the slope of the appropriate input characteristic at the quiescent point Q gives h_{ie}. In Fig. 11-4b, h_{ie} is given by the slope of the line EF, which is drawn tangent to the characteristic curves at the point Q.

The Parameter h_{re}   Finally, from Eq. (11-9),

$$h_{re} = \frac{\partial v_B}{\partial v_C} \approx \frac{\Delta v_B}{\Delta v_C}\bigg|_{I_B} = \frac{v_{B2} - v_{B1}}{v_{C2} - v_{C1}} \tag{11-15}$$

A vertical line on the input characteristics of Fig. 11-4b represents constant base current. The parameter h_{re} can now be obtained as the change in base voltage, $v_{B2} - v_{B1}$, divided by the change in collector voltage, $v_{C1} - v_{C2}$, for a constant base current I_B, at the quiescent point Q. Since $h_{re} \approx 10^{-4}$, then $\Delta v_B \ll \Delta v_C$, and hence the above method, although correct in principle, is very inaccurate in practice.

The procedure outlined here for the determination of the common-emitter h parameters may also be used to obtain the common-base and common-collector h parameters from the appropriate input and output characteristic curves.

Hybrid-parameter Variations   From the discussion in this section we have seen that once a quiescent point Q is specified, the h parameters can be obtained from the slopes and spacing between curves at this point. Since the characteristic curves are not in general straight lines, equally spaced for equal changes in I_B (Fig. 11-4a) or V_{CE} (Fig. 11-4b), it is clear that the values of the h parameters depend upon the position of the quiescent point on the curves. Moreover, from our discussion in Chap. 9, we know that the shape and actual numerical values of the characteristic curves depend on the junction temperature. Hence the h parameters also will depend on temperature. Most transistor specification sheets include curves of the variation of the h parameters with the quiescent point and temperature. Such curves are shown for a typical silicon p-n-p transistor in Fig. 11-5a and b. These curves are plotted with respect to the values of a specific operating point, say -5 V collector-to-emitter voltage and -1 mA collector current. The variation in h parameters as shown

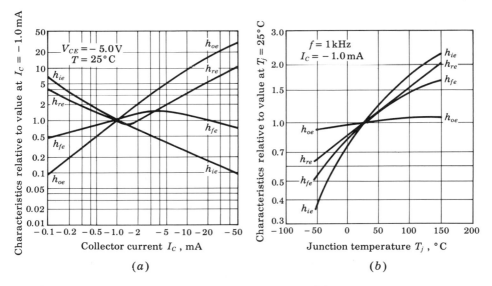

(a)   (b)

Fig. 11-5 Variation of common-emitter h parameters (a) with collector current normalized to unity at $V_{CE} = -5.0$ V and $I_C = -1.0$ mA for the type 2N996 diffused-silicon planar epitaxial transistor; (b) with junction temperature, normalized to unity at $T_j = 25°C$. (Courtesy of Fairchild Semiconductor.)

in Fig. 11-5a is for a constant junction temperature of 25°C and a frequency of 1 kHz. Manufacturers usually also provide curves of h parameters versus V_{CE}, although this variation with V_{CE} is often not significant. Specifically, h_{fe} is more sensitive to I_C than to V_{CE}. Most transistors exhibit a well-defined maximum in the value of h_{fe} as a function of collector or emitter current. Such a maximum in the variation of h_{fe} with emitter current and temperature is shown in Fig. 11-6 for an n-p-n double-diffused silicon mesa transistor.

Fig. 11-6 Variation of h_{fe} with emitter current for the type 2N1573 silicon mesa transistor. (Courtesy of Texas Instruments, Inc.)

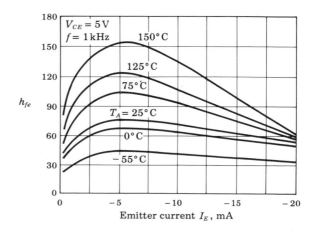

TABLE 11-2 Typical h-parameter values for a transistor (at $I_E = 1.3$ mA)

Parameter	CE	CC	CB
$h_{11} = h_i$	1,100 Ω	1,100 Ω	21.6 Ω
$h_{12} = h_r$	2.5×10^{-4}	~ 1	2.9×10^{-4}
$h_{21} = h_f$	50	-51	-0.98
$h_{22} = h_o$	25 μA/V	25 μA/V	0.49 μA/V
$1/h_o$	40 K	40 K	2.04 M

Table 11-2 shows values of h parameters for the three different transistor configurations of a typical junction transistor.

11-4   MEASUREMENT OF h PARAMETERS[3]

Based on the definitions given in Secs. 11-1 and 11-2, simple experiments may be carried out for the direct measurement of the hybrid parameters. Consider the circuit of Fig. 11-7. The desired quiescent conditions are obtained from adjustable supplies V_{CC}, V_{EE}, and the resistor R_2. The impedance of the tank circuit ($\sim$500 K) at the audio frequency (1 kHz) at which the measurements are made is large compared with the transistor input resistance R_i. The value of R_1 (1 M) is large compared with R_i, and the reactances of C_1, C_2, and C_3 are negligible at the frequency of the sinusoidal generator V_s.

Note that we now use capital letters to represent phasor rms voltages and currents. Hence, Δv_B, Δi_B, Δv_C, and Δi_C of the preceding section are replaced by V_b, I_b, V_c, and I_c, respectively. We may consider the signal-input current to be $I_b = V_s/R_1$. Since R_L is generally 50 Ω, we may consider the transistor output port as short-circuited to the signal.

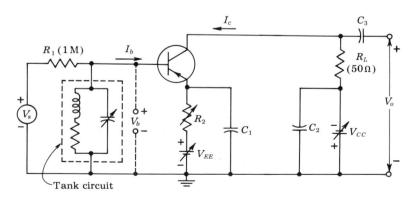

Fig. 11-7 Circuit for measuring h_{ie} and h_{fe}.

The value of h_{ie} is given by Eq. (11-14):

$$h_{ie} = \frac{V_b}{I_b}\bigg|_{V_c=0} = \frac{V_b R_1}{V_s} \tag{11-16}$$

Hence the input resistance h_{ie} may be calculated from the two measured voltages V_s and V_b.

For the parameter h_{fe} we have from Eq. (11-12)

$$h_{fe} = \frac{I_c}{I_b}\bigg|_{V_c=0} = \frac{V_o R_1}{V_s R_L} \tag{11-17}$$

since $I_c = V_o/R_L$. Thus h_{fe} is obtained from the two measured voltages V_o and V_s.

The circuit of Fig. 11-8 may be used to measure h_{re} and h_{oe}. The signal is now applied to the collector circuit using a transformer. Because the impedance of the tank circuit is large compared with R_i, the base circuit may be considered effectively open-circuited as far as the signal is concerned.

We then obtain from Eq. (11-15)

$$h_{re} = \frac{V_b}{V_c}\bigg|_{I_b=0} = \frac{V_b}{V_c} \tag{11-18}$$

The output conductance is defined by Eq. (11-13):

$$h_{oe} = \frac{I_c}{V_c}\bigg|_{I_b=0} = \frac{V_o}{R_L V_c} \tag{11-19}$$

Hence h_{oe} is obtained from the measured voltages V_o and V_c.

In measuring V_o, V_b, and V_c it is necessary to ground one side of the voltmeter to avoid stray pickup. This can be done by using a high input resistance voltmeter with one side connected, through a capacitor, to point A, or to the base or to the collector, and with the other side of the meter grounded.

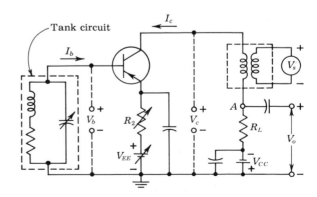

Fig. 11-8 Circuit for measuring h_{re} and h_{oe}.

TABLE 11-3 Approximate conversion formulas for transistor parameters
(numerical values are for a typical transistor Q)

Symbol	Common emitter	Common collector	Common base	T equivalent circuit
h_{ie}	$1{,}100\ \Omega$	$h_{ic}\dagger$	$\dfrac{h_{ib}}{1 + h_{fb}}$	$r_b + \dfrac{r_e}{1 - a}$
h_{re}	2.5×10^{-4}	$1 - h_{rc}\dagger$	$\dfrac{h_{ib}h_{ob}}{1 + h_{fb}} - h_{rb}$	$\dfrac{r_e}{(1 - a)r_c}$
h_{fe}	50	$-(1 + h_{fc})\dagger$	$-\dfrac{h_{fb}}{1 + h_{fb}}$	$\dfrac{a}{1 - a}$
h_{oe}	$25\ \mu\text{A/V}$	$h_{oc}\dagger$	$\dfrac{h_{ob}}{1 + h_{fb}}$	$\dfrac{1}{(1 - a)r_c}$
h_{ib}	$\dfrac{h_{ie}}{1 + h_{fe}}$	$-\dfrac{h_{ic}}{h_{fc}}$	$21.6\ \Omega$	$r_e + (1 - a)r_b$
h_{rb}	$\dfrac{h_{ie}h_{oe}}{1 + h_{fe}} - h_{re}$	$h_{rc} - \dfrac{h_{ic}h_{oc}}{h_{fc}} - 1$	2.9×10^{-4}	$\dfrac{r_b}{r_c}$
h_{fb}	$-\dfrac{h_{fe}}{1 + h_{fe}}$	$-\dfrac{1 + h_{fc}}{h_{fc}}$	-0.98	$-a$
h_{ob}	$\dfrac{h_{oe}}{1 + h_{fe}}$	$-\dfrac{h_{oc}}{h_{fc}}$	$0.49\ \mu\text{A/V}$	$\dfrac{1}{r_c}$
h_{ic}	$h_{ie}\dagger$	$1{,}100\ \Omega$	$\dfrac{h_{ib}}{1 + h_{fb}}$	$r_b + \dfrac{r_e}{1 - a}$
h_{rc}	$1 - h_{re} \approx 1\dagger$	1	1	$1 - \dfrac{r_e}{(1 - a)r_c}$
h_{fc}	$-(1 + h_{fe})\dagger$	-51	$-\dfrac{1}{1 + h_{fb}}$	$-\dfrac{1}{1 - a}$
h_{oc}	$h_{oe}\dagger$	$25\ \mu\text{A/V}$	$\dfrac{h_{ob}}{1 + h_{fb}}$	$\dfrac{1}{(1 - a)r_c}$
a	$\dfrac{h_{fe}}{1 + h_{fe}}$	$\dfrac{1 + h_{fc}}{h_{fc}}$	$-h_{fb}$	0.980
r_c	$\dfrac{1 + h_{fe}}{h_{oe}}\dagger$	$-\dfrac{h_{fc}}{h_{oc}}\dagger$	$\dfrac{1}{h_{ob}}$	$2.04\ \text{M}$
r_e	$\dfrac{h_{re}}{h_{oe}}\dagger$	$\dfrac{1 - h_{rc}}{h_{oc}}\dagger$	$h_{ib} - \dfrac{h_{rb}}{h_{ob}}(1 + h_{fb})\dagger$	$10\ \Omega$
r_b	$h_{ie} - \dfrac{h_{re}}{h_{oe}}(1 + h_{fe})\dagger$	$h_{ic} + \dfrac{h_{fc}}{h_{oc}}(1 - h_{rc})\dagger$	$\dfrac{h_{rb}}{h_{ob}}\dagger$	$590\ \Omega$

† Exact.

11-5   CONVERSION FORMULAS FOR THE PARAMETERS OF THE THREE TRANSISTOR CONFIGURATIONS[4]

Very often it is necessary to convert from one set of transistor parameters to another set. Some transistor manufacturers specify all four common-emitter h parameters; others specify h_{fe}, h_{ib}, h_{ob}, and h_{rb}. In Table 11-3 we give approximate conversion formulas between the CE, CC, and CB h parameters. For completeness, we also include the T-model parameters, although we postpone until Sec. 11-9 the discussion of the T model. Exact formulas are given in Ref. 4, but are seldom required. Those conversions marked with a dagger in Table 11-3 are exact.

The conversion formulas can be obtained using the definitions of the parameters involved and Kirchhoff's laws. The general procedure is illustrated in the following examples.

EXAMPLE Find, in terms of the CB h parameters, (a) h_{re} and (b) h_{ie}.

Solution a. The CB h-parameter circuit of Fig. 11-9a is redrawn in Fig. 11-9b as a CE configuration. The latter corresponds in every detail to the former, except that the emitter terminal E is made common to the input and output ports. By definition,

$$h_{re} = \frac{V_{be}}{V_{ce}}\bigg|_{I_b=0} = \frac{V_{bc} + V_{ce}}{V_{ce}}\bigg|_{I_b=0} = \left(1 + \frac{V_{bc}}{V_{ce}}\right)\bigg|_{I_b=0}$$

If $I_b = 0$, then $I_e = -I_c$, and the current I in h_{ob} in Fig. 11-9b is $I = (1 + h_{fb})I_e$. Since h_{ob} represents a conductance,

$$I = h_{ob}V_{bc} = (1 + h_{fb})I_e$$

Applying KVL to the output mesh of Fig. 11-9b,

$$h_{ib}I_e + h_{rb}V_{cb} + V_{bc} + V_{ce} = 0$$

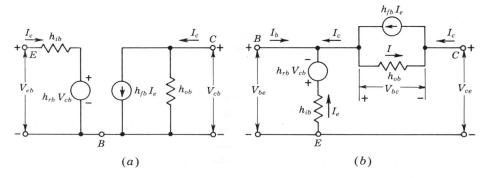

(a)   (b)

Fig. 11-9 (a) The CB hybrid model. (b) The circuit in (a) redrawn in a CE configuration.

Combining the last two equations yields

$$\frac{h_{ib}h_{ob}}{1 + h_{fb}} V_{bc} - h_{rb}V_{bc} + V_{bc} + V_{ce} = 0$$

or

$$\frac{V_{bc}}{V_{ce}} = \frac{-(1 + h_{fb})}{h_{ib}h_{ob} + (1 - h_{rb})(1 + h_{fb})}$$

Hence

$$h_{re} = 1 + \frac{V_{bc}}{V_{ce}} = \frac{h_{ib}h_{ob} - (1 + h_{fb})h_{rb}}{h_{ib}h_{ob} + (1 - h_{rb})(1 + h_{fb})}$$

This is an exact expression. The simpler approximate formula is obtained by noting that, for the typical values given in Table 11-2,

$$h_{rb} \ll 1 \quad \text{and} \quad h_{ob}h_{ib} \ll 1 + h_{fb}$$

Hence

$$h_{re} \approx \frac{h_{ib}h_{ob}}{1 + h_{fb}} - h_{rb}$$

which is the formula given in Table 11-3.

b. By definition,

$$h_{ie} = \frac{V_{be}}{I_b} \bigg|_{V_{ce}=0}$$

If we connect terminals C and E together in Fig. 11-9b, we obtain Fig. 11-10. From the latter figure we see that

$$V_{cb} = -V_{be}$$

Applying KVL to the left-hand mesh, we have

$$V_{bc} + h_{ib}I_e + h_{rb}V_{cb} = 0$$

Combining these two equations yields

$$I_e = -\frac{1 - h_{rb}}{h_{ib}} V_{be}$$

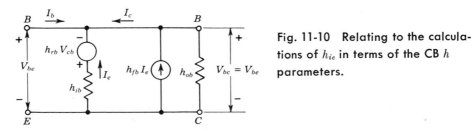

Fig. 11-10 Relating to the calculations of h_{ie} in terms of the CB h parameters.

Applying KCL to node B, we obtain

$$I_b + I_e + h_{fb}I_e - h_{ob}V_{be} = 0$$

or

$$I_b = (1 + h_{fb}) \frac{1 - h_{rb}}{h_{ib}} V_{be} + h_{ob}V_{be}$$

Hence

$$h_{ie} = \frac{V_{be}}{I_b} = \frac{h_{ib}}{h_{ib}h_{ob} + (1 - h_{rb})(1 + h_{fb})}$$

This is the exact expression. If we make use of the same inequalities as in part a, namely, $h_{rb} \ll 1$ and $h_{ob}h_{ib} \ll 1 + h_{fb}$, the above equation reduces to

$$h_{ie} \approx \frac{h_{ib}}{1 + h_{fb}}$$

which is the formula given in Table 11-3.

11-6   ANALYSIS OF A TRANSISTOR AMPLIFIER CIRCUIT USING h PARAMETERS

To form a transistor amplifier it is only necessary to connect an external load and signal source as indicated in Fig. 11-11 and to bias the transistor properly. The two-port active network of Fig. 11-11 represents a transistor in any one of the three possible configurations. In Fig. 11-12 we treat the general case (connection not specified) by replacing the transistor with its small-signal hybrid model. The circuit used in Fig. 11-12 is valid for any type of load whether it be a pure resistance, an impedance, or another transistor. This is true because the transistor hybrid model was derived without any regard to the external circuit in which the transistor is incorporated. The only restriction is the requirement that the h parameters remain substantially constant over the operating range.

Assuming sinusoidally varying voltages and currents, we can proceed with the analysis of the circuit of Fig. 11-12, using the phasor (sinor) notation to represent the sinusoidally varying quantities. The quantities of interest are *the current gain, the input impedance, the voltage gain,* and *the output impedance.*

Fig. 11-11   A basic amplifier circuit.

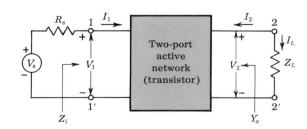

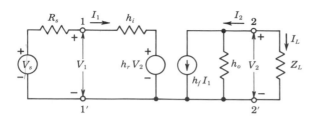

Fig. 11-12 The transistor in Fig. 11-11 is replaced by its h-parameter model.

The Current Gain, or Current Amplification, A_I For the transistor amplifier stage, A_I is defined as the ratio of output to input currents, or

$$A_I \equiv \frac{I_L}{I_1} = -\frac{I_2}{I_1} \tag{11-20}$$

From the circuit of Fig. 11-12, we have

$$I_2 = h_f I_1 + h_o V_2 = h_f I_1 - I_2 Z_L h_o \tag{11-21}$$

Substituting $V_2 = -I_2 Z_L$ in Eq. (11-21), we obtain

$$A_I = -\frac{I_2}{I_1} = -\frac{h_f}{1 + h_o Z_L} \tag{11-22}$$

The Input Impedance Z_i The resistance R_s in Figs. 11-11 and 11-12 represents the signal-source resistance. The impedance we see looking into the amplifier input terminals (1, 1′) is the amplifier *input impedance Z_i*, or

$$Z_i \equiv \frac{V_1}{I_1} \tag{11-23}$$

From the input circuit of Fig. 11-12, we have

$$V_1 = h_i I_1 + h_r V_2 \tag{11-24}$$

Hence

$$Z_i = \frac{h_i I_1 + h_r V_2}{I_1} = h_i + h_r \frac{V_2}{I_1} \tag{11-25}$$

Substituting

$$V_2 = -I_2 Z_L = A_I I_1 Z_L \qquad A_I = I_2 / I_1 \tag{11-26}$$

in Eq. (11-25), we obtain

$$Z_i = h_i + h_r A_I Z_L = h_i - \frac{h_f h_r}{Y_L + h_o} \tag{11-27}$$

where use has been made of Eq. (11-22) and the fact that the load admittance is $Y_L \equiv 1/Z_L$. Note that *the input impedance is a function of the load impedance.*

The Voltage Gain, or Voltage Amplification, A_V The ratio of output voltage V_2 to input voltage V_1 gives the voltage gain of the transistor, or

$$A_V \equiv \frac{V_2}{V_1} \tag{11-28}$$

From Eq. (11-26) we have

$$A_V = \frac{A_I I_1 Z_L}{V_1} = \frac{A_I Z_L}{Z_i} \qquad \tag{11-29}$$

$z_i = \dfrac{v_1}{I_1}$

The Output Admittance Y_o For the transistor in Figs. 11-11 and 11-12, Y_o is defined as

$$Y_o \equiv \frac{I_2}{V_2} \qquad \text{with } V_s = 0 \tag{11-30}$$

From Eq. (11-21),

$$Y_o = h_f \frac{I_1}{V_2} + h_o \qquad \tag{11-31}$$

$I_2 = h_f I_1 + h_o V_2$

From Fig. 11-12, with $V_s = 0$,

$$R_s I_1 + h_i I_1 + h_r V_2 = 0 \tag{11-32}$$

or

$$\frac{I_1}{V_2} = -\frac{h_r}{h_i + R_s} \tag{11-33}$$

Substituting the expression for I_1/V_2 from Eq. (11-33) in Eq. (11-31), we obtain

$$Y_o = h_o - \frac{h_f h_r}{h_i + R_s} \tag{11-34}$$

Note that *the output admittance is a function of the source resistance.* If the source impedance is resistive, as we have assumed, then Y_o is real (a conductance).

In the above definition of $Y_o = 1/Z_o$, we have considered the load Z_L external to the amplifier. If the output impedance of the amplifier stage with Z_L included is desired, this loaded impedance can be calculated as the parallel combination of Z_L and Z_o.

The Voltage Amplification A_{Vs}, Taking into Account the Resistance R_s of the Source This overall voltage gain A_{Vs} is defined by

$$A_{Vs} \equiv \frac{V_2}{V_s} = \frac{V_2}{V_1}\frac{V_1}{V_s} = A_V \frac{V_1}{V_s} \tag{11-35}$$

From the equivalent input circuit of the amplifier, shown in Fig. 11-13a,

$$V_1 = \frac{V_s Z_i}{Z_i + R_s}$$

Then

$$A_{Vs} = \frac{A_V Z_i}{Z_i + R_s} = \frac{A_I Z_L}{Z_i + R_s} \tag{11-36}$$

where use has been made of Eq. (11-29). Note that, if $R_s = 0$, then $A_{Vs} = A_V$. Hence A_V *is the voltage gain for an ideal voltage source* (one with zero internal resistance). In practice, the quantity A_{Vs} is more meaningful than A_V since,

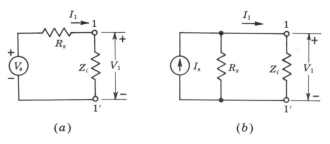

Fig. 11-13 Input circuit of a transistor amplifier using
(a) a Thévenin's equivalent for the source and (b) a
Norton's equivalent for the source.

usually, the source resistance has an appreciable effect on the overall voltage amplification. For example, if Z_i is resistive and equal in magnitude to R_s, then $A_{Vs} = 0.5A_V$.

The Current Amplification A_{Is}, Taking into Account the Source Resistance R_s If the input source is a current generator I_s in parallel with a resistance R_s, as indicated in Fig. 11-13b, then this *overall current gain* A_{Is} is defined by

$$A_{Is} \equiv \frac{-I_2}{I_s} = \frac{-I_2}{I_1}\frac{I_1}{I_s} = A_I\frac{I_1}{I_s} \tag{11-37}$$

From Fig. 11-13b,

$$I_1 = \frac{I_sR_s}{Z_i + R_s}$$

and hence

$$A_{Is} = \frac{A_IR_s}{Z_i + R_s} \tag{11-38}$$

Note that if $R_s = \infty$, then $A_{Is} = A_I$. Hence A_I *is the current gain for an ideal current source* (one with infinite source resistance).

Independent of the transistor characteristics, the voltage and current gains, taking source impedance into account, are related by

$$A_{Vs} = A_{Is}\frac{Z_L}{R_s} \tag{11-39}$$

This relationship is obtained by dividing Eq. (11-36) by Eq. (11-38), and is valid provided that the current and voltage generators have the *same* source resistance R_s.

The Operating Power Gain A_p The average power delivered to the load Z_L in Fig. 11-11 is $P_2 = |V_2|\,|I_L|\cos\theta$, where θ is the phase angle between V_2 and I_L. Assume that Z_L is resistive. Then, since the h parameters are real at low frequencies, the power delivered to the load is $P_2 = V_2I_L = -V_2I_2$. Since the input power is $P_1 = V_1I_1$, the *operating power gain* A_p of the transistor is defined as

$$A_p \equiv \frac{P_2}{P_1} = -\frac{V_2I_2}{V_1I_1} = A_VA_I = A_I{}^2\frac{R_L}{R_i} \tag{11-40}$$

TABLE 11-4   Small-signal analysis of a transistor amplifier

$$A_I = -\frac{h_f}{1 + h_o Z_L}$$

$$Z_i = h_i + h_r A_I Z_L = h_i - \frac{h_f h_r}{h_o + Y_L}$$

$$A_V = \frac{A_I Z_L}{Z_i}$$

$$Y_o = h_o - \frac{h_f h_r}{h_i + R_s} = \frac{1}{Z_o}$$

$$A_{Vs} = \frac{A_V Z_i}{Z_i + R_s} = \frac{A_I Z_L}{Z_i + R_s} = \frac{A_{Is} Z_L}{R_s}$$

$$A_{Is} = \frac{A_I R_s}{Z_i + R_s}$$

Summary   The important formulas derived above are summarized for ready reference in Table 11-4.   Note that the expressions for A_V, A_{Vs}, and A_{Is} do not contain the hybrid parameters, and hence are valid regardless of what equivalent circuit we use for the transistor.   In particular, these expressions are valid at high frequencies, where the h parameters are functions of frequency or where we may prefer to use another model for the transistor (for example, the hybrid-Π model of Sec. 13-5).

EXAMPLE   The transistor of Fig. 11-11 is connected as a common-emitter amplifier, and the h parameters are those given in Table 11-2.   If $R_L = R_s = 1,000\ \Omega$, find the various gains and the input and output impedances.

Solution   In making the small-signal analysis of this circuit it is convenient, first, to calculate A_I, then obtain R_i from A_I, and A_V from both these quantities. Using the expressions in Table 11-4 and the h parameters from Table 11-2,

$$A_I = -\frac{h_{fe}}{1 + h_{oe} R_L} = -\frac{50}{1 + 25 \times 10^{-6} \times 10^3} = -48.8$$

$$R_i = h_{ie} + h_{re} A_I R_L = 1,100 - 2.5 \times 10^{-4} \times 48.8 \times 10^3 = 1,088\ \Omega$$

$$A_V = \frac{A_I R_L}{R_i} = \frac{-48.8 \times 10^3}{1.088 \times 10^3} = -44.8$$

$$A_{Vs} = \frac{A_V R_i}{R_i + R_s} = -44.8 \times \frac{1,088}{2,088} = -23.3$$

$$A_{Is} = \frac{A_I R_s}{R_i + R_s} = \frac{-48.8 \times 10^3}{2.088 \times 10^3} = -23.3$$

Note that, since $R_s = R_L$, then $A_{Vs} = A_{Is}$.

$$Y_o = h_{oe} - \frac{h_{fe}h_{re}}{h_{ie} + R_s} = 25 \times 10^{-6} - \frac{50 \times 2.5 \times 10^{-4}}{2,100} = 19.0 \times 10^{-6} \text{ mho}$$

$$= 19.0 \text{ } \mu A/V$$

or

$$Z_o = \frac{1}{Y_o} = \frac{10^6}{19.0} \Omega = 52.6 \text{ K}$$

Finally, the power gain is given by

$$A_p = A_V A_I = 44.8 \times 48.8 = 2,190$$

11-7   COMPARISON OF TRANSISTOR AMPLIFIER CONFIGURATIONS

From Table 11-4 the values of current gain, voltage gain, input impedance, and output impedance are calculated as a function of load and source impedances. These are plotted in Figs. 11-14 to 11-17 for each of the three configurations. A study of the shapes and relative amplitudes of these curves is instructive. The asymptotic end points of these plots (for R_L or R_s equal to zero or infinity) are indicated in Table 11-5.

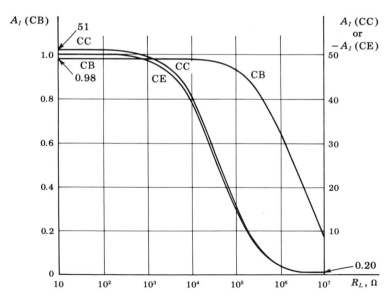

Fig. 11-14 The current gain A_I of the typical transistor of Table 11-2 as a function of its load resistance.

The CE Configuration   From the curves and Table 11-5, it is observed that only the common-emitter stage is capable of both a voltage gain and a current gain greater than unity.   This configuration is the most versatile and useful of the three connections.

Note that R_i and R_o vary least with R_L and R_s, respectively, for the CE circuit.   Also observe that the magnitudes of R_i and R_o lie between those for the CB and CC configurations.

To realize a gain nominally equal to $(A_{Vs})_{max}$ would require not only that a zero-impedance voltage source be used, but also that R_L be many times larger than the output impedance.   Normally, however, so large a value of R_L is not feasible.   Suppose, for example, that a manufacturer specifies a maximum collector voltage of, say, 30 V.   Then we should not be inclined to use a collector supply voltage in excess of this maximum voltage, since in such a case the collector voltage would be exceeded if the transistor were driven to cutoff.   Suppose, further, that the transistor is designed to carry a collector current of, say, 5 mA when biased in the middle of its active region. Then the load resistor should be selected to have a resistance of about $\frac{1.5}{5} = 3$ K. We compute for the CE configuration a voltage gain under load of $A_V = -129$ (for $R_s = 0$).   Of course, the load resistance may be smaller than 3 K, as,

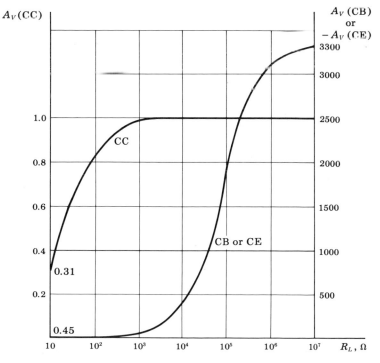

Fig. 11-15   The voltage gain of the typical transistor of Table 11-2 as a function of its load resistance.

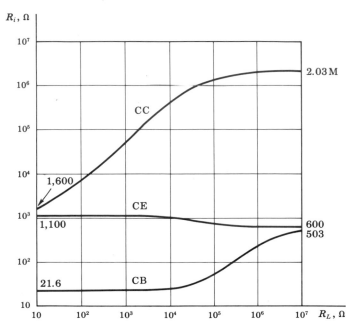

Fig. 11-16 The input resistance of the typical transistor of Table 11-2 as a function of its load resistance.

TABLE 11-5   Asymptotic values of transistor gains and resistances
(for numerical values of h parameters see Table 11-2)

Quantity	h-parameter expression	CE	CC	CB
$(A_{Is})_{max}$ $(R_L = 0, R_s = \infty)$	$-h_f$	-50	51	0.98
R_i $(R_L = 0)$	h_i	$1{,}100\ \Omega$	$1{,}100\ \Omega$	$21.6\ \Omega$
R_i $(R_L = \infty)$	$\dfrac{\Delta}{h_o}$	$600\ \Omega$	$2.04\ M$	$600\ \Omega$
$(A_{Vs})_{max}$ $(R_L = \infty, R_s = 0)$	$-\dfrac{h_f}{\Delta}$	$-3{,}330$	1	$3{,}330$
R_o $(R_s = 0)$	$\dfrac{h_i}{\Delta}$	$73.3\ K$	$21.6\ \Omega$	$73.5\ K$
R_o $(R_s = \infty)$	$\dfrac{1}{h_o}$	$40\ K$	$40\ K$	$2.04\ M$
Δ	$h_i h_o - h_r h_f$	15×10^3	51.0	2.94×10^{-4}

for example, when a transistor is used to drive another transistor. Or in some applications a higher value of R_L may be acceptable, although load resistances in excess of 10 K are unusual.

The CB Configuration   For the common-base stage, A_I is less than unity, A_V is high (approximately equal to that of the CE stage), R_i is the lowest, and R_o is the highest of the three configurations.   The CB stage has few applications.   It is sometimes used to match a very low impedance source, to drive a high-impedance load, or as a noninverting amplifier with a voltage gain greater than unity.   It is also used as a constant-current source (for example, as a sweep circuit to charge a capacitor linearly[5]).

The CC Configuration   For the common-collector stage, A_I is high (approximately equal to that of the CE stage), A_V is less than unity, R_i is the highest, and R_o is the lowest of the three configurations.   This circuit finds wide application as a buffer stage between a high-impedance source and a low-impedance load.   This use is analogous to that of the cathode follower, and this transistor circuit is called an *emitter follower*.

Summary   The foregoing characteristics are summarized in Table 11-6, where the various quantities are calculated for $R_L = 3$ K and for the h parameters in Table 11-2.

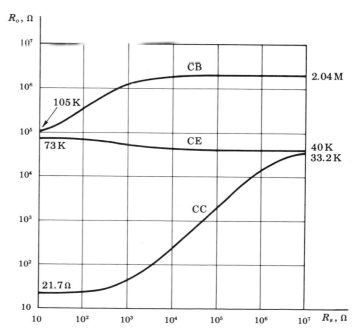

Fig. 11-17   The output resistance of the typical transistor of Table 11-2 as a function of its source resistance.

TABLE 11-6   Comparison of transistor configurations

Quantity	CE	CC	CB
A_I	High (-46.5)	High (47.5)	Low (0.98)
A_V	High (-131)	Low (0.99)	High (131)
R_i $(R_L = 3$ K$)$	Medium $(1,065 \ \Omega)$	High $(144$ K$)$	Low $(22.5 \ \Omega)$
R_o $(R_s = 3$ K$)$	Medium high $(45.5$ K$)$	Low $(80.5 \ \Omega)$	High $(1.72$ M$)$

11-8   LINEAR ANALYSIS OF A TRANSISTOR CIRCUIT

There are many transistor circuits which do not consist simply of the CE, CB, or CC configurations discussed above.   For example, a CE amplifier may have a feedback resistor from collector to base, as in Fig. 10-5, or it may have an emitter resistor, as in Fig. 10-6.   Furthermore, a circuit may consist of several transistors which are interconnected in some manner.   An analytic determination of the small-signal behavior of even relatively complicated amplifier circuits may be made by following these simple rules:

1. Draw the actual wiring diagram of the circuit neatly.
2. Mark the points B (base), C (collector), and E (emitter) on this circuit diagram.   Locate these points as the start of the equivalent circuit.   Maintain the same relative positions as in the original circuit.
3. Replace each transistor by its h-parameter model (Table 11-1).
4. Transfer all circuit elements from the actual circuit to the equivalent circuit of the amplifier.   Keep the relative positions of these elements intact.
5. Replace each independent dc source by its internal resistance.   The ideal voltage source is replaced by a short circuit, and the ideal current source by an open circuit.
6. Solve the resultant linear circuit for mesh or branch currents and node voltages by applying Kirchhoff's current and voltage laws (KCL and KVL).

It should be emphasized that it is not necessary to use the foregoing general approach for a circuit consisting of a cascade of CE, CB, and/or CC stages.   Such configurations are analyzed very simply in Chap. 12 by direct applications of the formulas in Table 11-4.

11-9   THE PHYSICAL MODEL OF A CB TRANSISTOR

The circuit designer finds the small-signal model of the transistor described by the hybrid parameters very convenient for circuit analysis.   As indicated in Sec. 11-1, these h parameters characterize a general two-port network. When this model is applied to a specific transistor, the values of the hybrid parameters are measured experimentally (Sec. 11-4) by the user or by the manufacturer.   The device designer, on the other hand, prefers to use a model containing circuit parameters whose values can be determined directly from the physical properties of the transistor.   We now attempt to obtain such a small-signal equivalent circuit which brings into evidence the physical mechanisms taking place within the device.

To be specific, consider the grounded-base configuration.   Looking into the emitter, we see a forward-biased diode.   Hence, between input terminals E and B', there is a dynamic resistance r_e', obtained as the slope of the (forward-biased) emitter-junction volt-ampere characteristic.   Looking back into the output terminals C and B', we see a back-biased diode.   Hence, between these terminals, there is a dynamic resistance r_c' obtained as the slope of the (reverse-biased) collector-junction volt-ampere characteristic.   From the physical behavior of a transistor as discussed in Chap. 9, we know that the collector current is proportional to the emitter current.   Hence a current generator αi_e is added across r_c', resulting in the equivalent circuit of Fig. 11-18.

The Early Feedback Generator   The equivalent circuit of Fig. 11-18 is unrealistic because it indicates a lack of dependence of emitter current on collector voltage.   Actually, there is some such small dependence, and the physical reason for this relationship is not hard to find.   As indicated in Sec. 9-7, an increase in the magnitude of the collector voltage effectively narrows the base width W, a phenomenon known as the *Early effect*.[6]   The minority-carrier current in the base in the active region is proportional to the slope of the injected minority-carrier density curve.   From Fig. 0 23 we see that this slope increases as W decreases.   Hence the emitter current injected into the base increases with reverse collector voltage.   This effect of collector voltage $v_{cb'}$ on emitter current may be taken into account by including a voltage source $\mu v_{cb'}$ in series with r_e', as indicated in Fig. 11-19.   A little thought should convince the reader that the polarity shown for generator $\mu v_{cb'}$ is consistent with the physical explanation just given.

The Base-spreading Resistance   To complete the equivalent circuit of Fig. 11-18, we must take into account the ohmic resistances of the three transistor regions.   Since the base section is very thin, the base current passes through a region of extremely small cross section.   Hence this resistance $r_{bb'}$, called the *base-spreading resistance*, is large, and may be of the order of several

Fig. 11-18   A simplified physical model of a CB transistor.

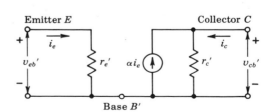

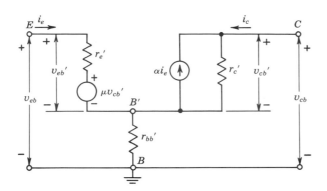

Fig. 11-19 A more complete physical model of a CB transistor than that indicated in Fig. 11-18.

hundred ohms. On the other hand, the collector and emitter ohmic resistances are only a few ohms, and may usually be neglected. If the external connection to the base is designated by B, then between the fictitious internal base node B' and B we must place a resistance $r_{bb'}$, as indicated in Fig. 11-19.

If the base-spreading resistance could be neglected so that B and B' coincided, the circuit of Fig. 11-19 would be identical with the hybrid model of Fig. 11-2, with

$$r'_e = h_{ib} \qquad \mu = h_{rb} \qquad \alpha = -h_{fb} \qquad \text{and} \qquad r'_c = \frac{1}{h_{ob}}$$

The T Model The circuit of Fig. 11-19 contains elements each of which has been identified with the physics of the transistor. However, this circuit, which includes a dependent voltage generator, a dependent current generator, and three resistors, is fairly complicated to use in circuit analysis. By means of network transformations it is possible to eliminate the voltage generator and obtain the simpler T model of Fig. 11-20. This new circuit should be considered in conjunction with Table 11-7. This tables gives the transformation equations and, in addition, specifies typical values of the parameters in each of the circuits. The derivation of the equations of transformation is an entirely straightforward matter. It is necessary only to find v_{eb} as a function of i_e and i_c (and also to determine v_{cb} as a function of i_e and i_c) for both circuits and to require that the corresponding equations be identical.

TABLE 11-7 Typical parameter values and the equations of transformation between the circuits of Figs. 11-19 and 11-20

Parameter in Fig. 11-19	Transformation equations	Parameter in Fig. 11-20
$r'_e = 40\ \Omega$	$r_e = r'_e - (1-\alpha)\mu r'_c$	$r_e = 20\ \Omega$
$\mu = 5 \times 10^{-4}$	$r'_b = \mu r'_c$	$r'_b = 1\ \text{K}$
$r'_c = 2\ \text{M}$	$r_c = (1-\mu)r'_c$	$r_c = 2\ \text{M}$
$\alpha = 0.98$	$a = \dfrac{\alpha - \mu}{1 - \mu}$	$a = 0.98$

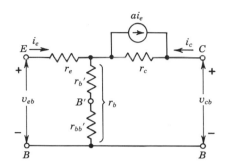

Fig. 11-20   The T model of a CB transistor.

The transformed circuit, we observe, accounts for the effect of the collector circuit on the emitter circuit essentially through the resistor r_b' rather than through the generator $\mu v_{cb'}$.   Note from Table 11-7 that $r_c \approx r_c'$, $a \approx \alpha$, and $r_e \approx r_e'/2$.   The resistor r_b in the base leg is given by $r_b \equiv r_b' + r_{bb'}$, where r_b' and $r_{bb'}$ are resistances of comparable magnitudes.

The circuit components in the T model cannot be interpreted directly in terms of the physical mechanisms in the transistor.   Values for these elements are difficult to obtain experimentally.   And, finally, the analysis of a circuit is somewhat simpler in terms of the h parameters than through the use of the T equivalent circuit.   For these three reasons the T model is not used in this text.   It is included here because of its historical significance and because we refer to this circuit when we discuss the transistor at high frequencies (Sec. 13-1).   The relationships between the hybrid parameters and those in the T equivalent circuit are given in Table 11-3.

11-10   A VACUUM–TUBE–TRANSISTOR ANALOGY[7]

It is possible to draw a very rough analogy between a transistor and a vacuum tube.   In this analogy the base, emitter, and collector of a transistor are identified, respectively, with the grid, cathode, and plate of a vacuum tube. Correspondingly, the grounded-base, grounded-emitter, and grounded-collector configurations are identified, respectively, with the grounded-grid, grounded-cathode, and grounded-plate (cathode-follower) vacuum-tube circuits, as in Fig. 11-21.

Consider, for example, the circuits of Fig. 11-21a.   For the tube circuit, we find that, in the normal amplifier region, $|I_k| = |I_p|$.   In the transistor circuit, in the active region, we find that $|I_e| \approx |I_c|$, the difference between I_e and I_c being of the order of 2 percent.   In both the transistor and tube circuits of Fig. 11-21a, we find that the input impedance is low because of the large current at low voltage which must be furnished by the driving generator. Also, both circuits are capable of considerable voltage gain without inverting the input signal.

The transistor configuration of Fig. 11-21b has a higher input imped-

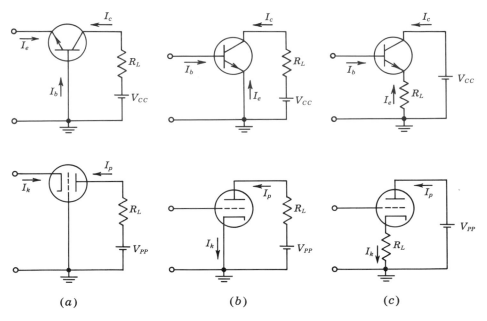

Fig. 11-21   Analogous transistor and vacuum-tube circuits.   (a) Grounded base
and grounded grid.   (b) Common emitter and common cathode.   (c) Emitter follower and cathode follower.

ance than the CB circuit.   As a voltage amplifier, a large gain with polarity
inversion is possible.   In all these respects the grounded-emitter configuration
is analogous to the grounded-cathode vacuum-tube amplifier stage.

In Fig. 11-21c, the grounded-collector (emitter-follower) configuration is
compared with the grounded-plate (cathode-follower) circuit.   In the emitter-
follower circuit the input current is relatively small, and the voltage difference
between base and emitter is essentially the small voltage drop across the forward-biased emitter junction when operating in the active region.   Hence we
may expect the input voltage and the output voltage, as in a cathode follower,
to be nominally the same.   The emitter follower, as the cathode follower,
provides a voltage gain slightly less than unity without polarity inversion.
The emitter follower may also be expected to handle an input signal comparable
in size with the collector supply voltage.   The input-current swing from cutoff
to saturation is the same for grounded-emitter and grounded-collector operation, but in the grounded-collector operation the input-voltage swing is larger.

The cutoff region of the transistor corresponds to the region in the vacuum
tube where the grid voltage is larger than the cutoff bias.   The active region
of the transistor corresponds to the region in which the tube operates as a
linear amplifier.   This region covers not only the region within the grid base,
but also the region of positive grid voltages, where the tube operates linearly.

The saturation region of the transistor corresponds to the tube region where the grid is so positive and the plate voltage is so low that the plate current is almost independent of grid voltage (Fig. D-3).   The transistor base takes current at all points in its active region, whereas in the tube the grid draws appreciable current only when it is positive.   The analogy may be improved by assuming that cutoff occurs in the tube at zero grid bias; i.e., the grid base is zero.   Also, the volt-ampere transistor characteristics are shaped more like pentode curves than like triode characteristics.

It need hardly be emphasized that the analogies drawn above are far from exact.   On several occasions we have already noted that a transistor is a more complicated device than a vacuum tube.   In the former the current is due to charge carriers of both signs moving in a solid, whereas in the latter the current is carried by electrons in a vacuum.   There is nothing in a vacuum tube corresponding to minority-carrier storage in a transistor.   The low-frequency input impedance of a grounded-cathode or cathode-follower circuit is infinite, whereas a transistor has a relatively low input impedance in all three configurations.   The low-frequency equivalent circuit of a tube contains only two parameters, μ and r_p (or g_m and r_p), whereas four parameters, h_{11}, h_{12}, h_{22}, and h_{21}, are required in the corresponding transistor small-signal equivalent circuit.

The analogies are principally useful as mnemonic aids.   For example, we may note that the most generally useful tube circuit is the grounded-cathode circuit.   We may then expect from our analogy that the grounded-emitter configuration will occupy the same preferred position in the transistor configurations.   This anticipated result is borne out in practice.

Tubes versus Transistors   The semiconductor device has replaced the vacuum tube in many applications because the bipolar transistor possesses the following advantages over the tube:

1. The transistor has no filament, and hence requires no standby power or heating time.
2. It is smaller and lighter than a tube.
3. It has longer life and hence greater reliability.
4. It may operate with low voltages and power dissipation.
5. It is mechanically more rugged and cannot be microphonic.
6. It is a more ideal switch.
7. The transistor is readily adapted to microminiaturization, as described in Chap. 15 on Integrated Circuits.
8. Because there are two types of transistors (n-p-n and p-n-p), some circuit designs are possible which have no tube counterparts.

Wherever space, weight, or power is at a premium, the circuits are transistorized.   Digital computers (large-scale or special-purpose), hearing aids, electronic circuits for space vehicles, and portable equipment fall into this category.   The future of extremely complex systems lies in the direction of microminiaturization, using transistor technology.   However, there are applications where the tube will continue to be used because of the following disadvantages of the semiconductor triode:

1. The transistor characteristics are very temperature-sensitive.
2. The transistor is damaged by nuclear radiation.
3. It is easily damaged by transient overloads.
4. The maximum output power (100 W) is lower than from a tube (300 kW).
5. The upper frequency response (1 GHz) is lower than from a tube (10 GHz).
6. It is difficult to obtain voltage swings in excess of about 100 V.
7. Under some operating conditions transistors are noisier than tubes.
8. The spread in the characteristics of a given type of transistor is often very great.

Systems involving high voltage, high power, or high frequencies (and particularly those requiring several of these characteristics simultaneously) use tubes. Such applications include communications transmitters, radar indicators, oscilloscopes, and test equipment. Systems which must operate under unusual environments of temperature or nuclear radiation use tubes. Also, systems designed some time ago, and still operative, use tubes. Such equipment is often in production today because it is not economically feasible to redesign the system using semiconductor devices.

REFERENCES

1. IRE Standards on Semiconductor Symbols, *Proc. IRE*, vol. 44, pp. 935–937, July, 1956.

2. "Transistor Manual," 7th ed., General Electric Co., pp. 52–55, Syracuse, N.Y., 1964.

3. Ref. 2, pp. 477–482.

4. Electronics Reference Sheet, *Electronics*, Apr. 1, 1957, p. 190.

5. Millman, J., and H. Taub: "Pulse, Digital, and Switching Waveforms," pp. 528–532, McGraw-Hill Book Company, New York, 1965.

6. Early, J. M.: Effects of Space-charge Layer Widening in Junction Transistors, *Proc. IRE*, vol. 40, pp. 1401–1406, November, 1952.

7. Giacoletto, L. J.: Junction Transistor Equivalent Circuits and Vacuum-tube Analogy, *Proc. IRE*, vol. 40, pp. 1490–1493, November, 1952.
   Dosse, J.: "The Transistor," pp. 104–123, D. Van Nostrand Company, Inc., Princeton, N.J., 1964.

12 / LOW-FREQUENCY TRANSISTOR AMPLIFIER CIRCUITS

In the preceding chapter we consider the small-signal analysis of a single stage of amplification. Very often, in practice, a number of stages are used in cascade to amplify a signal from a source, such as a phonograph pickup, to a level which is suitable for the operation of another transducer, such as a loudspeaker. In this chapter we consider the problem of cascading a number of transistor amplifier stages. In addition, various special transistor circuits of practical importance are examined in detail. Also, simplified approximate methods of solution are presented. All transistor circuits in this chapter are examined at low frequencies, where the transistor internal capacitances may be neglected.

12-1   CASCADING TRANSISTOR AMPLIFIERS[1]

When the amplification of a single transistor is not sufficient for a particular purpose, or when the input or output impedance is not of the correct magnitude for the intended application, two or more stages may be connected in cascade; i.e., the output of a given stage is connected to the input of the next stage, as shown in Fig. 12-1. In the circuit of Fig. 12-2a the first stage is connected common-emitter, and the second is a common-collector stage. Figure 12-2b shows the small-signal circuit of the two-stage amplifier, with the biasing arrangements omitted for simplicity.

In order to analyze a circuit such as the one of Fig. 12-2, we make use of the general expressions for A_I, Z_i, A_V, and Y_o from Table 11-4. It is necessary that we have available the h parameters for the specific transistors used in the circuit. The h-parameter values for a specific transistor are usually obtained from the manufacturer's data sheet.

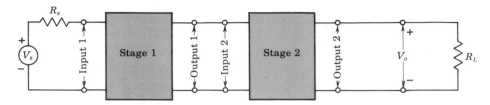

Fig. 12-1   Two cascaded stages.

Since most vendors specify the common-emitter h parameters, it may be necessary (depending on whether a certain stage is CE, CC, or CB) to convert them with the aid of Table 11-3 to the appropriate CC or CB values. In addition, the h parameters must be corrected for the operating bias conditions (Fig. 11-5).

EXAMPLE   Shown in Fig. 12-2 is a two-stage amplifier circuit in a CE-CC configuration.   The transistor parameters at the corresponding quiescent points are

$$h_{ie} = 2\text{ K} \qquad h_{fe} = 50 \qquad h_{re} = 6 \times 10^{-4} \qquad h_{oe} = 25\ \mu\text{A/V}$$

$$h_{ic} = 2\text{ K} \qquad h_{fc} = -51 \qquad h_{rc} = 1 \qquad h_{oc} = 25\ \mu\text{A/V}$$

Find the input and output impedances and individual, as well as overall, voltage and current gains.

Solution   We note that, in a cascade of stages, the collector resistance of one stage is shunted by the input impedance of the next stage.   Hence it is advantageous to start the analysis with the last stage.   In addition, it is convenient (as already noted in Sec. 11-6) to compute, first, the current gain, then the input impedance and the voltage gain.   Finally, the output impedance may be calculated if desired by starting this analysis with the first stage and proceeding toward the output stage.

The second stage.   From Table 11-4, with $R_L = R_{e2}$, the current gain of the last stage is

$$A_{I2} = -\frac{I_{e2}}{I_{b2}} = \frac{-h_{fc}}{1 + h_{oc}R_{e2}} = \frac{51}{1 + 25 \times 10^{-6} \times 5 \times 10^{3}} = 45.3$$

The input impedance R_{i2} is

$$R_{i2} = h_{ic} + h_{rc}A_{I2}R_{e2} = 2 + 45.3 \times 5 = 228.5\text{ K}$$

Note the high input impedance of the CC stage.   The voltage gain of the second stage is

$$A_{V2} = \frac{V_o}{V_2} = A_{I2}\frac{R_{e2}}{R_{i2}} = \frac{45.3 \times 5}{228.5} = 0.99$$

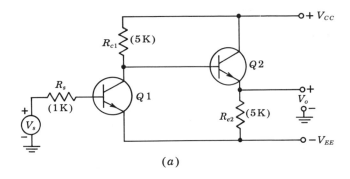

(a)

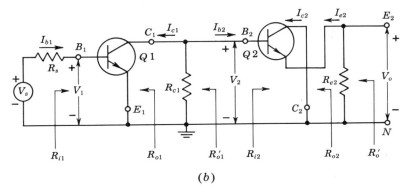

(b)

Fig. 12-2 (a) Common-emitter—common-collector amplifier. (b) Small signal circuit of the CE CC amplifier. (The component values refer to the example in Sec. 12-1.)

The first stage. We observe that the net load resistance R_{L1} of this stage is the parallel combination of R_{c1} and R_{i2} (written in symbolic form, $R_{L1} = R_{c1} \| R_{i2}$), or

$$R_{L1} = \frac{R_{c1}R_{i2}}{R_{c1} + R_{i2}} = \frac{5 \times 228.5}{233.5} = 4.9 \text{ K}$$

Hence

$$A_{I1} = -\frac{I_{c1}}{I_{b1}} = \frac{-h_{fe}}{1 + h_{oe}R_{L1}} = \frac{-50}{1 + 25 \times 10^{-6} \times 4.9 \times 10^{3}} = -44.5$$

The input impedance of the first stage, which is also the input impedance of the cascaded amplifier, is given by

$$R_{i1} = h_{ie} + h_{rc}A_{I1}R_{L1} = 2 - 6 \times 10^{-4} \times 44.5 \times 4.9 = 1.87 \text{ K}$$

The voltage gain of the first stage is

$$A_{V1} = \frac{V_2}{V_1} = \frac{A_{I1}R_{L1}}{R_{i1}} = \frac{-44.5 \times 4.9}{1.87} = -116.6$$

The output admittance of the first transistor is, from Eq. (11-39) or Table 11-4,

$$Y_{o1} = h_{oe} - \frac{h_{fe}h_{re}}{h_{ie} + R_s} = 25 \times 10^{-6} - \frac{50 \times 6 \times 10^{-4}}{2 \times 10^3 + 1 \times 10^3} = 15 \times 10^{-6} \text{ mho}$$

$$= 15 \ \mu A/V$$

Hence

$$R_{o1} = \frac{1}{Y_{o1}} = \frac{10^6}{15} \ \Omega = 66.7 \ K$$

The output impedance of the *first stage, taking R_{c1} into account*, is $R_{o1} \| R_{c1}$, or

$$R'_{o1} = \frac{R_{c1}R_{o1}}{R_{c1} + R_{o1}} = \frac{5 \times 66.7}{5 + 66.7} = 4.65 \ K$$

The output resistance of the last stage. The effective source resistance R'_{s2} for the second transistor $Q2$ is $R_{o1} \| R_{c1}$. Thus $R'_{s2} = R'_{o1} = 4.65 \ K$, and

$$Y_{o2} = h_{oc} - \frac{h_{fc}h_{rc}}{h_{ic} + R'_{s2}} = 25 \times 10^{-6} - \frac{(-51)(1)}{2 \times 10^3 + 4.65 \times 10^3}$$

$$= 7.70 \times 10^{-3} \text{ A/V}$$

Hence $R_{o2} = 1/Y_{o2} = 130 \ \Omega$, where R_{o2} is the output impedance of transistor $Q2$ under open-circuit conditions. The output impedance R'_o of the amplifier, taking R_{e2} into account, is $R_{o2} \| R_{e2}$, or

$$R'_o = \frac{R_{o2}R_{e2}}{R_{o2} + R_{e2}} = \frac{130 \times 5,000}{130 + 5,000} = 127 \ \Omega$$

The overall current and voltage gains. The total current gain of both stages is

$$A_I = -\frac{I_{e2}}{I_{b1}} = -\frac{I_{e2}}{I_{b2}}\frac{I_{b2}}{I_{c1}}\frac{I_{c1}}{I_{b1}} = -A_{I2}\frac{I_{b2}}{I_{c1}}A_{I1} \tag{12-1}$$

From Fig. 12-3, we have

$$\frac{I_{b2}}{I_{c1}} = -\frac{R_{c1}}{R_{i2} + R_{c1}} \tag{12-2}$$

Hence

$$A_I = A_{I2}A_{I1}\frac{R_{c1}}{R_{i2} + R_{c1}} = 45.3 \times (-44.5) \times \frac{5}{228.5 + 5} = -43.2 \tag{12-3}$$

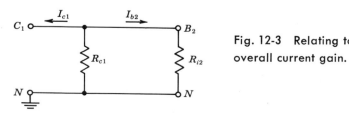

Fig. 12-3 Relating to the calculation of overall current gain.

For the voltage gain of the amplifier, we have

$$A_V = \frac{V_o}{V_1} = \frac{V_o}{V_2}\frac{V_2}{V_1} = A_{V2}A_{V1} \tag{12-4}$$

or

$$A_V = 0.99 \times (-116.6) = -115$$

The voltage gain can also be obtained from

$$A_V = A_I \frac{R_{e2}}{R_{i1}} = -43.2 \times \frac{5}{1.87} = -115$$

The overall voltage gain, taking the source impedance into account, is given by

$$A_{Vs} = \frac{V_o}{V_s} = A_V \frac{R_{i1}}{R_{i1} + R_s} = -115 \times \frac{1.87}{1.87 + 1} = -75.3$$

Table 12-1 summarizes the results obtained in the solution of this problem.

TABLE 12-1   Results of the example on page 324

	Transistor Q2 CC	Transistor Q1 CE	Both stages CE-CC
A_I	45.3	−44.5	−43.2
R_i	228.5 K	1.87 K	1.87 K
A_V	0.99	−116.6	−115
R_o'	127 Ω	4.65 K	127 Ω

12-2   *n*–STAGE CASCADED AMPLIFIER

The function of a low-level amplifier is to raise a weak signal to a usable level, perhaps from the range of microvolts to several volts. This is usually done by cascading several transistors in the common-emitter connection. A typical two-stage cascaded CE audio amplifier with biasing arrangements and coupling capacitors included is shown in Fig. 12-4.

We now examine in detail the small-signal operation of an amplifier consisting of *n* cascaded common-emitter stages, as shown in Fig. 12-5. The biasing arrangements and coupling capacitors have been omitted for simplicity.

The Voltage Gain   We observe from Fig. 12-5 that the resultant voltage gain is given by the product of the individual voltage gains of each stage. This statement is verified as follows:

$$A_{V1} \equiv \frac{V_2}{V_1} = \frac{\text{output voltage of first stage}}{\text{input voltage of first stage}} = A_1\underline{/\theta_1}$$

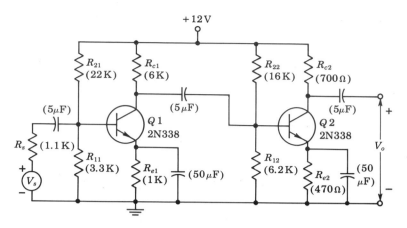

Fig. 12-4 Practical two-stage CE audio amplifier. (Courtesy of Texas Instruments, Inc.)

where A_1 is the magnitude of the voltage gain of the first stage, and θ_1 is the phase angle between output and input voltage of this stage. Similarly,

$$A_{Vk} \equiv \frac{V_{k+1}}{V_k} = \frac{\text{output voltage of } k\text{th stage}}{\text{input voltage of } k\text{th stage}} = A_k \underline{/\theta_k}$$

The resultant voltage gain is defined as

$$A_V \equiv \frac{V_o}{V_1} = \frac{\text{output voltage of } n\text{th stage}}{\text{input voltage of first stage}} = A \underline{/\theta}$$

Since

$$\frac{V_o}{V_1} \equiv \frac{V_2}{V_1} \frac{V_3}{V_2} \frac{V_4}{V_3} \cdots \frac{V_n}{V_{n-1}} \frac{V_o}{V_n} \tag{12-5}$$

it follows from these expressions that

$$A_V = A_{V1} A_{V2} \cdots A_{Vn}$$

$$= A_1 A_2 \cdots A_n \underline{/\theta_1 + \theta_2 + \cdots + \theta_n} = A \underline{/\theta} \tag{12-6}$$

or

$$A = A_1 A_2 \cdots A_n \qquad \theta = \theta_1 + \theta_2 + \cdots + \theta_n \tag{12-7}$$

The magnitude of the voltage gain equals the product of the magnitudes of the voltage gains of each stage. Also, the resultant phase shift of a multistage amplifier equals the sum of the phase shifts introduced by each stage.

The voltage gain of the kth stage is, from Table 11-4,

$$A_{Vk} = \frac{A_{Ik} R_{Lk}}{R_{ik}} \tag{12-8}$$

where R_{Lk} is the effective load at the collector of the kth transistor. The quantities in Eq. (12-8) are evaluated by starting with the last stage and proceeding to the first.   Thus the current gain and the input impedance of the nth stage are given in Table 11-4, respectively, as

$$A_{In} = \frac{-h_{fe}}{1 + h_{oe}R_{Ln}} \qquad R_{in} = h_{ie} + h_{re}A_{In}R_{Ln} \qquad (12\text{-}9)$$

where $R_{Ln} = R_{cn}$.   The effective load $R_{L,n-1}$ on the $(n-1)$st stage is $R_{c,n-1} \| R_{in}$, or

$$R_{L,n-1} = \frac{R_{c,n-1}R_{in}}{R_{c,n-1} + R_{in}} \qquad (12\text{-}10)$$

Now the amplification $A_{I,n-1}$ of the next to the last stage is obtained from Eq. (12-9) by replacing R_{Ln} by $R_{L,n-1}$.   The input impedance of the $(n-1)$st stage is obtained by replacing n by $n-1$ in Eq. (12-9).   Proceeding in this manner, we can calculate the base-to-collector current gains of every stage, including the first.   From Eq. (12-8) we then obtain the voltage gain of each stage.

The Current Gain   Without first finding the voltage amplification of each stage as indicated above, we can obtain the resultant voltage gain from

$$A_V = A_I \frac{R_{cn}}{R_{i1}} \qquad (12\text{-}11)$$

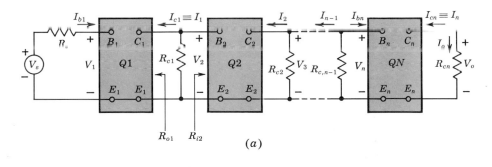

(a)

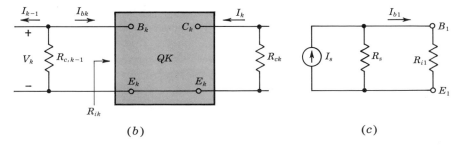

(b)   (c)

Fig. 12-5   (a) n transistor CE stages in cascade.   (b) The kth stage.   (c) The transistor input stage driven from a current source.

where A_I is the current gain of the n-stage amplifier. Since A_I is defined as the ratio of the output current I_o of the last stage to the input (base) current I_{b1} of the first stage,

$$A_I \equiv \frac{I_o}{I_{b1}} = -\frac{I_{cn}}{I_{b1}} = -\frac{I_n}{I_{b1}} \tag{12-12}$$

where $I_{cn} \equiv I_n$ is the collector current of the nth stage. We now obtain expressions from which to calculate A_I in terms of the circuit parameters. Since

$$\frac{I_n}{I_{b1}} \equiv \frac{I_1}{I_{b1}} \frac{I_2}{I_1} \cdots \frac{I_{n-1}}{I_{n-2}} \frac{I_n}{I_{n-1}}$$

then

$$A_I = A_{I1}A'_{I2} \cdots A'_{I,n-1}A'_{In} \tag{12-13}$$

where

$$A_{I1} \equiv -\frac{I_1}{I_{b1}} = -\frac{I_{c1}}{I_{b1}} \qquad A'_{Ik} \equiv \frac{I_k}{I_{k-1}} \tag{12-14}$$

Note that A_{I1} is the *base-to-collector current gain* of the first stage, and A'_{Ik} is the *collector-to-collector current gain* of the kth stage ($k = 2, 3, \ldots, n$).

We now obtain the relationship between the collector-to-collector current gain $A'_{Ik} = I_k/I_{k-1}$ and the base-to-collector current amplification

$$A_{Ik} = -\frac{I_k}{I_{bk}}$$

where $I_{ck} \equiv I_k$ is the collector current and I_{bk} is the base current of the kth stage. From Fig. 12-5b,

$$I_{bk} = -I_{k-1}\frac{R_{c,k-1}}{R_{c,k-1} + R_{ik}} \tag{12-15}$$

Hence

$$A'_{Ik} = \frac{I_k}{I_{k-1}} = \frac{I_k}{I_{bk}}\frac{I_{bk}}{I_{k-1}} = \frac{A_{Ik}R_{c,k-1}}{R_{c,k-1} + R_{ik}} \tag{12-16}$$

The base-to-collector current gain A_{Ik} is found by starting with the output stage and proceeding to the kth stage, as indicated above in connection with Eqs. (12-9) and (12-10). The collector-to-collector gains are then found from Eq. (12-16), and the current gain of the n-stage amplifier, from Eq. (12-13).

If the input stage of Fig. 12-5a is driven from a current source, as indicated in Fig. 12-5c, the overall current gain is given by

$$A_{Is} = A_I\frac{R_s}{R_s + R_{i1}} \tag{12-17}$$

Input and Output Impedances   The input resistance of the amplifier is obtained, as indicated above, by starting with the last stage and proceeding toward the first stage.

The output impedance of each transistor stage and of the overall amplifier is calculated starting with the first stage and using Eq. (11-34). The output impedance R'_{ok} of the kth stage is the parallel combination of the output impedance R_{ok} of transistor QK and R_{ck}. The effective source impedance of the $(k + 1)$st stage is also R'_{ok}.

Power Gain   The total power gain of the n-stage amplifier is

$$A_P = \frac{\text{output power}}{\text{input power}} = -\frac{V_o I_n}{V_1 I_{b1}} = A_V A_I \qquad (12\text{-}18)$$

or

$$A_P = (A_I)^2 \frac{R_{cn}}{R_{i1}} \qquad (12\text{-}19)$$

Choice of the Transistor Configuration in a Cascade   It is important to note that the previous calculations of input and output impedances and voltage and current gains are applicable for any connection of the cascaded stages. The discussion has assumed that all stages are CE. However, they could be CC, CB, or combinations of all three possible connections.

Consider the following question: Which of the three possible connections must be used in cascade if maximum voltage gain is to be realized? For the intermediate stages, the common-collector connection is not used because the voltage gain of such a stage is less than unity. Hence it is not possible (without a transformer) to increase the overall voltage amplification by cascading common-collector stages.

Grounded-base RC-coupled stages also are seldom cascaded because the voltage gain of such an arrangement is approximately the same as that of the output stage alone. This statement may be verified as follows: The voltage gain of a stage equals its current gain times the effective load resistance R_L divided by the input resistance R_i. The effective load resistance R_L is the parallel combination of the actual collector resistance R_c and (except for the last stage) the input resistance R_i of the following stage. This parallel combination is certainly less than R_i, and hence, for identical stages, the effective load resistance is less than R_i. The maximum current gain is h_{fb}, which is less than unity (but approximately equal to unity). Hence the voltage gain of any stage (except the last, or output, stage) is less than unity. (This analysis is not strictly correct because the R_i is a function of the effective load resistance and hence will vary somewhat from stage to stage.)

Since the short-circuit current gain h_{fe} of a common-emitter stage is much greater than unity, it is possible to increase the voltage amplification by cascading such stages. We may now state that *in a cascade the intermediate transistors should be connected in a common-emitter configuration.*

The choice of the input stage may be decided by criteria other than the maximization of voltage gain. For example, the amplitude or the frequency response of the transducer V_s may depend upon the impedance into which it operates. Some transducers require essentially open-circuit or short-circuit operation. In many cases the common-collector or common-base stage is used at the input because of impedance considerations, even at the expense of voltage or current gain. Noise is another important consideration which may determine the selection of a particular configuration of the input stage.

12-3   THE DECIBEL

In many problems it is found very convenient to compare two powers on a logarithmic rather than on a linear scale. The unit of this logarithmic scale is called the decibel (abbreviated dB). The number N of decibels by which the power P_2 exceeds the power P_1 is defined by

$$N = 10 \log \frac{P_2}{P_1} \tag{12-20}$$

It should be noted that the specification of a certain power in decibels is meaningless unless a standard reference level is implied or is stated specifically. A negative value of N means that the power P_2 is less than the reference power P_1.

If the input and output impedances of an amplifier are equal resistances, then $P_2 = V_2^2/R$ and $P_1 = V_1^2/R$, where V_2 and V_1 are the output and input voltage drops. Under this condition, Eq. (12-20) reduces to

$$N = 20 \log \frac{V_2}{V_1} = 20 \log A_V \tag{12-21}$$

where A_V is the magnitude of the voltage gain of the unit. The input and output resistances are not equal, in general. However, this expression is adopted as a convenient definition of the decibel voltage gain of an amplifier, regardless of the magnitudes of the input and output resistances. That is, if the voltage amplification is 10, its decibel voltage gain is 20; if the voltage amplification is 100, the decibel voltage gain is 40; etc. If there is the possibility of confusion between voltage and power gain, the designation dBV can be used for decibel voltage gain.

The logarithm of the magnitude of the expression for voltage gain in Eq. (12-7) is given by

$$\log A_V = \log A_1 + \log A_2 + \cdots + \log A_n \tag{12-22}$$

By comparing this result with Eq. (12-21), which defines the decibel voltage gain, it is seen that *the overall decibel voltage gain of a multistage amplifier is the sum of the decibel voltage gains of the individual stages.*

The foregoing considerations are independent of the type of interstage coupling and are valid for both transistor and vacuum-tube amplifiers. However, it must be emphasized that, in calculating the gain of one stage, the loading effect of the next stage must be taken into account.

12-4   SIMPLIFIED COMMON–EMITTER HYBRID MODEL[2]

In the preceding chapter, and also in Sec. 12-1, we carried out detailed calculations of current gain, voltage gain, input, and output impedances, of illustrative transistor amplifier circuits.

In most practical cases it is appropriate to obtain approximate values of A_I, A_V, A_P, R_i, and R_o rather than to carry out the more lengthy exact calculations. We are justified in making such approximations because the h parameters themselves usually vary widely for the same type of transistor. Also, a better "physical feeling" for the behavior of a transistor circuit can be obtained from a simple approximate solution than from a more laborious exact calculation. Since the common-emitter connection is in general the most useful, we first concentrate our attention on the CE h-parameter model shown in Fig. 12-6a. How can we modify this model so as to make the analysis simple without greatly sacrificing accuracy? Since $1/h_{oe}$ in parallel with R_L is approximately equal to R_L if $1/h_{oe} \gg R_L$, then h_{oe} may be neglected in Fig. 12-6a provided that $h_{oe}R_L \ll 1$. Moreover, if we omit h_{oe} from this figure, the collector current I_c is given by $I_c = h_{fe}I_b$. Under these circumstances the magnitude of the voltage of the generator in the emitter circuit is

$$h_{re}|V_c| = h_{re}I_cR_L = h_{re}h_{fe}R_LI_b$$

Since $h_{re}h_{fe} \approx 0.01$, this voltage may be neglected in comparison with the $h_{ie}I_b$ drop across h_{ie}, provided that R_L is not too large. We therefore conclude that if the load resistance R_L is small, it is possible to neglect the parameters h_{re} and h_{oe} in the circuit of Fig. 12-6a and to obtain the approximate equivalent

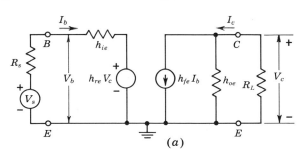

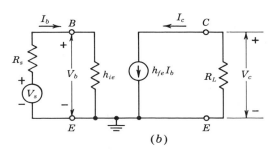

Fig. 12-6 (a) Exact CE hybrid model; (b) approximate CE model.

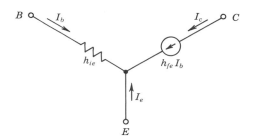

Fig. 12-7 Approximate hybrid model which may be used for all three configurations, CE, CC, or CB.

circuit of Fig. 12-6b. We are essentially making the assumption here that the transistor operates under short-circuit conditions. In subsequent discussion we investigate the error introduced in our calculations because of the nonzero load resistance. Specifically, we show that if $h_{oe}R_L \leq 0.1$, the error in calculating A_I, R_i, A_V, and R'_o for the CE connection is less than 10 percent.

Generalized Approximate Model The simplified hybrid circuit of Fig. 12-7 which we used in Fig. 12-6b for the CE circuit may also be used for the CC (or the CB) connection by simply grounding the appropriate terminal. The signal is connected between the input terminal and ground, and the load is placed between the output terminal and ground. We examine in detail in the following sections the errors introduced in our calculations by using the simplified model of Fig. 12-7 for the analysis of the CC and CB connections. In summary, we claim that two of the four h parameters, h_{ie} and h_{fe}, are sufficient for the approximate analysis of low-frequency transistor circuits, provided the load resistance R_L is no larger than $0.1/h_{oe}$. For the value of h_{oe} given in Table 11-2, R_L must be less than 4 K. The approximate circuit is always valid when CE transistors are operated in cascade because the low input impedance of a CE stage shunts the output of the previous stage so that the effective load resistance R'_L satisfies the condition $h_{oe}R'_L \leq 0.1$.

We now justify the validity of the proposed simplification for the CE configuration.

Current Gain From Table 11-4 the CE current gain is given by

$$A_I = \frac{-h_{fe}}{1 + h_{oe}R_L} \qquad (12\text{-}23)$$

Hence we immediately see that the approximation (Fig. 12-6b)

$$A_I \approx -h_{fe} \qquad (12\text{-}24)$$

overestimates the magnitude of the current gain by less than 10 percent if $h_{oe}R_L < 0.1$.

Input Impedance From Table 11-4 the input resistance is given by

$$R_i = h_{ie} + h_{re}A_I R_L \qquad (12\text{-}25)$$

which may be put in the form

$$R_i = h_{ie}\left(1 - \frac{h_{re}h_{fe}}{h_{ie}h_{oe}}\frac{|A_I|}{h_{fe}}h_{oe}R_L\right) \qquad (12\text{-}26)$$

Using the typical h-parameter values in Table 11-2, we find $h_{re}h_{fe}/h_{ie}h_{oe} \approx 0.5$. From Eq. (12-23), we see that $|A_I| < h_{fe}$. Hence, if $h_{oe}R_L < 0.1$, it follows from Eq. (12-26) that the approximation obtained from Fig. 12-6b, namely,

$$R_i = \frac{V_b}{I_b} \approx h_{ie} \qquad (12\text{-}27)$$

overestimates the input resistance by less than 5 percent.

Voltage Gain From Table 11-4 the voltage gain is given by

$$A_V = A_I\frac{R_L}{R_i} = -\frac{h_{fe}R_L}{h_{ie}} \qquad (12\text{-}28)$$

If we take the logarithm of this equation and then the differential, we obtain

$$\frac{dA_V}{A_V} = \frac{dA_I}{A_I} - \frac{dR_i}{R_i} \qquad (12\text{-}29)$$

From the preceding discussion the maximum errors for $h_{oe}R_L < 0.1$ are

$$\frac{dA_I}{A_I} = +0.1 \qquad \text{and} \qquad \frac{dR_i}{R_i} = +0.05$$

Hence, the maximum error in voltage gain is 5 percent, and the magnitude of A_V is overestimated by this amount.

Output Impedance The simplified circuit of Fig. 12-6b has infinite output resistance because, with $V_s = 0$ and an external voltage source applied at the output, we find $I_b = 0$, and hence $I_c = 0$. However, the true value depends upon the source resistance R_s and lies between 40 and 80 K (Fig. 11-17). For a maximum load resistance of $R_L = 4$ K, the output resistance of the stage, taking R_L into account, is 4 K, if the simplified model is used, and the parallel combination of 4 K with 40 K (under the worst case), if the exact solution is used. Hence, using the approximate model leads to a value of output resistance under load which is too large, but by no more than 10 percent.

The approximate solution for the CE configuration is summarized in the first column of Table 12-2.

12-5   SIMPLIFIED CALCULATIONS FOR THE COMMON–COLLECTOR CONFIGURATION

Figure 12-8 shows the simplified circuit of Fig. 12-7 with the collector grounded (with respect to the signal) and a load R_L connected between emitter and ground.

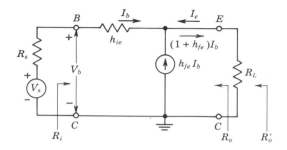

Fig. 12-8   Simplified hybrid model for the CC circuit.

Current Gain   From Fig. 12-8 we see that

$$A_I = -\frac{I_e}{I_b} = 1 + h_{fe} \tag{12-30}$$

From Tables 11-4 and 11-3, the *exact* expression for A_I is

$$A_I = \frac{-h_{fc}}{1 + h_{oc}R_L} = \frac{1 + h_{fe}}{1 + h_{oe}R_L} \tag{12-31}$$

Comparing these two equations, we conclude that when the simplified equivalent circuit of Fig. 12-8 is used, the current gain is overestimated by less than 10 percent if $h_{oe}R_L < 0.1$.

Input Resistance   From Fig. 12-8, we obtain

$$R_i = \frac{V_b}{I_b} = h_{ie} + (1 + h_{fe})R_L \tag{12-32}$$

Note that $R_i \gg h_{ie} \approx 1$ K even if R_L is as small as 0.5 K, because $h_{fe} \gg 1$. The expression for R_i is, from Tables 11-4 and 11-3,

$$R_i = h_{ic} + h_{rc}A_I R_L = h_{ie} + A_I R_L \tag{12-33}$$

where we have neglected h_{re} ($\sim 2.5 \times 10^{-4}$) compared with unity, and hence have written $h_{rc} = 1 - h_{re} = 1$. If we substitute from Eq. (12-30) in (12-33), we obtain Eq. (12-32). However, we have just concluded that Eq. (12-30) gives too high a value of A_I by at most 10 percent. Hence it follows that R_i, as calculated from Eq. (12-32) or Fig. 12-8, is also overestimated by less than 10 percent.

Voltage Gain   If Eq. (12-29) is used for the voltage gain, it follows from the same arguments as used in the CE case that there will be very little error in the value of A_V. An alternative proof is now given. The voltage gain of the emitter-follower is close to unity, and we obtain an expression for its deviation from unity. Using Eq. (12-33),

$$1 - A_V = 1 - \frac{A_I R_L}{R_i} = \frac{R_i - A_I R_L}{R_i} = \frac{h_{ie}}{R_i} \tag{12-34}$$

TABLE 12-2   Summary of approximate equations for $h_{oc}(R_e + R_L) \leq 0.1$†

	CE	CE with R_e	CC	CB
A_I	$-h_{fe}$	$-h_{fe}$	$1 + h_{fe}$	$-h_{fb} = \dfrac{h_{fe}}{1 + h_{fe}}$
R_i	h_{ie}	$h_{ie} + (1 + h_{fe})R_e$	$h_{ie} + (1 + h_{fe})R_L$	$h_{ib} = \dfrac{h_{ie}}{1 + h_{fe}}$
A_V	$-\dfrac{h_{fe}R_L}{h_{ie}}$	$-\dfrac{h_{fe}R_L}{R_i}$	$1 - \dfrac{h_{ie}}{R_i}$	$h_{fe}\dfrac{R_L}{h_{ie}}$
R_o	∞	∞	$\dfrac{R_s + h_{ie}}{1 + h_{fe}}$	∞
R'_o	R_L	R_L	$R_o \| R_L$	R_L

† $(R_i)_{\mathrm{CB}}$ is an underestimation by less than 10 percent. All other quantities except R_o are too large in magnitude by less than 10 percent.

This expression is nearly exact since the only approximation made is that $h_{rc} = 1 - h_{re}$ is replaced by unity. If, for example, $R_i = 10h_{ie}$, then $A_V = 0.9$. If, however, we use an approximate value of R_i which is 10 percent too high, then $h_{ie}/R_i = \frac{1}{11} = 0.09$ and $A_V = 0.91$. Hence the approximate calculation for A_V gives a value which is only 1 percent too high.

Output Impedance   In Fig. 12-8 the open-circuit output voltage is V_s and the short-circuit output current is

$$I = (1 + h_{fe})I_b = \frac{(1 + h_{fe})V_s}{h_{ie} + R_s}$$

Hence the output admittance of the transistor alone is, from Eq. (8-22),

$$Y_o = \frac{I}{V_s} = \frac{1 + h_{fe}}{h_{ie} + R_s} \tag{12-35}$$

From Tables 11-4 and 11-3, the expression for Y_o is

$$Y_o = h_{oc} - \frac{h_{fc}h_{rc}}{h_{ic} + R_s} = h_{oe} + \frac{1 + h_{fe}}{h_{ie} + R_s} \tag{12-36}$$

Even if we choose an abnormally large value of source resistance, say $R_s = 100$ K, then (using the typical h-parameter values in Table 11-2) we find that the second term in Eq. (12-36) is large (500 μA/V) compared with the first term (25 μA/V). Hence the value of the approximate output admittance given by Eq. (12-35) is smaller than the value given by Eq. (12-36) by less than 5 percent. The output resistance R_o of the transistor, calculated from the simplified model, namely,

$$R_o = \frac{h_{ie} + R_s}{1 + h_{fe}} \tag{12-37}$$

is an overestimation by less than 5 percent.   The output resistance R_o' of the stage, taking the load into account, is R_o in parallel with R_L.

The approximate solution for the CC configuration is summarized in the third column of Table 12-2.

EXAMPLE   Carry out the calculations for the two-stage amplifier of Fig. 12-2 using the simplified model of Fig. 12-7.

Solution   First note that, since $h_{oe}R_L = 25 \times 10^{-6} \times 5 \times 10^3 = 0.125$, which is slightly larger than 0.1, we may expect errors in our approximation somewhat larger than 10 percent.

For the CC output stage we have, from Table 12-2,

$$A_{I2} = 1 + h_{fe} = 51$$

$$R_{i2} = h_{ie} + (1 + h_{fe})R_L = 2 + (51)(5) = 257 \text{ K}$$

$$A_{V2} = \frac{A_{I2}R_L}{R_{i2}} = \frac{(51)(5)}{257} = 0.992$$

or alternatively,

$$A_{V2} = 1 - \frac{h_{ie}}{R_{i2}} = 1 - \frac{2}{257} = 0.992$$

For the CE input stage, we find, from Table 12-2,

$$A_{I1} = -h_{fe} = -50 \qquad R_{i1} = h_{ie} = 2 \text{ K}$$

The effective load on the first stage, its voltage gain, and output impedance are

$$R_{L1} = \frac{R_{c1}R_{i2}}{R_{c1} + R_{i2}} = \frac{(5)(257)}{262} = 4.9 \text{ K}$$

$$A_{V1} = \frac{A_{I1}R_{L1}}{R_{i1}} = \frac{-(50)(4.9)}{2} = -123$$

$$R_{o1}' = R_{c1} = 5 \text{ K}$$

Since R_{o1}' is the effective source impedance for $Q2$, then, from Table 12-2,

$$R_{o2} = \frac{h_{ie} + R_s}{1 + h_{fe}} = \frac{2,000 + 5,000}{51} = 137 \text{ }\Omega$$

$$R_{o2}' = \frac{R_{o2}R_{L2}}{R_{o2} + R_{L2}} = \frac{(137)(5,000)}{5,137} = 134 \text{ }\Omega$$

Finally, the overall voltage and current gains of the cascade are

$$A_V = A_{V1}A_{V2} = (-123)(0.992) = -122$$

$$A_I = A_{I1}A_{I2}\frac{R_{c1}}{R_{c1} + R_{i2}} = (-50)(51)\left(\frac{5}{5 + 257}\right) = -48.7$$

Alternatively, A_V may be computed from

$$A_V = A_I\frac{R_{L2}}{R_{i1}} = -\frac{48.7 \times 5}{2} = -122$$

Table 12-3 summarizes this solution, and should be compared with the exact values in Table 12-1. We find that the maximum errors are just slightly above 10 percent, as anticipated. It should also be noted that all the approximate values are numerically too large, as predicted.

TABLE 12-3   Approximate results of the example on page **338**

	Q2, CC	Q1, CE	Both stages
A_I	51	-50	-48.7
R_i	257 K	2 K	2 K
A_V	0.992	-123	-122
R_o'	134 Ω	5 K	134 Ω

12-6   SIMPLIFIED CALCULATIONS FOR THE COMMON–BASE CONFIGURATION

Figure 12-9 shows the simplified circuit of Fig. 12-7 with the base grounded and a load resistor R_L connected between collector and ground. Following procedures exactly analogous to those explained in Secs. 12-4 and 12-5 for the CE and CC configurations, respectively, the approximate formulas given in the fourth column of Table 12-2 may be obtained. Note that R_i is too small by less than 10 percent, whereas A_I, A_V, and R_o' are too large by no more than 10 percent.

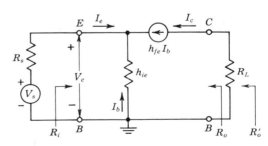

Fig. 12-9 Simplified hybrid model for the CB circuit.

12-7   THE COMMON–EMITTER AMPLIFIER
WITH AN EMITTER RESISTANCE

Very often a transistor amplifier consists of a number of CE stages in cascade. Since the voltage gain of the amplifier is equal to the product of the voltage gains of each stage, it becomes important to stabilize the voltage amplification of each stage. By stabilization of voltage or current gain, we mean that the amplification becomes essentially independent of the h parameters of the transistor. From our discussion in Sec. 11-3, we know that the transistor parameters depend on temperature, aging, and the operating point. Moreover, these parameters vary widely from device to device even for the same type of transistor.

The necessity for voltage stabilization is seen from the following example: Two commercially built six-stage amplifiers are to be compared. If each stage of the first has a gain which is only 10 percent below that of the second, the overall amplification of the latter is $(0.9)^6 = 0.53$ (or about one-half that of the former). And this value may be below the required specification. A simple and effective way to obtain voltage-gain stabilization is to add an emitter resistor R_e to a CE stage, as indicated in the circuit of Fig. 12-10. This stabilization is a result of the feedback provided by the emitter resistor. The general concept of feedback is discussed in Chap. 17.

We show in this section that the presence of R_e has the following effects on the amplifier performance, in addition to the beneficial effect on bias stability discussed in Sec. 10-4: It leaves the current gain A_I essentially unchanged; it increases the input impedance by $(1 + h_{fe})R_e$; it increases the output impedance; and under the condition $(1 + h_{fe})R_e \gg h_{ie}$, it stabilizes the

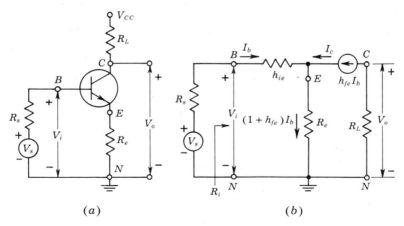

(a)   (b)

Fig. 12-10   (a) Common-emitter amplifier with an emitter resistor. The base biasing network (R_1R_2 of Fig. 12-13a) is not indicated. (b) Approximate small-signal equivalent circuit.

voltage gain, which becomes essentially equal to $-R_L/R_e$ (and thus is independent of the transistor).

The Approximate Solution An approximate analysis of the circuit of Fig. 12-10a can be made using the simplified model of Fig. 12-7 as shown in Fig. 12-10b.

The current gain is, from Fig. 12-10b,

$$A_I = \frac{-I_c}{I_b} = \frac{-h_{fe}I_b}{I_b} = -h_{fe} \tag{12-38}$$

The current gain equals the short-circuit value, and is unaffected by the addition of R_e.

The input resistance, as obtained from inspection of Fig. 12-10b, is

$$R_i = \frac{V_i}{I_b} = h_{ie} + (1 + h_{fe})R_e \tag{12-39}$$

The input resistance is augmented by $(1 + h_{fe})R_e$, and may be very much larger than h_{ie}. For example, if $R_e = 1$ K and $h_{fe} = 50$, then

$$(1 + h_{fe})R_e = 51 \text{ K} \gg h_{ie} \approx 1 \text{ K}$$

Hence an emitter resistance greatly increases the input resistance.

The voltage gain is

$$A_V = \frac{A_I R_L}{R_i} = \frac{-h_{fe}R_L}{h_{ie} + (1 + h_{fe})R_e} \tag{12-40}$$

Clearly, the addition of an emitter resistance greatly reduces the voltage amplification. This reduction in gain is often a reasonable price to pay for tho improvement in stability. We note that, if $(1 + h_{fe})R_e \gg h_{ie}$, and since $h_{fe} \gg 1$, then

$$A_V \approx \frac{-h_{fe}}{1 + h_{fe}} \frac{R_L}{R_e} \approx \frac{-R_L}{R_e} \tag{12-41}$$

Subject to the above approximations, A_V is completely stable (if stable resistances are used for R_L and R_e), since it is independent of all transistor parameters.

The output resistance of the transistor alone (with R_L considered external) is infinite for the approximate circuit of Fig. 12-10b, just as it was for the CE amplifier of Sec. 12-4 with $R_e = 0$. Hence the output impedance of the stage, including the load, is R_L.

Looking into the Base, Collector, and Emitter of a Transistor On the basis of Eq. (12-39), we draw the equivalent circuit of Fig. 12-11a from which to calculate the base current with the signal source applied. This network is the equivalent circuit "looking into the base." From it we obtain

$$I_b = \frac{V_s}{R_s + h_{ie} + (1 + h_{fe})R_e} \tag{12-42}$$

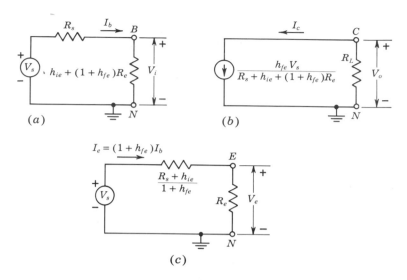

Fig. 12-11 (a) Equivalent circuit "looking into the base" of Fig. 12-10. This circuit gives (approximately) the correct base current. (b) Equivalent circuit "looking into the collector" of Fig. 12-10. This circuit gives (approximately) the correct collector current. (c) Equivalent circuit "looking into the emitter" of Fig. 12-10. This circuit gives (approximately) the correct emitter voltage V_e and the correct emitter and base currents.

Since the output voltage at the collector is

$$V_o = -I_c R_L = -h_{fe} I_b R_L = \frac{-h_{fe} V_s R_L}{R_s + h_{ie} + (1 + h_{fe}) R_e} \tag{12-43}$$

and since the output impedance is infinite, the Norton's equivalent output circuit is as given in Fig. 12-11b. This network "looking into the collector" gives the correct collector voltage. This equivalent circuit emphasizes that (subject to our approximations) the transistor behaves like an ideal current source and that the collector current is h_{fe} times the base current.

From Fig. 12-10b and Eq. (12-42) we find the emitter-to-ground voltage to be

$$V_{en} \equiv V_e = (1 + h_{fe}) I_b R_e = \frac{V_s R_e}{(R_s + h_{ie})/(1 + h_{fe}) + R_e} \tag{12-44}$$

This same expression may be obtained from Fig. 12-11c, which therefore represents the equivalent circuit "looking into the emitter."

Validity of the Approximations For the CE case, with $R_e = 0$, the approximate equivalent circuit of Fig. 12-7 is valid if $h_{oe} R_L \leq 0.1$. What is the corresponding restriction for the circuit with $R_e \neq 0$? We can answer this question and, at the same time, obtain an exact solution, if desired, by proceeding as indicated in Fig. 12-12. The exact value of the current gain of Fig. 12-12a (which is the same as that of Fig. 12-10a) is $A_I = -I_c/I_b$. The two amplifiers of Fig. 12-12a and b are equivalent in the sense that the base and collector currents are the same in the two circuits. This fact can be verified by writing the KVL equations for the two loops of each of the amplifiers.

The effective load impedance R'_L is, from Fig. 12-12b,

$$R'_L = R_L + \frac{A_I - 1}{A_I} R_e \qquad (12\text{-}45)$$

We know from the above approximate solution that $A_I \approx -h_{fe}$, and since $h_{fe} \gg 1$, then $R'_L \approx R_L + R_e$. Since in Fig. 12-12b the emitter is grounded and the collector resistance is R'_L, the approximate two-parameter (h_{ie} and h_{fe}) circuit is valid, provided that

$$h_{oe}R'_L = h_{oe}(R_L + R_e) \leq 0.1 \qquad (12\text{-}46)$$

This condition means that the sum of R_L and R_e is no more than a few thousand ohms, say 4 K for $1/h_{oe} = 40$ K. Furthermore, R_e is usually several times smaller than R_L in order to have an appreciable voltage gain [Eq. (12-41)].

The approximate solution for the CE amplifier with an emitter resistor R_e is summarized in the second column of Table 12-2.

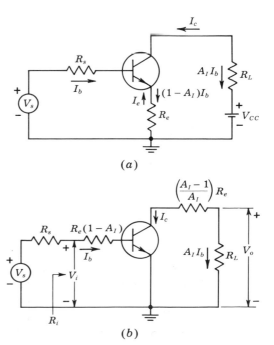

Fig. 12-12 (a) Transistor amplifier stage with unbypassed emitter resistor R_e. (b) Small-signal equivalent circuit.

(a)

(b)

The Exact Solution   If the above inequality (12-46) is not satisfied for a particular amplifier, an exact solution can readily be obtained by referring to Fig. 12-12b and to Table 11-4.   For example, the current gain is

$$A_I = \frac{-h_{fe}}{1 + h_{oe}R'_L} = \frac{-h_{fe}}{1 + h_{oe}\left(R_L + \dfrac{A_I - 1}{A_I}R_e\right)} \tag{12-47}$$

From this equation we can solve explicitly for A_I, and we obtain

$$A_I = \frac{h_{oe}R_e - h_{fe}}{1 + h_{oe}(R_L + R_e)} \tag{12-48}$$

If the inequality (12-46) is satisfied, then $h_{oe}R_e \ll h_{fe}$, and the exact expression (12-48) reduces to $A_I \approx -h_{fe}$ in agreement with Eq. (12-38).

The exact expression for the input resistance is, from Fig. 12-12b and Table 11-4,

$$R_i = \frac{V_i}{I_b} = (1 - A_I)R_e + h_{ie} + h_{re}A_IR'_L \tag{12-49}$$

where R'_L is given by Eq. (12-45).   Usually, the third term on the right-hand side can be neglected, compared with the other two terms.   The exact expression for the voltage amplification is

$$A_V = \frac{A_IR_L}{R_i} \tag{12-50}$$

where the exact values for A_I and R_i from Eqs. (12-48) and (12-49) must be used.

The exact expression for the output impedance (with R_L considered external to the amplifier) is found, as outlined in Prob. 12-14, to be

$$R_o = \frac{1}{h_{oe}}\frac{(1 + h_{fe})R_e + (R_s + h_{ie})(1 + h_{oe}R_e)}{R_e + R_s + h_{ie} - h_{re}h_{fe}/h_{oe}} \tag{12-51}$$

Note that, if $R_e \gg R_s + h_{ie}$ and $h_{oe}R_e \ll 1$, then

$$R_o \approx \frac{1 + h_{fe}}{h_{oe}} = \frac{1}{h_{ob}} \tag{12-52}$$

where the conversion formula (Table 11-3) from the CE to the CB h parameters is used.   Since $1/h_{ob} \approx 2$ M, we see that the addition of an emitter resistor greatly increases the output resistance of a CE stage.   This statement is true even if R_e is of the same order of magnitude as R_s and h_{ie}.   For example, for $R_e = R_s = 1$ K, and using the h-parameter values in Table 11-3, we find from Eq. (12-51) that $R_o = 817$ K, which is at least ten times the output resistance for an amplifier with $R_e = 0$ (Fig. 11-17).

12-8   THE EMITTER FOLLOWER

Figure 12-13a is the circuit diagram of a common-collector transistor amplifier. This configuration is called the *emitter follower*, and is similar to the cathode follower in its operation, although there are a number of important differences worth noting.   First, this amplifier has a voltage gain which is very close to unity (much closer to unity for typical loads than the cathode follower). Second, the voltage drop across the emitter resistor (from emitter to ground) may be either positive or negative, depending on whether an *n-p-n* or a *p-n-p* transistor is used.   In the case of the cathode follower, the drop across the cathode resistor is always positive.   Third, the input resistance of the emitter follower, although high (tens or hundreds of kilohms), is low compared with that of a cathode follower.   Fourth, the output resistance of the emitter follower is much lower (perhaps by a factor of 10) than that of a cathode follower.

In the discussion on cascading transistor stages in Sec. 12-2, we note that the common-collector stage is not used as an intermediate stage, but rather the most common use for the emitter follower is as a circuit which performs the function of impedance transformation over a wide range of frequencies with voltage gain close to unity.   In addition, the emitter follower increases the power level of the signal.

The input circuit of Fig. 12-13a includes the biasing resistors R_1, R_2, and the blocking capacitor C.   This circuit may be simplified by the use of Thévenin's theorem.   Let $R' = R_1\|R_2$.   If, at the lowest frequency under consideration, the reactance of C is small compared with $R_s + R'$, we may neglect the effect of this capacitor.   The equivalent input circuit is then indicated in Fig. 12-13b, where

$$R_b = R_s\|R' \qquad R' = R_1\|R_2 \qquad \text{and} \qquad V_g = \frac{V_s R'}{R_s + R'} \tag{12-53}$$

If the input resistance of the amplifier is $R_i \equiv V_i/I_b$, the input resistance R_i', taking the bleeder into account, is $R_i' = R'\|R_i$.   The impedance which the source V_s sees is $R_i'' = R_s + R_i'$.

The voltage V_i at the input terminals of the amplifier is

$$V_i = \frac{V_s R_i'}{R_s + R_i'} \tag{12-54}$$

The circuit of Fig. 12-13b is examined in some detail in Sec. 12-5, where we obtain approximate, as well as exact, expressions for A_I, R_i, A_V, and R_o. The approximate formulas are given in the third column of Table 12-2, with R_L replaced by R_e, and R_s replaced by R_b.   The approximate equivalent circuits looking into the base and emitter are given in Fig. 12-11a and c, respectively, where V_s is replaced by V_g.   For exact expressions for A_I, R_i, A_V, and Y_o, the reader is referred to Eqs. (12-31), (12-33), (12-34), and (12-36), respectively.

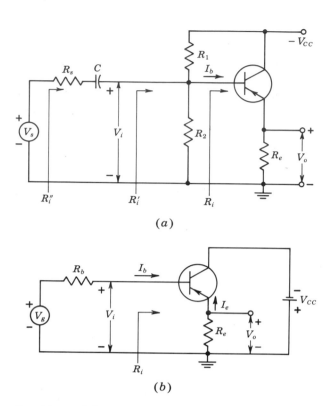

Fig. 12-13 (a) The circuit of an emitter follower, including the biasing resistors R_1 and R_2. (b) The input circuit is replaced by its Thévenin's equivalent.

Extreme Values of R_i and A_V It is interesting to calculate A_V for the largest load for which the approximate equivalent circuit is valid, namely, $R_L = 4$ K (for $1/h_{oe} = 40$ K). From Eqs. (12-32) and (12-34) and Table 11-2,

$$R_i = 1.1 + (51)(4) = 205 \text{ K}$$

$$A_V = 1 - \frac{1.1}{205} = 1 - 0.0054 = 0.9946$$

If a triode is used in a cathode-follower configuration, the maximum gain obtained for infinite load resistance is $\mu/(\mu + 1)$. A value of $\mu = 200$ would be required to obtain $A_V = 0.995$. Since such a large value of μ is difficult to obtain with a triode, we see that an emitter follower can give a value of A_V much closer to unity than can be obtained with a cathode follower [provided that the emitter follower is driven from a very low impedance; Eq. (12-58)].

Let us now calculate R_i and A_V for an infinite load resistance. Of course, we must now use the exact formulas, Eqs. (12-31) and (12-33), rather than the approximations, Eqs. (12-30) and (12-32).   With $R_L = R_e \to \infty$,

$$A_I = \frac{1 + h_{fe}}{1 + h_{oe}R_e} \approx \frac{1 + h_{fe}}{h_{oe}R_e} \to 0 \tag{12-55}$$

$$R_i = h_{ie} + A_I R_e \approx h_{ie} + \frac{1 + h_{fe}}{h_{oe}} \approx \frac{1 + h_{fe}}{h_{oe}} = \frac{1}{h_{ob}} \tag{12-56}$$

where use has been made of the transformation from the CE to the CB h parameters in Table 11-3.   We have proved that, even if the emitter resistance is infinite, the input resistance of an emitter follower is finite and equals $1/h_{ob} \approx 2$ M.   This result is evident from an inspection of Fig. 12-13b, where we see that, with $R_e \to \infty$, the input resistance is the resistance between base and collector.   However, by definition, h_{ob} is the admittance between collector and base, with zero emitter current ($R_e \to \infty$), and therefore $R_i = 1/h_{ob}$.

The input resistance R_i', taking the bleeder R_1R_2 into account, will be much smaller than a megohm.   Methods for increasing the input resistance of a transistor circuit are given in Sec. 12-10.

For $R_e \to \infty$, Eq. (12-34) becomes

$$1 - A_V = \frac{h_{ie}}{R_i} \approx \frac{h_{ie}h_{oe}}{1 + h_{fe}} \tag{12-57}$$

If we use the h-parameter values in Table 11-2, we find

$$A_V = 1 - 5.4 \times 10^{-4} = 0.99946$$

This value is probably somewhat optimistic (too close to unity) because, for a large value of R_e, and hence a small value of transistor current, h_{ie} will be larger and h_{fe} smaller than the nominal values in Table 11-4.

The voltage gain $A_V \equiv V_o/V_i$ gives the amplification between the output and the input to the base.   The overall gain A_{Vs}, taking the signal-source impedance into account, gives the amplification between the output and the signal source V_s.   Thus

$$A_{Vs} \equiv \frac{V_o}{V_s} = \frac{V_o}{V_i}\frac{V_i}{V_s} = A_V \frac{R_i'}{R_s + R_i'} \tag{12-58}$$

where use has been made of Eq. (12-54).   Hence, in order for A_{Vs} to be very close to unity, it is required that A_V be very nearly unity and, in addition, that R_s be extremely small compared with R_i'.   This latter condition may be difficult to satisfy in practice (Sec. 12-10).

The Effect of a Collector-circuit Resistor   It is important to investigate the effect of the presence in the collector circuit of a resistance R_c in Fig. 12-13. Such a resistance is frequently added in the circuit to protect the transistor against an accidental short circuit across R_e or a large input-voltage swing. From Fig. 12-12a we see that the relationship between the CE current gain A_{Ie} (designated simply A_I in the figure) and the CC current gain A_{Ic} is

$$A_{Ic} = 1 - A_{Ie} \qquad (12\text{-}59)$$

where

$$A_{Ic} = -\frac{I_e}{I_b} \quad \text{and} \quad A_{Ie} = -\frac{I_c}{I_b}$$

Substituting Eq. (12-48) in Eq. (12-59) with R_L replaced by R_c, we obtain the exact expression

$$A_{Ic} = \frac{1 + h_{oe}R_c + h_{fe}}{1 + h_{oe}(R_c + R_e)} \qquad (12\text{-}60)$$

The value of R_i is obtained from Eq. (12-49), with A_I replaced by A_{Ie} and R_L by R_c. The voltage gain of the emitter follower with R_c present in the collector circuit is obtained as follows:

$$A_V = \frac{V_o}{V_i} = A_{Ic}\frac{R_e}{R_i} \qquad (12\text{-}61)$$

Subject to the restriction $h_{oe}(R_c + R_e) \ll 1$, the approximate formulas given in the third column of Table 12-2 are valid, and the protection resistor R_c has no effect on the small-signal operation of the emitter follower.

12-9   MILLER'S THEOREM

We digress briefly to discuss a theorem which is used in the next section and also in connection with several other topics in this book. Consider an arbitrary circuit configuration with N distinct nodes, 1, 2, 3, . . . , N, as indicated in Fig. 12-14a. Let the node voltages be V_1, V_2, V_3, . . . , V_N, where $V_N = 0$

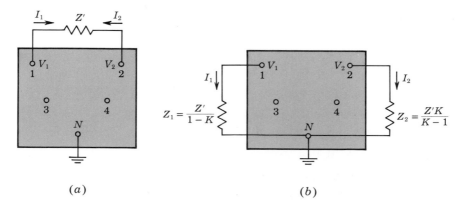

(a)   (b)

Fig. 12-14 Pertaining to Miller's theorem. By definition, $K \equiv V_2/V_1$. The networks in (a) and (b) have identical node voltages. Note that $I_1 = -I_2$.

and N is the reference or ground node. Nodes 1 and 2 (referred to as N_1 and N_2) are interconnected with an impedance Z'. We postulate that we know the ratio $V_2|V_1$. Designate the ratio V_2/V_1 by K, which in the sinusoidal steady state will be a complex number and, more generally, will be a function of the Laplace transform variable s. We shall now show that the current I_1 drawn from N_1 through Z' can be obtained by disconnecting terminal 1 from Z' and by bridging an impedance $Z'/(1 - K)$ from N_1 to ground, as indicated in Fig. 12-14b.

The current I_1 is given by

$$I_1 = \frac{V_1 - V_2}{Z'} = \frac{V_1(1 - K)}{Z'} = \frac{V_1}{Z'/(1 - K)} = \frac{V_1}{Z_1} \tag{12-62}$$

Therefore, if $Z_1 \equiv Z'/(1 - K)$ were shunted across terminals N_1-N, the current I_1 drawn from N_1 would be the same as that from the original circuit. Hence, KCL applied at N_1 leads to the same expression in terms of the node voltages for the two configurations (Fig. 12-14a and b).

In a similar way, it may be established that the correct current I_2 drawn from N_2 may be calculated by removing Z' and by connecting between N_2 and ground an impedance Z_2, given by

$$Z_2 \equiv \frac{Z'}{1 - 1/K} = \frac{Z'K}{K - 1} \tag{12-63}$$

Since identical nodal equations (KCL) are obtained from the configurations of Fig. 12-14a and b, then these two networks are equivalent. It must be emphasized that this theorem will be useful in making calculations only if it is possible to find the value of K by some independent means.

Let us apply the above theorem to the grounded-cathode stage, taking interelectrode capacitances into account. Terminal N is the cathode (Fig. 8-19), whereas nodes 1 and 2 are the grid and plate, respectively. Then Z' represents the capacitive reactance between grid and plate, or $Z' = -j/\omega C_{gp}$, and K represents the voltage gain between input and output. If R_p = plate-circuit resistance, r_p = plate resistance, and $R'_p = R_p \| r_p$, then, in the midband region, $K \approx -g_m R'_p$. Shunting the input terminals of the amplifier is an effective impedance Z_1, as in Fig. 12-14b, given by

$$Z_1 = \frac{Z'}{1 - K} = \frac{-j}{\omega C_{gp}(1 + g_m R'_p)} \tag{12-64}$$

Clearly, Z_1 is the reactance of a capacitance whose value is $C' \equiv C_{gp}(1 + g_m R'_p)$. The total input capacitance C_1 of the stage is C' augmented by the direct capacitance C_{gk} between grid and cathode, or

$$C_1 = C_{gk} + C_{gp}(1 + g_m R'_p) \tag{12-65}$$

This result agrees with Eq. (8-44), first derived by Miller.[3] Hence the transformation indicated in Fig. 12-14 is referred to as *Miller's theorem*.

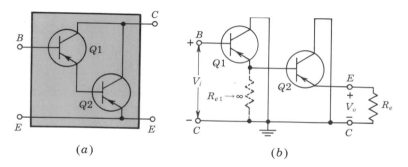

(a)   (b)

Fig. 12-15 (a) Darlington pair. Some vendors package this device as a single composite transistor with only three external leads. (b) The Darlington circuit drawn as two cascaded CC stages.

12-10   HIGH–INPUT–RESISTANCE TRANSISTOR CIRCUITS[4]

In some applications the need arises for an amplifier with a high input impedance. For input resistances smaller than about 500 K, the emitter follower discussed in Sec. 12-8 is satisfactory. In order to achieve larger input impedances, the circuit shown in Fig. 12-15a, called the *Darlington connection*, is used.† Note that two transistors form a composite pair, the input resistance of the second transistor constituting the emitter load for the first. More specifically, the Darlington circuit consists of two cascaded emitter followers with infinite emitter resistance in the first stage, as shown in Fig. 12-15b.

The Darlington composite emitter follower will be analyzed by referring to Fig. 12-16. Assuming that $h_{oe}R_e \leq 0.1$ and $h_{fe}R_e \gg h_{ie}$, we have, from Table 12-2, for the current gain and the input impedance of the second stage,

$$A_{I2} = \frac{I_0}{I_2} \approx 1 + h_{fe} \qquad R_{i2} \approx (1 + h_{fe})R_e \qquad (12\text{-}66)$$

Since the effective load for transistor $Q1$ is R_{i2}, which usually does not meet the requirement $h_{oe}R_{i2} \leq 0.1$, we must use the exact expression of Eq. (12-31) for the current gain of the first transistor:

$$A_{I1} = \frac{I_2}{I_i} = \frac{1 + h_{fe}}{1 + h_{oe}R_{i2}} = \frac{1 + h_{fe}}{1 + h_{oe}(1 + h_{fe})R_e} \qquad (12\text{-}67)$$

and since $h_{oe}R_e \leq 0.1$, we have

$$A_{I1} \approx \frac{1 + h_{fe}}{1 + h_{oe}h_{fe}R_e} \qquad (12\text{-}68)$$

† For many applications the field-effect transistor (Chap. 14) with its extremely high input impedance would be preferred to the Darlington pair.

The overall current gain for Fig. 12-16 is

$$A_I = \frac{I_o}{I_i} = \frac{I_o}{I_2}\frac{I_2}{I_i} = A_{I2}A_{I1}$$

or

$$A_I \approx \frac{(1 + h_{fe})^2}{1 + h_{oe}h_{fe}R_e} \qquad (12\text{-}69)$$

Similarly, for the input resistance of $Q1$, we must use Eq. (12-33):

$$R_{i1} = h_{ie} + A_{I1}R_{i2} \approx \frac{(1 + h_{fe})^2 R_e}{1 + h_{oe}h_{fe}R_e} \qquad (12\text{-}70)$$

This equation for the input resistance of the Darlington circuit is valid for $h_{oe}R_e \le 0.1$, and should be compared with the input resistance of the single-stage emitter follower given by Eq. (12-32). If $R_e = 4$ K, and using the h parameters of Table 11-2, we obtain $R_{i2} = 205$ K for the emitter follower and $R_{i1} = 1.73$ M for the Darlington circuit. We also find $A_I = 427$, which is much higher than the current gain of the emitter follower ($= 51$).

The voltage gain of the Darlington circuit is close to unity, but its deviation from unity is slightly greater than that of the emitter follower. This result should be obvious because Fig. 12-16 represents two emitter followers in cascade (and the product of two numbers, each less than unity, is smaller than either number). If we make use of Eq. (12-34), we obtain

$$1 - A_{V2} = \frac{h_{ie}}{R_{i2}} \qquad 1 - A_{V1} = \frac{h_{ie}}{R_{i1}} \approx \frac{h_{ie}}{A_{I1}R_{i2}} \qquad (12\text{-}71)$$

where $A_{V2} = V_o/V_2$ and $A_{V1} = V_2/V_i$. Finally, we have, for $A_V = V_o/V_i$,

$$A_V = A_{V1}A_{V2} = \left(1 - \frac{h_{ie}}{R_{i2}}\right)\left(1 - \frac{h_{ie}}{A_{I1}R_{i2}}\right) \approx 1 - \frac{h_{ie}}{A_{I1}R_{i2}} - \frac{h_{ie}}{R_{i2}} \qquad (12\text{-}72)$$

and since $A_{I1}R_{i2} \gg R_{i2}$, expression (12-72) becomes

$$A_V \approx 1 - \frac{h_{ie}}{R_{i2}} \qquad (12\text{-}73)$$

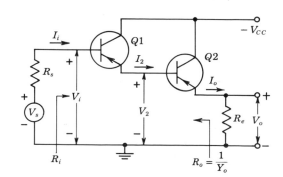

Fig. 12-16   Darlington emitter follower.

This result indicates that the voltage gain of the Darlington circuit used as an emitter follower is essentially the same as the voltage gain of the emitter follower consisting of transistor $Q2$ alone, but very slightly smaller.

The output resistance R_{o1} of $Q1$ is, from Eq. (12-35),

$$R_{o1} = \frac{R_s + h_{ie}}{1 + h_{fe}}$$

and hence the output resistance of the second transistor $Q2$ is, approximately,

$$R_{o2} \approx \frac{\dfrac{R_s + h_{ie}}{1 + h_{fe}} + h_{ie}}{1 + h_{fe}} = \frac{R_s + h_{ie}}{(1 + h_{fe})^2} + \frac{h_{ie}}{1 + h_{fe}} \tag{12-74}$$

We can now conclude from the foregoing discussion, and specifically from Eqs. (12-69), (12-70), (12-73), and (12-74), that the Darlington emitter follower has a higher current gain, a higher input resistance, a voltage gain less close to unity, and a lower output resistance than does a single-stage emitter follower.

Practical Considerations   We have assumed in the above computations that the h parameters of $Q1$ and $Q2$ are identical. In reality, this is usually not the case, because the h parameters depend on the quiescent conditions of $Q1$ and $Q2$. Since the emitter current of $Q1$ is the base current of $Q2$, the quiescent current of the first stage is much smaller than that of the second. Hence h_{fe} may be much smaller for $Q1$ than for $Q2$, and h_{ie} may be much larger for $Q1$ than for $Q2$ (Fig. 11-5). In order to have reasonable operating current in the first transistor, the second may have to be a power stage.

A second major drawback of the Darlington transistor pair is that the leakage current of the first transistor is amplified by the second, and hence the overall leakage current may be high.

For these two reasons, a Darlington connection of three or more transistors is usually impractical.

The composite transistor pair of Fig. 12-15a can, of course, be used as a common-emitter amplifier. The advantage of this pair would be a very high overall h_{fe}, nominally equal to the product of the CE short-circuit current gains of the two transistors. In fact, Darlington integrated transistor pairs are commercially available with h_{fe} as high as 30,000.

If the condition $h_{oe}R_e \ll 1$ is not satisfied, an exact analysis of the Darlington circuit must be made. We may proceed as in Sec. 12-1, using the CC h parameters of each stage, or we may derive the h parameters of the composite pair in terms of the parameters h' and h'' of $Q1$ and $Q2$, respectively.

The Biasing Problem   In discussing the Darlington transistor pair, we have emphasized its value in providing high-input impedance. However, we have oversimplified the problem by disregarding the effect of the biasing arrangement used in the circuit. Figure 12-13a shows a typical biasing network (resistors R_1 and R_2). The input resistance R_i' of the stage of the emitter follower of Fig. 12-13a consists of $R_i \| R'$, where $R' \equiv R_1 \| R_2$. Assume that the input circuit is modified as in Fig. 12-17 by the addition of R_3 but with $C' = 0$ (that is, for the moment, ignore the presence of C'). Now R' is increased to $R_3 + R_1 \| R_2$. However, since R_i is usually much greater than R', it is seen that $R_i' \approx R'$, which may be a few hundred kilohms at most.

To overcome the decrease in the input resistance due to the biasing network, the input circuit of Fig. 12-17 is modified by the addition of C' between the emitter and the junction of R_1 and R_2. The capacitance C' is chosen large enough to act as a short circuit at the lowest frequency under consideration. Hence the bottom of R_3 is effectively connected to the output (the emitter), whereas the top of R_3 is at the input (the base). Since the input voltage is V_i and the output voltage is $V_o = A_V V_i$, the circuit of Fig. 12-14 and Miller's theorem can be used to calculate the current drawn by R_3 from the input signal. We can then see that the biasing arrangement R_1, R_2, and R_3 represents an effective input resistance of

$$R_{\text{eff}} = \frac{R_3}{1 - A_V} \tag{12-75}$$

Since, for an emitter follower, A_V approaches unity, then R_{eff} becomes extremely large. For example, with $A_V = 0.995$ and $R_3 = 100$ K, we find $R_{\text{eff}} = 20$ M. Note that the quiescent base current passes through R_3, and hence that a few hundred kilohms is probably an upper limit for R_3.

The above effect, when $A_V \to |1$, is called *bootstrapping*. The term arises from the fact that, if one end of the resistor R_3 changes in voltage, the other end of R_3 moves through the same potential difference; it is as if R_3 were "pulling itself up by its bootstraps." The input resistance of the CC amplifier as given by Eq. (12-34) is $R_i = h_{ie}/(1 - A_V)$. Since this expression is of the form of Eq. (12-75), here is an example of bootstrapping of the resistance h_{ie} which appears between base and emitter.

In making calculations of A_I, R_i, and A_V, we should, in principle, take into account that the emitter follower is loaded, not only by R_e and $R_1 \| R_2$, but also by R_3. The extent to which R_3 loads the emitter follower is calcu-

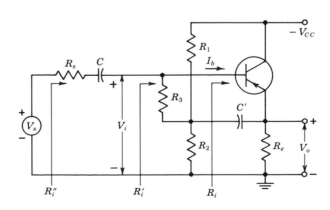

Fig. 12-17 The bootstrap principle increases the effective value of R_3.

lated as follows: The emitter end of R_3 is at a voltage A_V times as large as the base end of R_3. From Fig. 12-14, illustrating Miller's theorem, the effective resistance seen looking from the emitter to ground is not R_3 but, exaggerated by the Miller effect, is

$$R_{3M} = \frac{A_V R_3}{A_V - 1} \tag{12-76}$$

Since A_V is positive and slightly less than unity, then R_{3M} is a (negative) resistance of large magnitude. Since R_{3M} is paralleled with the appreciably smaller resistors R_e and $R_1 \| R_2$, the effect of R_3 will usually be quite negligible.

Bootstrapped Darlington Circuit We find in the preceding section that, even neglecting the effect of the resistors R_1, R_2, and R_3 and assuming infinite emitter resistance, the maximum input resistance is limited to $1/h_{ob} \approx 2$ M. Since $1/h_{ob}$ is the resistance between base and collector, the input resistance

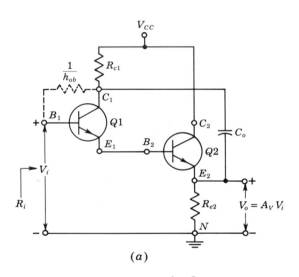

(a)

Fig. 12-18 (a) The bootstrapped Darlington circuit. (b) The equivalent circuit.

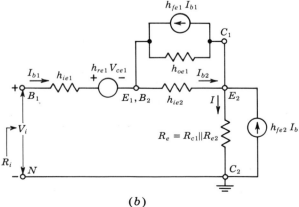

(b)

can be greatly increased by bootstrapping the Darlington circuit through the addition of C_o between the first collector C_1 and the second emitter E_2, as indicated in Fig. 12-18a. Note that the collector resistor R_{c1} is essential because, without it, R_{e2} would be shorted to ground. If the input signal changes by V_i, then E_2 changes by $A_V V_i$ and (assuming that the reactance of C_o is negligible) the collector changes by the same amount. Hence $1/h_{ob}$ is now effectively increased to $1/(h_{ob})(1 - A_V) \approx 400$ M, for a voltage gain of 0.995.

An expression for the input resistance R_i of the bootstrapped Darlington pair can be obtained using the equivalent circuit of Fig. 12-18b. The effective resistance R_e between E_2 and ground is $R_e = R_{c1} \| R_{e2}$. If $h_{oe} R_e \leq 0.1$, then $Q2$ may be represented by the approximate h-parameter model. However, the exact hybrid model as indicated in Fig. 12-18b must be used for $Q1$. Since $1/h_{oe1} \gg h_{ie2}$, then h_{oe1} may be omitted from this figure. Solving for V_i/I_{b1}, we obtain (Prob. 12-21)

$$R_i \approx h_{fe1} h_{fe2} R_e \qquad (12\text{-}77)$$

This equation shows that the input resistance of the bootstrapped Darlington emitter follower is essentially equal to the product of the short-circuit current gains and the effective emitter resistance. If $h_{fe1} = h_{fo2} = 50$ and $R_e = 4$ K, then $R_i \approx 10$ M. If transistors with current gains of the order of magnitude of 100 instead of 50 were used, an input resistance of 40 M would be obtained.

The biasing arrangement of Fig. 12-17 would also be used in the circuit of Fig. 12-18. Hence, the input resistance taking into account the bootstrapping both at the base and at the collector of $Q1$ would be $R_{eff} \| h_{fe1} h_{fe2} R_e$, where R_{eff} is given in Eq. (12-75).

12-11   THE CASCODE TRANSISTOR CONFIGURATION[5]

The cascode transistor configuration shown in Fig. 12-19 consists of a CE stage in series with a CB stage (the collector current of $Q1$ equals the emitter current of $Q2$). This circuit should be compared with the vacuum-tube triode cascode amplifier discussed in Sec. 8-10. In the case of the tube cascode connection, two triodes are used in a series circuit and the combination behaves like a pentode. In the circuit shown in Fig. 12-19 transistors $Q1$ and $Q2$ in cascode act like a single CE transistor with negligible internal feedback (negligible h_{re}) and very small output conductance for an open-circuited input.

Derivation of Parameter Values   To verify the above statement let us compute the h parameters of the $Q1$-$Q2$ combination. From our discussion in Sec. 11-1 and Fig. 12-19,

$$h_{11} = \frac{V_1}{I_1} \bigg|_{V_2 = 0}$$

However, if $V_2 = 0$, then the load of $Q1$ consists of h_{ib2}, which, from Table 11-3,

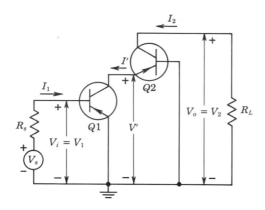

Fig. 12-19 The cascode configuration. (Supply voltages are not indicated.)

is about 20 Ω. Hence transistor $Q1$ is effectively short-circuited, and

$$h_{11} \approx h_{ie} \tag{12-78}$$

Similarly, we have for the short-circuit current gain

$$h_{21} = \frac{I_2}{I_1}\bigg|_{V_2=0} = \frac{I'}{I_1}\frac{I_2}{I'}\bigg|_{V_2=0} = -h_{fe}h_{fb} \approx h_{fe} \tag{12-79}$$

since $-h_{fb} = \alpha \approx 1$.

The output conductance with input open-circuited is given by

$$h_{22} = \frac{I_2}{V_2}\bigg|_{I_1=0}$$

If $I_1 = 0$, the output resistance of $Q1$ is equal to $1/h_{oe} \approx 40$ K. Hence the equivalent source resistance for transistor $Q2$ is 40 K. From Fig. 11-17 we see that, for the CB connection, the output resistance R_o with $R_s = 40$ K is essentially the same as that for $R_s = \infty$, so that $R_o = 1/h_{ob}$. Therefore

$$h_{22} = \frac{1}{R_o} \approx h_{ob} \tag{12-80}$$

Finally, for the reverse open-circuit voltage amplification, we have

$$h_{12} = \frac{V_1}{V_2}\bigg|_{I_1=0} = \frac{V_1}{V'}\frac{V'}{V_2}\bigg|_{I_1=0} \approx h_{re}h_{rb} \tag{12-81}$$

Equation (12-81) is valid under the assumption that the output resistance of $Q1$ (which is $1/h_{oe} \approx 40$ K) represents an open-circuited emitter for $Q2$.

Summary Using the h parameters of the typical transistor of Table 11-2 and Eqs. (12-78) to (12-81), we find

$$\begin{aligned} h_i &= h_{11} \approx 1{,}100 \ \Omega \approx h_{ie} \\ h_f &= h_{21} = 0.98 \times 50 = 49 \approx h_{fe} \\ h_o &= h_{22} = 0.49 \ \mu\text{A/V} \approx h_{ob} \\ h_r &= h_{12} = 7.25 \times 10^{-8} \approx h_{re}h_{rb} \end{aligned} \tag{12-82}$$

Note that the input resistance and current gain (with the output short-circuited) are nominally equal to the corresponding parameter values for a single CE stage. The output resistance (with the input open-circuited) is approximately equal to the CB value of 2 M, which is much higher than the CE value of 40 K. The reverse open-circuit amplification parameter h_r is very much smaller for the cascode connection than for a single CE stage. In view of the foregoing discussion, it should be clear that the simplified model given in Fig. 12-7 is a better approximation for the cascode circuit than for a single transistor. As a matter of fact, calculations based upon this hybrid model will result in less than 10 percent error if the load resistance R_L satisfies the inequality $h_{ob}R_L < 0.1$ or for R_L less than about 200 K.

The small value of h_r for the cascode transistor pair makes this circuit particularly useful in tuned-amplifier design. The reduction in the "internal feedback" of the compound device reduces the probability of oscillation and results in improved stability of the circuit.

12-12   DIFFERENCE AMPLIFIERS[6]

The function of a *difference*, or *differential, amplifier* is, in general, to amplify the difference between two signals. The need for differential amplifiers arises in many physical measurements, in medical electronics, and in direct-coupled amplifier applications.

Figure 12-20 represents a linear active device with two input signals v_1, v_2 and one output signal v_o, each measured with respect to ground. In an ideal differential amplifier the output signal v_o should be given by

$$v_o = A_d(v_1 - v_2) \tag{12-83}$$

where A_d is the gain of the differential amplifier. Thus it is seen that any signal which is common to both inputs will have no effect on the output voltage. However, a practical differential amplifier cannot be described by Eq. (12-83) since, in general, the output depends not only upon the *difference signal* v_d of the two signals, but also upon the average level, called the *common-mode signal* v_c, where

$$v_d \equiv v_1 - v_2 \qquad \text{and} \qquad v_c \equiv \tfrac{1}{2}(v_1 + v_2) \tag{12-84}$$

For example, if one signal is $+50$ μV and the second is -50 μV, the output will not be exactly the same as if $v_1 = 1{,}050$ μV and $v_2 = 950$ μV, even though the difference $v_d = 100$ μV is the same in the two cases.

The Common-mode Rejection Ratio   The foregoing statements are now clarified, and a figure of merit for a difference amplifier is introduced. The

Fig. 12-20 The output is a linear function of v_1 and v_2. For an ideal differential amplifier, $v_o = A_d(v_1 - v_2)$.

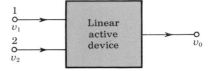

output of Fig. 12-20 can be expressed as a linear combination of the two input voltages

$$v_o = A_1 v_1 + A_2 v_2 \tag{12-85}$$

where A_1 (A_2) is the voltage amplification from input 1 (2) to the output under the condition that input 2 (1) is grounded. From Eqs. (12-84),

$$v_1 = v_c + \tfrac{1}{2} v_d \qquad \text{and} \qquad v_2 = v_c - \tfrac{1}{2} v_d \tag{12-86}$$

If these equations are substituted in Eq. (12-85), we obtain

$$v_o = A_d v_d + A_c v_c \tag{12-87}$$

where

$$A_d \equiv \tfrac{1}{2}(A_1 - A_2) \qquad \text{and} \qquad A_c \equiv A_1 + A_2 \tag{12-88}$$

The voltage gain for the difference signal is A_d, and that for the common-mode signal is A_c. We can measure A_d directly by setting $v_1 = -v_2 = 0.5$ V, so that $v_d = 1$ V and $v_c = 0$. Under these conditions the measured output voltage v_o gives the gain A_d for the difference signal [Eq. (12-87)]. Similarly, if we set $v_1 = v_2 = 1$ V, then $v_d = 0$, $v_c = 1$, and $v_o = A_c$. The output voltage now is a direct measurement of the common-mode gain A_c.

Clearly, we should like to have A_d large, whereas, ideally, A_c should equal zero. A quantity called the *common-mode rejection ratio*, which serves as a figure of merit for a difference amplifier, is

$$\rho \equiv \left| \frac{A_d}{A_c} \right| \tag{12-89}$$

From Eqs. (12-87) and (12-89) we obtain an expression for the output in the following form:

$$v_o = A_d v_d \left(1 + \frac{1}{\rho} \frac{v_c}{v_d} \right) \tag{12-90}$$

From this equation we see that the amplifier should be designed so that ρ is large compared with the ratio of the common-mode signal to the difference signal. For example, if $\rho = 1{,}000$, $v_c = 1$ mV, and $v_d = 1$ μV, the second term in Eq. (12-90) is equal to the first term. Hence, for an amplifier with a common-mode rejection ratio of 1,000, a 1-μV difference of potential between the two inputs gives the same output as a 1-mV signal applied with the same polarity to both inputs.

EXAMPLE (a) Consider the situation referred to above where the first set of signals is $v_1 = +50$ μV and $v_2 = -50$ μV and the second set is $v_1 = 1{,}050$ μV and $v_2 = 950$ μV. If the common-mode rejection ratio is 100, calculate the percentage difference in output voltage obtained for the two sets of input signals. (b) Repeat part a if $\rho = 10{,}000$.

Solution a. In the first case, $v_d = 100$ μV and $v_c = 0$, so that, from Eq. (12-90), $v_o = 100 A_d$ μV.

In the second case, $v_d = 100$ μV, the same value as in part a, but now $v_c = \frac{1}{2}(1{,}050 + 950) = 1{,}000$ μV, so that, from Eq. (12-90),

$$v_o = 100A_d\left(1 + \frac{10}{\rho}\right) = 100A_d(1 + \tfrac{10}{100}) \qquad \mu V$$

These two measurements differ by 10 percent.

b. For $\rho = 10{,}000$, the second set of signals results in an output

$$v_o = 100A_d(1 + 10 \times 10^{-4}) \qquad \mu V$$

whereas the first set of signals gives an output $v_o = 100A_d$ μV. Hence the two measurements now differ by only 0.1 percent.

The Emitter-coupled Difference Amplifier The circuit of Fig. 12-21 is an excellent difference amplifier if the emitter resistance R_e is large. This statement can be justified as follows: If $V_{s1} = V_{s2} = V_s$, then from Eq. (12-87), we have $V_d = V_{s1} - V_{s2} = 0$ and $V_o = A_cV_s$. However, if $R_e = \infty$, then because of the symmetry of Fig. 12-21, we obtain $I_{e1} = I_{e2} = 0$. Since $I_{b2} \ll I_{c2}$, then $I_{c2} \approx I_{e2}$, and it follows that $V_o = 0$. Hence the common-mode gain A_c becomes zero, and the common-mode rejection ratio is infinite for $R_e = \infty$ and a symmetrical circuit.

We now analyze the emitter-coupled circuit for a finite value of R_e. A_c can be evaluated by setting $V_{s1} = V_{s2} = V_s$ and making use of the symmetry of Fig. 12-21. This circuit can be bisected as in Fig. 12-22a. An analysis of this circuit (Prob. 12-28), using Eqs. (12-48) to (12-50) and neglecting the term in h_{re} in Eq. (12-49), yields

$$A_c = \frac{V_o}{V_s} = \frac{(2h_{oe}R_e - h_{fe})R_c}{2R_e(1 + h_{fe}) + (R_s + h_{ie})(2h_{oe}R_e + 1)} \qquad (12\text{-}91)$$

provided that $h_{oe}R_c \ll 1$. Similarly, the difference mode gain A_d can be obtained by setting $V_{s1} = -V_{s2} = V_s/2$. From the symmetry of Fig. 12-21, we see that, if $V_{s1} = -V_{s2}$, then the emitter of each transistor is grounded for

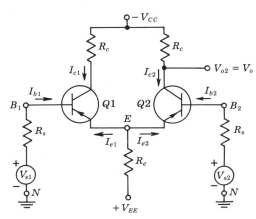

Fig. 12-21 Symmetrical emitter-coupled difference amplifier.

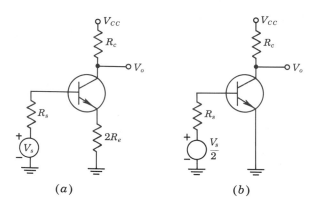

Fig. 12-22 Equivalent circuit for a symmetrical difference amplifier used to determine (a) the common-mode gain A_c and (b) the difference gain A_d.

(a)   (b)

small-signal operation. Under these conditions the circuit of Fig. 12-22b can be used to obtain A_d. Hence

$$A_d = \frac{V_o}{V_s} = \frac{1}{2}\frac{h_{fe}R_c}{R_s + h_{ie}} \tag{12-92}$$

provided $h_{oe}R_c \ll 1$.

The common-mode rejection ratio can now be obtained using Eqs. (12-91) and (12-92).

From Eq. (12-91) it is seen that the common-mode rejection ratio increases with R_e as predicted above. There are, however, practical limitations on the magnitude of R_e because of the quiescent dc voltage drop across it; the emitter supply V_{EE} must become larger as R_e is increased in order to maintain the quiescent current at its proper value. If the operating currents of the transistors are allowed to decrease, this will lead to higher h_{ie} values and lower values of h_{fe}. This can be seen from Fig. 11-5. Both of these effects will tend to decrease the common-mode rejection ratio.

Difference Amplifier Supplied with a Constant Current Frequently, in practice, R_e is replaced by a transistor circuit, as in Fig. 12-23, in which R_1, R_2, and R_3 can be adjusted to give the same quiescent conditions for $Q1$ and $Q2$ as the original circuit of Fig. 12-21. This modified circuit of Fig. 12-23 presents a very high effective emitter resistance R_e for the two transistors $Q1$ and $Q2$. Since R_e is also the effective resistance looking into the collector of transistor $Q3$, it is given by Eq. (12-51). In Sec. 12-7 it is verified that R_e will be hundreds of kilohms even if R_3 is as small as 1 K.

We now verify that transistor $Q3$ acts as an approximately constant current source, subject to the conditions that the base current and the base-to-emitter voltage of $Q3$ are negligible. The voltage across R_2 (and hence also across R_3) is $V_{EE}R_2/(R_1 + R_2)$. Hence the emitter current $I_E = I_{E1} + I_{E2}$ in Fig. 12-23 is given by

$$I_E = I_3 = \frac{V_{EE}R_2}{R_3(R_1 + R_2)} \tag{12-93}$$

Since this current is independent of the signal voltages V_{s1} and V_{s2}, then $Q3$ acts to supply the difference amplifier consisting of $Q1$ and $Q2$ with the constant current I_E.

Consider that $Q1$ and $Q2$ are identical and that $Q3$ is a true constant-current source. Under these circumstances we can demonstrate that the common-mode gain is zero. Assume that $V_{s1} = V_{s2} = V_s$, so that from the symmetry of the circuit, the collector current I_{c1} (the increase over the quiescent value for $V_s = 0$) in $Q1$ equals the current I_{c2} in $Q2$. However, since the total current increase $I_{c1} + I_{c2} = 0$ if $I_E = $ constant, then $I_{c1} = I_{c2} = 0$ and $A_c = V_{o2}/V_s = -I_{c2}R_c/V_s = 0$.

Practical Considerations Since the h parameters vary with the quiescent current, the common-mode rejection ratio depends upon the Q point. The values of h_{fe} and $1/h_{oe}$ should be as large as possible, and h_{ie} as small as possible. A reasonable set of values might be $h_{fe} = 100$, $h_{ie} = 2$ K, $1/h_{oe} = 100$ K, and $h_{re} = 2.5 \times 10^{-4}$. For $R_3 = 27$ K, $R_s = 1$ K, and $R_1R_2/(R_1 + R_2) = 1$ K, we find from Eqs. (12-51), (12-91), and (12-92) that $R_e = 9.95$ M and $\rho = 338{,}000$. More elaborate transistor configurations giving higher values of ρ are found in the literature.[6] For the analysis of nonsymmetrical differential circuits the reader is referred to Ref. 6.

In some applications the choice of V_{s1} and V_{s2} as the input voltages is not realistic because the resistances R_{s1} and R_{s2} represent the output impedances of the voltage generators V_{s1} and V_{s2}. In such a case we use as input voltages the base-to-ground voltages V_{b1} and V_{b2} of $Q1$ and $Q2$, respectively.

The differential amplifier is often used in dc applications. It is difficult to design dc amplifiers using transistors because of drift due to variations of h_{fe}, V_{BE}, and I_{CBO} with temperature. A shift in any of these quantities changes the output voltage and cannot be distinguished from a change in input-signal voltage. Using the techniques of integrated circuits (Chap. 15), it is possible

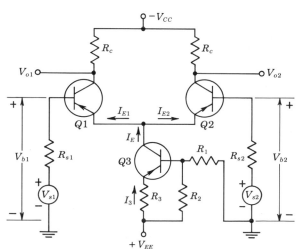

Fig. 12-23 Differential amplifier with constant-current stage in the emitter circuit. Nominally, $R_{s1} = R_{s2}$.

to construct a difference amplifier with $Q1$ and $Q2$ having almost identical properties. Under these conditions any parameter changes due to temperature will cancel and will not vary the output. A number of manufacturers† sell devices designed specifically for difference-amplifier applications. These consist of two high-gain *n-p-n* silicon planar transistors in the same hermetically sealed enclosure. The manufacturer guarantees that for equality of collector currents the maximum difference in base voltages is 5 mV, that the base-voltage differential at fixed collector current will not exceed 10 μV/°C, and that h_{fe} of one transistor will not differ from h_{fe} of the other by more than 10 percent. It has been found[7] that a substantial reduction in thermal drift is obtained if the two transistors are operated with equal V_{BE} instead of equal collector current.

Difference amplifiers may be cascaded in order to obtain larger amplifications for the difference signal and also better common-mode rejection. Outputs V_{o1} and V_{o2} are taken from each collector (Fig. 12-23) and are coupled directly to the two bases, respectively, of the next stage.

Finally, the differential amplifier may be used as an emitter-coupled phase inverter. For this application the signal is applied to one base, whereas the second base is not excited (but is, of course, properly biased). The output voltages taken from the collectors are equal in magnitude and 180° out of phase.

REFERENCES

1. Coblenz, A., and H. L. Owens: Cascading Transistor Amplifier Stages, *Electronics*, vol. 27, pp. 158–161, January, 1954.

2. Dion, D. F.: Common Emitter Transistor Amplifiers, *Proc. IRE*, vol. 46, p. 920, May, 1958.

3. Miller, J. M.: Dependence of the Input Impedance of a Three-electrode Vacuum Tube upon the Load in the Plate Circuit, *Natl. Bur. Std. (U.S.) Res. Papers*, vol. 15, no. 351, pp. 367–385, 1919.

4. Levine, I.: High Input Impedance Transistor Circuits, *Electronics*, vol. 33, pp. 50–54, September, 1960.

5. James, J. R.: Analysis of the Transistor Cascode Configuration, *Electron. Eng.*, vol. 32, pp. 44–48, 1960.

6. Slaughter, D. W.: The Emitter-coupled Differential Amplifier. *IRE Trans. Circuit Theory*, vol. CT-3, pp. 51–53, 1956.
   Middlebrook, R. D.: Differential Amplifiers, John Wiley & Sons. Inc.. New York, 1963.

7. Hoffait, A. H., and R. D. Thornton: Limitations of Transistor DC Amplifiers, *Proc. IEEE*, vol. 52, no. 2, pp. 179–184, February, 1964.

† Fairchild Semiconductor Corporation, Sprague Electric Co., Texas Instruments, Inc., and Motorola, Inc.

13 / THE HIGH-FREQUENCY TRANSISTOR

At low frequencies it is assumed that the transistor responds instantly to changes of input voltage or current. Actually, such is not the case because the mechanism of the transport of charge carriers from emitter to collector is essentially one of diffusion. Hence, in order to find out how the transistor behaves at high frequencies, it is necessary to examine this diffusion mechanism in more detail. Such an analysis[1] is complicated, and the resulting equations are suggestive of those encountered in connection with a lossy transmission line. This result could have been anticipated in view of the fact that some time delay must be involved in the transport of charge across the base region by the diffusion process. A model based upon the transmission-line equations would be quite accurate, but unfortunately, the resulting equivalent circuit is too complicated to be of practical use. Hence it is necessary to make approximations. Of course, the cruder the approximation, the simpler the circuit becomes. It is therefore a matter of engineering judgment to decide when we have a reasonable compromise between accuracy and simplicity.

13-1 THE HIGH-FREQUENCY T MODEL

Experience shows that, as a first reasonable approximation, the diffusion phenomenon can be taken into account by modifying the basic common-base T model of Fig. 11-19 as follows: The collector resistor r'_c is shunted by a capacitor C_c, and the emitter resistor r'_e is shunted by a capacitor C_e, as indicated in Fig. 13-1. Also, the dependent current generator is made proportional to the current i_1 in r'_e and *not* to the emitter current i_e. The low-frequency alpha is designated by α_o. If an input current step is applied, then initially this current is

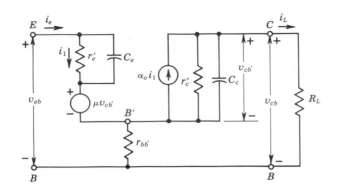

Fig. 13-1 Transistor T model at high frequencies.

bypassed by C_e and i_1 remains zero. Hence the output current starts at zero and rises slowly with time. Such a response is roughly what we expect because of the diffusion process. A better approximation is to replace C_e and r'_e by a lumped transmission line consisting of resistance-capacitance sections, but as already emphasized, such an equivalent circuit is too complicated to be useful.

The physical significance of C_e is not difficult to find. It represents the sum of the diffusion capacitance C_{De} and the transition capacitance C_{Te} across the emitter junction, $C_e = C_{De} + C_{Te}$. The diffusion capacitance is directly proportional to the quiescent emitter current. Usually, $C_{De} \gg C_{Te}$ (except for very small values of emitter current), and hence C_e is approximately equal to the diffusion capacitance C_{De}. Since the collector junction is reverse-biased, the collector diffusion capacitance C_{Dc} is negligible, so that C_c is essentially equal to the collector transition capacitance C_{Tc}. Usually, C_e is at least 30 times as large as C_c.

The High-frequency Alpha We shall assume that the input excitation is sinusoidal of frequency $f = \omega/2\pi$. Then, using capital letters for phasor currents, we have, from Fig. 13-1,

$$I_1 r'_e = \frac{I_e}{1/r'_e + j\omega C_e}$$

or

$$I_1 = \frac{I_e}{1 + jf/f_\alpha} \tag{13-1}$$

where

$$f_\alpha \equiv \frac{1}{2\pi r'_e C_e} \tag{13-2}$$

It is possible to consider the current generator to be proportional to the emitter current (rather than the current through r'_e) provided that we allow the proportionality factor α to be a complex function of frequency. Thus, if we write

$$\alpha_o I_1 = \alpha I_e \tag{13-3}$$

then, from Eq. (13-1),

$$\alpha = \frac{\alpha_o}{1 + jf/f_\alpha} \tag{13-4}$$

The magnitude of the complex or high-frequency alpha α is α_o at zero frequency and falls to $0.707\alpha_o$ at $f = f_\alpha$. This frequency f_α is called the *alpha cutoff frequency*. The diffusion equation leads to a solution for α equal to the hyperbolic secant of a complex quantity. If this expression is expanded into a power series in the variable f/f_α and only the first two terms are retained, Eq. (13-4) is obtained (Prob. 13-1). Hence Eq. (13-4) and the equivalent circuit of Fig. 13-1 are valid at frequencies which are appreciably less than f_α (up to perhaps $f_\alpha/2$). General-purpose transistors have values of f_α in the range of hundreds of kilohertz. High-frequency transistors may have alpha cutoff frequencies in the tens, hundreds, or even thousands of megahertz. Since $\alpha = -h_{fb}$, the symbol f_{hfb} is sometimes used for f_α.

The Approximate CB T Model If the load resistance R_L is small, the output voltage v_{cb}, and hence $v_{cb'}$, will be small. Since $\mu \approx 10^{-4}$, we can neglect the Early generator $\mu v_{cb'}$. Under these circumstances the network of Fig. 13-1 reduces to the circuit of Fig. 13-2, which is known as *the approximate CB high-frequency model*. The order of magnitudes of the parameters in Fig. 13-2 are

$$r'_e \approx 20 \ \Omega \qquad r_{bb'} \approx 100 \ \Omega \qquad r'_c \approx 1 \ \text{M}$$

$$C_c \approx 1\text{--}50 \ \text{pF} \qquad \text{and} \qquad C_e \approx 30\text{--}10{,}000 \ \text{pF}$$

13-2   THE COMMON–BASE SHORT–CIRCUIT–CURRENT FREQUENCY RESPONSE

Consider a transistor in the common-base configuration excited by a sinusoidal current I_e of frequency f. What is the frequency dependence of the load current I_L under short-circuited conditions? If terminals C and B are connected together in Fig. 13-2, then $r_{bb'}$, r'_c, and C_c are placed in parallel. Since $r'_c \gg r_{bb'}$,

Fig. 13-2 The approximate high-frequency T model.

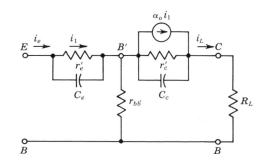

we may omit r_c'. Usually, $r_{bb'}C_c \ll r_e'C_e$, and under these circumstances, the response is determined by the larger time constant $r_e'C_e$. Hence we shall also omit C_c from Fig. 13-2. With these simplifications, $I_L = \alpha_o I_1$, or from Eqs. (13-3) and (13-4), the common-base short-circuit current gain is given by

$$A_{ib} \equiv \frac{I_L}{I_e} = \frac{\alpha_o I_1}{I_e} = \alpha = \frac{\alpha_o}{1 + jf/f_\alpha} \tag{13-5}$$

The magnitude of α and its phase angle θ are given by

$$|\alpha| = \frac{\alpha_o}{\sqrt{1 + (f/f_\alpha)^2}} \qquad \theta = -\arctan \frac{f}{f_\alpha} \tag{13-6}$$

If $f = f_\alpha$, $\alpha = \alpha_o/\sqrt{2}$, and $20 \log |\alpha/\alpha_o| = -20 \log \sqrt{2} = -3$ dB. Hence *the alpha cutoff frequency f_α is called the 3-dB frequency of the CB short-circuit current gain.* Equation (13-6) also predicts that α has undergone a 45° phase shift in comparison with its low-frequency value. This calculated amplitude response is in close agreement with experiment, but the phase-shift calculation may well be far off.

The reason for the discrepancy is that our lumped-circuit equivalent representation of the transistor is simply not accurate enough. It is found, empirically, that the discrepancy between calculation and experiment can be very substantially reduced by introducing an "excess-phase" factor[2] in the expression for α, so that Eq. (13-5) becomes

$$\alpha = \frac{\alpha_o}{1 + j(f/f_\alpha)} \epsilon^{-jmf/f_\alpha} \tag{13-7}$$

In this equation m is an adjustable parameter that ranges from about 0.2 for a diffusion transistor to about unity for a drift transistor. Diffusion transistors are transistors in which the base doping is uniform, so that minority carriers cross the base entirely through diffusion. In drift transistors the doping is nonuniform, and an electric field exists in the base that causes a drift of minority carriers which adds to the diffusion current.

13-3 THE ALPHA CUTOFF FREQUENCY

Obviously, for high-frequency applications we want f_α to be very large. In order to construct a transistor with a definite value of f_α, it is necessary to know all the parameters upon which f_α depends. As a first step toward obtaining the desired equation for f_α, an expression for the emitter capacitance will be obtained.

The Diffusion Capacitance Refer to Fig. 13-3, which represents the injected hole concentration vs. distance in the base region of a *p-n-p* transistor. The base width W is assumed to be small compared with the diffusion length L_B of the minority carriers. Since the collector is reverse-biased, the injected charge concentration P at the collector junction is essentially zero (Fig. 9-24). If $W \ll L_B$, then P varies almost linearly from the value $P(0)$ at the emitter to zero at the collector, as indicated in Fig. 13-3. The stored base charge Q_B is the average concentration $P(0)/2$ times the volume of the base WA (where A is the base cross-sectional area) times the electronic charge e; that is,

$$Q_B = \tfrac{1}{2}P(0)AWe \qquad\qquad (13\text{-}8)$$

The diffusion current is [from Eq. (5-32)]

$$I = -AeD_B \frac{dP}{dx} = AeD_B \frac{P(0)}{W} \qquad\qquad (13\text{-}9)$$

where D_B is the diffusion constant for minority carriers in the base. Combining Eqs. (13-8) and (13-9),

$$Q_B = \frac{IW^2}{2D_B} \qquad\qquad (13\text{-}10)$$

The emitter diffusion capacitance C_{De} is given by the rate of change of Q_B with respect to emitter voltage V, or

$$C_{De} = \frac{dQ_B}{dV} = \frac{W^2}{2D_B}\frac{dI}{dV} = \frac{W^2}{2D_B}\frac{1}{r'_e} \qquad\qquad (13\text{-}11)$$

where $r'_e \equiv dV/dI$ is the emitter-junction incremental resistance. From Eq. (6-41) and neglecting junction recombination, $r'_e = V_T/I_E$, where $V_T = \bar{k}T/e$, $\bar{k} =$ Boltzmann's constant in $J/°K$, $T =$ absolute temperature, and $e =$ electronic charge [Eq. (3-34)]. Hence

$$C_{De} = \frac{W^2 I_E}{2D_B V_T} \qquad\qquad (13\text{-}12)$$

which indicates that *the diffusion capacitance is proportional to the emitter bias current* I_E. Since D_B varies[3] approximately inversely with T, and V_T is proportional to T, then C_{De} is almost independent of temperature. Except for very small values of I_E, the diffusion capacitance is much greater than the transition capacitance C_T, and hence $C_e = C_{De} + C_{Te} \approx C_D$.

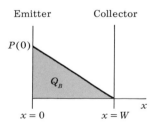

Fig. 13-3 Minority-carrier charge distribution in the base region.

Dependence of f_α upon Base Width or Transit Time From Eqs. (13-2) and (13-11), and since $C_e \approx C_{De}$, then

$$2\pi f_\alpha = \omega_\alpha = \frac{1}{r_e' C_e} = \frac{2D_B}{W^2} \tag{13-13}$$

This equation indicates that the alpha cutoff frequency varies inversely as the square of the base thickness W. For a p-n-p germanium transistor with

$$W = 1 \text{ mil} = 2.54 \times 10^{-3} \text{ cm} = 25.4 \text{ microns}$$

Eq. (13-13) predicts an $f_\alpha = 2.3$ MHz.

An interesting interpretation of ω_α is now obtained. By combining Eqs. (13-10) and (13-13),

$$I = Q_B \omega_\alpha \tag{13-14}$$

If t_B is the *base transit time* (the number of seconds it takes a carrier to cross the base), then in time t_B an amount of charge equal to the base charge Q_B reaches the collector. The resulting current is

$$I = \frac{Q_B}{t_B} \tag{13-15}$$

From Eqs. (13-14) and (13-15) we have that $\omega_\alpha = 1/t_B$, or that the *alpha cutoff (angular) frequency is the reciprocal of the base transit time.*

13-4   THE COMMON–EMITTER SHORT–CIRCUIT–CURRENT FREQUENCY RESPONSE

The T model of Fig. 13-2 is applicable in the CE configuration if E is grounded, the signal is applied to B, and the load is placed between C and E. The CE short-circuit current gain A_{ie} is obtained by shorting the collector terminal C to E as indicated in Fig. 13-4. Since $r_c' \gg r_e$ and $C_e \gg C_c$, we may omit the parallel elements r_c' and C_c, and then $I_L = \alpha_o I_1 = \alpha I_e$. But from KCL,

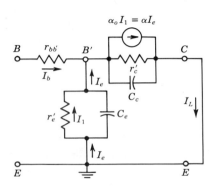

Fig. 13-4 The T circuit in the CE configuration under short-circuit conditions.

$I_L = I_b + I_e$, so that $I_e(1 - \alpha) = -I_b$. Finally,

$$A_{ie} = \frac{I_L}{I_b} = \frac{\alpha I_e}{I_b} = \frac{-\alpha(\omega)}{1 - \alpha(\omega)} \tag{13-16}$$

Using Eq. (13-4), A_{ie} may be put in the form

$$A_{ie} = \frac{-\beta_o}{1 + jf/f_\beta} \tag{13-17}$$

where

$$\beta_o \equiv \frac{\alpha_o}{1 - \alpha_o} \tag{13-18}$$

and

$$f_\beta \equiv f_\alpha(1 - \alpha_o) \tag{13-19}$$

At zero frequency the CE short-circuit current amplification is $\beta_o \approx h_{fe}$ and the corresponding CB parameter is $\alpha_o = -h_{fb}$. Hence Eq. (13-18) is consistent with the conversion in Table 11-3.

The CE 3-dB frequency, or the beta cutoff frequency, is f_β (also designated f_{hfe} or $f_{\alpha e}$). From Eqs. (13-18) and (13-19)

$$\beta_o f_\beta = h_{fe} f_\beta = \alpha_o f_\alpha \tag{13-20}$$

Since α_o is close to unity, the high-frequency response for the CE configuration is much worse than that for the CB circuit. However, the amplification for the CE configuration is much greater than that for the CB circuit. Note that the so-called *short-circuit-current gain-bandwidth product* (amplification times 3-dB frequency) is the same for both configurations.

13-5   THE HYBRID-PI (Π) COMMON–EMITTER TRANSISTOR MODEL[4]

In Chap. 11 it is emphasized that the common-emitter circuit is the most important practical configuration. Hence we now seek a CE model which will be valid at high frequencies. The circuit of Fig. 13-1 can be used in the CE configuration, but it is too complicated to be useful for analysis. On the other hand, the model of Fig. 13-4 (with a load R_L between C and E instead of the short circuit) is fairly simple but inaccurate (except for small values of R_L) because it neglects the Early generator.

A circuit, called *the hybrid-Π, or Giacoletto, model*, which does not have the above defects, is indicated in Fig. 13-5. Analyses of circuits using this model are not too difficult and give results which are in excellent agreement with experiment at all frequencies for which the transistor gives reasonable amplification. Furthermore, the resistive components in this circuit can be obtained (Sec. 13-6) from the low-frequency h parameters. All parameters (resistances and capacitances) in the model are assumed to be independent of frequency.

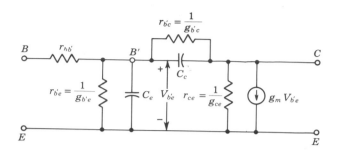

Fig. 13-5 The hybrid-Π model for a transistor in the CE configuration.

They may vary with the quiescent operating point, but under given bias conditions are reasonably constant for small-signal swings.

Discussion of Circuit Components   The internal node B' is not physically accessible.   The ohmic base-spreading resistance $r_{bb'}$ is represented as a lumped parameter between the external base terminal and B'.

For small changes in the voltage $V_{b'e}$ across the emitter junction, the excess-minority-carrier concentration injected into the base is proportional to $V_{b'e}$, and therefore the resulting small-signal collector current, with the collector shorted to the emitter, is proportional to $V_{b'e}$.   This effect accounts for the current generator $g_m V_{b'e}$ in Fig. 13-5.

The increase in minority carriers in the base results in increased recombination base current, and this effect is taken into account by inserting a conductance $g_{b'e}$ between B' and E.   The excess-minority-carrier storage in the base is accounted for by the diffusion capacitance C_e connected between B' and E (Sec. 13-3).

The Early effect (Sec. 9-7) indicates that the varying voltage across the collector-to-emitter junction results in *base-width modulation*.   A change in the effective base width causes the emitter (and hence collector) current to change because the slope of the minority-carrier distribution in the base changes.   This feedback effect between output and input is taken into account by connecting $g_{b'c}$ between B' and C.   The conductance between C and E is g_{ce}.

Finally, the collector-junction barrier capacitance is included in C_c.   Sometimes it is necessary to split the collector-barrier capacitance in two parts and connect one capacitance between C and B' and another between C and B.   The last component is known as the overlap-diode capacitance.

Hybrid-pi Parameter Values   Typical magnitudes for the elements of the hybrid-pi model for a germanium transistor at room temperature and for $I_C = 1.3$ mA are

$$g_m = 50 \text{ mA/V} \qquad r_{bb'} = 100 \ \Omega \qquad r_{b'e} = 1 \text{ K}$$

$$r_{b'c} = 4 \text{ M} \qquad r_{ce} = 80 \text{ K} \qquad C_c = 3 \text{ pF} \qquad C_e = 100 \text{ pF}$$

That these values are reasonable is justified in the following section.

13-6 HYBRID–PI CONDUCTANCES IN TERMS OF LOW–FREQUENCY h PARAMETERS

We now demonstrate that all the resistive components in the hybrid-pi model can be obtained from the h parameters in the CE configuration. These h parameters are supplied by the manufacturers or can be easily measured (Chap. 11).

Transistor Transconductance g_m Figure 13-6 shows a p-n-p transistor in the CE configuration with the collector shorted to the emitter for time-varying signals. In the active region the collector current is given by Eq. (9-7), repeated here for convenience, with $\alpha_N = \alpha_o$:

$$I_C = I_{CO} - \alpha_o I_E$$

The transconductance g_m is defined by

$$g_m \equiv \frac{\partial I_C}{\partial V_{B'E}}\bigg|_{V_{CE}} = -\alpha_o \frac{\partial I_E}{\partial V_{B'E}} = \alpha_o \frac{\partial I_E}{\partial V_E} \tag{13-21}$$

In the above we have assumed that α_N is independent of V_E. For a p-n-p transistor $V_E = -V_{B'E}$ as shown in Fig. 13-6. If the emitter diode resistance is r'_e (Fig. 13-2), then $r'_e = \partial V_E/\partial I_E$, and hence

$$g_m = \frac{\alpha_o}{r'_e} \tag{13-22}$$

To evaluate r'_e, note from Eq. (9-19), with $V_C \approx -V_{CC}$, that

$$I_E = a_{11}\epsilon^{V_E/V_T} - a_{11} - a_{12} \tag{13-23}$$

At cutoff, V_E is very negative and $I_E = -a_{11} - a_{12}$. Since the cutoff current is very small, we neglect it in Eq. (13-23). Hence

$$I_E \approx a_{11}\epsilon^{V_E/V_T}$$

and

$$\frac{1}{r'_e} = \frac{\partial I_E}{\partial V_E} \approx \frac{a_{11}\epsilon^{V_E/V_T}}{V_T} = \frac{I_E}{V_T} \tag{13-24}$$

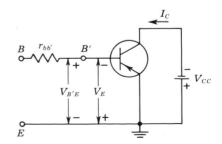

Fig. 13-6 Pertaining to the derivation of g_m.

Substituting Eq. (13-24) in Eq. (13-22), we obtain

$$g_m = \frac{\alpha_o I_E}{V_T} = \frac{I_{CO} - I_C}{V_T} \tag{13-25}$$

For a p-n-p transistor I_C is negative. For an n-p-n transistor I_C is positive, but the foregoing analysis (with $V_E = +V_{B'E}$) leads to $g_m = (I_C - I_{CO})/V_T$. Hence, for either type of transistor g_m is positive. Since $|I_C| \gg |I_{CO}|$, then g_m is given by

$$g_m \approx \frac{|I_C|}{V_T} \tag{13-26}$$

where, from Eq. (3-34), $V_T = T/11,600$. Note that g_m *is directly proportional to current and inversely proportional to temperature.* At room temperature

$$g_m = \frac{|I_C|(\text{mA})}{26} \tag{13-27}$$

For $I_C = 1.3$ mA, $g_m = 0.05$ mho $= 50$ mA/V. For $I_C = 10$ mA, $g_m \approx 400$ mA/V. These values are much larger than the transconductances obtained with tubes.

The Input Conductance $g_{b'e}$ In Fig. 13-7a we show the hybrid-pi model valid at low frequencies, where all capacitances are negligible. Figure 13-7b represents the same transistor, using the h-parameter equivalent circuit.

From the component values given in Sec. 13-5, we see that $r_{b'c} \gg r_{b'e}$. Hence I_b flows into $r_{b'e}$ and $V_{b'e} \approx I_b r_{b'e}$. The short-circuit collector current is given by

$$I_c = g_m V_{b'e} \approx g_m I_b r_{b'e}$$

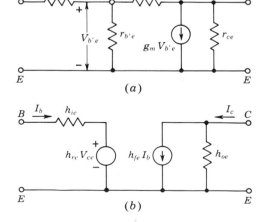

(a)

(b)

Fig. 13-7 (a) The hybrid-pi model at low frequencies; (b) the h-parameter model at low frequencies.

The short-circuit current gain h_{fe} is defined by

$$h_{fe} = \frac{I_c}{I_b}\bigg|_{V_{CE}} = g_m r_{b'e}$$

or

$$r_{b'e} = \frac{h_{fe}}{g_m} = \frac{h_{fe} V_T}{|I_c|} \qquad \text{or} \qquad g_{b'e} = \frac{g_m}{h_{fe}} \tag{13-28}$$

Note that, over the range of currents for which h_{fe} remains fairly constant, $r_{b'e}$ *is directly proportional to temperature and inversely proportional to current.* Observe in Fig. 11-5a that at both very low and very high currents, h_{fe} decreases.

Since $g_m = \alpha_o/r_e'$ and $h_{fe} \approx \alpha_o/(1 - \alpha_o)$, then $r_{b'e}$ may be expressed in terms of the T-model emitter resistor r_e' as

$$r_{b'e} = \frac{h_{fe}}{g_m} = \frac{r_e'}{1 - \alpha_o} \tag{13-29}$$

The Feedback Conductance $g_{b'c}$ With the input open-circuited, h_{re} is defined as the reverse voltage gain, or from Fig. 13-7a with $I_b = 0$,

$$h_{re} = \frac{V_{b'e}}{V_{ce}} = \frac{r_{b'e}}{r_{b'e} + r_{b'c}} \tag{13-30}$$

or

$$r_{b'e}(1 - h_{re}) = h_{re} r_{b'c}$$

Since $h_{re} \ll 1$, then to a good approximation

$$r_{b'e} = h_{re} r_{b'c} \qquad \text{or} \qquad g_{b'c} = h_{re} g_{b'e} \tag{13-31}$$

Since $h_{re} \approx 10^{-4}$, Eq. (13-31) verifies that $r_{b'c} \gg r_{b'e}$.

It is found that h_{re} is quite insensitive to current and temperature. Therefore $r_{b'c}$ has the same dependence upon $|I_c|$ and T as does $r_{b'e}$.

The Base-spreading Resistance $r_{bb'}$ The input resistance with the output shorted is h_{ie}. Under these conditions $r_{b'e}$ is in parallel with $r_{b'c}$. Using Eq. (13-31), we have $r_{b'e} \| r_{b'c} \approx r_{b'e}$, and hence

$$h_{ie} = r_{bb'} + r_{b'e} \tag{13-32}$$

or

$$r_{bb'} = h_{ie} - r_{b'e} \tag{13-33}$$

Incidentally, note from Eqs. (13-28) and (13-32) that the short-circuit input impedance h_{ie} varies with current and temperature in the following manner:

$$h_{ie} = r_{bb'} + \frac{h_{fe} V_T}{|I_C|} \tag{13-34}$$

The Output Conductance g_{ce} With the input open-circuited, this conductance is defined as h_{oe}. For $I_b = 0$, we have

$$I_c = \frac{V_{ce}}{r_{ce}} + \frac{V_{ce}}{r_{b'c} + r_{b'e}} + g_m V_{b'e} \tag{13-35}$$

With $I_b = 0$, we have, from Eq. (13-30), $V_{b'e} = h_{re}V_{ce}$, and from Eq. (13-35), we find

$$h_{oe} \equiv \frac{I_c}{V_{ce}} = \frac{1}{r_{ce}} + \frac{1}{r_{b'c}} + g_m h_{re} \tag{13-36}$$

where we made use of the fact that $r_{b'c} \gg r_{b'e}$. If we substitute Eqs. (13-28) and (13-31) in Eq. (13-36), we have

$$h_{oe} = g_{ce} + g_{b'c} + g_{b'e}h_{fe}\frac{g_{b'c}}{g_{b'e}}$$

or

$$g_{ce} = h_{oe} - (1 + h_{fe})g_{b'c} \tag{13-37}$$

If $h_{fe} \gg 1$, this equation may be put in the form [using Eqs. (13-29) and (13-31)]

$$g_{ce} \approx h_{oe} - g_m h_{re} \tag{13-38}$$

Summary If the CE h parameters at low frequencies are known at a given collector current I_C, the conductances or resistances in the hybrid-II circuit are calculable from the following five equations in the order given:

$$g_m = \frac{|I_C|}{V_T}$$

$$r_{b'e} = \frac{h_{fe}}{g_m} \quad \text{or} \quad g_{b'e} = \frac{g_m}{h_{fe}}$$

$$r_{bb'} = h_{ie} - r_{b'e} \tag{13-39}$$

$$r_{b'c} = \frac{r_{b'e}}{h_{re}} \quad \text{or} \quad g_{b'c} = \frac{h_{re}}{r_{b'e}}$$

$$g_{ce} = h_{oe} - (1 + h_{fe})g_{b'c} = \frac{1}{r_{ce}}$$

For the typical h parameters in Table 11-2, at $I_C = 1.3$ mA and room temperature, we obtain the component values listed on page 370.

The Hybrid-pi Capacitances The collector-junction capacitance $C_c = C_{b'c}$ is the measured CB output capacitance with the input open ($I_E = 0$), and is usually specified by manufacturers as C_{ob}. Since in the active region the collector junction is reverse-biased, then C_c is a transition capacitance, and hence varies as V_{CE}^{-n}, where n is $\frac{1}{2}$ or $\frac{1}{3}$ for an abrupt or gradual junction, respectively (Sec. 6-9).

Since $C_e = C_{b'e}$ represents, principally, the diffusion capacitance across the emitter junction, it is directly proportional to the current and is approximately independent of temperature (Sec. 13-3). Experimentally, C_e is determined from a measurement of the frequency f_T at which the CE short-circuit

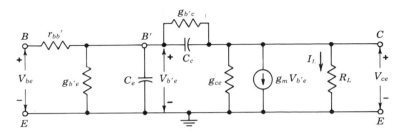

Fig. 13-8   The hybrid-II circuit for a single transistor with a resistive load R_L.

current gain drops to unity.   We verify in Sec. 13-7 that

$$C_e \approx \frac{g_m}{2\pi f_T} \tag{13-40}$$

Reasonable values for these capacitances are

$$C_c = 3 \text{ pF} \qquad C_e = 100 \text{ pF}$$

13-7   THE CE SHORT–CIRCUIT CURRENT GAIN OBTAINED WITH THE HYBRID–PI MODEL

Consider a single-stage CE transistor amplifier, or the last stage of a cascade. The load R_L on this stage is the collector-circuit resistor, so that $R_c = R_L$. In this section we assume that $R_L = 0$, whereas the circuit with $R_L \neq 0$ is analyzed in the next section.   To obtain the frequency response of the transistor amplifier, we use the hybrid-II model of Fig. 13-5, which is repeated for convenience in Fig. 13-8.   Representative values of the circuit components are specified on page 370 for a transistor intended for use at high frequencies. We use these values as a guide in making simplifying assumptions.

The approximate equivalent circuit from which to calculate the short-circuit current gain is shown in Fig. 13-9.   A current source furnishes a sinusoidal input current of magnitude I_i, and the load current is I_L.   We have neglected $g_{b'c}$, which should appear across terminals $B'C$, because $g_{b'c} \ll g_{b'e}$. And of course g_{ce} disappears, because it is in shunt with a short circuit.   An additional approximation is involved, in that we have neglected the current

Fig. 13-9   Approximate equivalent circuit for the calculation of the short-circuit CE current gain.

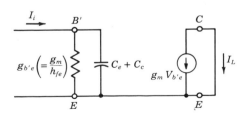

delivered directly to the output through $g_{b'c}$ and C_c. We see shortly that this approximation is justified.

The load current is $I_L = -g_m V_{b'e}$, where

$$V_{b'e} = \frac{I_i}{g_{b'e} + j\omega(C_e + C_c)} \tag{13-41}$$

The current amplification under short-circuited conditions is

$$A_i = \frac{I_L}{I_i} = \frac{-g_m}{g_{b'e} + j\omega(C_e + C_c)} \tag{13-42}$$

Using the results given in Eqs. (13-39), we have

$$A_i = \frac{-h_{fe}}{1 + j(f/f_\beta)} \tag{13-43}$$

where the frequency at which the CE short-circuit current gain falls by 3 dB is given by

$$f_\beta = \frac{g_{b'e}}{2\pi(C_e + C_c)} = \frac{1}{h_{fe}} \frac{g_m}{2\pi(C_e + C_c)} \tag{13-44}$$

The frequency range up to f_β is referred to as the *bandwidth* of the circuit. Note that the value of A_i at $\omega = 0$ is $-h_{fe}$, in agreement with the definition of $-h_{fe}$ as the low-frequency short-circuit CE current gain. The expression for f_β obtained in Sec. 13-4 from the high-frequency T model is essentially the same as that given in Eq. (13-44). (See also Prob. 13-12.)

Since, for a single-time-constant circuit, the 3-dB frequency f_2 is given by $f_2 = 1/2\pi RC$, where R is the resistance in parallel with the capacitance, we could have written f_β by inspection as

$$f_\beta = \frac{1}{2\pi r_{b'e}(C_e + C_c)}$$

in agreement with Eq. (13-44).

The Parameter f_T We introduce now f_T, which is defined as the *frequency at which the short-circuit common-emitter current gain attains unit magnitude.* Since $h_{fe} \gg 1$, we have, from Eqs. (13-43) and (13-44), that f_T is given by

$$f_T \approx h_{fe} f_\beta = \frac{g_m}{2\pi(C_e + C_c)} \approx \frac{g_m}{2\pi C_e} \tag{13-45}$$

since $C_e \gg C_c$. Hence, from Eq. (13-43),

$$A_i \approx \frac{-h_{fe}}{1 + jh_{fe}(f/f_T)} \tag{13-46}$$

The parameter f_T is an important high-frequency characteristic of a transistor. Like other transistor parameters, its value depends on the operating conditions of the device. Typically, the dependence of f_T on collector current is as shown in Fig. 13-10.

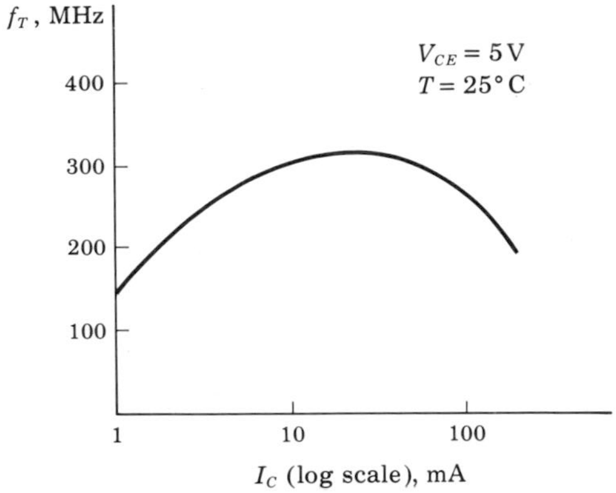

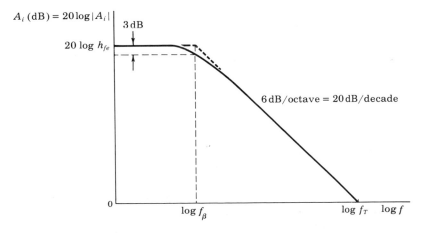

Fig. 13-10   Variation of f_T with collector current.

Since $f_T \approx h_{fe}f_\beta$, this parameter may be given a second interpretation. It represents the *short-circuit current-gain–bandwidth product;* that is, for the CE configuration with the output shorted, f_T is the product of the low-frequency current gain and the upper 3-dB frequency.   For our typical transistor (page 370), f_T = 80 MHz and f_β = 1.6 MHz.   It is to be noted from Eq. (13-45) that there is a sense in which gain may be sacrificed for bandwidth, and vice versa.   Thus, if two transistors are available with equal f_T, the transistor with lower h_{fe} will have a correspondingly larger bandwidth.

In Fig. 13-11, A_i expressed in decibels (i.e., 20 log $|A_i|$) is plotted against frequency on a logarithmic frequency scale.   When $f \ll f_\beta$, $A_i \approx -h_{fe}$, and A_i (dB) approaches asymptotically the horizontal line A_i (dB) = 20 log h_{fe}. When $f \gg f_\beta$, $|A_i| \approx h_{fe}f_\beta/f = f_T/f$, so that A_i (dB) = 20 log f_T − 20 log f. Accordingly, A_i (dB) − 0 dB at $f − f_T$.   And for $f \gg f_\beta$, the plot approaches

Fig. 13-11   The short-circuit CE current gain vs. frequency (plotted on a log-log scale).

as an asymptote a straight line passing through the point $(f_T, 0)$ and having a slope which causes a decrease in A_i (dB) of 6 dB per octave, or 20 dB per decade. The intersection of the two asymptotes occurs at the "corner" frequency $f = f_\beta$, where A_i is down by 3 dB.

Earlier, we neglected the current delivered directly to the output through $g_{b'c}$ and C_c. Now we may see that this approximation is justified. Consider, say, the current through C_c. The magnitude of this current is $\omega C_c V_{b'e}$, whereas the current due to the controlled generator is $g_m V_{b'e}$. The ratio of currents is $\omega C_c / g_m$. At the highest frequency of interest f_T, we have, from Eq. (13-45), using the typical values of Fig. 13-8,

$$\frac{\omega C_c}{g_m} = \frac{2\pi f_T C_c}{g_m} = \frac{C_c}{C_e + C_c} \approx 0.03$$

In a similar way the current delivered to the output through $g_{b'c}$ may be shown to be negligible.

The frequency f_T is often inconveniently high to allow a direct experimental determination of f_T. However, a procedure is available which allows a measurement of f_T at an appreciably lower frequency. We note from Eq. (13-43) that, for $f \gg f_\beta$, we may neglect the unity in the denominator and write $|A_i|f \approx h_{fe}f_\beta = f_T$ from Eq. (13-45). Accordingly, at some particular frequency f_1 (say f_1 is five or ten times f_β), we measure the gain $|A_{i1}|$. The parameter f_T may be calculated now from $f_T = f_1|A_{i1}|$. In the case of our typical transistor, for which $f_T = 80$ MHz and $f_\beta = 1.6$ MHz, the frequency f_1 may be $f_1 = 5 \times 1.6 = 8.0$ MHz, a much more convenient frequency than 80 MHz.

The experimentally determined value of f_T is used to calculate the value of C_e in the hybrid-II circuit. From Eq. (13-45),

$$C_e = \frac{g_m}{2\pi f_T} \tag{13-47}$$

From Eqs. (13-20) and (13-45), $f_T \approx h_{fe}f_\beta = \alpha_o f_\alpha$. Hence it is expected that f_α and f_T should be almost equal. Experimentally, it is found that in diffusion transistors $f_\alpha \approx 1.2 f_T$, whereas in drift transistors $f_\alpha \approx 2 f_T$. These values may be accounted for if the excess-phase factor for α in Eq. (13-7) is taken into consideration.

13-8   CURRENT GAIN WITH RESISTIVE LOAD

To minimize the complications which result when the load resistor R_L in Fig. 13-8 is not zero, we find it convenient to deal with the parallel combination of $g_{b'c}$ and C_c, using Miller's theorem of Sec. 12-9. We identify $V_{b'e}$ with V_1 in Fig. 12-14 and V_{ce} with V_2. On this basis the circuit of Fig. 13-8 may be replaced by the circuit of Fig. 13-12a. Here $K \equiv V_{ce}/V_{b'e}$. This circuit is still rather complicated because it has two independent time constants, one

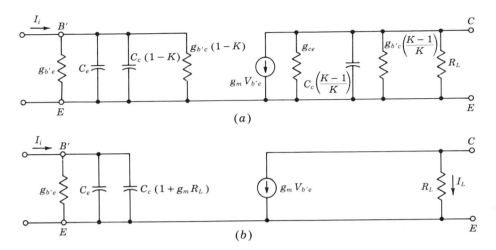

Fig. 13-12 (a) Approximate equivalent circuit for calculation of response of a transistor amplifier stage with a resistive load; (b) further simplification of the equivalent circuit.

associated with the input circuit and one associated with the output. We now show that in a practical situation the output time constant is negligible in comparison with the input time constant, and may be ignored. Let us therefore delete the output capacitance $C_c(K - 1)/K$, consider the resultant circuit, and then show that the reintroduction of the output capacitance makes no significant change in the performance of the circuit.

Since $K \equiv V_{ce}/V_{b'e}$ is (approximately) the voltage gain, we normally have $|K| \gg 1$. Hence $g_{b'c}(K - 1)/K \approx g_{b'c}$. Since $g_{b'c} \ll g_{ce}$ ($r_{b'c} \approx 1$ M and $r_{ce} \approx 80$ K), we may omit $g_{b'c}$ from Fig. 13-12a. In a wideband amplifier, R_L seldom exceeds 2 K. The conductance g_{ce} may be neglected compared with R_L, and the output circuit consists of the current generator $g_m V_{b'e}$ feeding the load R_L, as indicated in Fig. 13-12b. Even if the above approximations were not valid for some particular transistor or load, the analysis to follow is still valid provided that R_L is interpreted as the parallel combination of the collector-circuit resistor, r_{ce} and $r_{b'c}$.

By inspection of Fig. 13-12b, $K = V_{ce}/V_{b'e} = -g_m R_L$. For $g_m = 50$ mA/V and $R_L = 2,000$ Ω, $K = -100$. For this maximum value of K, conductance $g_{b'c}(1 - K) \approx 0.025$ mA/V is negligible compared with $g_{b'e} \approx 1$ mA/V. Hence the circuit of Fig. 13-12a is reduced to that shown in Fig. 13-12b. The load resistance R_L has been restricted to a maximum value of 2 K because, at values of R_L much above 2,000 Ω, the capacitance $C_c(1 + g_m R_L)$ becomes excessively large and the bandpass correspondingly small.

Now let us return to the capacitance $C_c(K - 1)/K \approx C_c$, which we neglected above. For $R_L = 2,000$ Ω,

$$R_L C_c = 2 \times 10^3 \times 3 \times 10^{-12} = 6 \times 10^{-9} \text{ sec} = 6 \text{ nsec}$$

The input time constant is

$$r_{b'e}[C_e + C_c(1 + g_m R_L)] = 10^3(100 + 3 \times 101)10^{-12} \text{ sec} = 403 \text{ nsec}$$

It is therefore apparent that the bandpass of the amplifier will be determined by the time constant of the input circuit and that, in the useful frequency range of the stage, the capacitance C_c will not make itself felt in the output circuit. Of course, if the transistor works into a highly capacitive load, this capacitance will have to be taken into account, and it then might happen that the output time constant will predominate.

The circuit of Fig. 13-12b is different from the circuit of Fig. 13-9 only in that a load R_L has been included and that C_c has been augmented by $g_m R_L C_c$. To the accuracy of our approximations, the low-frequency current gain A_{Io} under load is the same as the low-frequency gain A_{io} with output shorted. Therefore

$$A_{Io} = -h_{fe}$$

However, the 3-dB frequency is now f_2 (rather than f_β), where

$$f_2 = \frac{1}{2\pi r_{b'e} C} = \frac{g_{b'e}}{2\pi C} \tag{13-48}$$

where

$$C \equiv C_e + C_c(1 + g_m R_L) \tag{13-49}$$

13-9   TRANSISTOR AMPLIFIER RESPONSE, TAKING SOURCE RESISTANCE INTO ACCOUNT

In the preceding discussions we assumed that the transistor stage was driven from an ideal current source, that is, a source of infinite resistance. We now remove that restriction and consider that the source has a resistive impedance R_s. We may represent the source by its Norton's equivalent, as in Fig. 13-13a, or by its Thévenin's equivalent, as in Fig. 13-13b. At low frequencies (and with $R_s = \infty$) the current gain is $A_{Io} \equiv I_L/I_i = -g_m V_{b'e}/g_{b'e} V_{b'e} = -h_{fe}$, from Eq. (13-28). Therefore the low-frequency current gain, taking the load

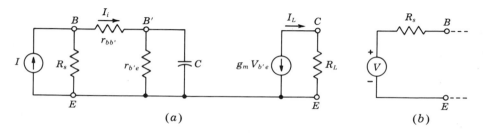

Fig. 13-13 (a) A transistor is driven by a generator of resistance R_s which is represented by its Norton's equivalent circuit. (b) The generator is represented by its Thévenin's equivalent.

and source impedances into account, is

$$A_{Iso} \equiv \frac{I_L}{I} = \frac{I_L}{I_i}\frac{I_i}{I} = -h_{fe}\frac{R_s}{R_s + r_{bb'} + r_{b'e}} = \frac{-h_{fe}R_s}{R_s + h_{ie}} \tag{13-50}$$

since $h_{ie} = r_{bb'} + r_{b'e}$. Note that A_{Iso} is independent of R_L. The 3-dB frequency is determined by the time constant consisting of C and the equivalent resistance R shunted across C. Accordingly,

$$f_2 = \frac{1}{2\pi RC} \tag{13-51}$$

where C is given by Eq. (13-49), and R is the parallel combination of $R_s + r_{bb'}$ and $r_{b'e}$, namely,

$$R \equiv \frac{(R_s + r_{bb'})r_{b'e}}{R_s + h_{ie}} \tag{13-52}$$

From Eq. (11-39) we have that the voltage gain A_{Vso} at low frequency, taking load and source impedances into account, is

$$A_{Vso} = A_{Iso}\frac{R_L}{R_s} = \frac{-h_{fe}R_L}{R_s + h_{ie}} \tag{13-53}$$

Note that A_{Vso} increases linearly with R_L. The 3-dB frequency for voltage gain A_{Vs} is also given by Eq. (13-51). Note that f_2 increases as the load resistance is decreased because C is a linear function of R_L. At $R_L = 0$, the 3-dB frequency is finite (unlike the vacuum-tube amplifier, which has infinite bandpass for zero plate-circuit resistance; Sec. 16-6) and from Eq. (13-47) is given by

$$f_2 = \frac{1}{2\pi R(C_e + C_c)} = \frac{f_T}{g_m R} = \frac{f_\beta}{g_{b'e}R} \qquad R_L = 0 \tag{13-54}$$

For $R_s = 0$, this quantity is of the order of $f_T/5 \approx 10f_\beta$, and for $R_s = 1$ K (and $R_L = 0$), $f_2 \approx f_T/25 \approx 2f_\beta$. Of course, for $R_L = 0$, the voltage gain is zero. In practice, when $R_L \neq 0$, much lower 3-dB frequencies than those indicated above will be obtained.

The equality in 3-dB frequencies for current and voltage gains applies only in the case of a fixed source resistance. The voltage gain A_V (for the case of an ideal voltage source) and the current gain A_I (for the case of an ideal current source) do not have the same value of f_2. In the former case, $R_s = 0$, and in the latter case, $R_s = \infty$. Equation (13-51) applies in both cases provided that, for A_V, we use $R = R_V$, where, from Eq. (13-52) with $R_s = 0$,

$$R_V = \frac{r_{bb'}r_{b'e}}{r_{bb'} + r_{b'e}} = \frac{r_{bb'}r_{b'e}}{h_{ie}} \tag{13-55}$$

and for A_I we use $R = R_I$, where, from Eq. (13-52) with $R_s = \infty$,

$$R_I = r_{b'e} \tag{13-56}$$

Since $R_V \ll R_I$, the 3-dB frequency f_{2V} for an ideal voltage source is higher than f_{2I} for an ideal current source.

The Gain-Bandwidth Product   This product is found in Prob. 13-18 to be

$$|A_{Vso}f_2| = \frac{g_m}{2\pi C} \frac{R_L}{R_s + r_{bb'}} = \frac{f_T}{1 + 2\pi f_T C_c R_L} \frac{R_L}{R_s + r_{bb'}} \tag{13-57}$$

$$|A_{Iso}f_2| = \frac{f_T}{1 + 2\pi f_T C_c R_L} \frac{R_s}{R_s + r_{bb'}} \tag{13-58}$$

The quantities f_2, A_{Iso}, and A_{Vso}, which characterize the transistor stage, depend on both R_L and R_s.   The form of this dependence, as well as the order of magnitude of these quantities, may be seen in Fig. 13-14.   Here f_2 has been plotted as a function of R_L, up to $R_L = 2,000\ \Omega$, for several values of R_s.   The topmost f_2 curve in Fig. 13-14 for $R_s = 0$ corresponds to ideal-voltage-source drive.   The current gain is zero, and the voltage gain ranges from zero at $R_L = 0$ to 90.9 at $R_L = 2,000\ \Omega$.   Note that a source impedance of only 100 Ω reduces the bandwidth by a factor of about 1.8.   The bottom curve has $R_s = \infty$ and corresponds to the ideal current source.   The voltage gain is zero for all R_L if $R_s = \infty$.   For any R_L the bandwidth is highest for lowest R_s.

In the case of a vacuum-tube stage of amplification, the gain-bandwidth product is a useful number (Sec. 16-6).   For a transistor amplifier consist-

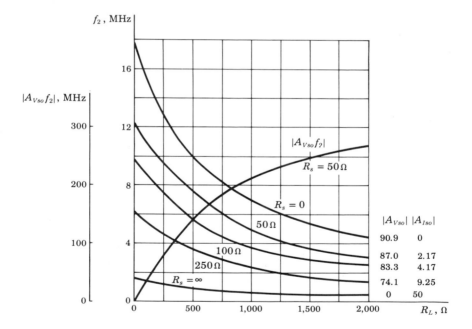

Fig. 13-14   Bandwidth f_2 as a function of R_L, with source resistance as a parameter, for an amplifier consisting of one CE transistor whose parameters are given in Sec. 13-5.   Also, the gain-bandwidth product for a 50-Ω source is plotted.   The tabulated values of $|A_{Vso}|$ correspond to $R_L = 2,000\ \Omega$ and to the values of R_s on the curves.   The values of $|A_{Iso}|$ are independent of R_L.

ing of a single stage, however, the gain-bandwidth product is ordinarily not a useful parameter: it is not independent of R_s and R_L and varies widely with both. The current-gain–bandwidth product decreases with increasing R_L and increases with increasing R_s. The voltage-gain–bandwidth product increases with increasing R_L and decreases with increasing R_s. Even if we know the gain-bandwidth product at a particular R_s and R_L, we cannot use the product to determine the improvement, say, in bandwidth corresponding to a sacrifice in gain. For if we change the gain by changing R_s or R_L or both, generally, the gain-bandwidth product will no longer be the same as it had been.

Summary The high-frequency response of a transistor amplifier is obtained by applying Eqs. (13-49) to (13-53). We now show that only four independent transistor device parameters appear in these equations. Hence these four (h_{fe}, f_T, h_{ie}, and $C_c = C_{ob}$) are usually specified by manufacturers of high-frequency transistors.

From the operating current I_C and the temperature T, the transconductance is obtained [Eqs. (13-39)] as $g_m = |I_C|/V_T$ and is independent of the particular device under consideration. Knowing g_m, we can find, from Eqs. (13-39) and (13-40),

$$r_{b'e} = \frac{h_{fe}}{g_m} \qquad r_{bb'} = h_{ie} - r_{b'e} \qquad C_e \approx \frac{g_m}{2\pi f_T}$$

If R_s and R_L are given, then all quantities in Eqs. (13-49) to (13-53) are known. We have therefore verified that the frequency response may be determined from the four parameters h_{fe}, f_T, h_{ie}, and C_e.

REFERENCES

1. Phillips, A. B.: "Transistor Engineering," chaps. 13 and 14, McGraw-Hill Book Company, New York, 1962.
   Pritchard, R. L.: Electric-network Representations of Transistors: A Survey, *IRE Trans. Circuit Theory*, vol. CT-3, no. 1, pp. 5–21, March, 1956.
   Searle, C. L., A. R. Boothroyd, E. J. Angelo, Jr., P. E. Gray, and D. O. Pederson: "Elementary Circuit Properties of Transistors," vol. 3, Semiconductor Electronics Education Committee, John Wiley & Sons, Inc., New York, 1964.

2. Thomas, D. E., and J. L. Moll: Junction Transistor Short-circuit Current Gain and Phase Determination, *Proc. IRE*, vol. 46, no. 6, pp. 1177–1184, June, 1958.

3. Phillips, A. B.: "Transistor Engineering," pp. 129–130, McGraw-Hill Book Company, New York, 1962.

4. Giacoletto, L. J.: Study of *p-n-p* Alloy Junction Transistors from DC through Medium Frequencies, *RCA Rev.*, vol. 15, no. 4, pp. 506–562, December, 1954.
   Searle, C. L., A. B. Boothroyd, E. J. Angelo, Jr., P. E. Gray, and D. O. Pederson: "Elementary Circuit Properties of Transistors," vol. 3, chap. 3, Semiconductor Electronics Education Committee, John Wiley & Sons, Inc., New York, 1964.

14 / FIELD–EFFECT TRANSISTORS

The field-effect transistor[1] is a semiconductor device which depends for its operation on the control of current by an electric field. There are two types of field-effect transistors, the *junction field-effect transistor* (abbreviated JFET, or simply FET) and the *insulated-gate field-effect transistor* (IGFET), more commonly called the *metal-oxide-semiconductor (MOS) transistor* (MOST or MOSFET).

The principles on which these devices operate, as well as the differences in their characteristics, are examined in this chapter. Representative circuits making use of FET transistors are also presented.

The FET enjoys several advantages over the conventional transistor:

1. Its operation depends upon the flow of majority carriers only. It is therefore a *unipolar* (one type of carrier) device. The vacuum tube is another example of a unipolar device. The conventional transistor is a bipolar device.

2. It is relatively immune to radiation.

3. It exhibits a high input resistance, typically many megohms.

4. It is less noisy than a tube or a bipolar transistor.

5. It exhibits no offset voltage at zero drain current, and hence makes an excellent signal chopper.[2]

6. It has thermal stability (Sec. 14-4).

The main disadvantage of the FET is its relatively small gain-bandwidth product in comparison with that which can be obtained with a conventional transistor.

14-1   THE JUNCTION FIELD–EFFECT TRANSISTOR

The structure of an *n-channel* field-effect transistor is shown in Fig. 14-1. Ohmic contacts are made to the two ends of a semiconductor bar of *n*-type material (if *p*-type silicon is used, the device is referred to as a *p-channel* FET). Current is caused to flow along the length of the bar because of the voltage supply connected between the ends. This current consists of majority carriers which in this case are electrons. The following FET notation is standard.

Source The *source* S is the terminal through which the majority carriers enter the bar. Conventional current entering the bar at S is designated by I_S.

Drain The *drain* D is the terminal through which the majority carriers leave the bar. Conventional current entering the bar at D is designated by I_D. The drain-to-source voltage is called V_{DS}, and is positive if D is more positive than S.

Gate On both sides of the *n*-type bar of Fig. 14-1, heavily doped (p^+) regions of acceptor impurities have been formed by alloying, by diffusion, or by any other procedure available for creating *p-n* junctions. These impurity regions are called the *gate G*. Between the gate and source a voltage V_{GS} is applied in the direction to reverse-bias the *p-n* junction. Conventional current entering the bar at G is designated I_G.

Channel The region in Fig. 14-1 of *n*-type material between the two gate regions is the *channel* through which the majority carriers move from source to drain.

FET Operation It is necessary to recall that on the two sides of the reverse-biased *p-n* junction (the transition region) there are space-charge regions (Sec. 6-9). The current carriers have diffused across the junction, leaving only uncovered positive ions on the *n* side and negative ions on the *p* side. The electric lines of field intensity which now originate on the positive ions and terminate on the negative ions are precisely the source of the voltage drop across the junction. As the reverse bias across the junction increases, so also does the thickness of the region of immobile uncovered charges. The conductivity of this region is nominally zero because of the unavailability of current carriers. Hence we see that the effective width of the *channel* in Fig. 14-1 will become progressively decreased with increasing reverse bias. Accordingly, for a fixed drain-to-source voltage, the drain current will be a function of the reverse-biasing voltage across the gate junction. The term *field effect* is used to describe this device because the mechanism of current control is the *effect* of the extension, with increasing reverse bias, of the *field* associated with the region of uncovered charges.

FET Static Characteristics The circuit, symbol, and polarity conventions for a FET are indicated in Fig. 14-2. The direction of the arrow at the gate

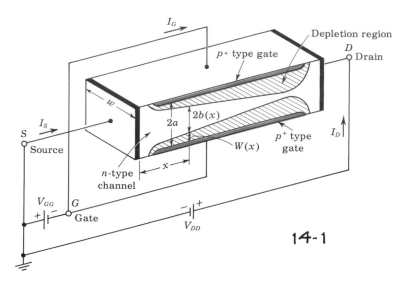

14-1

Fig. 14-1   The basic structure of an n-channel field-effect transistor.   The normal polarities of the drain-to-source and gate-to-
source supply voltages are shown.   In a p-channel FET the voltages would be reversed.

of the junction FET in Fig. 14-2 indicates the direction in which gate current
would flow if the gate junction were forward-biased.   The common-source
drain characteristics for a typical n-channel FET shown in Fig. 14-3 give I_D
against V_{DS}, with V_{GS} as a parameter.   To see qualitatively why the characteristics have the form shown, consider, say, the case for which $V_{GS} = 0$.   For
$I_D = 0$, the channel between the gate junctions is entirely open.   In response
to a small applied voltage V_{DS}, the n-type bar acts as a simple semiconductor
resistor, and the current I_D increases linearly with V_{DS}.   With increasing current, the ohmic voltage drop between the source and the channel region reverse-
biases the junction, and the conducting portion of the channel begins to con-
strict.   Because of the ohmic drop along the length of the channel itself, the

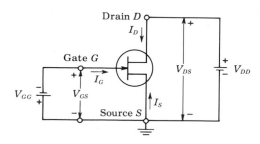

Fig. 14-2   Circuit symbol for an
n-channel FET.   (For a p-channel
FET the arrow at the gate junction points in the opposite direction.)   For an n-channel FET, I_D
and V_{DS} are positive and V_{GS} is
negative.   For a p-channel FET, I_D
and V_{DS} are negative and V_{GS} is
positive.

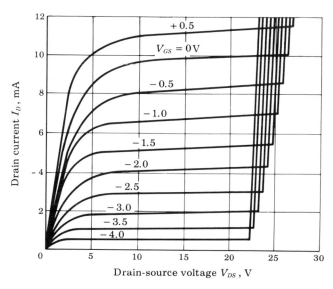

Fig. 14-3 Common-source drain characteristics of an n-channel field-effect transistor. (Courtesy Texas Instruments, Inc.)

constriction is not uniform, but is more pronounced at distances farther from the source, as indicated in Fig. 14-1. Eventually, a voltage V_{DS} is reached at which the channel is "pinched off." This is the voltage, not too sharply defined in Fig. 14-3, where the current I_D begins to level off and approach a constant value. It is, of course, in principle not possible for the channel to close completely and thereby reduce the current I_D to zero. For if such, indeed, could be the case, the ohmic drop required to provide the necessary back bias would itself be lacking. Note that each characteristic curve has an ohmic region for small values of V_{DS}, where I_D is proportional to V_{DS}. Each also has a constant-current region for large values of V_{DS}, where I_D responds very slightly to V_{DS}.

If now a gate voltage V_{GS} is applied in the direction to provide additional reverse bias, pinch-off will occur for smaller values of $|V_{DS}|$, and the maximum drain current will be smaller. This feature is brought out in Fig. 14-3. Note that a plot for a silicon FET is given even for $V_{GS} = +0.5$ V, which is in the direction of forward bias. We note from Table 9-1 that, actually, the gate current will be very small, because at this gate voltage the Si junction is barely at the cutin voltage V_γ. The similarity between the FET characteristics and those of a pentode tube need hardly be belabored.

The maximum voltage that can be applied between any two terminals of the FET is the lowest voltage that will cause avalanche breakdown (Sec. 6-12) across the gate junction. From Fig. 14-3 it is seen that avalanche occurs at a lower value of $|V_{DS}|$ when the gate is reverse-biased than for $V_{GS} = 0$. This is caused by the fact that the reverse-bias gate voltage adds to the drain voltage, and hence increases the effective voltage across the gate junction.

We note from Fig. 14-2 that the *n*-channel FET requires zero or negative gate bias and positive drain voltage, and it is therefore similar to a vacuum tube. The *p*-channel FET which requires opposite voltage polarities behaves like a vacuum tube in which the cathode emits positive ions instead of electrons. Either end of the channel may be used as a source. We can remember supply polarities by using the channel type, *p* or *n*, to designate the polarity of the *source* side of the drain supply. The field-effect transistor existed as a laboratory device from 1952 to 1962. The reason why no large-scale production and use of this device took place is that semiconductor-device technology only recently reached the degree of refinement required for the production of a thin, lightly doped layer between two more heavily doped layers of opposite type.

A Practical FET Structure　The structure shown in Fig. 14-1 is not practical because of the difficulties involved in diffusing impurities into both sides of a semiconductor wafer. Figure 14-4 shows a single-ended-geometry junction FET where diffusion is from one side only. The substrate is of *p*-type material onto which an *n*-type channel is epitaxially grown (Sec. 15-2). A *p*-type gate is then diffused into the *n*-type channel. The substrate which may function as a second gate is of relatively low resistivity material. The diffused gate is also of very low resistivity material, allowing the depletion region to spread mostly into the *n*-type channel.

14-2　　THE PINCH–OFF VOLTAGE V_P

We derive an expression for the gate reverse voltage V_P that removes all the free charge from the channel using the physical model described in the preceding section. This analysis was first made by Shockley,[1] using the structure of Fig. 14-1. In this device a slab of *n*-type semiconductor is sandwiched between two layers of *p*-type material, forming two *p-n* junctions.

Assume that the *p*-type region is doped with N_A acceptors per cubic meter, that the *n*-type region is doped with N_D donors per cubic meter, and that the

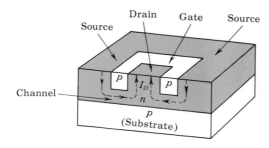

Fig. 14-4　Single-ended-geometry junction FET.

junction formed is abrupt.   The assumption of an abrupt junction is the same
as that made in Sec. 6-9 and Fig. 6-12, and is chosen for simplicity.   Moreover, if $N_A \gg N_D$, we see from Eq. (6-44) that $W_p \ll W_n$, and using Eq. (6-47),
we have, for the space-charge width, $W_n(x) = W(x)$ at a distance x along the
channel in Fig. 14-1:

$$W(x) = a - b(x) = \left\{ \frac{2\epsilon}{eN_D} [V_o - V(x)] \right\}^{\frac{1}{2}} \tag{14-1}$$

where $\epsilon =$ dielectric constant of channel material
   $e \cdot=$ magnitude of electronic charge
   $V_o =$ junction contact potential at x (Fig. 6-1d)
$V(x) =$ applied potential across space-charge region at x and is a negative
         number for an applied reverse bias
$a - b(x) =$ penetration $W(x)$ of depletion region into channel at a point x
         along channel (Fig. 14-1)
   If the drain current is zero, $b(x)$ and $V(x)$ are independent of x and
$b(x) = b$.   If in Eq. (14-1) we substitute $b(x) = b = 0$ and solve for V, on the
assumption that $|V_o| \ll |V|$, we obtain the pinch-off voltage V_P, the diode
reverse voltage that removes all the free charge from the channel.   Hence

$$|V_P| = \frac{eN_D}{2\epsilon} a^2 \tag{14-2}$$

If we substitute V_{GS} for V and $a - b$ for x in Eq. (6-46), we obtain, using
Eq. (14-2),

$$V_{GS} = \left(1 - \frac{b}{a} \right)^2 V_P \tag{14-3}$$

The voltage V_{GS} in Eq. (14-3) represents the reverse bias across the gate
junction and is independent of distance along the channel if $I_D = 0$.

EXAMPLE   For an n-channel silicon FET with $a = 3 \times 10^{-4}$ cm and $N_D = 10^{15}$
electrons/cm^3, find (a) the pinch-off voltage and (b) the channel half-width for
$V_{GS} = \frac{1}{2}V_P$ and $I_D = 0$.

Solution   a. The relative dielectric constant of silicon is given in Table 5-1 as
12, and hence $\epsilon = 12\epsilon_o$.   Using the value of e and ϵ_o from Appendixes A and B,
we have, from Eq. (14-2), expressed in mks units,

$$V_P = \frac{1.60 \times 10^{-19} \times 10^{21} \times (3 \times 10^{-6})^2}{2 \times 12 \times (36\pi \times 10^9)^{-1}} = 6.8 \text{ V}$$

b. Solving Eq. (14-3) for b, we obtain for $V_{GS} = \frac{1}{2}V_P$

$$b = a \left[1 - \left(\frac{V_{GS}}{V_P} \right)^{\frac{1}{2}} \right] = (3 \times 10^{-4})[1 - (\tfrac{1}{2})^{\frac{1}{2}}] = 0.87 \times 10^{-4} \text{ cm}$$

Hence the channel width has been reduced to about one-third its value for $V_{GS} = 0$.

14-3   THE JFET VOLT–AMPERE CHARACTERISTICS

Assume, first, that a small voltage V_{DS} is applied between drain and source. The resulting small drain current I_D will then have no appreciable effect on the channel profile. Under these conditions we may consider the effective channel cross section A to be constant throughout its length. Hence $A = 2bw$, where $2b$ is the channel width corresponding to zero drain current as given by Eq. (14-3) for a specified V_{GS}, and w is the channel dimension perpendicular to the b direction, as indicated in Fig. 14-1.

Since no current flows in the depletion region, then, using Ohm's law [Eq. (5-1)], we obtain for the drain current

$$I_D = AeN_D\mu_n\mathcal{E} = 2bweN_D\mu_n\frac{V_{DS}}{L} \tag{14-4}$$

where L is the length of the channel.

Substituting b from Eq. (14-3) in Eq. (14-4), we have

$$I_D = \frac{2aweN_D\mu_n}{L}\left[1 - \left(\frac{V_{GS}}{V_P}\right)^{\frac{1}{2}}\right]V_{DS} \tag{14-5}$$

The ON Resistance $r_d(\text{ON})$ Equation (14-5) describes the volt-ampere characteristics of Fig. 14-3 for very small V_{DS}, and it suggests that under these conditions the FET behaves like an ohmic resistance whose value is determined by V_{GS}. The ratio V_{DS}/I_D at the origin is called the ON *drain resistance $r_d(\text{ON})$*. For a JFET we obtain from Eq. (14-5), with $V_{GS} = 0$,

$$r_d(\text{ON}) = \frac{L}{2aweN_D\mu_n} \tag{14-6}$$

For the device values given in the illustrative example in this section and with $L/w = 1$, we find that $r_d(\text{ON}) = 3.3$ K. For the dimensions and concentration used in commercially available FETs and MOSFETs (Sec. 14-5), values of $r_d(\text{ON})$ ranging from about 100 Ω to 100 K are measured. This parameter is important in switching applications where the FET is driven heavily ON. The bipolar transistor has the advantage over the field-effect device in that R_{CS} is usually only a few ohms, and hence is much smaller than $r_d(\text{ON})$. However, a bipolar transistor has the disadvantage for chopper applications[2] of possessing an offset voltage (Sec. 9-14), whereas the FET characteristics pass through the origin, $I_D = 0$ and $V_{DS} = 0$.

The Pinch-off Region   We now consider the situation where an electric field $\mathcal{E}_x$ appears along the x axis. If a substantial drain current I_D flows, the drain end of the gate is more reverse-biased than the source end, and hence the boundaries of the depletion region are not parallel to the center of the channel, but converge as shown in Fig. 14-1. If the convergence of the depletion region is gradual, the previous one-dimensional analysis is valid[1] in a thin slice of the channel of thickness Δx and at a distance x from the source.

Subject to this condition of the "gradual" channel, the current may be written by inspection of Fig. 14-1 as

$$I_D = 2b(x)weN_D\mu_n\mathcal{E}_x \tag{14-7}$$

As V_{DS} increases, $\mathcal{E}_x$ and I_D increase, whereas $b(x)$ decreases because the channel narrows and hence the current density $J = I_D/2b(x)w$ increases. We now see that complete pinch-off ($b = 0$) cannot take place because, if it did, J would become infinite, which is a physically impossible condition. If J were to increase without limit, then, from Eq. (14-7), so also would $\mathcal{E}_x$, provided that μ_n remains constant. It is found experimentally,[3,4] however, that the mobility is a function of electric field intensity and remains constant only for $\mathcal{E}_x < 10^3$ V/cm in n-type silicon. For moderate fields, 10^3 to 10^4 V/cm, the mobility is approximately inversely proportional to the square root of the applied field. For still higher fields, such as are encountered at pinch-off, μ_n is inversely proportional to $\mathcal{E}_x$. In this region the drift velocity of the electrons ($v_x = \mu_n\mathcal{E}_x$) remains constant, and Ohm's law is no longer valid. From Eq. (14-7) we now see that both I_D and b remain constant, thus explaining the constant-current portion of the V-I characteristic of Fig. 14-3.

What happens[4] if V_{DS} is increased beyond pinch-off, with V_{GS} held constant? As explained above, the minimum channel width $b_{\min} = \delta$ has a small nonzero constant value. This minimum width occurs at the drain end of the bar. As V_{DS} is increased, this increment in potential causes an increase in $\mathcal{E}_x$ in an adjacent channel section toward the source. Referring to Fig. 14-5, the velocity-limited region L' increases with V_{DS}, whereas δ remains at a fixed value.

The Region before Pinch-off   We have verified that the FET behaves as an ohmic resistance for small V_{DS} and as a constant-current device for large V_{DS}. An analysis giving the shape of the volt-ampere characteristic between these two extremes is complicated. It has already been mentioned that in this region the mobility is at first independent of electric field and then μ

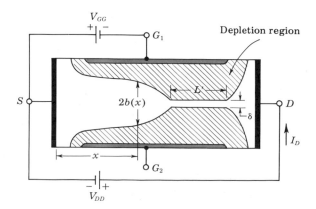

Fig. 14-5   After pinch-off, as V_{DS} is increased, then L' increases but δ and I_D remain essentially constant. (G_1 and G_2 are tied together.)

varies with $\mathcal{E}_x^{-\frac{1}{2}}$ for larger values of $\mathcal{E}_x$ (before pinch-off). Taking this relationship into account, it is possible[3-5] to obtain an expression for I_D as a function of V_{DS} and V_{GS} which agrees quite well with experimentally determined curves.

The Transfer Characteristic In amplifier applications the FET is almost always used in the region beyond pinch-off (also called the *constant-current, pentode,* or *current-saturation region*). Let the saturation drain current be designated by I_{DS}, and its value with the gate shorted to the source ($V_{GS} = 0$) by I_{DSS}. It has been found[6] that the transfer characteristic, giving the relationship between I_{DS} and V_{GS}, can be approximated by the parabola

$$I_{DS} = I_{DSS} \left(1 - \frac{V_{GS}}{V_P}\right)^2 \tag{14-8}$$

This simple parabolic approximation gives an excellent fit, with the experimentally determined transfer characteristics for FETs made by the diffusion process.

Cutoff Consider a FET operating at a fixed value of V_{DS} in the pentode region. As V_{GS} is increased in the direction to reverse-bias the gate junction, the conducting channel will narrow. When $V_{GS} = V_P$, the channel width is reduced to zero, and from Eq. (14-7), $I_{DS} = 0$. With a physical device some leakage current $I_D(\text{OFF})$ still flows even under the cutoff condition $|V_{GS}| > |V_P|$. A manufacturer usually specifies a maximum value of $I_D(\text{OFF})$ at a given value of V_{GS} and V_{DS}. Typically, a value of a few nanoamperes may be expected for $I_D(\text{OFF})$ for a silicon FET.

The gate reverse current, also called *the gate cutoff current,* designated by I_{GSS}, gives the gate-to-source current, with the drain shorted to the source for $|V_{GS}| > |V_P|$. Typically, I_{GSS} is of the order of a few nanoamperes for a silicon device.

14-4   THE FET SMALL-SIGNAL MODEL

The linear small-signal equivalent circuit for the FET can be obtained in a manner analogous to that used to derive the corresponding model for a vacuum tube or a transistor. We employ the same notation in labeling time-varying and dc currents and voltages as used in Secs. 7-9 and 9-13 for the vacuum tube and transistor. We can formally express the drain current i_D as a function f of the gate voltage v_{GS} and drain voltage v_{DS} by

$$i_D = f(v_{GS}, v_{DS}) \tag{14-9}$$

The Transconductance g_m and Drain Resistance r_d We now proceed as in Sec. 8-4. If both the gate and drain voltages are varied, the change in drain current is given approximately by the first two terms in the Taylor's series expansion of Eq. (14-9), or

$$\Delta i_D = \frac{\partial i_D}{\partial v_{GS}}\bigg|_{V_{DS}} \Delta v_{GS} + \frac{\partial i_D}{\partial v_{DS}}\bigg|_{V_{GS}} \Delta v_{DS} \tag{14-10}$$

In the small-signal notation of Sec. 8-1, $\Delta i_D = i_d$, $\Delta v_{GS} = v_{gs}$, and $\Delta v_{DS} = v_{ds}$, so that Eq. (14-10) becomes

$$i_d = g_m v_{gs} + \frac{1}{r_d} v_{ds} \tag{14-11}$$

where

$$g_m \equiv \frac{\partial i_D}{\partial v_{GS}}\bigg|_{V_{DS}} \approx \frac{\Delta i_D}{\Delta v_{GS}}\bigg|_{V_{DS}} = \frac{i_d}{v_{gs}}\bigg|_{V_{DS}} \tag{14-12}$$

is the *mutual conductance*, or *transconductance*. It is also often designated by y_{fs} or g_{fs} and called the *(common-source) forward transadmittance*. The second parameter r_d in Eq. (14-11) is the *drain (or output) resistance*, and is defined by

$$r_d = \frac{\partial v_{DS}}{\partial i_D}\bigg|_{V_{GS}} \approx \frac{\Delta v_{DS}}{\Delta i_D}\bigg|_{V_{GS}} = \frac{v_{ds}}{i_d}\bigg|_{V_{GS}} \tag{14-13}$$

The reciprocal of r_d is the drain conductance g_d. It is also designated by y_{os} and g_{os} and called the (common-source) output conductance.

The parameters g_m and r_d are completely analogous to the vacuum-tube parameter g_m and r_p. An *amplification factor* μ for a FET may be defined, just as it is for a tube, by

$$\mu \equiv \frac{\partial v_{DS}}{\partial v_{GS}}\bigg|_{I_D} = \frac{\Delta v_{DS}}{\Delta v_{GS}}\bigg|_{I_D} = \frac{v_{ds}}{v_{gs}}\bigg|_{I_D} \tag{14-14}$$

Proceeding as in Sec. 8-4, we verify that μ, r_d, and g_m are related by

$$\mu = r_d g_m \tag{14-15}$$

A circuit for measuring g_m is given in Fig. 14-6a. It follows from Eq. (14-12) that (if $|V_2| \ll V_{DD}$, so that $V_{DS} = $ const)

$$g_m = \frac{I_d}{V_1} = \frac{V_2/R_d}{V_1} = \frac{V_2}{V_1 R_d} \tag{14-16}$$

Similarly, the circuit of Fig. 14-6b allows r_d to be measured. From Eq. (14-13) it follows that

$$r_d = \frac{V_2}{I_d} = \frac{V_2}{V_1/R_d} = \frac{V_2 R_d}{V_1} \tag{14-17}$$

An expression for g_m is obtained by applying the definition of Eq. (14-12) to Eq. (14-8). The result is

$$g_m = g_{mo}\left(1 - \frac{V_{GS}}{V_P}\right) \tag{14-18}$$

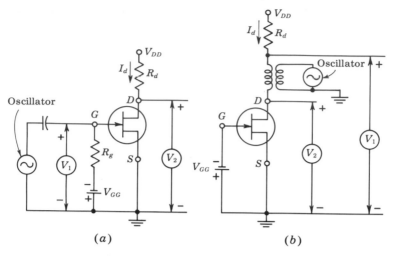

Fig. 14-6   Test circuits for measuring (a) g_m and (b) r_d.   The rms voltages V_1 and V_2 are measured with ac high-impedance voltmeters.

where g_{mo} is the value of g_m for $V_{GS} = 0$, and is given by

$$g_{mo} = \frac{-2I_{DSS}}{V_P} \qquad (14\text{-}19)$$

Since I_{DSS} and V_P are of opposite sign, g_{mo} is always positive.   This relationship, connecting g_{mo}, I_{DSS}, and V_P, has been verified experimentally.[7]   Since g_{mo} can be measured with the circuit of Fig. 14-6a for $V_{GG} = 0$, and I_{DSS} can be read on a dc milliammeter placed in the drain lead of the same circuit (with zero gate excitation), Eq. (14-19) gives a method for obtaining V_P.

The dependence of g_m upon V_{GS} is indicated in Fig. 14-7 for the 2N3277 FET (with $V_P \approx 4.5$ V) and the 2N3278 FET (with $V_P \approx 7$ V).   The linear relationship predicted by Eq. (14-18) is seen to be only approximately valid.

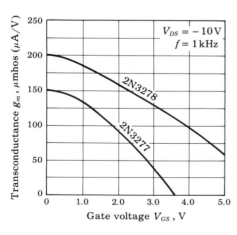

Fig. 14-7   Transconductance g_m versus gate voltage for types 2N3277 and 2N3278 FETs.   (Courtesy of Fairchild Semiconductor Company.)

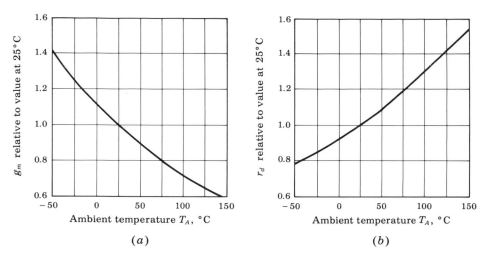

(a)   (b)

Fig. 14-8   (a) Normalized transconductance g_m versus ambient temperature T_A and (b) normalized drain resistance r_d versus T_A (for the 2N3277 and the 2N3278 FETs with $V_{DS} = -10$ V, $V_{GS} = 0$ V, and $f = 1$ kHz). (Courtesy of Fairchild Semiconductor.)

Temperature Dependence   Curves of g_m and r_d versus temperature are given in Fig. 14-8a and b.   The drain current I_{DS} has the same temperature variation as does g_m.   The principal reason for the negative temperature coefficient of I_{DS} is that the mobility decreases with increasing temperature.[9] Since this majority-carrier current decreases with temperature (unlike the bipolar transistor whose minority-carrier current increases with temperature), the troublesome phenomenon of *thermal runaway* (Sec. 10-10) is not encountered with field-effect transistors.

The FET Model   We note that Eq. (14-11) is identical with Eq. (8-13) for the triode provided that k (*cathode*) is replaced by s (*source*), that p (*plate*) is replaced by d (*drain*), and the g is now identified as *gate* (instead of *grid*). Hence the small-signal tube equivalent circuit of Fig. 8-8 is valid for the FET. This model is repeated in Fig. 14-9, with the appropriate change of notation. In this figure we have also included the capacitances which exist between pairs of nodes (corresponding to the high-frequency triode model of Fig. 8-19).   The capacitor C_{gs} represents the barrier capacitance between gate and source, and

Fig. 14-9   Small-signal FET
model.

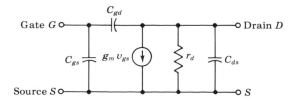

TABLE 14-1   Range of parameter values for a FET

Parameter	JFET	MOSFET†
g_m	0.1–10 mA/V	0.1–20 mA/V or more
r_d	0.1–1 M	1–50 K
C_{ds}	0.1–1 pF	0.1–1 pF
C_{gs}, C_{gd}	1–10 pF	1–10 pF
r_{gs}	$>10^8\ \Omega$	$>10^{10}\ \Omega$
r_{gd}	$>10^8\ \Omega$	$>10^{14}\ \Omega$

† Discussed in Sec. 14-5.

C_{gd} is the barrier capacitance between gate and drain. The element C_{ds} represents the drain-to-source capacitance of the channel.

The order of magnitudes of the parameters in the model for a diffused-junction FET is given in Table 14-1. Since the gate junction is reverse-biased, the gate-source resistance r_{gs} and the gate-drain resistance r_{gd} are extremely large, and hence have not been included in the model of Fig. 14-9.

14-5   THE INSULATED–GATE FET (MOSFET)

In preceding sections we developed the volt-ampere characteristics and small-signal properties of the junction field-effect transistor. We now turn our attention to the insulated-gate FET, or metal-oxide-semiconductor FET,[9] which promises to be of even greater commercial importance than the junction FET.

The n-channel MOSFET consists of a lightly doped p-type substrate into which two highly doped n^+ regions are diffused, as shown in Fig. 14-10. These n^+ sections, which will act as the source and drain, are separated by about 1 mil. A thin layer of insulating silicon dioxide (SiO_2) is grown over the surface of the structure, and holes are cut into the oxide layer, allowing contact with the source and drain. Then the gate-metal area is overlaid on the oxide,

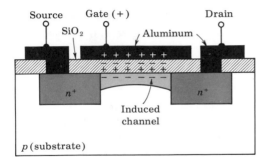

Fig. 14-10 Channel enhancement in a MOSFET. (Courtesy of Motorola Semiconductor Products, Inc.)

covering the entire channel region.   Simultaneously, metal contacts are made
to the drain and source, as shown in Fig. 14-10.   The contact to the metal
over the channel area is the gate terminal.

The metal area of the gate, in conjunction with the insulating dielectric
oxide layer and the semiconductor channel, forms a parallel-plate capacitor.
The insulating layer of silicon dioxide is the reason why this device is called
the insulated-gate field-effect transistor.   This layer results in an extremely
high input resistance (10^{10} to 10^{15} Ω) for the MOSFET.

The Enhancement MOSFET   If we ground the substrate for the structure
of Fig. 14-10 and apply a positive voltage at the gate, an electric field will be
directed perpendicularly through the oxide.   This field will end on "induced"
negative charges on the semiconductor site, as shown in Fig. 14-10.   The negative charge of electrons which are minority carriers in the p-type substrate
forms an "inversion layer."   As the positive voltage on the gate increases, the
induced negative charge in the semiconductor increases.   The region beneath
the oxide now has n-type carriers, the conductivity increases, and current
flows from source to drain through the induced channel.   Thus the drain current is "enhanced" by the positive gate voltage, and such a device is called an
enhancement-type MOS.

The volt-ampere drain characteristics of an n-channel enhancement-mode
MOSFET are given in Fig. 14-11a, and its transfer curve, in Fig. 14-11b.   The
current I_{DSS} at $V_{GS} \leq 0$ is very small, being of the order of a few nanoamperes.
As V_{GS} is made positive, the current I_D increases slowly at first, and then
much more rapidly with an increase in V_{GS}.   The manufacturer sometimes
indicates the *gate-source threshold voltage* V_{GST} at which I_D reaches some
defined small value, say 10 μA.   A current $I_D(\text{ON})$, corresponding approximately to the maximum value given on the drain characteristics, and the
value of V_{GS} needed to obtain this current are also usually given on the manufacturer's specification sheets.

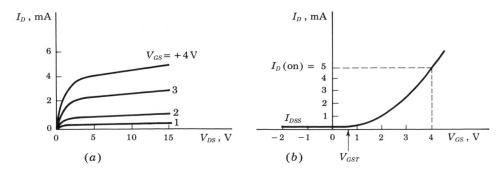

Fig. 14-11   (a) The drain characteristics, and (b) the transfer curve (for $V_{DS} =$
10 V) of an n-channel enhancement-type MOSFET.

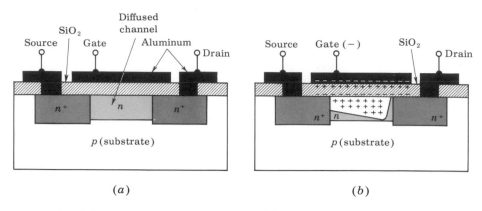

Fig. 14-12 (a) A depletion-type MOSFET. (b) Channel depletion with the application of a negative gate voltage. (Courtesy of Motorola Semiconductor Products, Inc.)

The Depletion MOSFET A second type of MOSFET can be made if, to the basic structure of Fig. 14-10, an n channel is diffused between the source and the drain, as shown in Fig. 14-12a. With this device an appreciable drain current I_{DSS} flows for zero gate-to-source voltage, $V_{GS} = 0$. If the gate voltage is made negative, positive charges are induced in the channel through the SiO_2 of the gate capacitor. Since the current in a FET is due to majority carriers (electrons for an n-type material), the induced positive charges make the channel less conductive, and the drain current drops as V_{GS} is made more negative. The redistribution of charge in the channel causes an effective depletion of majority carriers, which accounts for the designation *depletion* MOSFET. Note in Fig. 14-12b that, because of the voltage drop due to the drain current, the channel region nearest the drain is more depleted than is the volume near the source. This phenomenon is analogous to that of pinch-off occurring in a JFET at the drain end of the channel (Fig. 14-1). As a matter of fact, the volt-ampere characteristics of the depletion-mode MOS and the JFET are quite similar.

A MOSFET of the depletion type just described may also be operated in an enhancement mode. It is only necessary to apply a positive gate voltage so that negative charges are induced into the n-type channel. In this manner the conductivity of the channel increases and the current rises above I_{DSS}. The volt-ampere characteristics of this device are indicated in Fig. 14-13a, and the transfer curve is given in Fig. 14-13b. The depletion and enhancement regions, corresponding to V_{GS} negative and positive, respectively, should be noted. The manufacturer sometimes indicates the *gate-source cutoff voltage* $V_{GS}(\text{OFF})$, at which I_D is reduced to some specified negligible value at a recommended V_{DS}. This gate voltage corresponds to the pinch-off voltage V_P of a JFET.

The foregoing discussion is applicable in principle also to the p-channel

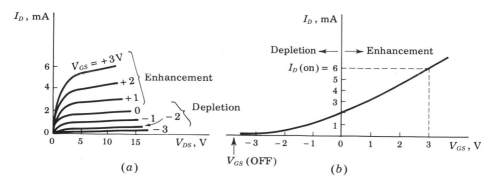

Fig. 14-13   (a) The drain characteristics and (b) the transfer curve (for $V_{DS} = 10$ V) for an n-channel MOSFET which may be used in either the enhancement or the depletion mode.

MOSFET.   For such a device the signs of all currents and voltages in the volt-ampere characteristics of Figs. 14-11 and 14-13 must be reversed.

Circuit Symbols   It is possible to bring out the connection to the substrate externally so as to have a tetrode device.   Most MOSFETs, however, are triodes, with the substrate internally connected to the source.   The circuit symbols used by several manufacturers are indicated in Fig. 14-14.   Sometimes the symbol of Fig. 14-2 for the JFET is also used for the MOSFET, with the understanding that G_2 is internally connected to S.

Small-signal MOSFET Circuit Model[10]   If the small bulk resistances of the source and drain are neglected, the small-signal equivalent circuit of the MOSFET between terminals $G (= G_1)$, S, and D is identical with that given in Fig. 14-9 for the JFET.   The transconductance g_m and the interelectrode capacitances have comparable values for the two types of devices.   However, as noted in Table 14-1 on page 396, the drain resistance r_d of the MOSFET is very much smaller than that of the JFET.   The magnitude of r_d for a MOSFET is comparable with the plate resistance of a triode, whereas r_d for a JFET has a value approximating the r_p of a pentode.   It should also be noted in Table 14-1 that the input resistance r_{gs} and the feedback resistance r_{gd} are very much larger for the MOSFET than for the JFET.

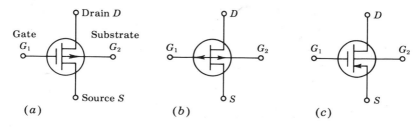

Fig. 14-14   Three circuit symbols for a p-channel MOSFET.

If the substrate terminal G_2 is not connected to the source, the model of Fig. 14-9 must be generalized as follows: Between node G_2 and S, a diode $D1$ is added to represent the p-n junction between the substrate and the source. Similarly, a second diode $D2$ is included between G_2 and D to account for the p-n junction formed by the substrate and the drain.

14-6   THE COMMON–SOURCE AMPLIFIER

The three basic JFET or MOSFET configurations are the common-source (CS), common-drain (CD), and common-gate (CG). The configurations are shown in Fig. 14-15 for a p-channel JFET. Unless specifically stated otherwise, the circuits discussed throughout this chapter apply equally well to JFETs or MOSFETs.

Voltage Gain   The circuit of Fig. 14-16a is the basic CS amplifier configuration. If the FET is replaced by the circuit model of Fig. 14-9, we obtain the circuit of Fig. 14-16b, which is equivalent to that of Fig. 8-19b for a CK triode amplifier with interelectrode capacitances taken into account. [In Fig. 8-19 the voltage source μV_i in series with r_p may be transformed into a current source $\mu V_i/r_p = g_m V_i$, in parallel with r_p (Sec. 8-5).] Hence the voltage gain $A_V = V_o/V_i$ for the CS amplifier as given by Eq. (8-39), which is repeated here, using FET notation,

$$A_V = \frac{-g_m + Y_{gd}}{Y_L + Y_{ds} + g_d + Y_{gd}} \tag{14-20}$$

where $Y_L = 1/Z_L$ = admittance corresponding to Z_L
$\quad Y_{ds} = j\omega C_{ds}$ = admittance corresponding to C_{ds}
$\quad g_d = 1/r_d$ = conductance corresponding to r_d
$\quad Y_{gd} = j\omega C_{gd}$ = admittance corresponding to C_{gd}

At low frequencies the FET capacitances can be neglected. Under these con-

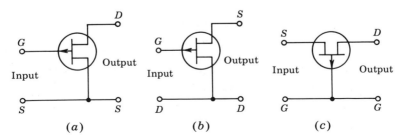

Fig. 14-15   The three FET configurations: (a) CS, (b) CD, and (c) CG.

ditions, $Y_{ds} = Y_{gd} = 0$, and Eq. (14-20) reduces to

$$A_V = \frac{-g_m}{Y_L + g_d} = -\frac{g_m Z_L}{1 + g_d Z_L} = -g_m Z_L' \qquad (14\text{-}21)$$

where $Z_L' \equiv r_d \| Z_L$. This equation is identical with Eq. (8-40).

Input Admittance An inspection of Fig. 14-16b reveals that the gate circuit is not isolated from the drain circuit. Since Figs. 14-16b and 8-19 are identical, the input admittance is given by Eq. (8-42), or

$$Y_i = Y_{gs} + (1 - A_V) Y_{gd} \qquad (14\text{-}22)$$

This expression indicates that for a field-effect transistor to possess negligible input admittance over a wide range of frequencies, the gate-source and gate-drain capacitances must be negligible. Also, as explained in Sec. 8-12, it is possible for the input resistance to be negative for an inductive load, and the circuit may oscillate.

Input Capacitance (Miller Effect) Consider a FET with a drain-circuit resistance R_d. From the previous discussion it follows that within the audio-frequency range, the gain is given by the simple expression $A_V = -g_m R_d'$, where R_d' is $R_d \| r_d$. In this case, Eq. (14-22) becomes

$$\frac{Y_i}{j\omega} \equiv C_i = C_{gs} + (1 + g_m R_d') C_{gd} \qquad (14\text{-}23)$$

This increase in input capacitance C_i over the capacitance from gate to source is caused by the familiar (Sec. 8-12) *Miller effect.*

This input capacitance is important in the operation of cascaded amplifiers, as is discussed in Sec. 8-12 in connection with vacuum tubes.

Output Resistance For the common-source amplifier of Fig. 14-16a, the

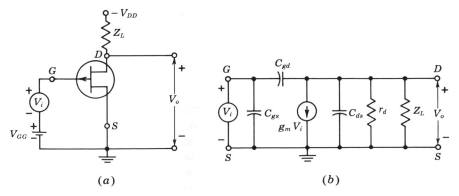

(a)   *(b)*

Fig. 14-16 (a) The common-source amplifier circuit; (b) small-signal equivalent circuit of CS amplifier.

output resistance R_o is given by the parallel combination of r_d and R_d, or

$$R_o = \frac{r_d R_d}{r_d + R_d} \tag{14-24}$$

Equation (14-24) is valid at low frequencies, where the effect of the capacitors in Fig. 14-16b is negligible, and with a resistive load, $Z_L = R_d$.

EXAMPLE   A MOSFET has a drain-circuit resistance R_d of 100 K and operates at 20 kHz.   Calculate the voltage gain of this device as a single stage, and then as the first transistor in a cascaded amplifier consisting of two identical stages. The MOSFET parameters are $g_m = 1.6$ mA/V, $r_d = 44$ K, $C_{gs} = 3.0$ pF, $C_{ds} = 3.8$ pF, and $C_{gd} = 2.8$ pF.

Solution   The numerical values of the circuit parameters for this particular MOSFET are identical with the parameter values of the triode used in the example of Sec. 8-12.   The solution of this example is therefore the same as that given in Sec. 8-12.   Hence

$$(A_V)_{\text{second stage}} = -48.6$$
and
$$(A_V)_{\text{first stage}} = 38.8/143.3°$$

14-7   THE COMMON–DRAIN AMPLIFIER, OR SOURCE FOLLOWER

The CD-amplifier connection shown in Fig. 14-17 is analogous to the cathode follower discussed in Sec. 8-14.   The voltage gain of this circuit is given by Eq. (8-53), or in FET notation,

$$A_V = \frac{(g_m + j\omega C_{gs})R_s}{1 + (g_m + g_d + j\omega C_T)R_s} \tag{14-25}$$

where $C_T \equiv C_{gs} + C_{ds} + C_{sn}$, and C_{sn} represents the capacitance from source to ground.

At low frequencies the gain reduces to

$$A_V \approx \frac{g_m R_s}{1 + (g_m + g_d)R_s} \tag{14-26}$$

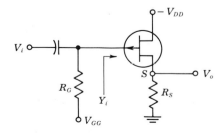

Fig. 14-17   Source-follower circuit.

Note that the amplification is positive and has a value less than unity.   If $g_m R_s \gg 1$, then $A_V \approx g_m/(g_m + g_d) = \mu/(\mu + 1)$.

Input Admittance   The source follower offers the important advantage of lower input capacitance than the CS amplifier.   The input admittance Y_i is given by Eq. (8-55), or

$$Y_i = j\omega C_{gd} + j\omega C_{gs}(1 - A_V) \tag{14-27}$$

Output Admittance   The output admittance Y_o, with R_s considered external to the amplifier, is given by Eq. (8-58), or

$$Y_o = g_m + g_d + j\omega C_T \tag{14-28}$$

At low frequencies the output resistance R_o is

$$R_o = \frac{1}{g_m + g_d} \approx \frac{1}{g_m} \tag{14-29}$$

since $g_m \gg g_d$.   For $g_m = 2$ mA/V, then $R_o = 500\ \Omega$.

The source follower is used for the same applications as the cathode follower, those requiring high input impedance and low output impedance (Sec. 8-8).

14-8   A GENERALIZED FET AMPLIFIER

The analysis of the CS amplifier with a source resistance R_s, the CG configuration, and the CD circuit at low frequencies is made by considering the generalized configuration in Fig. 14-18.   This circuit contains three independent signal sources, v_i in series with the gate, v_s in series with the source, and v_a in series with the drain.   For the CS amplifier, $v_s = v_a = 0$, and the output is v_{o1} taken at the drain.   For the CG circuit, $v_i = v_a = 0$, the signal is v_s with a source resistance R_s, and the output is v_{o1}.   For the source follower, $R_d = 0$, $v_s = v_a = 0$, the signal voltage is v_i, and the output is v_{o2} taken at the source. (The signal-source resistance is unimportant since it is in series with a gate which draws negligible current.)   If the effect of the ripple voltage in the power supply V_{DD} is to be investigated, v_a will be included in the circuit to represent these small changes in V_{DD}.

The Output from the Drain   From the analysis given in Secs. 8-6 and 8-8 we obtain the Thévenin's equivalent circuit from drain to ground (Fig. 14-19a) and from source to ground (Fig. 14-19b).   From the former circuit we conclude that *"looking into the drain"* of the FET we see (*for small-signal operation*) *an equivalent circuit consisting of two generators in series, one of $-\mu$ times the gate-signal voltage v_i and the second $(\mu + 1)$ times the source-signal voltage v_s and the resistance $r_d + (\mu + 1)R_s$.*   Note that the voltage v_s and the resistance in the source lead are both multiplied by the same factor, $\mu + 1$.

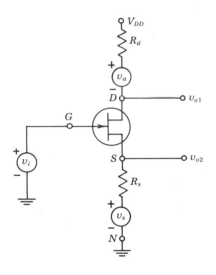

Fig. 14-18 A generalized FET amplifier.

The CS Amplifier with an Unbypassed Source Resistance From Fig. 14-19a, with $v_s = v_a = 0$, we obtain for the voltage gain, $A_V \equiv v_{o1}/v_i$,

$$A_V = \frac{-\mu R_d}{r_d + (\mu + 1)R_s + R_d} = \frac{-g_m R_d}{1 + g_m R_s + g_d(R_s + R_d)} \tag{14-30}$$

Note that, for $R_s = 0$, this result reduces to that given in Eq. (14-21), with Z_L replaced by R_d. The minus sign indicates a 180° phase shift between input and output.

The resistance R_o, looking into the drain, is increased by $(\mu + 1)R_s$ from its value r_d for $R_s = 0$. The net output resistance R'_o, taking R_d into account, is

$$R'_o = [r_d + (\mu + 1)R_s] \| R_d \tag{14-31}$$

We observe that the addition of R_s reduces the voltage gain and increases the output impedance. The input impedance is in excess of 100 M since the gate junction is reverse-biased.

The CG Amplifier From Fig. 14-19a, with $v_i = v_a = 0$, we obtain for the voltage gain, $A_V \equiv v_{o1}/v_s$,

$$A_V = \frac{(\mu + 1)R_d}{r_d + (\mu + 1)R_s + R_d} = \frac{(g_m + g_d)R_d}{1 + g_m R_s + g_d(R_s + R_d)} \tag{14-32}$$

Since A_V is a positive number, there is no phase shift between input and output. Also, since $g_m \gg g_d$, the magnitude of the amplification is approximately the same as for the CS amplifier with $R_s \neq 0$.

The output resistance R'_o is given by Eq. (14-31), and unless R_s is quite small, R'_o will be much larger than $r_d \| R_d$. The input impedance R'_i between source and ground is obtained by inspection of Fig. 14-19b:

$$R'_i = \left(\frac{r_d + R_d}{\mu + 1}\right) \| R_s \tag{14-33}$$

The common-gate amplifier with its low input resistance and high output resistance has few applications. The CG circuit at high frequencies is considered in Prob. 14-11.

The Output from the Source   From Fig. 14-19b we conclude that *"looking into the source" of the FET we see (for small-signal operation) an equivalent circuit consisting of two generators in series, one of value $\mu/(\mu + 1)$ times the gate-signal voltage v_i and the second $1/(\mu + 1)$ times the drain-signal voltage v_a and a resistance $(r_d + R_d)/(\mu + 1)$. Note that the voltage v_a and the resistance in the drain circuit are both divided by the same factor, $\mu + 1$.*

The CD Amplifier   The voltage gain A_V of the source follower is obtained, by inspection, from Fig. 14-19b, with $v_s = v_a = 0$ and $R_d = 0$:

$$A_V \equiv \frac{v_{o2}}{v_i} = \frac{\mu R_s/(\mu + 1)}{r_d/(\mu + 1) + R_s} = \frac{g_m R_s}{1 + (g_m + g_d)R_s} \tag{14-34}$$

Note that this expression agrees with Eq. (14-26), obtained by setting $\omega = 0$ into the high-frequency formula for A_V. If $R_d \neq 0$, then A_V in Eq. (14-34) is modified only by the addition of the term $g_d R_d$ to the denominator.

The output impedance R_o of the source follower at low frequencies (with $R_d = 0$ and with R_s considered external to the amplifier) is, from Fig. 14-19b,

$$R_o = \frac{r_d}{\mu + 1} = \frac{1}{g_m + g_d} \tag{14-35}$$

which agrees with Eq. (14-29). The output impedance R_o', taking R_s into account, is $R_o' = R_o \| R_s$.

14-9   BIASING THE FET

The selection of an appropriate operating point (I_D, V_{GS}, V_{DS}) for a FET amplifier stage is determined by considerations similar to those given to tubes

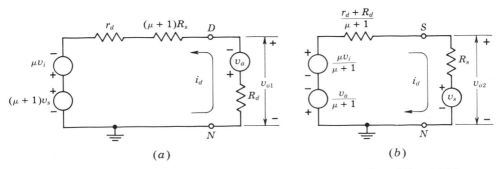

                  (a)   (b)

Fig. 14-19   The equivalent circuits for the generalized amplifier of Fig. 14-18 "looking into" (a) the drain and (b) the source. Note that $\mu = r_d g_m$.

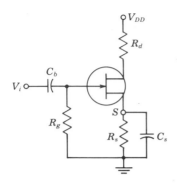

Fig. 14-20   Source self-bias circuit.

and transistors, as discussed in Sec. 7-13 and Chap. 10.   These considerations
are output-voltage swing, distortion, power dissipation, voltage gain, and drift
of drain current.   In most cases it is not possible to satisfy all desired specifications simultaneously.   In this section we examine several biasing circuits
for field-effect devices.

Source Self-bias   The configuration shown in Fig. 14-20 is the same as
that considered in connection with the biasing of vacuum tubes.   It can be
used to bias junction FET devices or depletion-mode MOS transistors.   For
a specified drain current I_D, the corresponding gate-to-source voltage V_{GS} can
be obtained either using Eq. (14-8) or from the plotted drain or transfer
characteristics.   Since the gate current is negligible, the source resistance R_s
can be found as the ratio of V_{GS} to the desired I_D.

EXAMPLE   The amplifier of Fig. 14-20 utilizes an n-channel FET for which
$V_P = -2.0$ V, $g_{mo} = 1.60$ mA/V, and $I_{DSS} = 1.65$ mA.   It is desired to bias the
circuit at $I_D = 0.8$ mA, using $V_{DD} = 24$ V.   Assume $r_d \gg R_d$.   Find (a) V_{GS},
(b) g_m, (c) R_s, (d) R_d, such that the voltage gain is at least 20 dB, with R_s bypassed
with a very large capacitance C_s.

Solution   *a.* Using Eq. (14-8), we have $0.8 = 1.65(1 + V_{GS}/2.0)^2$.   Solving,
$V_{GS} = -0.62$ V.

   b. Equation (14-18) now yields

$$g_m = 1.60 \left(1 - \frac{0.62}{2.0} \right) = 1.11 \text{ mA/V}$$

   c. $R_s = - \dfrac{V_{GS}}{I_D} = \dfrac{0.62}{0.8} = 0.77 \text{ K} = 770 \text{ }\Omega$

   d. Since 20 dB corresponds to a voltage gain of 10, then $A_V = g_m R_d \geq 10$, or

$$R_d \geq \frac{10}{1.11} = 9 \text{ K}$$

Biasing for Zero Current Drift[11]   Figure 14-21 shows the dependence of the transfer characteristics on temperature.   Observe from this figure that there exists a value of V_{GS} for which $I_D = I_Q$ does not change with temperature T. It is therefore possible to bias a field-effect transistor for zero drain-current drift.   An explanation of this effect is possible if we note that two factors affect the variation of drain current with T.   The first factor is the decrease of majority-carrier mobility with temperature.   As T increases, the lattice ions vibrate more vigorously, and hence the carriers cannot move as freely in the crystalline structure.   Thus, for a given field strength, their velocity is decreased, and this reduces the current.   It has been found[12] that the reduction in I_D is 0.7 percent/°C at a temperature of 25°C.

The second factor is the decrease of the width of the gate-to-channel barrier with increasing temperature.   This allows I_D to increase, and it has been found that the increase in I_D is equivalent to a change of 2.2 mV/°C in $|V_{GS}|$.   This is a similar phenomenon to that which gives a bipolar transistor a change of $|V_{BE}|$ of 2.5 mV/°C, as discussed in Sec. 6-7.

Since a change in gate voltage ΔV_{GS} causes a change in drain current of $g_m \Delta V_{GS}$, then the condition for zero drift is

$$0.007|I_D| = 0.0022 g_m \tag{14-36}$$

or

$$\frac{|I_D|}{g_m} = 0.314 \text{ V} \tag{14-37}$$

If we substitute Eqs. (14-8), (14-18), and (14-19) in Eq. (14-36), we obtain

$$|V_P| - |V_{GS}| = 0.63 \text{ V} \qquad \text{at } T = 25°C \tag{14-38}$$

Equation (14-38) gives the value of V_{GS} for zero drift if V_P is known.   If $V_P = 0.63$ V, $V_{GS} = 0$ and $I_D = I_{DSS}$.   From Eqs. (14-8), (14-18), and (14-38),

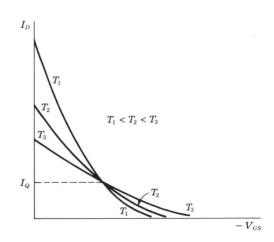

Fig. 14-21   Transfer characteristics for an *n*-channel FET as a function of temperature T.

$$I_D = I_{DSS} \left(\frac{0.63}{V_P}\right)^2 \tag{14-39}$$

and

$$g_m = g_{mo} \frac{0.63}{|V_P|} \tag{14-40}$$

Equations (14-39) and (14-40) can be used to specify the drain current and transconductance for zero drift of I_D with T. The parameters V_P, I_{DSS}, and g_{mo} in Eqs. (14-38) to (14-40) are measured at $T = 25°C$.

EXAMPLE It is desired to bias the amplifier stage of the previous example for zero drain-current drift. If $R_d = 10$ K, find (a) I_D for zero drift, (b) V_{GS}, (c) R_s, (d) the voltage gain, with R_s bypassed with a very large capacitance C_s.

Solution a. From Eq. (14-39),

$$I_D = 1.65 \left(\frac{0.63}{2}\right)^2 = 0.165 \text{ mA} = 165 \text{ } \mu A$$

b. From Eq. (14-38),

$$V_{GS} = -1.37 \text{ V}$$

c. Since $V_{GS} = -I_D R_s$,

$$R_s = \frac{1.37}{0.165} \text{ K} = 8.3 \text{ K}$$

d. From Eq. (14-40), we have

$$g_m = 1.60 \left(\frac{0.63}{2}\right) = 0.50 \text{ mA/V}$$

Hence $A_V \approx g_m R_d = 0.50 \times 10 = 5.0$.

We thus see that zero drift has been obtained at the expense of g_m and voltage gain, which are now one-half their values in the previous example.

Biasing against Device Variation FET manufacturers usually supply information on the maximum and minimum values of I_{DSS} and V_P at room temperature. They also supply data to correct these quantities for temperature variations. The transfer characteristics for a given type of n-channel FET may appear as in Fig. 14-22a, where the top and bottom curves are for extreme values of temperature and device variation. Assume that, on the basis of considerations previously discussed, it is necessary to bias the device at a drain current which will not drift outside of $I_D = I_A$ and $I_D = I_B$. Then the bias line $V_{GS} = -I_D R_s$ must intersect the transfer characteristics between the points A and B, as indicated in Fig. 14-22a. The slope of the bias line is determined by the source resistance R_s. For any transfer characteristic between the two extremes indicated, the current I_Q is such that $I_A < I_Q < I_B$, as desired.

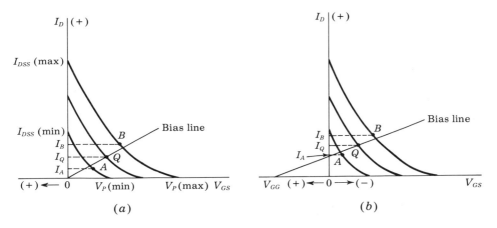

(a)   (b)

Fig. 14-22 Maximum and minimum transfer curves for an n-channel FET. The drain current must lie between I_A and I_B. The bias line can be drawn through the origin for the current limits indicated in (a), but this is not possible for the currents specified in (b).

Consider the physical situation indicated in Fig. 14-22b, where a line drawn to pass between points A and B does not pass through the origin. This bias line satisfies the equation

$$V_{GS} = V_{GG} - I_D R_s \tag{14-41}$$

Such a bias relationship may be obtained by adding a fixed bias to the gate in addition to the source self-bias, as indicated in Fig. 14-23a. A circuit requiring only one power supply and which can satisfy Eq. (14-41) is shown

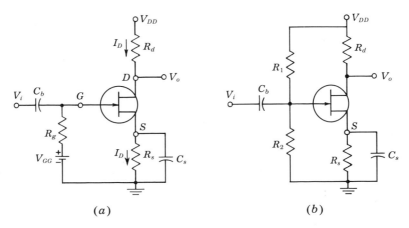

(a)   (b)

Fig. 14-23 (a) Biasing a FET with a fixed-bias V_{GG} in addition to self-bias through R_s. (b) A single power-supply configuration which is equivalent to the circuit in (a).

in Fig. 14-23b.   For this circuit

$$V_{GG} = \frac{R_2 V_{DD}}{R_1 + R_2} \qquad R_g = \frac{R_1 R_2}{R_1 + R_2}$$

We have assumed that the gate current is negligible.   It is also possible for V_{GG} to fall in the reverse-biased region so that the line in Fig. 14-22b intersects the axis of abscissa to the right of the origin.   Under these circumstances two separate supply voltages must be used.

EXAMPLE   FET 2N3684 is used in the circuit of Fig. 14-23b.   For this n-channel device the manufacturer specifies $V_P(\min) = -2$ V, $V_P(\max) = -5$ V, $I_{DSS}(\min) = 1.6$ mA, and $I_{DSS}(\max) = 7.05$ mA.   The extreme transfer curves are plotted in Fig. 14-24.   It is desired to bias the circuit so that $I_D(\min) = 0.8$ mA $= I_A$ and $I_D(\max) = 1.2$ mA $= I_B$ for $V_{DD} = 24$ V.   Find (a) V_{GG} and R_s, (b) the range of possible values in I_D if $R_s = 3.3$ K and $V_{GG} = 0$.

Solution   a. The bias line will lie between A and B as indicated if it is drawn to pass through the two points $V_{GS} = 0$, $I_D = 0.9$ mA, and $V_{GS} = -4$ V, $I_D = 1.1$ mA.   The slope of this line determines R_s, or

$$R_s = \frac{4 - 0}{1.1 - 0.9} = 20 \text{ K}$$

Then, from the first point and Eq. (14-41), we find

$$V_{GG} = I_D R_s = (0.9)(20) = 18 \text{ V}$$

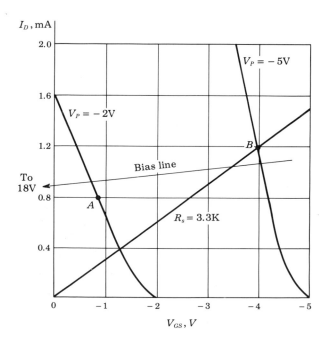

Fig. 14-24   Extreme transfer curves for the 2N3684 field-effect transistor. (Courtesy of Union Carbide Corporation.)

b. If $R_s = 3.3$ K, we see from the curves that $I_D(\text{min}) = 0.4$ mA and $I_D(\text{max}) = 1.2$ mA. The minimum current is far below the specified value of 0.8 mA.

Biasing the Enhancement MOSFET   The self-bias technique of Fig. 14-20 cannot be used to establish an operating point for the enhancement-type MOSFET because the voltage drop across R_s is in a direction to reverse-bias the gate, and a forward gate bias is required. The circuit of Fig. 14-25a can be used, and for this case we have $V_{GS} = V_{DS}$, since no current flows through R_f. If for reasons of linearity in device operation or maximum output voltage it is desired that $V_{GS} \neq V_{DS}$, then the circuit of Fig. 14-25b is suitable. We note that $V_{GS} = [R_1/(R_1 + R_f)]V_{DS}$. Both circuits discussed here offer the advantages of dc stabilization through the feedback introduced with R_f. However, the input impedance is reduced because, by Miller's theorem (Sec. 12-9), R_f corresponds to an equivalent resistance $R_i = R_f/(1 - A_V)$ shunting the amplifier input.

Finally, note that the circuit of Fig. 14-23b could also be used with the enhancement MOSFET, but the dc stability introduced in Fig. 14-25 through the feedback resistor R_f would then be missing.

14-10   UNIPOLAR–BIPOLAR CIRCUIT APPLICATIONS[12]

The main advantages of the unipolar transistor, or FET, are the very high input impedance, no offset voltage, and low noise. For these reasons a FET is most useful in a low-level high-input-impedance circuit, such as a signal chopper or the first stage of a unipolar-bipolar cascade combination. In this section we consider the advantages of some representative FET-bipolar transistor or FET-FET combinations.

Source Follower with Constant-current Supply   Consider the source follower of Fig. 14-17, where the g_m of the FET is 1 mA/V at $I_D = 1$ mA. In order to have $A_V \geq 0.98$, then, by Eq. (14-26), $R_s \geq 49$ K, provided $g_m \gg g_d$.

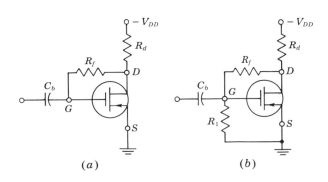

Fig. 14-25 (a) Drain-to-gate bias circuit for enhancement-mode MOS transistors; (b) improved version of (a).

(a) (b)

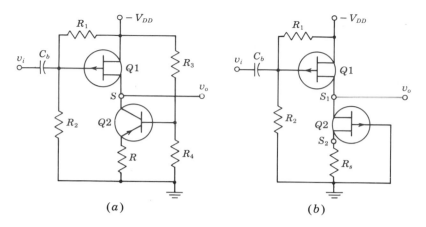

Fig. 14-26 A source follower with (a) a bipolar transistor and (b) a FET constant-current supply.

It is clear that the drain supply must exceed 49 V. Since most FETs have low breakdown voltages, it might be impractical to obtain $A_V \geq 0.98$ with this circuit.

This difficulty is circumvented in the configuration of Fig. 14-26a, which shows a source follower with the constant-current supply circuit discussed in Sec. 12-12. Here the effective source resistance of $Q1$ is the output impedance of $Q2$, whose value is given by Eq. (12-51). Since this dynamic source resistance is very high, then A_V approaches the maximum value of $\mu/(\mu + 1)$. Similarly, the source follower of Fig. 14-26b makes use of the high dynamic resistance $R'_s = r_d + (\mu + 1)R_s$ in the source circuit of $Q1$.

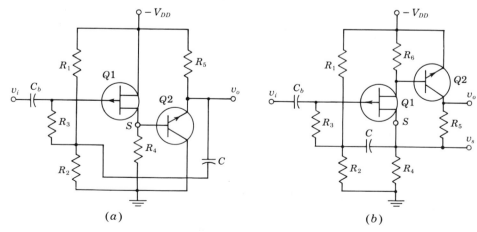

Fig. 14-27 Bootstrap circuits for very high input impedance.

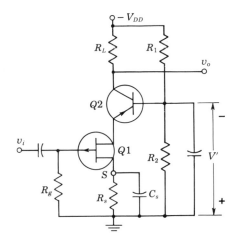

Fig. 14-28 Direct-coupled cascode circuit.

Bootstrap FET Circuits for Very High Input Impedance The input resistance in the circuits of Fig. 14-26 is essentially $R_1\|R_2$. If very high input impedance is desired, the bootstrap principle discussed in Sec. 12-10 must be invoked. The circuits of Fig. 14-27 employ a FET source follower with a bootstrapped bias network which allows input impedances on the order of tens of megohms to be obtained. In Fig. 14-27a, the output circuit is an emitter follower, and a voltage gain close to unity is possible. In Fig. 14-27b, the output is taken from the collector circuit of $Q2$, and hence this circuit is a low-noise high-input-impedance amplifier with $A_V = v_o/v_i > 1$. Expressions for A_V and also for v_s/v_i are given in Prob. 14-30.

The Cascode Amplifier Circuit This configuration is a version of the cascode circuit discussed in Secs. 8-10 and 12-11. In Fig. 14-28 a common-source FET drives a common-base bipolar transistor. The FET is biased at high I_D, thus giving high values of g_m. The advantage of this circuit is that the drain voltage V_{DD} can be high since the FET drain-to-source voltage $< V'$. A large supply V_{DD} allows the resistance R_L to be high, thus giving a large voltage gain and output swing. The cascode amplifier offers good isolation between output and input and is useful for high-frequency amplification.

14-11 THE FET AS A VOLTAGE–VARIABLE RESISTOR[13] (VVR)

In most linear applications of field-effect transistors the device is operated in the constant-current portion of its output characteristics. We now consider FET transistor operation in the region before pinch-off, where V_{DS} is small. In this region the FET is useful as a voltage-controlled resistor; i.e., the drain-to-source resistance is controlled by the bias voltage V_{GS}. In such an applica-

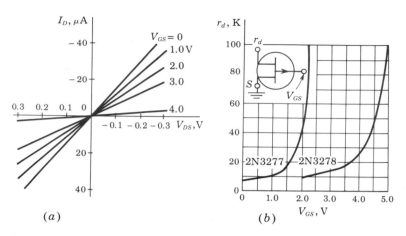

Fig. 14-29 (a) FET low-level drain characteristics for 2N3278.
(b) Small-signal FET resistance variation with applied gate voltage.
(Courtesy of Fairchild Semiconductor Company.)

tion the FET is also referred to as a *voltage-variable resistor* (VVR) or *voltage-dependent resistor* (VDR).

Figure 14-29a shows the low-level bidirectional characteristics of a FET. The slope of these characteristics gives r_d as a function of V_{GS}. Figure 14-29a has been extended into the third quadrant to give an idea of device linearity around $V_{DS} = 0$.

In our treatment of the junction FET characteristics in Sec. 14-3 we derive Eq. (14-5), which gives the drain-to-source conductance $g_d = I_D/V_{DS}$ for small values of V_{DS}. From this equation we have

$$g_d = g_{do}\left[1 - \left(\frac{V_{GS}}{V_P}\right)^{\frac{1}{2}}\right] \tag{14-42}$$

where g_{do} is the value of the drain conductance when the bias is zero. In Ref. 4 it is shown that g_{do} is equal to the value of the FET transconductance g_m measured for $V_{GS} = 0$ and for a drain voltage V_{DS} higher than the pinch-off voltage V_P. Variation of r_d with V_{GS} is plotted in Fig. 14-29b for the 2N3277 and 2N3278 FETs. The variation of r_d with V_{GS} can be closely approximated by the empirical expression

$$r_d = \frac{r_o}{1 - KV_{GS}} \tag{14-43}$$

where r_o = drain resistance at zero gate bias
  K = a constant, dependent upon FET type
  V_{GS} = gate-to-source voltage

Applications of the VVR Since the FET operated as described above acts like a variable passive resistor, it finds applications in many areas where

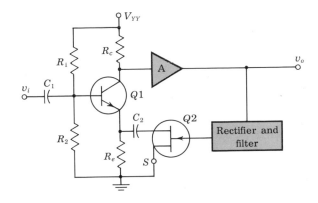

Fig. 14-30 AGC amplifier using the FET as a voltage-variable resistor.

this property is useful.   The VVR, for example, can be used to vary the voltage gain of a multistage amplifier A as the signal level is increased.   This action is called AGC, or *automatic gain control.*   A typical arrangement is shown in Fig. 14-30.   The signal is taken at a high-level point, rectified, and filtered to produce a dc voltage proportional to the output-signal level.   This voltage is applied to the gate of $Q2$, thus causing the ac resistance between the drain and source to change, as shown in Fig. 14-29b.   We thus may cause the gain of transistor $Q1$ to decrease as the output-signal level increases.   The dc bias conditions of $Q1$ are not affected by $Q2$ since $Q2$ is isolated from $Q1$ by means of capacitor C_2.

14-12   THE UNIJUNCTION TRANSISTOR

Another device whose construction is similar to that of the FET is indicated in Fig. 14-31.   A bar of high-resistivity n-type silicon of typical dimensions $8 \times 10 \times 35$ mils, called the base B, has attached to it at opposite ends two ohmic contacts, $B1$ and $B2$.   A 3-mil aluminum wire, called the *emitter E,*

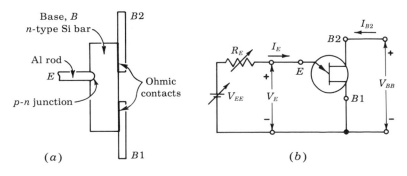

Fig. 14-31 Unijunction transistor. (a) Constructional details; (b) circuit symbol.

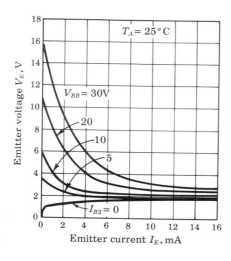

Fig. 14-32 Unijunction input character-istics for types 2N489 to 2N494. (Courtesy of General Electric Company.)

is alloyed to the base to form a *p-n* rectifying junction. This device was originally described in the literature as the *double-base diode,* but is now commercially available under the designation *unijunction transistor* (UJT). The standard symbol for this device is shown in Fig. 14-31*b*. Note that the emitter arrow is inclined and points toward $B1$ whereas the ohmic contacts $B1$ and $B2$ are brought out at right angles to the line which represents the base.

The principal constructional difference between the FET and the UJT is that the gate surface of the former is much larger than the emitter junction of the latter. The main operational difference between the two devices is that the FET is normally operated with the gate junction reverse-biased, whereas the useful behavior of the UJT occurs when the emitter is forward-biased.

As usually employed, a fixed interbase potential V_{BB} is applied between $B1$ and $B2$. The most important characteristic of the UJT is that of the input diode between E and $B1$. If $B2$ is open-circuited so that $I_{B2} = 0$, then the input volt-ampere relationship is that of the usual *p-n* junction diode as given by Eq. (6-31). In Fig. 14-32 the input current-voltage characteristics are plotted for $I_{B2} = 0$ and also for fixed values of interbase voltage V_{BB}. Each of the latter curves is seen to have a negative-resistance characteristic. A qualitative explanation of the physical origin of the negative resistance is given in Ref. 14. The principal application of the UJT is as a switch which allows the rapid discharge of a capacitor (Ref. 13).

REFERENCES

1. Shockley, W.: A Unipolar Field-effect Transistor, *Proc. IRE,* vol. 40, pp. 1365–1376, November, 1952.

Dacey, G. C., and I. M. Ross: The Field Effect Transistor, *Bell System Tech. J.,* vol. 34, pp. 1149–1189, November, 1955.

Wallmark, J. T., and H. Johnson: "Field-effect Transistors," Prentice-Hall, Inc., Englewood Cliffs, N.J., 1966.
Sevin, L. J.: "Field-effect Transistors," McGraw-Hill Book Company, New York, 1965.

2. Millman, J., and H. Taub: "Pulse, Digital, and Switching Waveforms," sec. 17-20, McGraw-Hill Book Company, New York, 1965.

3. Wallmark, J. T., and H. Johnson: "Field-effect Transistors," p. 115, Prentice-Hall, Inc., Englewood Cliffs, N.J., 1966.

4. Sevin, L. J.: "Field-effect Transistors," pp. 13–17, McGraw-Hill Book Company, New York, 1965.

5. Halladay, H. E., and A. Van Der Ziel: DC Characteristics of Junction Gate Field-effect Transistors, *IEEE Trans. Electron Devices*, vol. ED-13, no. 6, pp. 531–532, June, 1966.

6. Ref. 4, p. 21.

7. Ref. 4, p. 23.

8. Ref. 4, p. 34.

9. Ref. 3, pp. 187–215.

10. Ref. 3, pp. 256–259.

11. Hoerni, J. A., and B. Weir: Conditions for a Temperature Compensated Silicon Field Effect Transistor, *Proc. IEEE*, vol. 51, pp. 1058–1059, July, 1963.
Evans, L. L.: Biasing FETs for Zero dc Drift, *Electrotechnol.*, August, 1964, pp. 93–96.

12. Gosling, W.: A Drift Compensated FET-Bipolar Hybrid Amplifier, *Proc. IEEE*, vol. 53, pp. 323–324, March, 1965.

13. Bilotti, A.: Operation of a MOS Transistor as a Voltage Variable Resistor, *Proc. IEEE*, vol. 54, pp. 1093–1094, August, 1966.

14. Millman, J., and H. Taub: "Pulse, Digital, and Switching Waveforms," secs. 12-3 and 13-13, McGraw-Hill Book Company, New York, 1965.

15/INTEGRATED CIRCUITS

An integrated circuit consists of a single-crystal chip of silicon, typically 50 by 50 mils in cross section, containing both active and passive elements and their interconnections. Such circuits are produced by the same processes used to fabricate individual transistors and diodes. These processes include epitaxial growth, masked impurity diffusion, oxide growth, and oxide etching, using photolithography for pattern definition. A method of batch processing is used which offers excellent repeatability and is adaptable to the production of large numbers of integrated circuits at low cost. The main benefits derived from this technology are high reliability, size reduction, and low cost, as compared with the use of discrete components interconnected by conventional techniques. In this chapter we describe the basic processes involved in fabricating an integrated circuit.

15-1 BASIC MONOLITHIC INTEGRATED CIRCUITS[1,2]

We now examine in some detail the various techniques and processes required to obtain the circuit of Fig. 15-1a in an integrated form, as shown in Fig. 15-1b. This configuration is called a monolithic integrated circuit because it is formed on a single silicon chip. The word "monolithic" is derived from the Greek *monos*, meaning "single," and *lithos*, meaning "stone." Thus a monolithic circuit is built into a single stone, or single crystal.

In this section we describe qualitatively a complete epitaxial-diffused fabrication process for integrated circuits. In subsequent sections we examine in more detail the epitaxial, photographic, and diffusion processes involved. The circuit of Fig. 15-1a is chosen for discussion because it contains typical components: a resistor, diodes,

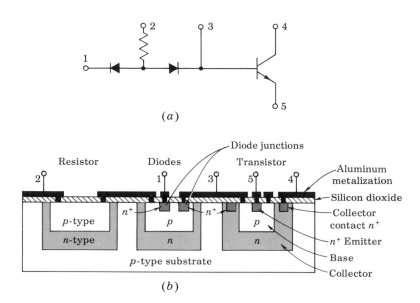

Fig. 15-1   (a) A circuit containing a resistor, two diodes, and a transistor.   (b) Cross-sectional view of the circuit in (a) when transformed into a monolithic form.   (After Phillips.[2])

and a transistor.   These elements (and also capacitors, with small values of capacitances) are the components encountered in integrated circuits.   The monolithic circuit is formed by the steps indicated in Fig. 15-2 and described below.

Step 1.   Epitaxial Growth   An n-type epitaxial layer, typically 25 microns thick, is grown onto a p-type substrate which has a resistivity of typically 10 Ω-cm, corresponding to $N_A = 1.4 \times 10^{15}$ atoms/cm^3.   The epitaxial process described in Sec. 15-2 indicates that the resistivity of the n-type epitaxial layer can be chosen independently of that of the substrate.   Values of from 0.1 to 0.5 Ω-cm are chosen for the n-type layer.   In contrast to the situation depicted in Fig. 15-2a, the epitaxial process is used with discrete transistors to obtain a thin high-resistivity layer on a low-resistivity substrate of *the same polarity*.   After polishing and cleaning, a thin layer (0.5 micron = 5,000 Å) of oxide, SiO$_2$, is formed over the entire wafer, as shown in Fig. 15-2a.   The SiO$_2$ is grown by exposing the epitaxial layer to an oxygen atmosphere while being heated to about 1000°C.   Silicon dioxide has the fundamental property of preventing the diffusion of impurities through it.   Use of this property is made in the following steps.

Step 2.   Isolation Diffusion   In Fig. 15-2b the wafer is shown with the oxide removed in four different places on the surface.   This removal is accom-

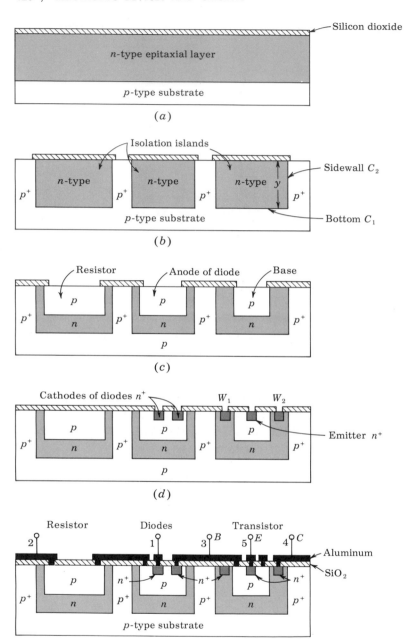

Fig. 15-2 The steps involved in fabricating a monolithic circuit (not drawn to scale). (a) Epitaxial growth; (b) isolation diffusion; (c) base diffusion; (d) emitter diffusion; (e) aluminum metalization.

plished by means of a photolithographic etching process described in Sec. 15-3. The remaining SiO_2 serves as a mask for the diffusion of acceptor impurities (in this case, boron). The wafer is now subjected to the so-called *isolation diffusion*, which takes place at the temperature and for the time interval required for the *p*-type impurities to penetrate the *n*-type epitaxial layer and reach the *p*-type substrate. We thus leave the shaded *n*-type regions in Fig. 15-2*b*. These sections are called *isolation islands*, or *isolated regions*, because they are separated by two back-to-back *p-n* junctions. Their purpose is to allow electrical isolation between different circuit components. For example, it will become apparent later in this section that a different isolation region must be used for the collector of each separate transistor. The *p*-type substrate must always be held at a negative potential with respect to the isolation islands in order that the *p-n* junctions be reverse-biased. If these diodes were to become forward-biased in an operating circuit, then, of course, the isolation would be lost.

It should be noted that the concentration of acceptor atoms ($N_A \approx 5 \times 10^{20}$ cm^{-3}) in the region between isolation islands will generally be much higher (and hence indicated as p^+) than in the *p*-type substrate. The reason for this higher density is to prevent the depletion region of the reverse-biased isolation-to-substrate junction from extending into p^+-type material (Sec. 6-9) and possibly connecting two isolation islands.

Parasitic Capacitance It is now important to consider that these isolation regions, or junctions, are connected by a significant barrier, or transition capacitance C_{Ts}, to the *p*-type substrate, which capacitance can affect the operation of the circuit. Since C_{Ts} is an undesirable by-product of the isolation process, it is called the *parasitic capacitance*.

The parasitic capacitance is the sum of two components, the capacitance C_1 from the bottom of the *n*-type region to the substrate (Fig. 15-2*b*) and C_2 from the sidewalls of the isolation islands to the p^+ region. The bottom component, C_1, results from an essentially step junction due to the epitaxial growth (Sec. 15-2) and hence varies inversely as the square root of the voltage V between the isolation region and the substrate (Sec. 6-9). The sidewall capacitance C_2 is associated with a diffused graded junction, and it varies as $V^{-\frac{1}{3}}$. For this component the junction area is equal to the perimeter of the isolation region times the thickness y of the epitaxial *n*-type layer. The total capacitance is of the order of a few picofarads.

Step 3. Base Diffusion During this process a new layer of oxide is formed over the wafer, and the photolithographic process is used again to create the pattern of openings shown in Fig. 15-2*c*. The *p*-type impurities (boron) are diffused through these openings. In this way are formed the transistor base regions as well as resistors, the anode of diodes, and junction capacitors (if any). It is important to control the depth of this diffusion so that it is shallow and does not penetrate to the substrate. The resistivity of the base layer will generally be much higher than that of the isolation regions.

Step 4. Emitter Diffusion A layer of oxide is again formed over the entire surface, and the masking and etching processes are used again to open windows in the p-type regions, as shown in Fig. 15-2d. Through these openings are diffused n-type impurities (phosphorus) for the formation of transistor emitters, the cathode regions for diodes, and junction capacitors.

Additional windows (such as W_1 and W_2 in Fig. 15-2d) are often made into the n regions to which a lead is to be connected, using aluminum as the ohmic contact, or interconnecting metal. During the diffusion of phosphorus a heavy concentration (called n^+) is formed at the points where contact with aluminum is to be made. Aluminum is a p-type impurity in silicon, and a large concentration of phosphorus prevents the formation of a p-n junction when the aluminum is alloyed to form an ohmic contact.[4]

Step 5. Aluminum Metalization All p-n junctions and resistors for the circuit of Fig. 15-1a have been formed in the previous steps. It is now necessary to interconnect the various components of the integrated circuit as dictated by the desired circuit. In order to make these connections, a fourth set of windows is opened into a newly formed SiO_2 layer, as shown in Fig. 15-2e, at the points where contact is to be made. The interconnections are made first, using vacuum deposition of a thin even coating of aluminum over the entire wafer. The photoresist technique is now applied to etch away all undesired aluminum areas, leaving the desired pattern of interconnections shown in Fig. 15-2e between resistors, diodes, and transistors.

In production a large number (several hundred) of identical circuits such as that of Fig. 15-1a are manufactured simultaneously on a single wafer. After the metalization process has been completed, the wafer is scribed with a diamond-tipped tool and separated into individual chips. Each chip is then mounted on a ceramic wafer and is attached to a suitable header. The package leads are connected to the integrated circuit by stitch bonding[1] of a 1-mil aluminum or gold wire from the terminal pad on the circuit to the package lead (Fig. 15-2b).

Summary In this section the epitaxial-diffused method of fabricating integrated circuits is described. We have encountered the following processes:

1. Epitaxy
2. Silicon dioxide growth
3. Photoetching
4. Diffusion
5. Vacuum evaporation of aluminum

Using these techniques, it is possible to produce the following elements on the same chip: transistors, diodes, resistors, capacitors, and aluminum interconnections. Other techniques have been used also, such as the triple-diffused

process and the diffused-collector process.[1]   The method just described, however, is in more general use because of a number of inherent advantages.[1]

15-2   EPITAXIAL GROWTH[1]

The epitaxial process produces a thin film of single-crystal silicon from the
gas phase upon an existing crystal wafer of the same material.   The epitaxial
layer may be either p-type or n-type.   The growth of an epitaxial film with
impurity atoms of boron being trapped in the growing film is shown in Fig. 15-3.
    The basic chemical reaction used to describe the epitaxial growth of pure
silicon is the hydrogen reduction of silicon tetrachloride:

$$SiCl_4 + 2H_2 \xrightleftharpoons{1200°C} Si + 4HCl \tag{15-1}$$

Since it is required to produce epitaxial films of specific impurity concentrations, it is necessary to introduce impurities such as phosphine for n-type
doping or biborane for p-type doping into the silicon tetrachloride–hydrogen
gas stream.   An apparatus for the production of an epitaxial layer is shown in
Fig. 15-4.   In this system a long cylindrical quartz tube is encircled by a
radio-frequency induction coil.   The silicon wafers are placed on a rectangular
graphite rod called a *boat*.   The boat is inserted in the reaction chamber, and
the graphite is heated inductively to about 1200°C.   At the input of the
reaction chamber a control console permits the introduction of various gases
required for the growth of appropriate epitaxial layers.   Thus it is possible
to form an almost abrupt step p-n junction similar to the junction shown in
Fig. 6-12.

Fig. 15-3   The epitaxial
growth of an epitaxial film
showing impurity (boron)
atoms being trapped in the
growing film.   (Courtesy of
Motorola, Inc.[1])

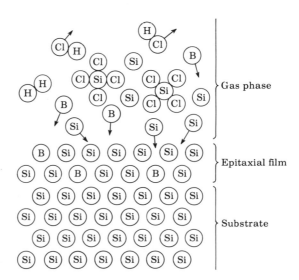

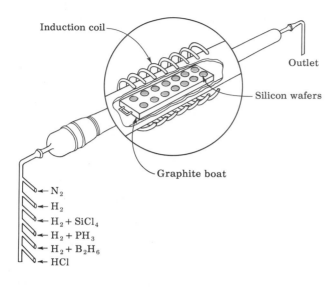

Fig. 15-4   A diagrammatic representation of a system for production growth of silicon epitaxial films. (Courtesy of Motorola, Inc.[1])

15-3   MASKING AND ETCHING[1]

The monolithic technique described in Sec. 15-1 requires the selective removal of the SiO_2 to form openings through which impurities may be diffused.   The photoetching method used for this removal is illustrated in Fig. 15-5.   During the photolithographic process the wafer is coated with a uniform film of a photosensitive emulsion (such as the Kodak *photoresist* KPR).   A large black-and-white layout of the desired pattern of openings is made and then reduced photographically.   This negative, or stencil, of the required dimensions is placed as a mask over the photoresist, as shown in Fig. 15-5*a*.   By exposing the KPR to ultraviolet light through the mask, the photoresist becomes polymerized under the transparent regions of the stencil.   The mask is now removed, and the wafer is "developed" by using a chemical (such as trichloroethylene) which dissolves the unexposed (unpolymerized) portions of the photoresist film and leaves the surface pattern as shown in Fig. 15-5*b*.

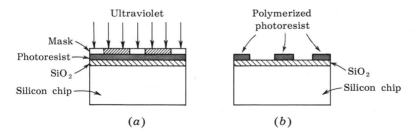

Fig. 15-5   Photoetching technique.   (a) Masking and exposure to ultraviolet radiation.   (b) The photoresist after development.

The emulsion which was not removed in development is now *fixed*, or *cured*, so that it becomes resistant to the corrosive etches used next. The chip is immersed in an etching solution of hydrofluoric acid, which removes the oxide from the areas through which dopants are to be diffused. Those portions of the SiO_2 which are protected by the photoresist are unaffected by the acid. After etching and diffusion of impurities, the resist mask is removed (stripped) with a chemical solvent (hot H_2SO_4) and by means of a mechanical abrasion process.

15-4   DIFFUSION OF IMPURITIES[5]

The most important process in the fabrication of integrated circuits is the diffusion of impurities into the silicon chip. We now examine the basic theory connected with this process. The solution to the diffusion equation will give the effect of temperature and time on the diffusion distribution.

The Diffusion Law The continuity equation derived in Sec. 5-9 for charged particles is equally valid for neutral atoms. Since diffusion does not involve electron-hole recombination or generation ($\tau_p = \infty$) and since no electric field is present ($\mathcal{E} = 0$), Eq. (5-46) now reduces to

$$\frac{\partial N}{\partial t} = D \frac{\partial^2 N}{\partial x^2} \tag{15-2}$$

where N is the particle concentration in atoms per unit volume as a function of distance x from the surface and time t, and D is the diffusion constant in area per unit time. This diffusion equation is also called Fick's second law.

The Complementary Error Function If an intrinsic silicon wafer is exposed to a volume of gas having a uniform concentration N_o atoms per unit volume of n-type impurities, such as phosphorus, these atoms will diffuse into the silicon crystal, and their distribution will be as shown in Fig. 15-6a. If the diffusion is allowed to proceed for extremely long times, the silicon will become uniformly doped with N_o phosphorus atoms per unit volume. The basic assumptions made here are that the surface concentration of impurity atoms remains at N_o for all diffusion times and that $N(x) = 0$ at $t = 0$ for $x > 0$.

If Eq. (15-2) is solved and the above boundary conditions are applied,

$$N(x, t) = N_o\left(1 - \text{erf}\,\frac{x}{2\,\sqrt{Dt}}\right) = N_o\,\text{erfc}\,\frac{x}{2\,\sqrt{Dt}} \tag{15-3}$$

where erfc y means the error-function complement of y, and the *error function* of y is defined by

$$\text{erf}\,y \equiv \frac{2}{\sqrt{\pi}} \int_0^y \epsilon^{-\lambda^2}\,d\lambda \tag{15-4}$$

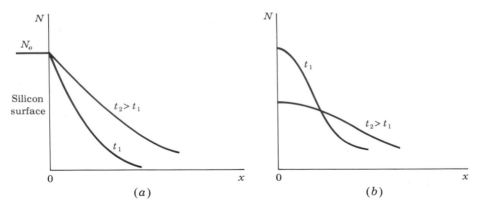

Fig. 15-6 The concentration N as a function of distance x into a silicon chip for two values t_1 and t_2 of the diffusion time. (a) The surface concentration is held constant at N_o per unit volume. (b) The total number of atoms on the surface is held constant at Q per unit area.

and is tabulated in Ref. 3. The function erfc $y = 1 - \text{erf } y$ is plotted in Fig. 15-7.

The Gaussian Distribution If a specific number Q of impurity atoms per unit area are deposited on one face of the wafer and then if the material is heated, the impurity atoms will again diffuse into the silicon. When the boundary conditions $\int_0^\infty N(x)\, dx = Q$ for all times and $N(x) = 0$ at $t = 0$ for $x > 0$ are applied to Eq. (15-2), we find

$$N(x, t) = \frac{Q}{\sqrt{\pi D t}}\, \epsilon^{-x^2/4Dt} \tag{15-5}$$

Equation (15-5) is known as the Gaussian distribution, and is plotted in Fig. 15-6b for two times. It is noted from the figure that as time increases, the surface concentration decreases. The area under each curve is the same, however, since this area represents the total amount of impurity being diffused, and this is a constant amount Q. Note that in Eqs. (15-3) and (15-5) time t and the diffusion constant D appear only as a product Dt.

Solid Solubility[1,6] The designer of integrated circuits may wish to produce a specific diffusion profile (say the complementary error function of an n-type impurity). In deciding which of the available impurities (such as phosphorus, arsenic, antimony) can be used, it is necessary to know if the number of atoms per unit volume required by the specific profile of Eq. (15-3) is less than the diffusant's *solid solubility*. The solid solubility is defined as the maximum concentration N_o of the element which can be dissolved in the solid silicon

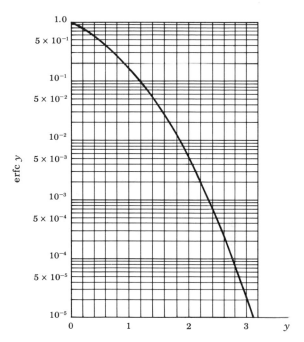

Fig. 15-7 The complementary error function plotted on semilogarithmic paper.

at a given temperature.   Figure 15-8 shows solid solubilities of some impurity elements.   It can be seen that since for phosphorus the solid solubility is approximately 10^{21} atoms/cm^3, and for pure silicon we have 5×10^{22} atoms/ cm^3, the maximum concentration of phosphorus in silicon is 2 percent.   For most of the other impurity elements the solubility is a small fraction of 1 percent.

Diffusion Coefficients   Temperature affects the diffusion process because higher temperatures give more energy, and thus higher velocities, to the dif-

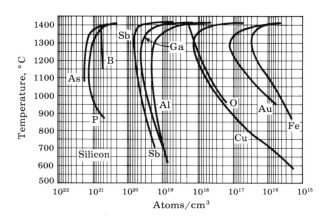

Fig. 15-8 Solid solubilities of some impurity elements in silicon. (After Trumbore,[6] courtesy of Motorola, Inc.[1])

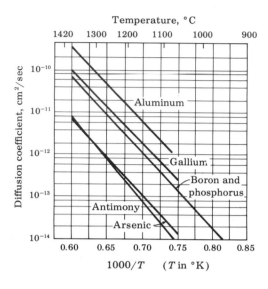

Fig. 15-9 Diffusion coefficients as a function of temperature for some impurity elements in silicon. (After Fuller and Ditzenberger,[5] courtesy of Motorola, Inc.[1])

fusant atoms. It is clear that the diffusion coefficient is a function of temperature, as shown in Fig. 15-9. From this figure it can be deduced that the diffusion coefficient could be doubled for a few degrees increase in temperature. This critical dependence of D on temperature has forced the development of accurately controlled diffusion furnaces, where temperatures in the range of 1000 to 1300°C can be held to a tolerance of ± 0.5°C or better. Since time t in Eqs. (15-3) and (15-5) appears in the product Dt, an increase in either diffusion constant or diffusion time has the same effect on diffusant density.

Note from Fig. 15-9 that the diffusion coefficients, for the same temperature, of the n-type impurities (antimony and arsenic) are lower than the coefficients for the p-type impurities (gallium and aluminum), but that phosphorus (n-type) and boron (p-type) have the same diffusion coefficients.

Typical Diffusion Apparatus Reasonable diffusion times require high diffusion temperatures (~ 1000°C). Therefore a high-temperature diffusion furnace, having a closely controlled temperature over the length (20 in.) of the hot zone of the furnace, is standard equipment in a facility for the fabrication of integrated circuits. Impurity sources used in connection with diffusion furnaces can be gases, liquids, or solids. For example, $POCl_3$, which is a liquid, is often used as a source of phosphorus. Figure 15-10 shows the apparatus used for $POCl_3$ diffusion. In this apparatus a carrier gas (mixture of nitrogen and oxygen) bubbles through the liquid-diffusant source and carries the diffusant atoms to the silicon wafers. Using this process, we obtain the complementary-error-function distribution of Eq. (15-3). A two-step procedure is used to obtain the Gaussian distribution. The first step involves *predeposition*, carried out at about 900°C, followed by *drive-in* at about 1100°C.

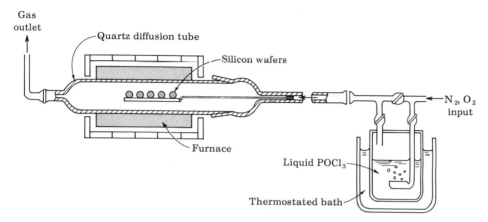

Fig. 15-10 Schematic representation of typical apparatus for $POCl_3$ diffusion. (Courtesy of Motorola, Inc.[1])

EXAMPLE A uniformly doped n-type silicon substrate of 0.5 Ω-cm resistivity is subjected to a boron diffusion with constant surface concentration of 5×10^{18} cm^{-3}. It is desired to form a p-n junction at a depth of 2.7 microns. At what temperature should this diffusion be carried out if it is to be completed in 2 hr?

Solution The concentration N of boron is high at the surface and falls off with distance into the silicon, as indicated in Fig. 15-6a. At that distance $x = x_j$ at which N equals the concentration n of the doped silicon wafer, the net impurity density is zero. For $x < x_j$, the net impurity density is positive, and for $x > x_j$, it is negative. Hence x_j represents the distance from the surface at which a junction is formed. We first find n from Eq. (5-2):

$$n = \frac{\sigma}{\mu_n e} = \frac{1}{(0.5)(1,300)(1.60 \times 10^{-19})} = 0.96 \times 10^{16}\ cm^{-3}$$

where all distances are expressed in centimeters and the mobility μ_n for silicon is taken from Table 5-1, on page 98. The junction is formed when $N = n$. For

$$\text{erfc } y = \frac{N}{N_o} = \frac{n}{N_o} = \frac{0.96 \times 10^{16}}{5 \times 10^{18}} = 1.92 \times 10^{-3}$$

we find from Fig. 15-7 that $y = 2.2$. Hence

$$2.2 = \frac{x_j}{2\sqrt{Dt}} = \frac{2.7 \times 10^{-4}}{2\sqrt{D \times 2 \times 3,600}}$$

Solving for D, we obtain $D = 5.2 \times 10^{-13}\ cm^2/sec$. This value of diffusion constant for boron is obtained from Fig. 15-9 at $T = 1130°C$.

15-5   TRANSISTORS FOR MONOLITHIC CIRCUITS[1,7]

A planar transistor made for monolithic integrated circuits, using epitaxy and diffusion, is shown in Fig. 15-11a.   Here the collector is electrically separated from the substrate by the reverse-biased isolation diodes.   Since the anode of the isolation diode covers the back of the entire wafer, it is necessary to make the collector contact on the top, as shown in Fig. 15-11a.   It is now clear that the isolation diode of the integrated transistor has two undesirable effects: it adds a parasitic shunt capacitance to the collector and a leakage current path.   In addition, the necessity for a top connection for the collector increases the collector-current path and thus increases the collector resistance and V_{CE}(sat).   All these undesirable effects are absent from the discrete epitaxial transistor shown in Fig. 15-11b.   What is then the advantage of the monolithic transistor?   A significant improvement in performance arises from the fact that integrated transistors are located physically close together and their electrical characteristics are closely matched.   For example, integrated transistors spaced within 30 mils (0.03 in.) have V_{BE} matching of better than 5 mV with less than 10 μV/°C drift and an h_{FE} match of ± 10 percent. These matched transistors make excellent difference amplifiers (Sec. 12-12).

The electrical characteristics of a transistor depend on the size and geometry of the transistor, doping levels, diffusion schedules, and the basic silicon material.   Of all these factors the size and geometry offer the greatest flexibility for design.   The doping levels and diffusion schedules are determined by the standard processing schedule used for the desired transistors in the integrated circuit.

Impurity Profiles for Integrated Transistors[1]   Figure 15-12 shows a typical impurity profile for a monolithic integrated circuit transistor.   The back-

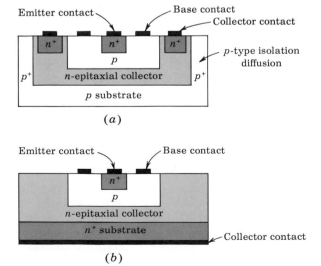

Fig. 15-11   Comparison of cross sections of (a) a monolithic integrated circuit transistor with (b) a discrete planar epitaxial transistor.   [For a top view of the transistor in (a) see Fig. 15-13.]

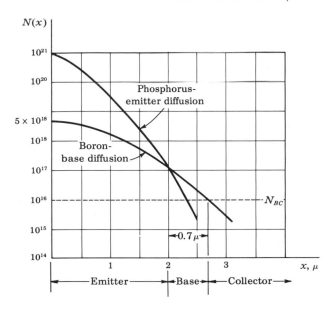

Fig. 15-12 A typical impurity profile in a monolithic integrated transistor. [Note that $N(x)$ is plotted on a logarithmic scale.]

ground, or epitaxial-collector, concentration N_{BC} is shown as a dashed line in Fig. 15-12. The base diffusion of p-type impurities (boron) starts with a surface concentration of 5×10^{18} atoms/cm³, and is diffused to a depth of 2.7 microns, where the collector junction is formed. The emitter diffusion (phosphorus) starts from a much higher surface concentration (close to the solid solubility) of about 10^{21} atoms/cm³, and is diffused to a depth of 2 microns, where the emitter junction is formed. This junction corresponds to the intersection of the base and emitter distribution of impurities. We now see that the base thickness for this monolithic transistor is 0.7 micron. The emitter-to-base junction is usually treated as a step junction, whereas the base-to-collector junction is considered a graded junction.

EXAMPLE (a) Obtain the equations for the impurity profiles in Fig. 15-12. (b) If the phosphorus diffusion is conducted at 1100°C, how long should be allowed for this diffusion?

Solution a. The base diffusion specifications are exactly those given in the example on page 429, where we find (with x expressed in microns) that

$$y = 2.2 = \frac{2.7}{2\sqrt{Dt}}$$

or

$$2\sqrt{Dt} = \frac{2.7}{2.2} = 1.23 \text{ microns}$$

Hence the boron profile, given by Eq. (15-3), is

$$N_B = 5 \times 10^{18} \text{ erfc } \frac{x}{1.23}$$

The emitter junction is formed at $x = 2$ microns, and the boron concentration here is

$$N_B = 5 \times 10^{18} \text{ erfc } \frac{2}{1.23} = 5 \times 10^{18} \times 2 \times 10^{-2}$$

$$= 1.0 \times 10^{17} \text{ cm}^{-3}$$

The phosphorus concentration N_P is given by

$$N_P = 10^{21} \text{ erfc } \frac{x}{2 \sqrt{Dt}}$$

At $x = 2$, $N_P = N_B = 1.0 \times 10^{17}$, so that

$$\text{erfc } \frac{2}{2 \sqrt{Dt}} = \frac{1.0 \times 10^{17}}{10^{21}} = 1.0 \times 10^{-4}$$

From Fig. 15-7, $2/(2 \sqrt{Dt}) = 2.7$ and $2 \sqrt{Dt} = 0.74$ micron. Hence the phosphorus profile is given by

$$N_P = 10^{21} \text{ erfc } \frac{x}{0.74}$$

b. From Fig. 15-9, at $T = 1100°C$, $D = 3.8 \times 10^{-13}$ cm²/sec. Solving for t from $2 \sqrt{Dt} = 0.74$ micron, we obtain

$$t = \frac{(0.37 \times 10^{-4})^2}{3.8 \times 10^{-13}} = 3,600 \text{ sec} = 60 \text{ min}$$

Monolithic Transistor Layout[1,2]   The physical size of a transistor determines the parasitic isolation capacitance as well as the junction capacitance. It is therefore necessary to use small-geometry transistors if the integrated circuit is designed to operate at high frequencies or high switching speeds. The geometry of a typical monolithic transistor is shown in Fig. 15-13.   The emitter rectangle measures 1 by 1.5 mils, and is diffused into a 2.5- by 4.0-mil base region.   Contact to the base is made through two metalized stripes on either side of the emitter.   The rectangular metalized area forms the ohmic contact to the collector region.   The rectangular collector contact of this transistor reduces the saturation resistance.   The substrate in this structure is located about 1 mil below the surface.   Since diffusion proceeds in three dimensions, it is clear that the *lateral-diffusion* distance will also be 1 mil.   The dashed rectangle in Fig. 15-13 represents the substrate area and is 6.5 by 8 mils.   A summary of the electrical properties[2] of this transistor for both the 0.5- and the 0.1-Ω-cm collectors is given in Table 15-1.

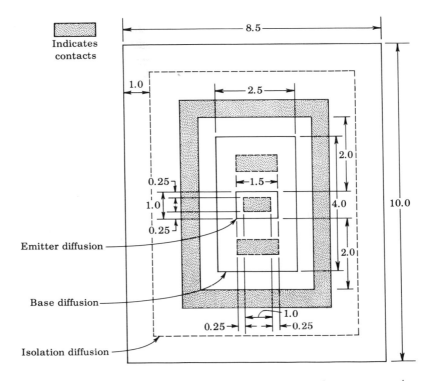

Fig. 15-13 A typical double-base stripe geometry of an integrated-circuit transistor. Dimensions are in mils. (For a side view of the transistor see Fig. 15-11.) (Courtesy of *Motorola Monitor*.)

TABLE 15-1   Characteristics for 1- by 1.5-mil double-base stripe monolithic transistors[2]

Transistor parameter	0.5 Ω-cm	0.1 Ω-cm†
BV_{CBO}, V	55	25
BV_{EBO}, V	7	5.5
BV_{CEO}, V	23	14
C_{Te} (forward bias), pF	6	10
C_{Te} at 0.5 V, pF	1.5	2.5
C_{Te} at 5 V, pF	0.7	1.5
h_{FE} at 10 mA	50	50
R_{CS}, Ω	75	15
V_{CE}(sat) at 5 mA, V	0.5	0.26
V_{BE} at 10 mA, V	0.85	0.85
f_T at 5 V, 5 mA, MHz	440	520

† Gold-doped.

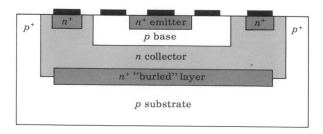

Fig. 15-14 Utilization of "buried" n^+ layer to reduce collector series resistance.

Buried Layer[1]   We noted above that the integrated transistor, because of the top collector contact, has a higher collector series resistance than a similar discrete-type transistor.   One common method of reducing the collector series resistance is by means of a heavily doped n^+ "buried" layer sandwiched between the p-type substrate and the n-type epitaxial collector, as shown in Fig. 15-14.   The buried-layer structure can be obtained by diffusing the n^+ layer into the substrate before the n-type epitaxial collector is grown or by selectively growing the n^+-type layer, using masked epitaxial techniques.

We are now in a position to appreciate one of the reasons why the integrated transistor is usually of the n-p-n type.   Since the collector region is subjected to heating during the base and emitter diffusions, it is necessary that the diffusion coefficient of the collector impurities be as small as possible, to avoid movement of the collector junction.   Since Fig. 15-9 shows that n-type impurities have smaller values of diffusion constant D than p-type impurities, the collector is usually n-type.   In addition, the solid solubility of some n-type impurities is higher than that of any p-type impurity, thus allowing heavier doping of the n^+-type emitter and other n^+ regions.

15-6   MONOLITHIC DIODES[1]

The diodes utilized in integrated circuits are made by using transistor structures in one of five possible connections (Prob. 15-9).   The three most popular diode structures are shown in Fig. 15-15.   They are obtained from a transistor

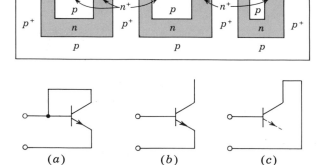

Fig. 15-15 Cross section of various diode structures. (a) Emitter-base diode with collector shorted to base; (b) emitter-base diode with collector open; and (c) collector-base diode (no emitter diffusion).

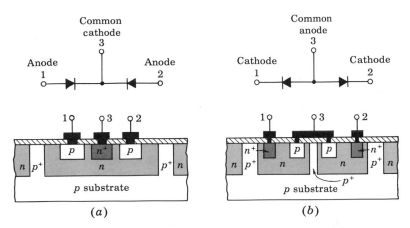

Fig. 15-16 Diode pairs. (a) Common-cathode pair, and (b) common-anode pair, using collector-base diodes.

structure by using (a) the emitter-base diode, with the collector short-circuited to the base; (b) the emitter-base diode, with the collector open; and (c) the collector-base diode, with the emitter open-circuited (or not fabricated at all). The choice of the diode type used depends upon the application and circuit performance desired. Collector-base diodes have the higher collector-base voltage-breakdown rating of the collector junction ($\sim$12 V minimum), and they are suitable for common-cathode diode arrays diffused within a single isolation island, as shown in Fig. 15-16a. Common-anode arrays can also be made with the collector-base diffusion, as shown in Fig. 15-16b. A separate isolation is required for each diode, and the anodes are connected by metalization.

The emitter-base diffusion is very popular for the fabrication of diodes provided that the reverse-voltage requirement of the circuit does not exceed the lower base-emitter breakdown voltage ($\sim$7 V). Common-anode arrays can easily be made with the emitter-base diffusion by using a multiple-emitter transistor within a single isolation area, as shown in Fig. 15-17. The collector

Fig. 15-17 A multiple-emitter n-p-n transistor. (a) Schematic, (b) monolithic surface pattern. If the base is connected to the collector, the result is a multiple-cathode diode structure with a common anode.

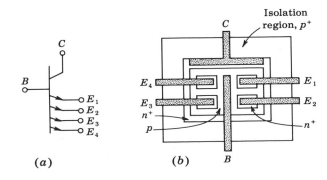

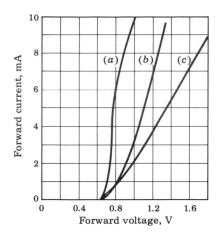

Fig. 15-18 Typical diode volt-ampere characteristics for the three diode types of Fig. 15-15. (a) Base-emitter (collector shorted to base); (b) base-emitter (collector open); (c) collector-base (emitter open). (Courtesy of Fairchild Semiconductor.[8])

may be either open or shorted to the base. The diode pair in Fig. 15-1 is constructed in this manner, with the collector floating (open).

Diode Characteristics The forward volt-ampere characteristics of the three diode types discussed above are shown in Fig. 15-18. It will be observed that the diode-connected transistor (emitter-base diode with collector shorted to the base) provides the highest conduction for a given forward voltage. The reverse recovery time for this diode is also smaller, one-third to one-fourth that of the collector-base diode.

15-7   INTEGRATED RESISTORS[1]

A resistor in a monolithic integrated circuit is very often obtained by utilizing the bulk resistivity of one of the diffused areas. The p-type base diffusion is most commonly used, although the n-type emitter diffusion is also employed. Since these diffusion layers are very thin, it is convenient to define a quantity known as the *sheet resistance R_S*.

Sheet Resistance If, in Fig. 15-19, the width w equals the length l, we have a square l by l of material with resistivity ρ, thickness y, and cross-sectional area $A = ly$. The resistance of this conductor (in ohms per square) is

$$R_S = \frac{\rho l}{ly} = \frac{\rho}{y} \tag{15-6}$$

Note that R_S is independent of the size of the square. Typically, the sheet resistance of the base and emitter diffusions whose profiles are given in Fig. 15-12 are 200 Ω/square and 2.2 Ω/square, respectively.

The construction of a base-diffused resistor is shown in Fig. 15-1 and is repeated in Fig. 15-20a. A top view of this resistor is shown in Fig. 15-20b.

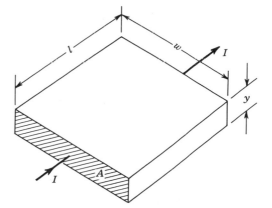

Fig. 15-19 Pertaining to sheet
resistance, ohms per square.

The resistance value may be computed from

$$R = \frac{\rho l}{yw} = R_s \frac{l}{w} \tag{15-7}$$

where l and w are the length and width of the diffused area, as shown in
the top view.   For example, a base-diffused-resistor stripe 1 mil wide and 10
mils long contains 10 (1 by 1 mil) squares, and its value is $10 \times 200 = 2,000 \ \Omega$.
Empirical[1,2] corrections for the end contacts are usually included in calculations
of R.

Resistance Values   Since the sheet resistance of the base and emitter
diffusions is fixed, the only variables available for diffused-resistor design are
stripe length and stripe width.   Stripe widths of less than one mil (0.001 in.)
are not normally used because a line-width variation of 0.0001 in. due to
mask drawing error or mask misalignment or photographic-resolution error
can result in 10 percent resistor-tolerance error.

The range of values obtainable with diffused resistors is limited by the
size of the area required by the resistor.   Practical range of resistance is 20 Ω

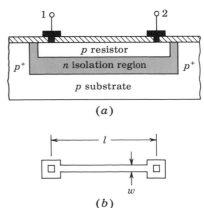

Fig. 15-20 A monolithic resistor. (a)
Cross-sectional view; (b) top view.

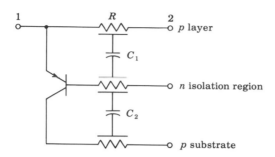

Fig. 15-21   The equivalent circuit of a diffused resistor.

to 30 K for a base-diffused resistor and 10 Ω to 1 K for emitter-diffused resistors.   The tolerance which results from profile variations and surface geometry errors[1] is as high as ± 10 percent of the nominal value at 25°C, with ratio tolerance of ± 3 percent.   For this reason the design of integrated circuits should, if possible, emphasize resistance ratios rather than absolute values.   The temperature coefficient for these heavily doped resistors is positive (for the same reason that gives a positive coefficient to the silicon sensistor, discussed in Sec. 10-9) and is $+0.06$ percent/°C from -55 to 0°C and $+0.20$ percent/°C from 0 to 125°C.

Equivalent Circuit   A model of the diffused resistor is shown in Fig. 15-21, where the parasitic capacitances of the base-isolation (C_1) and isolation-substrate (C_2) junctions are included.   In addition, it can be seen that a parasitic p-n-p transistor exists, with the substrate as collector, the isolation n-type region as base, and the resistor p-type material as the emitter.   Since the collector is reverse-biased, it is also necessary that the emitter be reverse-biased in order to keep the parasitic transistor at cutoff.   This condition is maintained by placing all resistors in the same isolation region and connecting the n-type isolation region surrounding the resistors to the *most positive* voltage present in the circuit.   Typical values of h_{fe} for this parasitic transistor range from 0.5 to 5.

Thin-film Resistors[1]   A technique of vapor thin-film deposition can also be used to fabricate resistors for integrated circuits.   The metal (usually nichrome, NiCr) film is deposited on the silicon dioxide layer, and masked etching is used to produce the desired geometry.   The metal resistor is then covered by an insulating layer, and apertures for the ohmic contacts are opened through this insulating layer.   Typical sheet-resistance values for nichrome thin-film resistors are 40 to 400 Ω/square, resulting in resistance values from about 20 Ω to 50 K.

15-8   INTEGRATED CAPACITORS AND INDUCTORS[1,2]

Capacitors in integrated circuits may be obtained by utilizing the transition capacitance of a reverse-biased p-n junction or by a thin-film technique.

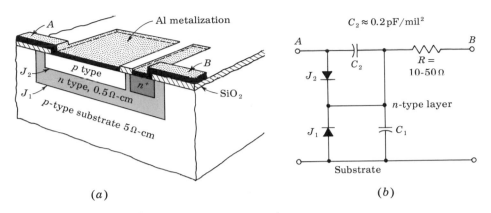

$$C_2 \approx 0.2\,\mathrm{pF/mil}^2$$

Fig. 15-22 (a) Junction monolithic capacitor. (b) Equivalent circuit. (Courtesy of Motorola, Inc.)

Junction Capacitors A cross-sectional view of a junction capacitor is shown in Fig. 15-22a. The capacitor is formed by the reverse-biased junction J_2, which separates the epitaxial n-type layer from the upper p-type diffusion area. An additional junction J_1 appears between the n-type epitaxial plane and the substrate, and a parasitic capacitance C_1 is associated with this reverse-biased junction. The equivalent circuit of the junction capacitor is shown in Fig. 15-22b, where the desired capacitance C_2 should be as large as possible relative to C_1. The value of C_2 depends on the junction area and impurity concentration. Since this junction is essentially abrupt, C_2 is given by Eq. (6-49). The series resistance R (10 to 50 Ω) represents the resistance of the n type layer.

It is clear that the substrate must be at the most negative voltage so as to minimize C_1 and isolate the capacitor from other elements by keeping junction J_1 reverse-biased. It should also be pointed out that the junction capacitor C_2 is polarized since the p-n junction J_2 must always be reverse-biased.

Thin-film Capacitors A metal-oxide-semiconductor (MOS) nonpolarized capacitor is indicated in Fig. 15-23a. This structure is a parallel-plate capa-

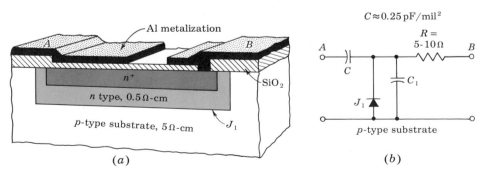

$$C \approx 0.25\,\mathrm{pF/mil}^2$$

Fig. 15-23 A MOS capacitor. (a) The structure and (b) the equivalent circuit.

TABLE 15-2   Integrated capacitor parameters

Characteristic	Diffused-junction capacitor	Thin-film MOS
Capacitance, pF/mil²..........	0.2	0.25–0.4
Maximum area, mil²..........	2×10^3	2×10^3
Maximum value, pF..........	400	800
Breakdown voltage, V..........	5–20	50–200
Voltage dependence..........	$kV^{-\frac{1}{2}}$	0
Tolerance, percent..........	±20	±20

citor with SiO_2 as the dielectric.   A surface thin film of metal (aluminum) is the top plate.   The bottom plate consists of the heavily doped n^+ region that is formed during the emitter diffusion.   A typical value for capacitance[8] is 0.4 pF/mil² for an oxide thickness of 500 Å, and the capacitance varies inversely with the thickness.

The equivalent circuit of the MOS capacitor is shown in Fig. 15-23b, where C_1 denotes the parasitic capacitance J_1 of the collector-substrate junction, and R is the small series resistance of the n^+ region.   Table 15-2 lists the range of possible values for the parameters of junction and MOS capacitors.

Inductors   No practical inductance values have been obtained at the present time (1967) on silicon substrates using semiconductor or thin-film techniques.   Therefore their use is avoided in circuit design wherever possible.   If an inductor is required, a discrete component is connected externally to the integrated circuit.

15-9   MONOLITHIC CIRCUIT LAYOUT[1,9]

In this section we describe how to transform the discrete circuit of Fig. 15-24a into the layout of the monolithic circuit shown in Fig. 15-25.   Circuits involving diodes and transistors, connected as in Fig. 15-24a, are called diode-transistor (DTL) *logic gates*.[10]

Design Rules for Monolithic Layout   The following 10 reasonable design rules are stated by Phillips:[9]

1. Redraw the schematic to satisfy the required pin connection with the minimum number of crossovers.
2. Determine the number of isolation islands from collector-potential considerations, and reduce the areas as much as possible.
3. Place all resistors having fixed potentials at one end in the same isolation island, and return that isolation island to the most positive potential in the circuit.
4. Connect the substrate to the most negative potential of the circuit.

5. In layout, allow an isolation border equal to twice the epitaxial thickness to allow for underdiffusion.

6. Use 1-mil widths for diffused emitter regions and $\frac{1}{2}$-mil widths for base contacts and spacings, and for collector contacts and spacings.

7. For resistors, use widest possible designs consistent with die-size limitations.

8. Always optimize the layout arrangement to maintain the smallest possible die size, and if necessary, compromise pin connections to achieve this.

9. Determine component geometries from the performance requirements of the circuit.

10. Keep all metalizing runs as short and as wide as possible, particularly at the emitter and collector output connections of the saturating transistor.

Pin Connections The circuit of Fig. 15-24a is redrawn in Fig. 15-24b, with the external leads labeled 1, 2, 3, . . . , 10 and arranged in the order in which they are connected to the header pins. The diagram reveals that the power-supply pins are grouped together, and also that the inputs are on adjacent pins. In general, the external connections are determined by the system in which the circuits are used.

Crossovers Very often the layout of a monolithic circuit requires two conducting paths (such as leads 5 and 6 in Fig. 15-24b) to cross over each other. This crossover cannot be made directly because it will result in electric contact between two parts of the circuit. Since all resistors are protected by the SiO₂ layer, any resistor may be used as a crossover region. In other words,

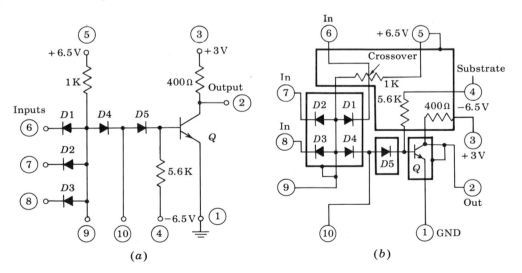

Fig. 15-24 (a) A DTL gate. (b) The schematic redrawn to indicate the 10 external connections arranged in the sequence in which they will be brought out to the header pins. The isolation regions are shown in heavy outline.

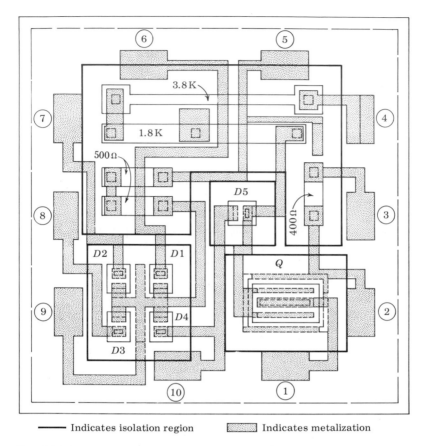

——— Indicates isolation region   ▨▨ Indicates metalization

Fig. 15-25 Monolithic design layout for the circuit of Fig. 15-24. (Courtesy of *Motorola Monitor*, Phoenix, Ariz.)

if aluminum metalization is run over a resistor, no electric contact will take place between the resistor and the aluminum.

Sometimes the layout is so complex that additional crossover points may be required. A diffused structure which allows a crossover is also possible.[1] This type of crossover should be avoided if at all possible because it requires a separate isolation region and it introduces undesired series resistance of the diffused region into the connection.

Isolation Islands The number of isolation islands is determined next. Since the transistor collector requires one isolation region, the heavy rectangle has been drawn in Fig. 15-24*b* around the transistor. It is shown connected to the output pin 2 because this isolation island also forms the transistor collector. Next, all resistors are placed in the same isolation island, and the island is then connected to the most positive voltage in the circuit, for reasons discussed in Sec. 15-7.

In order to determine the number of isolation regions required for the diodes, it is necessary first to establish which kind of diode will be fabricated. In this case, because of the low forward drop shown in Fig. 15-18, it was decided to make the common-anode diodes of the emitter-base type with the collector shorted to the base. Since the "collector" is at the "base" potential, it is required to have a single isolation island for the four common-anode diodes. Finally, the remaining diode is fabricated as an emitter-base diode, with the collector open-circuited, and thus it requires a separate isolation island.

The Fabrication Sequence   The final monolithic layout is determined by a trial-and-error process, having as its objective the smallest possible die size. This layout is shown in Fig. 15-25. The reader should identify the four isolation islands, the three resistors, the five diodes, and the transistor. It is

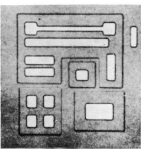

Isolation diffusion   Base diffusion

Fig. 15-26   Monolithic fabrication sequence for the circuit of Fig. 15-24. (Courtesy of *Motorola Monitor*, Phoenix, Ariz.)

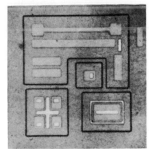

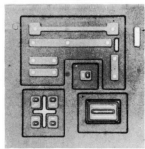

Emitter diffusion   Preohmic etch

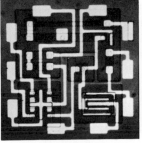

Metalization   Flat package assembly

interesting to note that the 5.6-K resistor has been achieved with a 2-mil-wide 1.8-K resistor in series with a 1-mil-wide 3.8-K resistor. In order to conserve space, the resistor was folded back on itself. In addition, two metalizing crossovers ran over this resistor.

From a layout such as shown in Fig. 15-25, the manufacturer produces the masks required for the fabrication of the monolithic integrated circuit. The production sequence which involves isolation, base, and emitter diffusions, preohmic etch, aluminum metalization, and the flat package assembly is shown in Fig. 15-26.

Large-scale Integration (LSI) The monolithic circuit layout shown in Fig. 15-25 contains one transistor, five diodes, and three resistors for a total of nine circuit elements. This number of elements per chip, or the component density, is determined primarily by cost considerations. Even if it were possible to fabricate and interconnect several hundred components per chip, the manufacturing cost per component would not necessarily decrease. The reason is that beyond a certain component density the cost per component increases again owing to circuit complexity, which tends to reduce the yield. At any given stage in the development of integrated-circuit techniques, there exists an optimum number of components per chip which will produce minimum cost per component.[11] In 1962, 10 components per circuit (chip) represented the optimum. In 1967 the optimum number is about 70. It is predicted[12] that by 1970 the optimum number will exceed 1,000. Large-scale integration (LSI) represents the process of fabricated large-component-density chips which represent complete subsystems or equipment components. A packaged LSI slice $2\frac{1}{2}$ in. square with 32 leads on each side is pictured in Ref. 12.

15-10   INTEGRATED FIELD–EFFECT TRANSISTORS[1,13]

The MOSFET is discussed in detail in Chap. 14. In this section we point out the advantages of this device as an integrated-circuit active element (Fig. 15-27).

Size Reduction The MOS integrated transistor typically occupies only 5 percent of the surface required by an epitaxial double-diffused transistor in a conventional integrated circuit. The double-base stripe 1- by 1.5-mil emitter integrated transistor normally requires about 10×9.5 mils of chip area, whereas the MOS requires 5 square mils.

Simple Fabrication Process Only one diffusion step is required to fabricate the MOS enhancement-type field-effect transistor. In this step (Fig. 15-27a) two heavily doped n-type regions are diffused into a lightly doped p-type substrate to form the drain and source. An insulating layer of oxide is grown, and holes are etched for the metal electrodes for the source

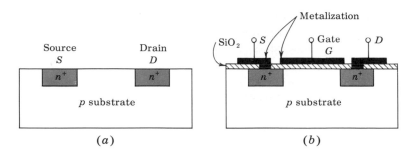

Fig. 15-27 An n-channel insulated-gate FET of the enhancement-mode type. (a) The source and drain are diffused into the substrate. (b) The completed device.

and drain. The metal for these contacts, as well as for the gate electrode, is then evaporated at the same time to complete the device shown in Fig. 15-27b.

Crossovers and Isolation Islands The crossovers between components of integrated MOS circuits are diffused at the same time as the source and drain. The resistive effects of crossover-diffused regions (with $R_S \approx 80\text{--}100 \ \Omega/\text{square}$) are negligible since these regions are in series with large-value load resistors of the order of 100 K normally used with FETs. Another important advantage is that no isolation regions are needed between MOS transistors because the p-n junctions are reverse-biased during the operation of the circuit.

The MOS as a Resistor for Integrated Circuits In our discussion of diffused resistors in Sec. 15-7, we show that 30 K is about the maximum resistance value possible (in 1967). Larger values may be obtained by using a MOS structure as shown in Fig. 15-28, where the gate and drain are tied together and a fixed voltage V_{DD} is applied between drain and ground. A

Fig. 15-28 The MOS as a resistor.

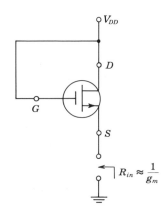

Thévenin's equivalent circuit looking into the source is obtained in Sec. 14-8. From Eq. (14-35) we find that the impedance seen looking into the source is approximately equal to $1/g_m$, assuming negligible drain conductance g_d. If, for example, $g_m = 10 \ \mu A/V$, we have $R = 1/g_m = 100 \ K$. This value of effective resistance requires approximately 5 square mils of active area as compared with 300 square mils of chip area to yield a diffused resistance of value 20 K.

15-11   ADDITIONAL ISOLATION METHODS

Electrical isolation between the different elements of a monolithic integrated circuit is accomplished by means of a diffusion which yields back-to-back *p-n* junctions, as indicated in Sec. 15-1. With the application of bias voltage to the substrate, these junctions represent reverse-biased diodes with a very high back resistance, thus providing adequate dc isolation. But since each *p-n* junction is also a capacitance, there remains that inevitable capacitive coupling between components and the substrate. These parasitic distributed capacitances thus limit monolithic integrated circuits to frequencies somewhat below those at which corresponding discrete circuits can operate.

Additional methods for achieving better isolation, and therefore improved frequency response, have been developed, and are discussed in this section.

Dielectric Isolation In this process[1,14] the diode-isolation concept is discarded completely. Instead, isolation, both electrical and physical, is achieved by means of a layer of solid dielectric which completely surrounds and separates the components from each other and from the common substrate. This passive layer can be silicon dioxide, silicon monoxide, ruby, or possibly a glazed ceramic substrate which is made thick enough so that its associated capacitance is negligible.

In a dielectric isolated integrated circuit it is possible to fabricate readily *p-n-p* and *n-p-n* transistors within the same silicon substrate. It is also simple to have both fast and charge-storage diodes and also both high- and low-frequency transistors in the same chip through selective gold diffusion—a process prohibited by conventional techniques because of the rapid rate at which gold diffuses through silicon unless impeded by a physical barrier such as a dielectric layer.

One isolation method employing silicon dioxide as the isolating material is the EPIC process,[12] developed by Motorola, Inc. This EPIC isolation method reduces parasitic capacitance by a factor of 10 or more. In addition, the insulating oxide precludes the need for a reverse bias between substrate and circuit elements. Breakdown voltage between circuit elements and substrate is in excess of 1,000 V, in contrast to the 20 V across an isolation junction.

Beam Leads The beam-lead concept[15] of Bell Telephone Laboratories was primarily developed to batch-fabricate semiconductor devices and integrated circuits.   This technique consists in depositing an array of thick (of the order of 1 mil) contacts on the surface of a slice of standard monolithic circuit, and then removing the excess semiconductor from under the contacts, thereby separating the individual devices and leaving them with semirigid beam leads cantilevered beyond the semiconductor.   The contacts serve not only as electrical leads, but also as the structural support for the devices; hence the name beam leads.   Chips of beam-lead circuits are mounted directly by leads, without 1-mil aluminum or gold wires.

Isolation within integrated circuits may be accomplished by the beam-

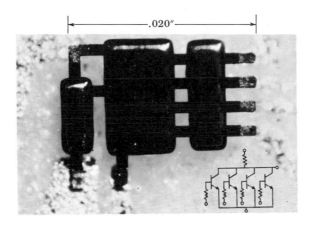

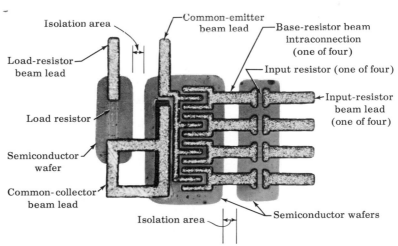

Fig. 15-29   The beam-lead isolation technique.   (a) Photomicrograph of logic circuit connected in a header.   (b) The underside of the same circuit, with the various elements identified.   (Courtesy of Bell Telephone Laboratories.)

lead structure. By etching away the unwanted silicon from under the beam leads which connect the devices on an integrated chip, isolated pads of silicon may be attained, interconnected by the beam leads. The only capacitive coupling between elements is then through the small metal-over-oxide overlay. This is much lower than the junction capacitance incurred with p-n junction-isolated monolithic circuits.

It should be pointed out that the dielectric and beam-lead isolation techniques involve additional process steps, and thus higher costs and possible reduction in yield of the manufacturing process.

Figure 15-29 shows photomicrographs of two different views of a logic circuit made using the beam-lead technique. The top photo shows the logic circuit connected in a header. The bottom photo shows the underside of the same circuit with the various elements identified. This device is made using conventional planar techniques to form the transistor and resistor regions. Electrical isolation is accomplished by removing all unwanted material between components. The beam leads then remain to support and intraconnect the isolated components.

Hybrid Circuits[1]   The hybrid circuit as opposed to the monolithic circuit consists of several component parts (transistors, diodes, resistors, capacitors, or complete monolithic circuits), all attached to the same ceramic substrate and employing wire bonding to achieve the interconnections. In these circuits electrical isolation is provided by the physical separation of the component parts, and in this respect hybrid circuits resemble beam-lead circuits.

REFERENCES

1. Motorola, Inc. (R. M. Warner, Jr., and J. N. Fordemwalt, eds.): "Integrated Circuits," McGraw-Hill Book Company, New York, 1965.

2. Phillips, A. B.: Monolithic Integrated Circuits, *IEEE Spectrum*, vol. 1, no. 6, pp. 83–101, June, 1964.

3. Jahnke, E., and F. Emde: "Tables of Functions," Dover Publications, New York, 1945.

4. Hunter, L. P.: "Handbook of Semiconductor Electronics," 2d ed., sec. 8, McGraw-Hill Book Company, New York, 1962.

5. Fuller, C. S., and J. A. Ditzenberger: Diffusion of Donor and Acceptor Elements in Silicon, *J. Appl. Phys.*, vol. 27, pp. 544–553, May, 1956.
   Barrer, P. M.: "Diffusion in and through Solids," Cambridge University Press, London, 1951.

6. Trumbore, F. A.: Solid Solubilities of Impurity Elements in Germanium and Silicon, *Bell System Tech. J.*, vol. 39, pp. 205–234, January, 1960.

7. King, D., and L. Stern: Designing Monolithic Integrated Circuits, *Semicond. Prod. Solid State Technol.*, March, 1965.

8. "Custom Microcircuit Design Handbook," Fairchild Semiconductor, Mountain View, Calif., 1963.

9. Phillips, A. B.: Designing Digital Monolithic Integrated Circuits, *Motorola Monitor*, vol. 2, no. 2, pp. 18–27, 1964.

10. Millman, J., and H. Taub: "Pulse, Digital, and Switching Waveforms," pp. 330–334, McGraw-Hill Book Company, New York, 1965.

11. Baker, O. R.: Aspects of Large Scale Integration, *1967 IEEE Intern. Conv. Dig.*, pp. 376–377, March, 1967.

12. Weber, S.: LSI: The Technologies Converge, *Electronics*, vol. 40, no. 4, pp. 124–127, February, 1967.

13. Farina, E. D., and D. Trotter: MOS Integrated Circuits, *Electronics*, vol. 38, no. 20, pp. 84–95, October, 1965.

14. Epic Process Isolates Integrated Circuit Elements with Silicon Dioxide, *Electro-Technol. (New York)*, July, 1964, p. 136.

15. Lepselter, M. P., et al.: Beam Leads and Integrated Circuits, *Proc. IEEE*, vol. 53, p. 405, April, 1965.
Lepselter, M. P.: Beam-lead Technology, *Bell System Tech. J.*, February, 1966, pp. 233–253.

16 / UNTUNED AMPLIFIERS

Frequently the need arises for amplifying a signal with a minimum of distortion. Under these circumstances the active devices involved must operate linearly. In the analysis of such circuits the first step is the replacement of the actual circuit by a linear model. Thereafter it becomes a matter of circuit analysis to determine the distortion produced by the transmission characteristics of the linear network.

The frequency range of the amplifiers discussed in this chapter extends from a few cycles per second (hertz), or possibly from zero, up to some tens of megahertz. The original impetus for the study of such wideband amplifiers was supplied because they were needed to amplify the pulses occurring in a television signal. Therefore such amplifiers are often referred to as *video amplifiers*. Basic amplifier circuits are discussed here. Modifications of these configurations to extend the frequency range of these amplifiers are considered in Ref. 1.

In this chapter, then, we consider the following problem: Given a low-level input waveform which is not necessarily sinusoidal but may contain frequency components from a few hertz to a few megahertz, how can this voltage signal be amplified with a minimum of distortion?

We also discuss many topics associated with the general problem of amplification, such as the classification of amplifiers, hum and noise in amplifiers, etc.

16-1 CLASSIFICATION OF AMPLIFIERS

Amplifiers are described in many ways, according to their frequency range, the method of operation, the ultimate use, the type of load, the method of interstage coupling, etc. The frequency classification

450

includes dc (from zero frequency), audio (20 Hz to 20 kHz), video or pulse (up to a few megahertz), radio-frequency (a few kilohertz to hundreds of megahertz), and ultrahigh-frequency (hundreds or thousands of megahertz) amplifiers.

The position of the quiescent point and the extent of the characteristic that is being used determine the method of operation. Whether the transistor or tube is operated as a Class A, Class AB, Class B, or Class C amplifier is determined from the following definitions.

Class A   A Class A amplifier is one in which the operating point and the input signal are such that the current in the output circuit (in the collector, plate, or drain electrode) flows at all times. A Class A amplifier operates essentially over a linear portion of its characteristic.

Class B   A Class B amplifier is one in which the operating point is at an extreme end of its characteristic, so that the quiescent power is very small. Hence either the quiescent current or the quiescent voltage is approximately zero. If the signal voltage is sinusoidal, amplification takes place for only one-half a cycle. For example, if the quiescent output-circuit current is zero, this current will remain zero for one-half a cycle.

Class AB   A Class AB amplifier is one operating between the two extremes defined for Class A and Class B. Hence the output signal is zero for part but less than one-half of an input sinusoidal signal cycle.

Class C   A Class C amplifier is one in which the operating point is chosen so that the output current (or voltage) is zero for more than one-half of an input sinusoidal signal cycle.

In the case of a vacuum-tube amplifier the suffix 1 may be added to the letter or letters of the class identification to denote that grid current does not flow during any part of the input cycle. The suffix 2 may be added to denote that grid current does flow during some part of the input cycle.

Amplifier Applications   The classification according to use includes voltage, power, current, or general-purpose amplifiers. In general, the load of an amplifier is an impedance. The two most important special cases are the idealized resistive load and the tuned circuit operating near its resonant frequency.

Class AB and Class B operation are used with untuned power amplifiers (Chap. 18), whereas Class C operation is used with tuned radio-frequency amplifiers. Many important waveshaping functions may be performed by Class B or C overdriven amplifiers. This chapter considers only the untuned audio or video voltage amplifier with a resistive load operated in Class A.

16-2   DISTORTION IN AMPLIFIERS

The application of a sinusoidal signal to the input of an ideal Class A amplifier will result in a sinusoidal output wave.   Generally, the output waveform is not an exact replica of the input-signal waveform because of various types of distortion that may arise, either from the inherent nonlinearity in the characteristics of the transistors or tubes or from the influence of the associated circuit.   The types of distortion that may exist either separately or simultaneously are called *nonlinear distortion, frequency distortion,* and *delay distortion.*

Nonlinear Distortion   This type of distortion results from the production of new frequencies in the output which are not present in the input signal. These new frequencies, or harmonics, result from the existence of a nonlinear dynamic curve for the active device; they are considered in some detail in Secs. 18-2 and 18-3.   This distortion is sometimes referred to as "amplitude distortion."

Frequency Distortion   This type of distortion exists when the signal components of different frequencies are amplified differently.   In either a transistor or a tube this distortion may be caused by the internal device capacitances, or it may arise because the associated circuit (for example, the coupling components or the load) is reactive.   Under these circumstances, the gain A is a complex number whose magnitude and phase angle depend upon the frequency of the impressed signal.   A plot of gain (magnitude) vs. frequency of an amplifier is called the *amplitude frequency-response characteristic.* If this plot is not a horizontal straight line over the range of frequencies under consideration, the circuit is said to exhibit frequency distortion over this range.

Delay Distortion   This distortion, also called *phase-shift distortion,* results from unequal phase shifts of signals of different frequencies.   This distortion is due to the fact that the phase angle of the complex gain A depends upon the frequency.

16-3   FREQUENCY RESPONSE OF AN AMPLIFIER

A criterion which may be used to compare one amplifier with another with respect to fidelity of reproduction of the input signal is suggested by the following considerations: Any arbitrary waveform of engineering importance may be resolved into a Fourier spectrum.   If the waveform is periodic, the spectrum will consist of a series of sines and cosines whose frequencies are all integral multiples of a fundamental frequency.   The fundamental frequency is the reciprocal of the time which must elapse before the waveform repeats itself.   If the waveform is not periodic, the fundamental period extends in a sense from a time $-\infty$ to a time $+\infty$.   The fundamental frequency is then infinitesimally small; the frequencies of successive terms in the Fourier series differ by an infinitesimal amount rather than by a finite amount; and the Fourier series becomes instead a Fourier integral. In either case the spectrum includes terms whose frequencies extend, in the general case, from zero frequency to infinity.

Fidelity Considerations Consider a sinusoidal signal of angular frequency ω represented by $V_m \sin(\omega t + \phi)$. If the voltage gain of the amplifier has a magnitude A and if the signal suffers a phase lag θ, then the output will be

$$AV_m \sin(\omega t + \phi - \theta) = AV_m \sin\left[\omega\left(t - \frac{\theta}{\omega}\right) + \phi\right]$$

Therefore, *if the amplification A is independent of frequency and if the phase shift θ is proportional to frequency (or is zero), then the amplifier will preserve the form of the input signal, although the signal will be delayed in time by an amount $D = \theta/\omega$.*

This discussion suggests that the extent to which an amplifier's amplitude response is not uniform, and its time delay is not constant with frequency, may serve as a measure of the lack of fidelity to be anticipated in it. In principle, it is really not necessary to specify both amplitude and delay response since, for most practical circuits, the two are related and, one having been specified, the other is uniquely determined. However, in particular cases, it may well be that either the time-delay or amplitude response is the more sensitive indicator of frequency distortion.

Low-frequency Response Video amplifiers of either the transistor or tube variety are almost invariably of the RC-coupled type. For such a stage the frequency characteristics may be divided into three regions: There is a range, called the *midband frequencies*, over which the amplification is reasonably constant and equal to A_o and over which the delay is also quite constant. For the present discussion we assume that the midband gain is normalized to unity, $A_o = 1$. In the second (low-frequency) region, below the midband, an amplifier stage behaves (Sec. 16-5) like the simple high-pass circuit of Fig. 16-1 of time constant $\tau_1 = R_1 C_1$. From this circuit we find that

$$V_o = \frac{V_i R_1}{R_1 - j/\omega C_1} = \frac{V_i}{1 - j/\omega R_1 C_1} \tag{16-1}$$

The voltage gain at low frequencies A_1 is defined as the ratio of the output

Fig. 16-1   A high-pass RC circuit may be used to calculate the low-frequency response of an amplifier.

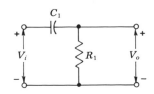

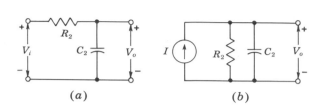

Fig. 16-2   (a) A low-pass RC circuit may be used to calculate the high-frequency response of an amplifier.   (b) The Norton's equivalent of the circuit in (a), where $I = V_i/R_2$.

voltage V_o to the input voltage V_i, or

$$A_1 \equiv \frac{V_o}{V_i} = \frac{1}{1 - jf_1/f} \qquad (16\text{-}2)$$

where

$$f_1 \equiv \frac{1}{2\pi R_1 C_1} \qquad (16\text{-}3)$$

The magnitude $|A_1|$ and the phase *lag* θ_1 of the gain are given by

$$|A_1| = \frac{1}{\sqrt{1 + (f_1/f)^2}} \qquad \theta_1 = -\arctan\frac{f_1}{f} \qquad (16\text{-}4)$$

At the frequency $f = f_1$, $A_1 = 1/\sqrt{2} = 0.707$, whereas in the midband region $(f \gg f_1)$, $A_1 \to 1$. Hence f_1 is that frequency at which the gain has fallen to 0.707 times its midband value A_o. From Eq. (12-21) this drop in signal level corresponds to a decibel reduction of $20 \log (1/\sqrt{2})$, or 3 dB. Accordingly, f_1 is referred to as *the lower 3-dB frequency*. From Eq. (16-3) we see that f_1 is that frequency for which the resistance R_1 equals the capacitive reactance $1/2\pi f_1 C_1$.

High-frequency Response In the third (high-frequency) region, above the midband, the amplifier stage behaves (Sec. 16-6) like the simple low-pass circuit of Fig. 16-2, with a time constant $\tau_2 = R_2 C_2$. Proceeding as above, we obtain for the magnitude $|A_2|$ and the phase *lag* θ_2 of the gain

$$|A_2| = \frac{1}{\sqrt{1 + (f/f_2)^2}} \qquad \theta_2 = \arctan\frac{f}{f_2} \qquad (16\text{-}5)$$

where

$$f_2 \equiv \frac{1}{2\pi R_2 C_2} \qquad (16\text{-}6)$$

Since at $f = f_2$ the gain is reduced to $1/\sqrt{2}$ times its midband value, then f_2 is called *the upper 3-dB frequency*. It also represents that frequency for which the resistance R_2 equals the capacitive reactance $1/2\pi f_2 C_2$. In the above expressions θ_1 and θ_2 represent the angle by which the output *lags* the input, neglecting the initial 180° phase shift through the amplifier. The frequency dependence of the gains in the high- and low-frequency range is to be seen in Fig. 16-3.

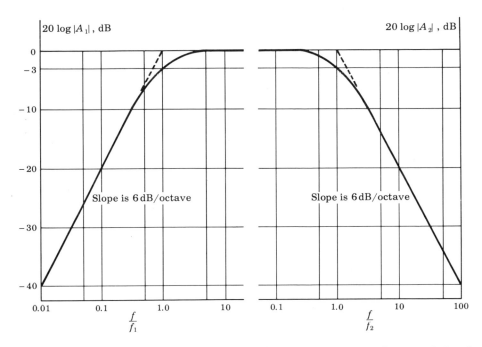

Fig. 16-3 A log-log plot of the amplitude frequency-response characteristic of an RC-coupled amplifier.

Bandwidth The frequency range from f_1 to f_2 is called the *bandwidth* of the amplifier stage. We may anticipate in a general way that a signal, all of whose Fourier components of appreciable amplitude lie well within the range f_1 to f_2, will pass through the stage without excessive distortion. This criterion must be applied, however, with caution.[2]

16-4   THE RC–COUPLED AMPLIFIER

A cascaded arrangement of common-cathode (CK) vacuum-tube stages is shown in Fig. 16-4a, of common-emitter (CE) transistor stages in Fig. 16-4b, and of common-source (CS) FET stages in Fig. 16-4c. The output Y_1 of one stage is coupled to the input X_2 of the next stage via a blocking capacitor C_b which is used to keep the dc component of the output voltage at Y_1 from reaching the input X_2. The resistor R_g is the grid (gate) leak, and the plate (collector) (drain) circuit resistor is R_p (R_c) (R_d). The cathode resistor R_k, the source resistor R_s, the emitter resistor R_e, the screen resistor R_{sc}, and the resistors R_1 and R_2 are used to establish the bias. The bypass capacitors, used to prevent loss of amplification due to negative feedback (Chap. 17), are C_k in the cathode, C_z in the emitter, C_s in the source, and C_{sc} in the screen circuit. Also present are interelectrode capacitances in the case of a tube, and junction

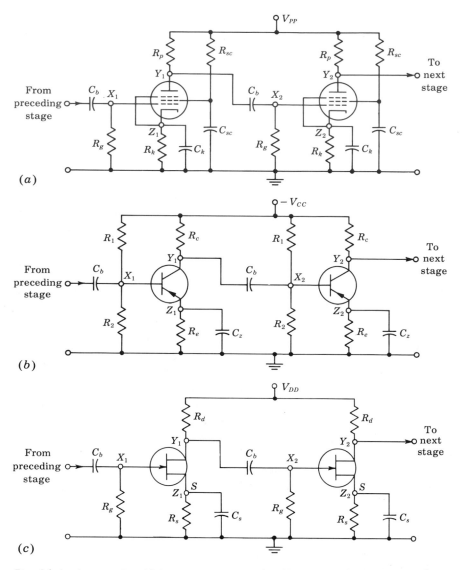

Fig. 16-4 A cascade of (a) common-cathode (CK) pentode stages; (b) common-emitter (CE) transistor stages; (c) common-source (CS) FET stages.

capacitances if a transistor is used. These are taken into account when we consider the high-frequency response, which is limited by their presence. In any practical mechanical arrangement of the amplifier components there are also capacitances associated with tube sockets and the proximity to the chassis of components (for example, the body of C_b) and signal leads. These stray capacitances are also considered later. We assume that the active device operates linearly, so that small-signal models are used throughout this chapter.

Fig. 16-5 A schematic representation of either a tube, FET, or transistor stage. Biasing arrangements and supply voltages are not indicated.

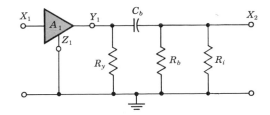

16-5 LOW–FREQUENCY RESPONSE OF AN RC–COUPLED STAGE

The effect of the bypass capacitors C_k, C_z, and C_s on the low-frequency characteristics is discussed in Sec. 16-10. For the present we assume that these capacitances are arbitrarily large and act as ac short circuits across R_k, R_e, and R_s, respectively. The effect of C_{sc} is considered in Ref. 3. A single intermediate stage of any of the cascades in Fig. 16-4 may be represented schematically as in Fig. 16-5. The resistor R_b represents the grid-leak resistor for a tube or the gate resistor R_g for a FET, and equals R_1 in parallel with R_2 if a transistor stage is under consideration. The resistor R_y represents R_p for a tube, R_o for a transistor, or R_d for a FET, and R_i represents the input resistance of the following stage.

The low-frequency equivalent circuit is obtained by neglecting all shunting capacitances and all junction capacitances, by replacing amplifier A_1 by its Norton's equivalent, as indicated in Fig. 16-6a. For a vacuum tube or field-effect transistor, $R_i = \infty$; the output impedance is $R_o - r_p\ (r_d)$ [the plate (drain) resistance]; and $I = g_m V_i$ (transconductance times grid or gate signal voltage). For a transistor these quantities may be expressed in terms of the CE hybrid parameters as in Sec. 11-2; $R_i \approx h_{ie}$ (for small values of R_o), $R_o = 1/h_{oe}$ (for a current drive), and $I = h_{fe}I_b$, where I_b is the base signal current. Let R'_o represent R_o in parallel with R_y, and let R'_i be R_i in parallel with R_b. Then, replacing I and R'_o by the Thévenin's equivalent, the single-time-constant high-pass circuit of Fig. 16-6b results. Hence, from Eq. (16-3),

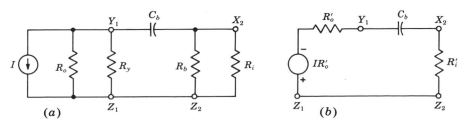

(a)

(b)

Fig. 16-6 (a) The low-frequency model of an RC-coupled amplifier; (b) an equivalent representation. For a tube or FET: $I = g_m V_i$, $R_o = r_p\ (r_d)$, $R_y = R_p\ (R_d)$, $R_b = R_g$, and $R_i = \infty$. For a transistor: $I = h_{fe}I_b$, $R_o \approx 1/h_{oe}$, $R_b = R_1||R_2$, $R_y = R_c$, and $R_i \approx h_{ie}$. Also, $R'_i = R_i||R_b$ and $R'_o = R_o||R_y$.

the lower 3-dB frequency is

$$f_1 = \frac{1}{2\pi(R'_o + R'_i)C_b} \tag{16-7}$$

This result is easy to remember since the time constant equals C_b multiplied by the sum of the effective resistances R'_o to the left of the blocking capacitor and R'_i to the right of C_b. For a vacuum-tube amplifier, $R'_i = R_g \gg R_p$. Since $R'_o < R_p$ because R'_o is R_p in parallel with R_o, then $R'_i = R_g \gg R'_o$ and $f_1 \approx 1/2\pi C_b R_g$. This same expression is valid for a FET.

EXAMPLE It is desired to have a low 3-dB frequency of not more than 10 Hz for an RC-coupled amplifier for which $R_y = 1$ K. What minimum value of coupling capacitance is required if (a) vacuum tubes or FETs with $R_g = 1$ M are used; (b) transistors with $R_i = 1$ K and $1/h_{oe} = 40$ K are used?

Solution a. From Eq. (16-7) we have

$$f_1 = \frac{1}{2\pi(R'_o + R'_i)C_b} \leq 10$$

or

$$C_b \geq \frac{1}{62.8(R'_o + R'_i)}$$

Since $R'_i = 1$ M and $R'_o < R_y = 1$ K, then $R'_o + R'_i \approx 1$ M and $C_b \geq 0.016$ μF.

b. From Eq. (11-34) we find for a transistor $R_o \geq 1/h_{oe} \approx 40$ K, and hence $R'_o \approx R_c = 1$ K. If we assume that $R_b \gg R_i = 1$ K, then $R'_i \approx 1$ K. Hence

$$C_b \geq \frac{1}{(62.8)(2 \times 10^3)} \text{ F} = 8.0 \text{ } \mu\text{F}$$

Note that because the input impedance of a transistor is much smaller than that of a FET or a tube, a coupling capacitor is required with the transistor which is 500 times larger than that required with the FET or tube. Fortunately, it is possible to obtain physically small electrolytic capacitors having such high capacitance values at the low voltages at which transistors operate.

16-6   HIGH–FREQUENCY RESPONSE OF A VACUUM–TUBE STAGE

For frequencies above the midband range we may neglect the reactance of the large series capacitance C_b. However, we must now include in Fig. 16-4 the output capacitance C_o from Y_1 to ground and the input capacitance C_i from X_2 to ground. To these capacitances must also be added the stray capacitance to ground. If the sum of all these shunt capacitances is called C, then the high-frequency model of Fig. 16-7 can be drawn. In order to keep the

Fig. 16-7 The high-frequency model of an RC-coupled stage using a pentode.

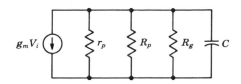

input capacitance C_i as small as possible, a pentode, rather than a triode, is used for the tube (Secs. 8-11 and 8-13). Hence r_p is of the order of magnitude of a megohm, as is also R_g, whereas R_p is at most a few kilohms. Therefore the parallel combination R of these three resistors can be approximated by R_p without introducing appreciable error. As predicted above (Fig. 16-2b), the amplifier stage at high frequencies behaves like a single-time-constant low-pass circuit, where $C_2 = C$ and $R_2 = R = r_p \| R_p \| R_g$.

Hence, from Eq. (16-6), the upper 3-dB frequency f_2 is given by

$$f_2 = \frac{1}{2\pi RC} \approx \frac{1}{2\pi R_p C} \tag{16-8}$$

In the midband region, where the shunting effect of C can be neglected ($X_c \gg R_p$), the output voltage is $V_o = -g_m RV_i$, and hence the midband gain $A_o \equiv V_o/V_i$ (for $R_p \ll r_p$ and $R_p \ll R_g$) is given by

$$A_o = -g_m R \approx -g_m R_p \tag{16-9}$$

Gain-Bandwidth Product   The upper 3-dB frequency of the amplifier may be improved by reducing the product $R_p C$. Every attempt should be made to reduce C by careful mechanical arrangement to decrease the shunt capacitance. The upper 3-dB frequency may also be increased by reducing R_p, but this reduces simultaneously the nominal amplifier gain. A figure of merit F which is very useful in comparing tube types is obtained by computing the product of A_o and f_2 in the limiting case where stray capacitance is considered to have been reduced to zero. From Eqs. (16-8) and (16-9) we have, since $C = C_i + C_o$,

$$F \equiv |A_o|f_2 = \frac{g_m}{2\pi(C_o + C_i)} \tag{16-10}$$

Since $f_2 \gg f_1$, the bandwidth $f_2 - f_1 \approx f_2$ and $|A_o|f_2 = F$ is called the *gain-bandwidth product*. It should be noted that f_2 varies inversely with plate-circuit resistance, whereas A_o is proportional to R_p, so that the gain-bandwidth product is a constant independent of R_p. It is possible to reduce R_p to such a low value that a midband gain $|A_o| = 1$ is obtained. Hence the figure of merit F may be interpreted as giving the maximum possible bandwidth obtainable with a given tube if R_p is adjusted for unity gain. For video pentodes such as the 6AK5, 6BH6, 6AU6, 6BC5, and 6CL6, values of g_m ranging from 5 to 11 millimhos (mA/V) and values of $C_o + C_i$ from 7 to 20 pF are obtainable. The value of F for all these tubes lies between 80 and 120 MHz, with the 6AK5 having the largest value.

An amplifier with a gain of unity is not very useful. Hence let us assume that $|A_o|$ is at least 2. Then $f_2 = F/|A_o| = 60$ MHz for the 6AK5 tube. In a practical circuit, the inevitable extra stray capacitance might easily reduce the bandwidth by a factor of 2. Hence we may probably take a bandwidth of 30 MHz as a reasonable estimate of a practical upper limit for an uncompensated tube amplifier using lumped parameters. If the desired gain is 10 instead of 2, the maximum 3-dB frequency is about 6 MHz.

The highest transconductance available in tubes is about 50 millimhos, and is obtained with frame grid pentodes having very close (0.05 mm) grid-to-cathode spacing. For example, the Amperex type 7788 pentode has $g_m = 50$ mA/V and $C_o + C_i \approx 20$ pF, corresponding to $F = 400$ MHz. With this tube a 3-dB frequency of about 20 MHz is possible with a gain of 10. If more bandwidth is needed, distributed amplifiers are used.[1]

The foregoing discussion is valid for any stage of a tube amplifier, including the output stage. For this last stage, C_i, representing the input capacitance to the following stage, is missing, and its place is taken by any shunt capacitance of the device being driven (say a cathode-ray tube).

The equivalent circuit of a FET is the same as that of a triode (Fig. 14-9). Hence the input capacitance of an internal stage may be very large because of the Miller effect (Sec. 8-12). This shunting capacitance limits the bandwidth of a FET.

16-7   CASCADED CE TRANSISTOR STAGES

The high-frequency analysis of a single-stage CE transistor amplifier, or the last stage of a cascade, is given in detail in Secs. 13-7 and 13-8. Since the input impedance of a transistor cannot be represented by a parallel resistance-capacitance combination, the analysis of an internal stage differs from that of the final stage.

We consider now the operation of one transistor amplifier stage in a cascade of many stages. Such a cascade is shown in Fig. 16-8. We omit from this diagram all supply voltages and components, such as coupling capacitors,

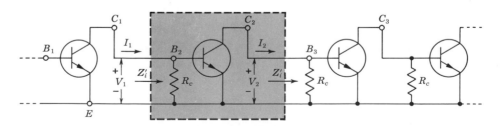

Fig. 16-8 An infinite cascade of CE stages. The dashed, shaded rectangle (block) encloses one stage.

which serve only to establish proper bias and do not affect the high-frequency response. The collector-circuit resistor R_c is included, however, since this resistor has an effect on both the gain and frequency response. The base-biasing resistors R_1 and R_2 in Fig. 16-4b are assumed to be large compared with R_c. If this condition is not satisfied, the symbol R_c represents the parallel combination of R_1, R_2, and the collector-circuit resistance. A complete stage from collector to collector is included in the shaded block. We define the current gain of the stage to be $A_{Is} \equiv I_2/I_1$. Each stage behaves like a current generator of impedance $R_s = R_c$ delivering current to the following stage. We define the voltage gain to be $A_V \equiv V_2/V_1$. Since we have specified V_1 as the voltage precisely at the stage input, then A_V is the gain for an ideal voltage source. We now prove that $A_{Is} = A_V$ for an infinite cascade of similar stages.

In a long chain of stages the input impedance Z_i between base and emitter of each stage is identical. Let Z_i' represent Z_i in parallel with R_c. Accordingly, $Z_i' = V_1/I_1 = V_2/I_2$, so that $I_2/I_1 = A_{Is} = V_2/V_1 = A_V$ in this special case.

We now calculate this gain $A_{Is} = A_V \equiv A$. For this purpose Fig. 16-9 shows the circuit details of the stage in the shaded block in Fig. 16-8. Also shown is the input portion of the next stage, so that we may take account of its loading effect on the stage of interest. The symbol K used in the expression $C_c(1 - K)$ for one of the capacitors is $K \equiv V_{ce}/V_{b'e}$. Figure 16-9 is obtained from Fig. 13-12a. The elements involving $g_{b'e}$ have been omitted since, as demonstrated in Sec. 13-8, their omission introduces little error.

The gain $A_o = I_2/I_1$ at low frequencies is given by Eq. (13-50), except with R_s replaced by R_c, and we have

$$A_o = \frac{-h_{fe}R_c}{R_c + h_{ie}} \tag{16-11}$$

To calculate the bandwidth we must evaluate K. From Fig. 16-9 we obtain for K an unwieldy expression. Since K is a function of frequency, the element marked $C_c(1 - K)$ is not a true capacitor, but rather is a complex network. Thus, in order to proceed with a simple solution which will give reasonable accuracy, we use the zero-frequency value of K. We show

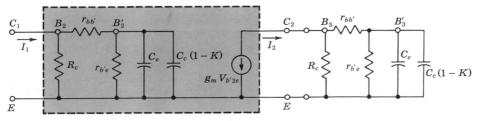

Fig. 16-9 The equivalent circuit of the enclosed stage of Fig. 16-8 ($K \equiv V_{ce}/V_{b'e}$).

below that the response obtained experimentally is somewhat better than that predicted by this analysis, and hence that we are erring in the conservative direction. At zero frequency, $K = K_o = -g_m R_L$, in which R_L is the resistive load on the transistor from C to E and consists of R_c in parallel with $r_{bb'} + r_{b'e} = h_{ie}$. Therefore

$$R_L = \frac{R_c h_{ie}}{R_c + h_{ie}} \tag{16-12}$$

and the total capacitance C from B_2' to E is

$$C = C_e + C_c(1 + g_m R_L) \tag{16-13}$$

The gain is $A = I_2/I_1 = -g_m V_{b'e}/I_1$, where $V_{b'e} = V_{b'2e}$ represents the voltage across C. Instead of calculating $V_{b'e}$ directly from the input network of Fig. 16-9, we again make the observation that this is a single-time-constant circuit. Hence we can calculate the 3-dB frequency f_2 by inspection. Since the capacitance C is charged through a resistance R consisting of $r_{b'e}$ in parallel with $R_c + r_{bb'}$, or

$$R = \frac{(R_c + r_{bb'})r_{b'e}}{R_c + h_{ie}} \tag{16-14}$$

the 3-dB frequency is

$$f_2 = \frac{1}{2\pi RC} \tag{16-15}$$

This half-power frequency is the same for the current gain and voltage gain.

In using the approximation $K = K_o = -g_m R_L$, we are making a conservative error, since K_o is the maximum magnitude of K and is attained only at zero frequency. Using K_o leads to the largest value of shunt capacitance C, and consequently to an overly low estimate of the bandwidth f_2.

From the equations above the gain-bandwidth product is found to be

$$|A_o f_2| = \frac{g_m}{2\pi C} \frac{R_c}{R_c + r_{bb'}} = \frac{f_T}{1 + 2\pi f_T C_c R_L} \frac{R_c}{R_c + r_{bb'}} \tag{16-16}$$

where R_L depends upon R_c, as indicated in Eq. (16-12).

Gain and Bandwidth Considerations   Our only adjustable parameter is R_c, and we now discuss its selection. At one extreme, if we set $R_c = 0$, we should simply shunt all output current away from the following transistor. As a matter of fact, it seems initially not unreasonable to set R_c arbitrarily high so as to avoid this shunting effect. However, as we reduce R_c and thereby lose gain, a compensating advantage appears. A reduction of R_c reduces R_L in Eq. (16-12) and also reduces R in Eq. (16-14). The reduction in R_L reduces $C = C_e + C_c(1 + g_m R_L)$, and this reduction, together with the reduction in R, increases f_2, as is seen in Eq. (16-15). It may be that a decrease in gain is more than compensated for by an increase in f_2. To investigate this point we differentiate the gain-bandwidth product $|A_o f_2|$ with respect to R_c. Setting the derivative equal to zero, we find that a maximum does occur. The value of R_c for which this optimum gain-bandwidth product is obtained is designated by $(R_c)_{opt}$ and is given by

$$(R_c)_{opt} = \frac{h_{ie}}{\sqrt{x - 1}} \qquad (16\text{-}17)$$

with

$$x = \frac{h_{fe} C_c}{C_e + C_c} \frac{h_{ie}}{r_{bb'}} \qquad (16\text{-}18)$$

In Fig. 16-10 we have plotted the gain, the bandwidth, and the gain-bandwidth product. The maximum which is apparent [at $R_c = 360 \ \Omega$, as found from Eq. (16-17)] is not particularly pronounced.[5] Nevertheless, there is enough of a falling off at values of R_c above or below $(R_c)_{opt}$ so that it may be worthwhile to operate near the maximum. It is important to bias the transistor so that at the quiescent point a large value of f_T is obtained (Fig. 13-10).

Note in Fig. 16-10 that $|A_o f_2|$ remains roughly constant for values of R_c in the neighborhood of $(R_c)_{opt}$ or for larger values of R_c. Hence, for a cascade of stages (as distinct from the single stage considered in Sec. 13-9), the gain-bandwidth product takes on some importance as a figure of merit.

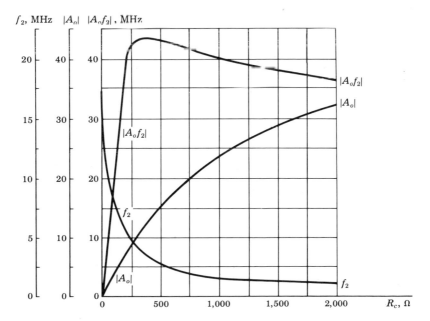

Fig. 16-10 Gain $|A_o|$, bandwidth f_2, and gain-bandwidth product $|A_o f_2|$ as a function of R_c for one stage of a CE cascade. The transistor parameters are given in Sec. 13-5.

For our typical transistor, $f_T = 80$ MHz, whereas the constant value of $|A_o f_2|$ in Fig. 16-10 is approximately 40 MHz, or $0.5 f_T$. A good general rule in choosing a transistor as a broadband amplifier is to assume $A_o f_2 \approx 0.6 f_T$. This conclusion is based upon calculations on more than twenty transistors for which the hybrid-Π parameters were known. These had values of f_T ranging from 700 kHz to 700 MHz. In each case $(R_c)_{opt}$ was found and the value of $A_o f_2$ at this optimum resistance was calculated. All values of gain-bandwidth product were in the range between 0.4 and $0.8 f_T$. The values of $A_o f_2$ were also calculated for several values of R_c besides $(R_c)_{opt}$, and it was confirmed that the gain-bandwidth product remained constant over a wide range of values of R_c.

It must be remembered that bandwidth cannot be exchanged for gain at low values of gain because $A_o f_2$ is not constant for small values of R_c or A_o. The maximum value of f_2, which occurs at $R_c = 0$ (and $A_o = 0$), is given by

$$(f_2)_{max} = \frac{f_T}{g_m R} = \frac{f_T h_{ie}}{h_{fe} r_{bb'}} \tag{16-19}$$

The design of the amplifier represents, as usual, a compromise between gain and bandwidth. If A_o is specified, the load R_c which must be used is found from Eq. (16-11). Then the bandwidth which will be obtained is found from Eq. (16-15). On the other hand, if the desired bandwidth is specified, then f_2 substituted into Eq. (16-15) will not allow a direct calculation of R_c. The reason for the difficulty is that R depends upon R_c and that

$$C = C_e + C_c(1 + g_m R_L)$$

is also a function of R_c through R_L, as given in Eq. (16-12). Under these circumstances an arbitrary value of R_c, say 1,000 Ω, is chosen, and f_2 is calculated. If this value is larger (smaller) than the desired value of f_2, the next approximation to R_c must be larger (smaller) than 1,000 Ω. By plotting f_2 versus R_c, the desired value of R_c can be found by interpolation.

The approximations which we have made in this analysis are valid if R_L is less than 2,000 Ω. Since R_L is the parallel combination of R_c and $h_{ie} \approx 1,100 \Omega$, there are no restrictions on the magnitude of R_c. As $R_c \to \infty$, $R_L = h_{ie}$ and $A_o = -h_{fe}$. The asymptotic limits in Fig. 16-10 are found to be $|A_o| = 50$, $f_2 = 0.59$ MHz, and $|A_o f_2| = 29.5$ MHz for $R_c \to \infty$.

The First and Final Stages   The results obtained above for an internal stage of a cascade are not valid for the first or last stage. For the first stage the equations in Sec. 13-9 for a single stage apply, provided that the load R_L is taken as the collector-circuit resistance in parallel with the input resistance of the second stage:

$$R_L = \frac{R_c h_{ie}}{R_c + h_{ie}}$$

For the last stage in a cascade use the formulas for a single stage, with R_s

equal to the collector-circuit resistance R_c of the preceding stage and with R_L equal to the R_c of the last stage.

16-8   STEP RESPONSE OF AN AMPLIFIER

An alternative criterion of amplifier fidelity is the response of the amplifier to a particular input waveform.   Of all possible available waveforms, the most generally useful is the step voltage.   In terms of a circuit's response to a step, the response to an arbitrary waveform may be written in the form of the superposition integral.   Another feature which recommends the step voltage is the fact that this waveform is one which permits small distortions to stand out clearly.   Additionally, from an experimental viewpoint, we note that excellent pulse (a short step) and square-wave (a repeated step) generators are available commercially.

As long as an amplifier can be represented by a single-time-constant circuit, the correlation between its frequency response and the output waveshape for a step input is that given below.   Quite generally, even for more complicated amplifier circuits, there continues to be an intimate relationship between the distortion of the leading edge of a step and the high-frequency response. Similarly, there is a close relationship between the low-frequency response and the distortion of the flat portion of the step.   We should, of course, expect such a relationship, since the high-frequency response measures essentially the ability of the amplifier to respond faithfully to rapid variations in signal, whereas the low-frequency response measures the fidelity of the amplifier for slowly varying signals.   An important feature of a step is that it is a combination of the most abrupt voltage change possible and of the slowest possible voltage variation.

Rise Time   The response of the low-pass circuit of Fig. 16-2 to a step input of amplitude V is exponential with a time constant R_2C_2.   Since the capacitor voltage cannot change instantaneously, the output starts from zero and rises toward the steady-state value V, as shown in Fig. 16-11.   The output

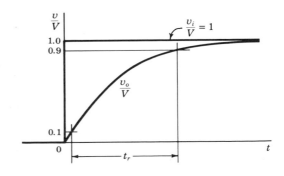

Fig. 16-11   Step-voltage response of the low-pass RC circuit.   The rise time t_r is indicated.

is given by

$$v_o = V(1 - e^{-t/R_2 C_2}) \tag{16-20}$$

The time required for v_o to reach one-tenth of its final value is readily found to be $0.1 R_2 C_2$, and the time to reach nine-tenths its final value is $2.3 R_2 C_2$. The difference between these two values is called the *rise time* t_r of the circuit and is shown in Fig. 16-11. The time t_r is an indication of how fast the amplifier can respond to a discontinuity in the input voltage. We have, using Eq. (16-6),

$$t_r = 2.2 R_2 C_2 = \frac{2.2}{2\pi f_2} = \frac{0.35}{f_2} \tag{16-21}$$

Note that the rise time is inversely proportional to the upper 3-dB frequency. For an amplifier with 1 MHz bandpass, $t_r = 0.35$ μsec.

Tilt or Sag   If a step of amplitude V is impressed on the high-pass circuit of Fig. 16-1, the output is

$$v_o = V\epsilon^{-t/R_1 C_1} \tag{16-22}$$

For times t which are small compared with the time constant $R_1 C_1$, the response is given by

$$v_o \approx V\left(1 - \frac{t}{R_1 C_1}\right) \tag{16-23}$$

From Fig. 16-12 we see that the output is tilted, and the percent tilt or sag in time t_1 is given by

$$P \equiv \frac{V - V'}{V} \times 100 = \frac{t_1}{R_1 C_1} \times 100\% \tag{16-24}$$

It is found[6] that this same expression is valid for the tilt of each half cycle of a symmetrical square wave of peak-to-peak value V and period T provided that we set $t_1 = T/2$. If $f = 1/T$ is the frequency of the square wave, then, using Eq. (16-3), we may express P in the form

$$P = \frac{T}{2 R_1 C_1} \times 100 = \frac{1}{2f R_1 C_1} \times 100 = \frac{\pi f_1}{f} \times 100\% \tag{16-25}$$

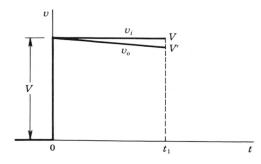

Fig. 16-12   The response v_o, when a step v_i is applied to a high-pass RC circuit, exhibits a tilt.

Note that the tilt is directly proportional to the lower 3-dB frequency. If we wish to pass a 50-Hz square wave with less than 10 percent sag, then f_1 must not exceed 1.6 Hz.

Square-wave Testing An important experimental procedure (called *square-wave testing*) is to observe with an oscilloscope the output of an amplifier excited by a square-wave generator. It is possible to improve the response of an amplifier by adding to it certain circuit elements,[1] which then must be adjusted with precision. It is a great convenience to be able to adjust these elements and to see simultaneously the effect of such an adjustment on the amplifier output waveform. The alternative is to take data, after each successive adjustment, from which to plot the amplitude and phase responses. Aside from the extra time consumed in this latter procedure, we have the problem that it is usually not obvious which of the attainable amplitude and phase responses corresponds to optimum fidelity. On the other hand, the step response gives immediately useful information.

It is possible, by judicious selection of two square-wave frequencies, to examine individually the high-frequency and low-frequency distortion. For example, consider an amplifier which has a high-frequency time constant of 1 μsec and a low-frequency time constant of 0.1 sec. A square wave of half period equal to several microseconds, on an appropriately fast oscilloscope sweep, will display the rounding of the leading edge of the waveform and will not display the tilt. At the other extreme, a square wave of half period approximately 0.01 sec on an appropriately slow sweep will display the tilt, and not the distortion of the leading edge.

It should *not* be inferred from the above comparison between steady-state and transient response that the phase and amplitude responses are of no importance at all in the study of amplifiers. The frequency characteristics are useful for the following reasons: In the first place, much more is known generally about the analysis and synthesis of circuits in the frequency domain than in the time domain, and for this reason the design of coupling networks is often done on a frequency-response basis. Second, it is often possible to arrive at least at a qualitative understanding of the properties of a circuit from a study of the steady-state-response circumstances where transient calculations are extremely cumbersome. Finally, it happens occasionally that an amplifier is required whose characteristics are specified on a frequency basis, the principal emphasis being to amplify a sine wave.

16-9   BANDPASS OF CASCADED STAGES

The upper 3-dB frequency for n cascaded stages is $f_2^{(n)}$ and equals the frequency for which the overall voltage gain falls to $1/\sqrt{2}$ (3 dB) of its midband value. Thus $f_2^{(n)}$ is calculated from

$$\left[\frac{1}{\sqrt{1 + (f_2^{(n)}/f_2)^2}} \right]^n = \frac{1}{\sqrt{2}}$$

to be

$$\frac{f_2^{(n)}}{f_2} = \sqrt{2^{1/n} - 1} \tag{16-26}$$

For example, for $n = 2$, $f_2^{(2)}/f_2 = 0.64$. Hence two cascade stages, each with a bandwidth $f_2 = 10$ kHz, have an overall bandwidth of 6.4 kHz. Similarly, three cascaded 10-kHz stages give a resultant upper 3-dB frequency of 5.1 kHz, etc.

If the lower 3-dB frequency for n cascaded stages is $f_1^{(n)}$, then corresponding to Eq. (16-26) we find

$$\frac{f_1^{(n)}}{f_1} = \frac{1}{\sqrt{2^{1/n} - 1}} \tag{16-27}$$

We see that a cascade of stages has a lower f_2 and a higher f_1 than a single stage, resulting in a shrinkage in bandwidth.

If the amplitude response for a single stage is plotted on log-log paper, the resulting graph will approach a straight line whose slope is 6 dB/octave both at the low and at the high frequencies, as indicated in Fig. 16-3. Hence every time the frequency f doubles (which, by definition, is one octave), the response drops by 6 dB. For an n-stage amplifier it follows that the amplitude response falls $6n$ dB/octave, or, equivalently, $20n$ dB/decade.

Step Response If the rise time of the individual cascaded stages is $t_{r1}, t_{r2}, \ldots, t_{rn}$ and if the input waveform rise time is t_{ro}, it is found that the output-signal rise time t_r is given (to within 10 percent) by

$$t_r \approx 1.1 \sqrt{t_{ro}^2 + t_{r1}^2 + t_{r2}^2 + \cdots + t_{rn}^2} \tag{16-28}$$

If, upon application of a voltage step, one RC-coupling circuit produces a tilt of P_1 percent and if a second stage gives a tilt of P_2 percent, the effect of cascading these two circuits is to produce a tilt of $P_1 + P_2$ percent. This result applies only if the individual tilts and the combined tilt are small enough so that in each case the response falls approximately linearly with time.

16-10 EFFECT OF AN EMITTER (OR A CATHODE) BYPASS CAPACITOR ON LOW–FREQUENCY RESPONSE

If an emitter resistor R_e is used for self-bias in an amplifier and if it is desired to avoid the degeneration, and hence the loss of gain due to R_e, we might attempt to bypass this resistor with a very large capacitance C_z. The circuit is indicated in Fig. 16-4b. It is shown below that the effect of this capacitor is to affect adversely the low-frequency response.

Consider the single stage of Fig. 16-13a. To simplify the analysis we assume that $R_1 \| R_2 \gg R_s$ and that the load R_c is small enough so that the simplified hybrid model of Fig. 12-7 is valid. The equivalent circuit subject

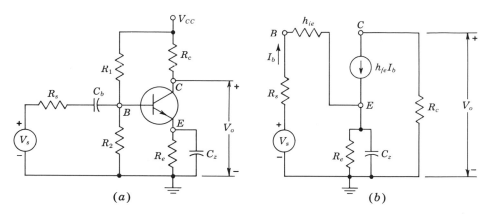

Fig. 16-13 (a) An amplifier with a bypassed emitter resistor; (b) the low-frequency simplified h-parameter model of the circuit in (a).

to these assumptions is shown in Fig. 16-13b. The blocking capacitor C_b is omitted from Fig. 16-13b; its effect is considered in Sec. 16-5.

The output voltage V_o is given by

$$V_o = -I_b h_{fe} R_c = -\frac{V_s h_{fo} R_c}{R_s + h_{ie} + Z'_e} \tag{16-29}$$

where

$$Z'_e \equiv (1 + h_{fe}) \frac{R_e}{1 + j\omega C_z R_e} \tag{16-30}$$

Substituting Eq. (16-30) in Eq. (16-29) and solving for the voltage gain A_V, we find

$$A_V = \frac{V_o}{V_s} = -\frac{h_{fe} R_c}{R + R'} \frac{1 + j\omega C_z R_e}{1 + j\omega C_z \dfrac{R_e R}{R + R'}} \tag{16-31}$$

where

$$R \equiv R_s + h_{ie} \qquad \text{and} \qquad R' \equiv (1 + h_{fe}) R_e \tag{16-32}$$

The midband gain A_o is obtained as $\omega \to \infty$, or

$$A_o = -\frac{h_{fe} R_c}{R} = \frac{-h_{fe} R_c}{R_s + h_{ie}} \tag{16-33}$$

Hence

$$\frac{A_V}{A_o} = \frac{1}{1 + R'/R} \frac{1 + jf/f_o}{1 + jf/f_p} \tag{16-34}$$

where

$$f_o \equiv \frac{1}{2\pi C_z R_e} \qquad f_p \equiv \frac{1 + R'/R}{2\pi C_z R_e} \tag{16-35}$$

Note that f_o determines the zero and f_p the pole of the gain A_V/A_o. Since usually $R'/R \gg 1$, then $f_p \gg f_o$, so that the pole and zero are widely separated.

For example, assuming $R_s = 0$, $R_e = 1$ K, $C_z = 100$ μF, $h_{fe} = 50$, $h_{ie} = 1.1$ K, and $R_c = 2$ K, we find $f_o = 1.6$ Hz and $f_p = 76$ Hz.

A plot of $20 \log |A_V/A_o|$ versus $\log f$ is indicated in Fig. 16-14. The piecewise linear curve shown dashed indicates the asymptotic behavior of the frequency response. This dashed characteristic is constant at $-20 \log (1 + R'/R)$ for $f < f_o$; it increases linearly at 6 dB/octave for $f_o < f < f_p$, and remains at 0 dB for $f > f_p$. Remembering that $f_p \gg f_o$ and using Eqs. (16-34) and (16-35), the magnitude of A_V/A_o becomes, for $f = f_p$,

$$\left| \frac{A_V}{A_o} \right| = \frac{1}{1 + R'/R} \frac{f_p/f_o}{\sqrt{1+1}} = \frac{1}{\sqrt{2}}$$

Hence $f = f_p$ is that frequency at which the gain has dropped 3 dB. Thus the lower 3-dB frequency f_1 is approximately equal to f_p. If the condition $f_p \gg f_o$ is *not* satisfied, then $f_1 \neq f_p$. As a matter of fact, a 3-dB frequency may not exist (Prob. 16-29).

Square-wave Response   Since the network in Fig. 16-13 is a single-time-constant circuit, the percentage tilt to a square wave is given by Eq. (16-25), or

$$P = \frac{\pi f_p}{f} \times 100 = \frac{1 + R'/R}{2 f C_z R_e} \times 100 \tag{16-36}$$

Since $R'/R \gg 1$,

$$P \approx \frac{R' \times 100}{2 f C_z R R_e} = \frac{1 + h_{fe}}{2 f (C_z)(R_s + h_{ie})} \times 100\% \tag{16-37}$$

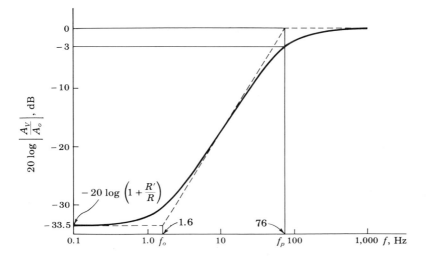

Fig. 16-14   The frequency response of an amplifier with a bypassed emitter resistor.   The numerical values correspond to the component values given at the top of this page.

Let us calculate the size of C_z so that we may reproduce a 50-Hz square wave with a tilt of less than 10 percent. Using the parameters given above, we obtain

$$C_z = \frac{(51)(100)}{(2)(50)(1{,}100)(10)} \text{ F} = 4{,}600 \ \mu\text{F}$$

Such a large value of capacitance is impractical, and it must be concluded that if very small tilts are to be obtained for very low frequency signals, the emitter resistor must be left unbypassed. The flatness will then be obtained at the sacrifice of gain because of the degeneration caused by R_e. If the loss in amplification cannot be tolerated, R_e cannot be used.

A Tube or FET Stage If the active device is a pentode (with $r_p \gg R_L + R_k$) instead of a transistor, the equivalent circuit of Fig. 16-15 must be used. An analysis of this circuit (Prob. 16-30) yields

$$\frac{A_V}{A_o} = \frac{1}{1 + g_m R_k} \frac{1 + jf/f_o}{1 + jf/f_p} \tag{16-38}$$

where

$$A_o \equiv -g_m R_L \qquad f_o \equiv \frac{1}{2\pi C_k R_k} \qquad f_p \equiv \frac{1 + g_m R_k}{2\pi C_k R_k} \tag{16-39}$$

These equations are analogous to Eqs. (16-34) and (16-35), and the frequency response is of the form indicated in Fig. 16-14. If $g_m R_k \gg 1$, the pole and zero frequencies are widely separated, and hence $f_1 \approx f_p$. Then, from Eq. (16-25), it follows that the percentage tilt to a square wave of frequency f is

$$P = \frac{\pi f_p}{f} \times 100 = \frac{1 + g_m R_k}{2 C_k R_k f} \times 100 \approx \frac{g_m}{2 C_k f} \times 100\% \tag{16-40}$$

Note that for $g_m R_k \gg 1$, P is independent of R_k. If g_m for a pentode is 5 mA/V (one-tenth that of a transistor), then for no more than a 10 percent output tilt with a 50-Hz square-wave input, the capacitor C_k must be at least

$$C_k = \frac{5 \times 10^{-3} \times 100}{2 \times 50 \times 10} \text{ F} = 500 \ \mu\text{F}$$

The analysis of a FET stage (with $r_d \gg R_L + R_s$) is identical with that for a pentode, except that C_k and R_k must be replaced by C_s and R_s, respectively.

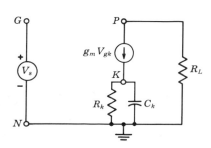

Fig. 16-15 The equivalent circuit of a pentode stage with a cathode impedance.

Practical Considerations Electrolytic capacitors are often used as emitter, cathode, or source bypass capacitors because they offer the greatest capacitance per unit volume. It is important to note that these capacitors have a series resistance which arises from the conductive losses in the electrolyte. This resistance, typically 1 to 20 Ω, must be taken into account in computing the midband gain of the stage.

If in a given stage both C_z and the coupling capacitor C_b are present, we can assume, first, C_z to be infinite and compute the lower 3-dB frequency due to C_b alone. We then calculate f_1 due to C_z by assuming C_b to be infinite. If the two cutoff frequencies are significantly different (by a factor of more than four or five times), the higher of the two is approximately the lower 3-dB frequency for the stage.

16-11   SPURIOUS INPUT VOLTAGES

It often happens that, with no apparent input signal to an amplifier, an output voltage of considerable magnitude may be obtained. The amplifier may be oscillating because some part of the output is inadvertently being fed back into the input.

Parasitic Oscillations Feedback may occur through the interelectrode capacitance from input to output of the active device, through lead inductances, stray wiring, etc., the exact path often being very difficult to determine. The undesired, or *parasitic*, oscillation may occur with any type of circuit, such as audio-, video-, or radio-frequency amplifier, oscillator, modulator, pulse waveform generating circuits, etc. Parasitic oscillations are particularly prevalent with circuits in which (physically) large tubes are used, tubes or transistors are operated in parallel or push-pull, and in power stages.[7] The frequency of oscillation may be in the audio range, but is usually much higher and often is so high (hundreds of megahertz) that its presence cannot be detected with an oscilloscope.

Parasitic oscillations can usually be eliminated by a change in circuit parameters, a rearrangement of wiring, some additional bypassing or shielding, a change of tube or transistor, the use of a radio-frequency inductor in the output circuit, radio-frequency chokes in series with filament leads, etc. A small resistance (50 to 1,000 Ω) placed in series with a grid and as close to the grid terminal as possible is often very effective in reducing high-frequency oscillations in a tube.

Hum Even if an amplifier is not oscillating, undesirable output voltages may be present in a vacuum-tube amplifier in the form of hum from the use of ac heated filaments.[8] There are several sources of this hum:

1. The magnetic field produced by the filament current will deflect the electron stream. During some portion of each half cycle the electrons may

be deflected to such an extent as to miss the plate. A 120-Hz hum results (if a 60-Hz power source is used).

2. Effective capacitances exist between each side of the heater and the grid. If these capacitances are not equal, an effective 60-Hz voltage is impressed upon the grid.

3. The heater-cathode insulation is not infinite. If self-bias is used, leakage will take place from the heater through this insulation resistance in series with the cathode impedance Z_k. The voltage across Z_k appears as hum.

4. The heating and cooling of the cathode, because the heating power is periodic, introduces a 120-Hz hum. This would not be true if the plate current were strictly space-charge-limited since it would then be independent of the temperature of the emitter. However, some parts of the cathode are at a low enough temperature so that some temperature-limited current exists. Furthermore, the effect of the initial velocities is a function of temperature.

Hum from the above sources can be eliminated completely only by using dc heating power.

In addition to hum that is inherent in the heater construction, some hum may appear from pickup resulting from the stray magnetic fields of the power transformer or from the fields produced by the heater current in the connecting leads. The effect of the former is negligible with properly shielded transformers, and that of the latter may be reduced if the heater leads are twisted. There may also be electrostatic pickup from the ac line. Finally, there is the possibility of pickup of radio-frequency signals radiated through space. These spurious voltages can often be eliminated by proper shielding or bypassing. Some of these sources of hum cause difficulties with transistors as well as with tubes. It should be emphasized that hum troubles are usually of importance only in the first stage of a high-gain amplifier, for the small spurious voltages introduced in this stage are amplified by all succeeding stages.

Microphonics The spurious output voltages caused by the vibrations of the electrodes arising from mechanical or acoustical jarring of the tube are called *microphonics*. Some tubes are much more microphonic than others of presumably identical construction, and this source of trouble can often be eliminated by changing tubes. In many cases, it is necessary to mount the tubes in rubber or in special supports. In addition, special tubes are available in which the microphonic effect, and also the heater hum effects outlined above, have been minimized. A transistor is, of course, completely nonmicrophonic because there can be no mechanical motion between the emitter, base, and collector.

16-12   NOISE

It is found that there is an inherent limit to the amplification obtainable from an amplifier even after the above-mentioned sources of hum have been eliminated.   Under these conditions, the output of the amplifier, when there is no impressed input signal, is called *amplifier noise*.[9]   If, therefore, only a very small voltage is available, such as a weak radio, television, radar, etc., signal, it may be impossible to distinguish the signal from the background noise.   The term *noise* arises from the fact that with no input, the output of an audio amplifier with the gain control set at a maximum is an audible hiss, or crackle.   In the case of a video amplifier the term *snow* is often used in place of noise because of the snowlike appearance on a TV screen when the set is tuned to a weak station.   The various noise sources in an amplifier are now considered.

Thermal, or Johnson, Noise   The electrons in a conductor possess varying amounts of energy by virtue of the temperature of the conductor.   The slight fluctuations in energy about the values specified by the most probable distribution are very small, but they are sufficient to produce small noise potentials within a conductor.   These random fluctuations produced by the thermal agitation of the electrons are called the *thermal*, or Johnson, noise.   The rms value of the thermal resistance noise voltage V_n over a frequency range $f_2 - f_1$ is given by the expression

$$V_n{}^2 = 4\bar{k}TRB \tag{16-41}$$

where $\bar{k}$ = Boltzmann constant, J/°K
$\quad T$ = resistor temperature, °K
$\quad R$ = resistance, Ω
$\quad B = f_2 - f_1$ = bandwidth, Hz

It should be observed that the same noise power exists in a given bandwidth regardless of the center frequency.   Such a distribution, which gives the same noise per unit bandwidth anywhere in the spectrum, is called *white noise*.

If the conductor under consideration is the input resistor to an ideal (noiseless) amplifier, the input noise voltage to the amplifier is given by Eq. (16-41).   An idea of the order of magnitude of the voltage involved is obtained by calculating the noise voltage generated in a 1-M resistance at room temperature over a 10-kHz bandpass.   Equation (16-41) yields for V_n the value 13 μV.   Clearly, if the bandpass of an amplifier is wider, the input resistance must be smaller, if excessive noise is to be avoided.   Thus, if the amplifier considered is 10 MHz wide, its input resistance cannot exceed 1,000 Ω, if the fluctuation noise is not to exceed that of the 10-kHz audio amplifier.

It is obvious that the bandpass of an amplifier should be kept as low as possible (without introducing excessive frequency distortion) because the noise power is directly proportional to the bandwidth.   The noise output squared from the amplifier due to R_s only is given by Eq. (16-41) provided that the value of $V_n{}^2$ is multiplied by $|A_{Vo}|^2$ and that the noise bandwidth B is defined by

$$B \equiv \frac{1}{|A_{Vo}|^2} \int_0^\infty |A_V(f)|^2 \, df \tag{16-42}$$

where A_{Vo} is the midband value of the voltage gain $A_V(f)$. We thus see that the noise bandwidth given by Eq. (16-42) may be different from the amplifier voltage gain bandwidth.

Shot Noise Among the various possible sources of noise in a tube, one of the most important is the *shot effect*. Normally, one assumes that the current in a tube under dc conditions is a constant at every instant. Actually, however, the current from the cathode to the anode consists of a stream of individual electrons, and it is only the time average flow which is constant. These fluctuations in the number of electrons emitted constitute the shot noise. If the cathode emission is temperature-limited, the rms noise current I_n in a diode is given by the expression

$$I_n{}^2 = 2eI_PB \qquad\qquad (16\text{-}43)$$

where e = electronic charge, C

$\quad I_P$ = emission current, A

$\quad B$ = bandwidth, Hz

If the load resistor is R, a noise voltage of magnitude I_nR will appear across the load. Temperature-limited diodes are used as constant-current white-noise generators for test purposes.

If the tube is space-charge-limited, the irregularities in emission are decreased, and the plate-current fluctuation is much less in a space-charge-limited tube than in one which is temperature-limited. This fact is explained qualitatively by the automatic-valve action of the space-charge cloud in the neighborhood of the cathode, as discussed in Sec. 7-1. The space-charge-limited noise power is of the order of 10 percent of the temperature-limited value.

Other Noise Sources in Tubes In addition to Johnson and shot noise, there are the following physical mechanisms for the generation of extraneous signals in a tube: *gas noise*, caused by the random ionization of the few molecules remaining in the tube; *secondary-emission noise*, arising from the random variations of secondary emission from the grid and plate; *flicker noise*, caused by the spontaneous emission of particles from an oxide-coated cathode, an effect particularly noticeable at low frequencies; and *induced grid noise*, resulting from the random nature of the electron stream near the grid. In addition to these, we also have in a pentode *partition noise*, which arises from the random fluctuation in the current division between the screen and the plate. Because of this partition effect, a pentode may be much noisier (perhaps by a factor of 10) than a triode. Hence the input stage to a high-gain amplifier is usually a triode. We should note that it is the input stage whose noise must be kept extremely low, because any noise generated in this tube is amplified by all the following stages.

Noise Figure A *noise figure NF* has been introduced in order to be able to specify quantitatively how noisy a circuit is. By definition, *NF* is the ratio of the noise power output of the circuit under consideration to the noise power output which would be obtained in the same bandwidth if the only source of noise were the thermal noise in the internal resistance R_s of the signal source. Thus the noise figure is a quantity which compares the noise in an actual amplifier with that in an ideal (noiseless) amplifier. Usually, NF is expressed in decibels.

We define the following symbols:

$$S_{Pi} (S_{Vi}) = \text{signal power (voltage) input}$$
$$N_{Pi} (N_{Vi}) = \text{noise power (voltage) input due to } R_s$$
$$S_{Po} (S_{Vo}) = \text{signal power (voltage) output}$$
$$N_{Po} (N_{Vo}) = \text{noise power (voltage) output due to } R_s \text{ and any noise}$$
$$\text{sources within the active device}$$

From Eq. (16-41), $N_{Vi} = V_n = (4\bar{k}TR_sB)^{\frac{1}{2}}$.

From the definition of noise figure

$$NF \equiv 10 \log \frac{\text{total noise power output}}{\text{noise power output due to } R_s} = 10 \log \frac{N_{Po}}{A_P N_{Pi}} \qquad (16\text{-}44)$$

where the power gain of the active device is $A_P \equiv S_{Po}/S_{Pi}$. Hence,

$$NF = 10 \log \frac{N_{Po} S_{Pi}}{S_{Po} N_{Pi}} = 10 \log \frac{S_{Pi}/N_{Pi}}{S_{Po}/N_{Po}} \qquad (16\text{-}45)$$

The quotient S_P/N_P is called the *signal-to-noise power ratio*. The noise figure is the input signal-to-noise power ratio divided by the output signal-to-noise power ratio. Expressed in decibels, the noise figure is given by the input signal-to-noise power ratio in decibels minus the output signal-to-noise power ratio in decibels. Since the signal and noise appear across the same load, Eq. (16-45) takes the form

$$NF = 20 \log \frac{S_{Vi}/N_{Vi}}{S_{Vo}/N_{Vo}} = 20 \log \frac{S_{Vi}}{N_{Vi}} - 20 \log \frac{S_{Vo}}{N_{Vo}} \qquad (16\text{-}46)$$

where S_V/N_V is called the *signal-to-noise voltage ratio*.

Measurement of Noise Figure A very simple method[10] for measuring the noise figure of an active device Q is indicated in Fig. 16-16. An audio sinusoidal generator V_s with source resistance R_s is connected to the input of

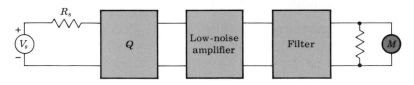

Fig. 16-16 A system used to measure the noise figure of an active device Q.

Q. The active device is cascaded with a low-noise amplifier and a filter, and the output of this system is measured on a true rms reading voltmeter M. The experimental procedure for determining NF is as follows:

1. Measure R_s and calculate $N_{Vi} \equiv V_n$ from Eq. (16-41). The bandwidth B is set by the filter.

2. Adjust the audio signal voltage so that it is ten times the noise voltage: $V_s = 10V_n$ or $S_{Vi} = 10N_{Vi}$. Measure the output voltage with M. For such a large signal-to-noise ratio ($S_{Vi}/N_{Vi} = 20$ dB) we may neglect the noise and assume that the voltmeter reading gives the signal output voltage S_{Vo}.

3. Set $V_s = 0$ and measure the output voltage N_{Vo} with M.

4. From Eq. (16-46) the noise figure is given by

$$NF = 20 - 20 \log \frac{S_{Vo}}{N_{Vo}} \tag{16-47}$$

where S_{Vo} and N_{Vo} are the meter readings obtained in measurements 2 and 3, respectively.

The low-noise amplifier is required only if the noise output of Q is too low to be detected with M. It should be pointed out that the amplifier-filter combination does not affect NF (for a given B) since the ratio S_{Vo}/N_{Vo} is used in Eq. (16-47).

The accuracy of the method described is based on the assumption that the output signal and noise can be measured separately. This is not strictly true since the noise cannot be turned off while measuring the output signal. It is found[10] that for a 20-dB input signal-to-noise ratio, transistor noise figures may be measured up to 10 dB with less than 0.5 dB error. The larger the S_{Vi}/N_{Vi}, the smaller is the error in this measurement. Usually the output signal voltage is monitored on an oscilloscope to make certain that the system operates linearly so that no clipping takes place and no 60-Hz hum is present.

If a filter with a very narrow bandwidth (a few hertz) is used, the foregoing measurement gives the *spot, single-frequency,* or *incremental noise figure.* On the other hand, if the filter bandwidth is large (from $f_1 = 10$ Hz to $f_2 = 10$ kHz), then the circuit of Fig. 16-16 gives the *broadband* or *integrated noise figure.* Other methods of measuring NF are available,[11,12] but these have the disadvantage of requiring a calibrated noise generator.

Transistor Noise[13]   In addition to thermal noise in a transistor, there is noise due to the random motion of the carriers crossing the emitter and collector junctions and to the random recombination of holes and electrons in the base. There is also a partition effect arising from the random fluctuation in the division of current between the collector and base. It is found that a transistor does not generate white noise, except over a midband region. Also, the amount of noise generated depends upon the quiescent conditions and the source resistance. Hence, in specifying the noise in a transistor, the center frequency, the operating point, and R_s must be given.

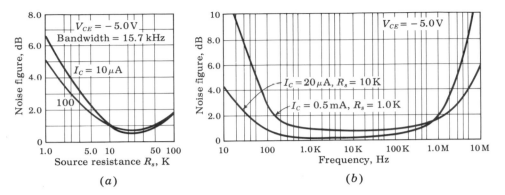

Fig. 16-17 Noise figure of a 2N3964 transistor. (a) Broadband NF as a function of source resistance; (b) spot NF as a function of frequency. (Courtesy of Fairchild Semiconductor Corp.)

Figure 16-17a and b show the noise figure vs. source resistance and frequency for the 2N3964 diffused planar resistor. There are three distinct regions in Fig. 16-16b. At low frequencies the noise varies approximately as $1/f$, and is called *excess* or *flicker* noise. The source of this noise is not clearly understood, but is thought to be caused by the recombination and generation of carriers on the surface of the crystal. In intermediate frequencies the noise is independent of frequency. This white noise is caused by the bulk resistance of the semiconductor material and the statistical variation of the currents (shot noise). The third region in Fig. 16-17b is characterized by an increase of the noise figure with frequency, and is essentially caused by a decrease in power gain with frequency.[12]

FET Noise[14] The field-effect transistor exhibits excellent noise characteristics. The main sources of noise in the FET are the thermal noise of the conducting channel, the shot noise caused by the gate leakage current, and the $1/f$ noise caused by surface effects. The FET is also superior, from a noise point of view, to a vacuum tube of comparable transconductance.[12]

The noise figure vs. frequency for the 2N2497 FET transistor is shown

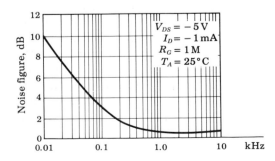

Fig. 16-18 The spot noise figure for a 2N2497 FET. (Courtesy of Texas Instruments, Inc.)

in Fig. 16-18. It should be pointed out that, unlike the bipolar transistor, the noise figure of the FET is essentially independent of the quiescent point (I_D and V_{DS}).

REFERENCES

1. Millman, J., and H. Taub: "Pulse, Digital, and Switching Waveforms," chap. 5, McGraw-Hill Book Company, New York, 1965.

2. Ref. 1, sec. 4-4.

3. Ref. 1, sec. 4-12.

4. Ref. 1, sec. 5-8.

5. Johannes, V.: "Transient Response of Transistor Video Amplifiers," sec. 1, University Microfilms, Ann Arbor, Mich., 1961.

6. Ref. 1, sec. 2-1.

7. Terman, F. E.: "Electronic and Radio Engineering," 4th ed., pp. 503–506, McGraw-Hill Book Company, New York, 1955.

8. RCA *Appl. Note* 88.

9. Van der Ziel, A.: "Noise," Prentice-Hall, Inc., Englewood Cliffs, N.J., 1954.
   Ref. 7, pp. 434–442, 796–798.
   Seely, S.: "Radio Electronics," pp. 143–149, McGraw-Hill Book Company, New York, 1956.
   Valley, G. E., Jr., and H. Wallman (eds.): "Vacuum Tube Amplifiers," MIT Radiation Laboratory Series, vol. 18, pp. 496–720, McGraw-Hill Book Company, New York, 1948.

10. Miller, J. R. (ed.): "Solid-state Communications," Texas Instruments Electronic Series, pp. 194–197, McGraw-Hill Book Company, New York, 1966.

11. Terman, F. E., and J. M. Pettit: "Electronic Measurements," pp. 362–379, McGraw-Hill Book Company, New York, 1952.

12. Dosse, J.: "The Transistor," 4th ed., pp. 144–152, D. Van Nostrand Company, Inc., Princeton, N.J., 1964.

13. Thornton, R. D., et al.: "Characteristics and Limitations of Transistors," Semiconductor Electronics Education Committee, vol. 4, John Wiley & Sons, Inc., New York, 1966.

14. Van der Ziel, A.: Thermal Noise in Field Effect Transistors, *Proc. IRE*, vol. 50, pp. 1808–1812, August, 1962.
    Van der Ziel, A.: "Electronics," chap. 23, Allyn and Bacon, Inc., Boston, 1966.
    Sevin, L. J.: "Field-effect Transistors," pp. 46–50, McGraw-Hill Book Company, New York, 1965.

17 / FEEDBACK AMPLIFIERS AND OSCILLATORS

In this chapter we introduce the concept of feedback and show how to modify the characteristics of an amplifier by combining a portion of the output signal with the external signal. Many advantages are to be gained from the use of negative (degenerative) feedback, and these are studied. It is possible for the feedback to be positive (regenerative), and the circuit may then oscillate. Examples of feedback amplifier and oscillator circuits are given.

17-1   CLASSIFICATION OF AMPLIFIERS

Before proceeding with the concept of feedback, it is useful to classify amplifiers into four broad categories,[1] as either *voltage, current, transconductance,* or *transresistance amplifiers*. This classification is based on the magnitudes of the input and output impedances of an amplifier relative to the source and load impedances, respectively.

Voltage Amplifier Figure 17-1a shows a Thévenin's equivalent circuit of a two-port network which represents an amplifier. If the amplifier input resistance R_i is large compared with the source resistance R_s, then $V_i \approx V_s$. If the external load resistance R_L is large compared with the output resistance R_o of the amplifier, then $V_o \approx A_v V_i \approx A_v V_s$. This amplifier provides a voltage output proportional to the voltage input, and the *proportionality factor is independent of the magnitudes of the source and load resistances*. Such a circuit is called a *voltage amplifier*. An ideal voltage amplifier must have infinite input resistance R_i and zero output resistance R_o. The symbol A_v in Fig. 17-1a represents V_o/V_i with $R_L = \infty$, and hence represents the open-circuit voltage amplification, or gain.

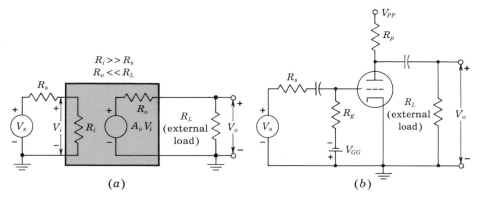

Fig. 17-1 (a) Thévenin's equivalent circuit of a voltage amplifier. (b) A simple vacuum-tube voltage amplifier. For this circuit $R_i = R_g$, $R_o = R_p \| r_p$, and $A_v = -g_m R_o$.

A practical circuit which approximates the ideal voltage amplifier is the simple triode-tube voltage amplifier shown in Fig. 17-1b. Note that the open-circuit voltage gain is computed with $R_L = \infty$, but with R_p in place.

Current Amplifier An ideal current amplifier[1] is defined as an amplifier which provides an output current proportional to the signal current, and *the proportionality factor is independent of R_s and R_L.* An ideal current amplifier must have zero input resistance R_i and infinite output resistance R_o. In practice, the amplifier has low input resistance and high output resistance. It drives a low-resistance load ($R_o \gg R_L$), and is driven by a high-resistance source ($R_i \ll R_s$). Figure 17-2a shows Norton's equivalent circuit of a current amplifier. Note that $A_i \equiv I_L/I_i$, with $R_L = 0$, representing the short-circuit current amplification, or gain. We see that if $R_i \ll R_s$, $I_i \approx I_s$, and if $R_o \gg R_L$, $I_L \approx A_i I_i \approx A_i I_s$. Hence the output current is proportional to the signal current. The characteristics of the four ideal amplifier types are summarized in Table 17-1.

A practical circuit which approximates the ideal current amplifier is the

TABLE 17-1   Ideal amplifier characteristics

Parameter	Amplifier type			
	Voltage	Current	Transconductance	Transresistance
R_i....................	∞	0	∞	0
R_o....................	0	∞	∞	0
Transfer characteristic..	$V_o = A_v V_s$	$I_L = A_i I_s$	$I_L = G_m V_s$	$V_o = R_m I_s$
Figure................	17-1	17-2	17-3	17-4

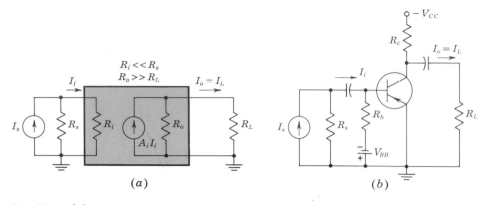

Fig. 17-2 (a) Norton's equivalent circuit of a current amplifier. (b) A simple common-emitter transistor current amplifier. For this circuit $R_b \gg R_i \approx h_{ie}$, $A_i = -h_{fe}$, $R_o \approx R_c$, assuming that $h_{oe}(R_c \| R_L) < 0.1$.

simple common-emitter transistor amplifier of Fig. 17-2b. The amplifier of Fig. 17-2b can be considered as a voltage amplifier if $R_s \ll h_{ie}$ and $R_L \gg R_o$. In that case the amplifier should be represented by its Thévenin's equivalent circuits at the input and the output ports.

Transconductance Amplifier The ideal transconductance amplifier[1] supplies an output current which is proportional to the signal voltage, independently of the magnitudes of R_s and R_L. This amplifier must have an infinite input resistance R_i and infinite output resistance R_o. A practical transconductance amplifier has a large input resistance $(R_i \gg R_s)$ and hence must be driven by a low-resistance source. It presents a high output resistance $(R_o \gg R_L)$ and hence drives a low-resistance load. The equivalent circuit of a transconductance amplifier is shown in Fig. 17-3a.

A practical transconductance amplifier using a pentode is shown in Fig. 17-3b. From the circuit of Fig. 17-3a we have that $V_i \approx V_s$ if $R_i \gg R_s$. Also, if $R_o \gg R_L$, then $I_L \approx G_m V_i \approx G_m V_s$. Hence the output current is proportional to the input-signal voltage. The proportionality factor is $G_m \equiv I_L / V_i$, with $R_L = 0$, and represents the short-circuit mutual or transfer conductance. Note that the voltage and current amplifiers of Figs. 17-1 and 17-2 may also be considered as imperfect transconductance amplifiers.

Transresistance Amplifier Finally, in Fig. 17-4a, we show the equivalent circuit of an amplifier which ideally supplies an output voltage V_o in proportion to the signal current I_s independently of R_s and R_L. This amplifier is called a *transresistance amplifier*. For a practical transresistance amplifier we must have $R_i \ll R_s$ and $R_o \ll R_L$. Hence the input and output resistances are low relative to the source and load resistances. From Fig. 17-4a we see that if $R_s \gg R_i$, $I_i \approx I_s$, and if $R_o \ll R_L$, $V_o \approx R_m I_i \approx R_m I_s$. Note that $R_m \equiv V_o / I_i$

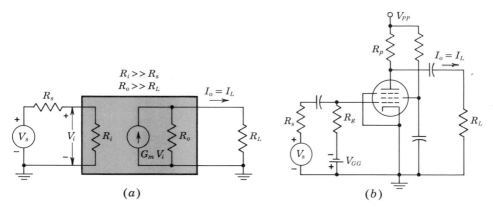

Fig. 17-3 (a) A transconductance amplifier is represented by a Thévenin's equivalent in its input circuit and a Norton's equivalent in its output circuit. (b) A pentode transconductance amplifier. For this circuit $R_i = R_g$, $R_o \approx R_p \gg R_L$, $G_m = -g_m$. A FET also approximates a transconductance amplifier provided that $R_o = R_d \| r_d \gg R_L$.

with $R_L = \infty$. In other words, R_m is the open-circuit mutual or transfer resistance.

The common-emitter circuit of Fig. 17-2b may be considered as a trans-resistance amplifier if $R_L \gg R_c$. In that case we convert the output current source into a voltage source, as indicated in Fig. 17-4b.

17-2   THE FEEDBACK CONCEPT[2]

In the preceding section we summarize the properties of four basic amplifier types. In each one of these circuits we may sample the output voltage or

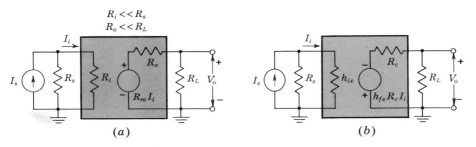

Fig. 17-4 (a) A transresistance amplifier is represented by a Norton's equivalent in its input circuit and a Thévenin's equivalent in its output circuit. (b) Equivalent circuit of a common-emitter transistor transresistance amplifier. For this circuit $R_i = h_{ie}$, $R_m = -h_{fe}R_c$, $R_o \approx R_c \ll R_L$, assuming that $h_{oe}(R_c\|R_L) < 0.1$.

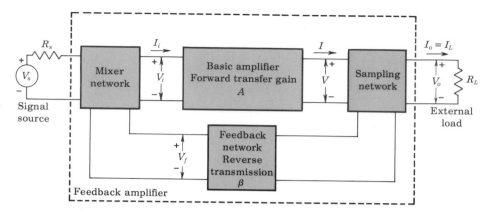

Fig. 17-5 Representation of any single-loop feedback connection around a basic amplifier. The transfer gain A may represent A_v, A_i, G_m, or R_m.

current by means of a suitable sampling network and apply this signal to the input through a feedback two-port network, as shown in Fig. 17-5. At the input the feedback signal is combined with the external (source) signal through a mixer network and is fed into the amplifier proper.

Feedback Network This block in Fig. 17-5 is usually a passive two-port network which may contain resistors, capacitors, and inductors. Very often it is simply a resistive configuration.

Sampling Network Several sampling blocks are shown in Fig. 17-6. In Fig. 17-6a the output voltage is sampled by connecting the feedback network *in shunt* across the output. In this case it is desirable that the input impedance of the feedback network be much greater than R_L so as not to load the output of the amplifier. Another feedback connection which samples the out-

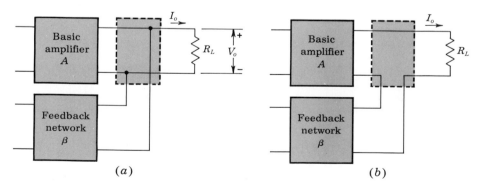

Fig. 17-6 Feedback connections at the output of a basic amplifier, sampling the output (a) voltage and (b) current.

put current is shown in Fig. 17-6b, where the feedback network is connected
in series with the output.   Here the input impedance of the feedback network
should be much smaller than R_L in order not to reduce the current gain appreciably (without feedback).   Other sampling networks are possible.

Mixing Network   Various mixing blocks are shown in Fig. 17-7.   Figure
17-7a and b show the simple and very common *series input* and *shunt input*
connections, respectively.   Figure 17-7c shows a mixing network consisting of
a single transistor, and in Fig. 17-7d we indicate a differential input connection.

Feedback may be classified as either *positive* or *negative*.   In the former
case any increase in the output signal results in a feedback signal into the input
in such a way as to increase further the magnitude of the output signal.   When
the feedback results in a decrease in the magnitude of the output signal, the
amplifier is said to have negative feedback.

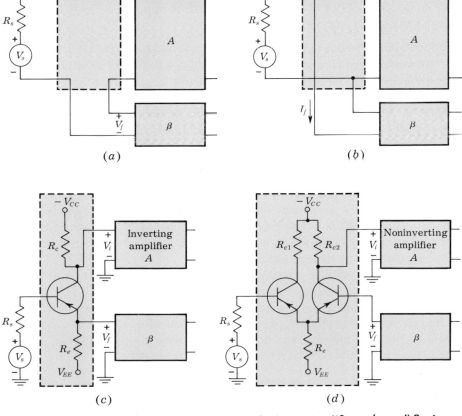

Fig. 17-7   Feedback connections at the input of a basic amplifier.   (a, c, d) Series
feedback.   (b) Shunt feedback.   In (c) and (d) the gain for V_s may not be the
same as the gain for V_f.

Transfer Ratio or Gain   The symbol A in Fig. 17-5 represents the ratio of the output signal to the input signal of the basic amplifier.   For an ideal amplifier the transfer ratio V/V_i is the voltage amplification or the *voltage gain* A_v.   Similarly the transfer ratio I/I_i is the current amplification or *current gain* A_i for an ideal current amplifier.   The ratio I/V_i of the ideal basic amplifier is the transconductance G_m, and V/I_i is the transresistance R_m.   Although G_m and R_m are defined as the ratio of two signals, one of these is a current and the other is a voltage waveform.   Hence, the symbol G_m or R_m does not represent an amplification in the usual sense of the word.   Nevertheless it is convenient to refer to each of the four quantities A_v, A_i, G_m, and R_m as a *transfer gain of the basic ideal amplifier* and to use the symbol A to represent any one of these quantities.

The symbol A_f is defined as the ratio of the output signal to the input signal of the amplifier configuration of Fig. 17-5 and is called the *transfer gain of the feedback amplifier*.   Hence A_f is used to represent any one of the four ratios V_o/V_s, I_o/I_s, I_o/V_s, and V_o/I_s.   The relationship between the transfer gain A_f with feedback and the gain A of the ideal amplifier without feedback is derived below [Eq. (17-4)].

Advantages of Negative Feedback   The usefulness of negative feedback lies in the fact that, in general, any of the four basic amplifier types discussed in Sec. 17-1 may be made to exhibit the properties of any other type by the proper application of negative feedback.   In addition, any one of the four basic amplifier types may be improved by the proper use of negative feedback. For example, the normally high input resistance of a voltage amplifier can be made higher, and its normally low output resistance can be lowered.   Also, the transfer gain A_f of the amplifier with feedback can be stabilized against variations of the h parameters of the transistors or the parameters of the FETs or tubes used in the amplifier.   Another important advantage of the proper use of negative feedback is the significant improvement in the frequency response and in the linearity of operation of the feedback amplifier compared with that of the amplifier without feedback.

It should be pointed out that all the advantages mentioned above are obtained at the expense of the gain A_f with feedback, which is lowered in comparison with the transfer gain A of an amplifier without feedback.   Also, under certain circumstances, discussed later in this chapter, a negative-feedback amplifier may become unstable and break into oscillations.   Special precautions must be taken to avoid this undesirable effect.

The Transfer Gain with Feedback   Any one of the output connections of Fig. 17-6 may be combined with any of the input connections of Fig. 17-7 to form the feedback amplifier of Fig. 17-5.   The analysis of the feedback amplifier can then be carried out by replacing each active element (transistor, FET, or vacuum tube) by its small-signal model and by writing Kirchhoff's

TABLE 17-2   Voltage and current signals in feedback amplifiers

Signal	Type of feedback			
	Voltage-series Fig. 17-9a	Current-series Fig. 17-9b	Current-shunt Fig. 17-9c	Voltage-shunt Fig. 17-9d
X_s	Voltage	Voltage	Current	Current
X_o	Voltage	Current	Current	Voltage
X_f	Voltage	Voltage	Current	Current
X_d	Voltage	Voltage	Current	Current

loop, or nodal, equations.   That approach, however, does not place in evidence the main characteristics of feedback.

As a first step toward a method of analysis which emphasizes the benefits of feedback, consider Fig. 17-8, which represents an ideal feedback amplifier. The basic amplifier of Fig. 17-8 may be an ideal voltage, transconductance, current, or transresistance amplifier connected in a feedback configuration, as indicated in Fig. 17-9.   The input signal X_s, the output signal X_o, the feedback signal X_f, and the difference signal X_d each represent either a voltage or a current, as indicated in Table 17-2.   The symbol indicated by the circle in Fig. 17-8 represents a mixing network whose output is the sum of the inputs, taking the sign shown at each input into account.   Thus

$$X_d = X_s - X_f \tag{17-1}$$

Since X_d represents the difference between the applied signal and that fed back to the input, X_d is called the *difference* or *error signal*.

Two major assumptions have been made in the idealized feedback circuit of Fig. 17-8.   The first assumption is that the basic amplifier is unilateral[3] from input to output (this is not valid if $h_{re} \neq 0$ for a CE transistor amplifier). The second assumption is that the passive bilateral feedback network is unilateral and transmits a signal from the output to the input but not in the opposite direction.   The reverse transmission factor β of the feedback network

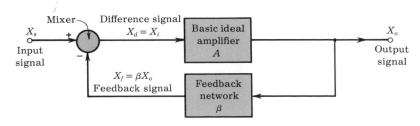

Fig. 17-8 Ideal single-loop feedback amplifier.

is defined by

$$X_f \equiv \beta X_o \tag{17-2}$$

The factor β is often a positive or a negative real number, but, in general, β is a complex function of the signal frequency. (This symbol should not be confused with the symbol β used previously for the CE short-circuit current gain.) The symbol X_o is the output voltage, or the output (load) current.

In Sec. 17-1 we show that for an ideal amplifier the output is proportional to the input and that this proportionality factor A is independent of the magnitude of the source and load impedances. Thus

$$X_o = A X_i = A X_d \tag{17-3}$$

By substituting Eqs. (17-1) and (17-2) into (17-3), we obtain for A_f, the gain with feedback,

$$A_f \equiv \frac{X_o}{X_s} = \frac{A}{1 + \beta A} \tag{17-4}$$

The quantity A in Eqs. (17-3) and (17-4) represents the transfer gain (A_v, A_i, G_m, or R_m) of the corresponding amplifier without feedback, used as the basic amplifier in Fig. 17-8. In the following section many of the desirable features of feedback are deduced, starting with the fundamental relationship given in Eq. (17-4).

If $|A_f| < |A|$, the feedback is termed *negative*, or *degenerative*. If $|A_f| > |A|$, the feedback is termed *positive*, or *regenerative*. From Eq. (17-4) we see that in the case of negative feedback, the gain of the basic ideal amplifier with feedback is divided by the factor $|1 + \beta A|$, which exceeds unity.

Loop Gain The signal X_d in Fig. 17-8 is multiplied by A in passing through the amplifier, is multiplied by β in transmission through the feedback network, and is multiplied by -1 in the mixing or differencing network. Such a path takes us from the input terminals around the loop consisting of the amplifier and feedback network back to the input; the product $-A\beta$ is called the *loop gain, loop transmission feedback factor*, or *return ratio*. Also, the amount of feedback introduced into an amplifier is often expressed in decibels by the definition

$$N = \text{dB of feedback} = 20 \log \left| \frac{A_f}{A} \right| = 20 \log \left| \frac{1}{1 + A\beta} \right|$$

If negative feedback is under consideration, N will be a negative number.

17-3 GENERAL CHARACTERISTICS OF NEGATIVE–FEEDBACK AMPLIFIERS[4]

Since negative feedback reduces the transfer gain, why is it used? The answer to this question is that it is used because many desirable characteristics are otained for the price of gain reduction.   We now examine some of the advantages of negative feedback.

Stability of Transfer Amplification   The variation due to aging, temperature, replacement, etc., of the circuit components and transistor or tube characteristics is reflected in a corresponding lack of stability of the amplifier transfer gain.   The fractional change in amplification with feedback is related to the fractional change without feedback by

$$\left|\frac{dA_f}{A_f}\right| = \frac{1}{|1 + \beta A|}\left|\frac{dA}{A}\right| \tag{17-5}$$

This equation is obtained by differentiating Eq. (17-4).   If the feedback is negative, so that $|1 + \beta A| > 1$, the feedback will have served to improve the gain stability of the amplifier.   For example, for an amplifier with 20 dB of negative feedback, $|1/(1 + A\beta)| = 0.1$, and a 1 percent change in the gain without feedback is reduced to a 0.1 percent change after feedback is introduced.

In particular, if $|\beta A| \gg 1$, then

$$A_f = \frac{A}{1 + \beta A} \approx \frac{A}{\beta A} = \frac{1}{\beta} \tag{17-6}$$

and the gain may be made to depend entirely on the feedback network.   The worst offenders with respect to stability are usually the vacuum tubes and transistors involved.   If the feedback network contains only stable passive elements, the improvement in stability may indeed be pronounced.

Feedback is used to improve stability in the following way: Suppose an amplifier of gain A_1 is required.   We start by building an amplifier of gain $A_2 = kA_1$, in which k is a large number.   Feedback is now introduced to divide the gain by the factor k.   The stability will be improved by the same factor k, since both gain and stability are divided by the factor $k = |1 + \beta A_2|$.   If now the instability of the amplifier of gain A_2 is not appreciably poorer than the instability of an amplifier of gain without feedback equal to A_1, this procedure will have been useful.   It often happens as a matter of practice that amplifier gain may be increased appreciably without a corresponding loss of stability.   Consider, for example, the case of a one-stage-triode voltage amplifier (Fig. 17-1b).   The gain is $A_v = -g_m R_o$; g_m is the tube transconductance; and $R_o = R_p \| r_p$.   The principal source of instability is in g_m.   Hence the fractional change in gain is the same for a given fractional change in g_m, independently of the size of R_p, the plate-circuit resistance.   However, the gain may be increased by increasing R_p.   Similarly, consider the transistor transresistance amplifier (Fig. 17-4b), where the transfer gain is $R_m = -h_{fe}R_c$ and the short-circuit current gain h_{fe} varies with temperature and device replacement.   Without worsening the stability, the gain may be increased by using a larger value of the collector-circuit resistance R_c.

Frequency Distortion   It follows from Eq. (17-6) that if the feedback network does not contain reactive elements, the overall gain is not a function of frequency. Under these circumstances a substantial reduction in frequency and phase distortion is obtained. If, on the other hand, a frequency-selective feedback network is used, so that β depends upon frequency, the amplification may depend markedly upon frequency. For example, it is possible to obtain an amplifier with a high-Q bandpass characteristic by using a feedback network which gives little feedback at the center of the band and a great deal of feedback on both sides of this frequency.

Nonlinear Distortion Suppose that a large amplitude signal is applied to a stage of an amplifier so that the operation of the device extends slightly beyond its range of linear operation, and as a consequence the output signal is slightly distorted. Negative feedback is now introduced, and the input signal is increased by the same amount by which the gain is reduced, so that the output-signal amplitude remains the same. For simplicity, let us consider that the input signal is sinusoidal and that the distortion consists, simply, of a second-harmonic signal generated within the active device. We assume that the second-harmonic component, in the absence of feedback, is equal to B_2. Because of the effects of feedback, a component B_{2f} actually appears in the output. To find the relationship that exists between B_{2f} and B_2, it is noted that the output will contain the term $-A\beta B_{2f}$, which arises from the component $-\beta B_{2f}$ that is fed back to the input. Thus the output contains two terms: B_2, generated in the transistor or tube, and $-A\beta B_{2f}$, which represents the effect of the feedback. Hence

$$B_2 - A\beta B_{2f} = B_{2f}$$

or

$$B_{2f} = \frac{B_2}{1 + A\beta} \tag{17-7}$$

Since A and β are generally functions of the frequency, they must be evaluated at the second-harmonic frequency.

The signal X_s to the feedback amplifier may be the actual signal externally available, or it may be the output of an amplifier preceding the feedback stage or stages under consideration. In order to multiply the input to the feedback amplifier by the factor $|1 + A\beta|$, it is necessary either to increase the nominal gain of the preamplifying stages or to add a new stage. If the full benefit of the feedback amplifier in reducing nonlinear distortion is to be obtained, these preamplifying stages must not introduce additional distortion, because of the increased output demanded of them. Since, however, appreciable harmonics are introduced only when the output swing is large, most of the distortion arises in the last stage. The preamplifying stages are of smaller importance in considerations of harmonic generation.

It has been assumed in the derivation of Eq. (17-7) that the small amount of additional distortion that might arise from the second-harmonic component fed back from the output to the input is negligible. This assumption leads to little error. Further, it must be noted that the result given by Eq. (17-7) applies only in the case of small distortion. The principle of superposition has been used in the derivation, and for this reason it is required that the device operate approximately linearly.

Reduction of Noise By employing the same reasoning as that in the discussion of nonlinear distortion, it can be shown that the noise introduced in an amplifier is multiplied by the factor $1/|1 + A\beta|$ if feedback is employed. If $|1 + A\beta|$ is much larger than unity, this would seem to represent a considerable reduction in the output noise. However, as noted above, for a given output the amplification of the preamplifier for a specified overall gain must be increased by the factor $|1 + A\beta|$. Since the noise generated is independent of the signal amplitude, there may be as much noise generated in the preamplifying stage as in the output stage. Furthermore, this additional noise will be amplified, as well as the signal, by the feedback amplifier, so that the complete system may actually be noisier than the original amplifier without feedback. If the additional gain required to compensate what is lost because of the presence of inverse feedback can be obtained by a readjustment of the circuit parameters rather than by the addition of an extra stage, a definite reduction will result from the presence of the feedback. In particular, the hum introduced into the circuit by a poorly filtered power supply may be decreased appreciably.

Nonideal Amplifiers Most transistor amplifiers are considered to be nonideal current amplifiers; triode-tube amplifiers are thought of as nonideal voltage amplifiers; pentode amplifiers and field-effect transistor (FET) amplifiers are considered to be nonideal transconductance amplifiers; and finally, some transistor amplifiers are treated as nonideal transresistance amplifiers. The characteristics discussed above for the idealized amplifier continue to remain valid, in general, for a physical (real or commercial) device. For example, in Sec. 17-6 we show that the voltage gain is stabilized for a nonideal amplifier connected into a feedback circuit, where the output *voltage* is sampled and fed back in *series* with the input. (We refer to such a connection simply as *voltage-series feedback*.) Similarly, for any of the other connections in Fig. 17-9, the transfer gain is stabilized, even if the amplifier is constructed with physical devices.

17-4 EFFECT OF NEGATIVE FEEDBACK UPON OUTPUT AND INPUT RESISTANCES[5]

In subsequent sections we examine the effect of negative feedback on the characteristics of a nonideal amplifier. We consider in detail the following four configurations:

1. Voltage-series feedback (Fig. 17-9a)
2. Current-series feedback (Fig. 17-9b)

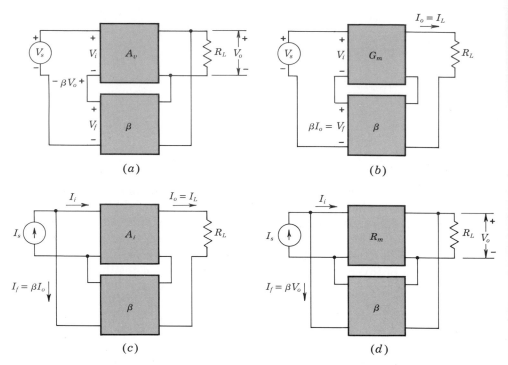

Fig. 17-9 Feedback-amplifier connections. (a) Voltage amplifier with voltage-series feedback. (b) Transconductance amplifier with current-series feedback. (c) Current amplifier with current-shunt feedback. (d) Transresistance amplifier with voltage-shunt feedback.

3. Current-shunt feedback (Fig. 17-9c)
4. Voltage-shunt feedback (Fig. 17-9d)

In this section we discuss qualitatively the effect of the methods of sampling and mixing upon the output resistance R_{of} and the input resistance R_{if} with feedback.

Output Resistance   Negative feedback which samples the output *voltage*, regardless of how this output signal is returned to the input, tends to *decrease the output resistance*. For example, if R_L increases so that v_o increases, the effect of feeding this voltage back to the input in a degenerative manner (negative feedback) is to cause v_o to increase less than it would if there were no feedback. Hence the output voltage tends to remain constant as R_L changes, which means that $R_{of} \ll R_L$. This argument leads to the conclusion that this type of feedback (sampling the output voltage) reduces the output resistance.

By similar reasoning to that given above, negative feedback which samples the output *current* will tend to hold this current constant. Hence an output-current source is created ($R_{of} \gg R_L$), and we conclude that this type of sampling connection increases the output resistance.

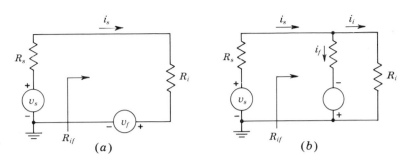

Fig. 17-10 The mixer circuit connections affect the input resistance. (a) Series input and (b) shunt input.

Input Resistance   If the feedback signal is returned to the input in *series* to oppose the applied voltage, regardless of whether it is obtained by sampling the output voltage or current, it tends to *increase the input resistance*.   Since the feedback voltage v_f opposes v_s, as indicated in Fig. 17-10a, the current i_s is less than it would be if v_f were absent.   Hence $R_{if} \equiv v_s/i_s - R_s$ is increased.

Negative feedback in which the output signal is fed back to the input in *parallel* tends to *decrease the input resistance*.   As indicated in Fig. 17-10b, the current i_s drawn from the signal source is increased over what it would be if there were no feedback current i_f.   Hence R_{if} is decreased because of this type of feedback.

Table 17-3 summarizes the characteristics of the four types of negative-feedback configurations.

17-5   VOLTAGE–SERIES FEEDBACK[1,4]

In order to investigate the effect of sampling the output voltage and returning a portion of it to the input in series and opposing the applied signal, let us

TABLE 17-3   Effect of negative feedback on amplifier characteristics

	Type of feedback			
	Voltage-series	Current-series	Current-shunt	Voltage-shunt
Figure....................	17-9a	17-9b	17-9c	17-9d
R_{of}.....................	Decreases	Increases	Increases	Decreases
R_{if}.....................	Increases	Increases	Decreases	Decreases
Improves................	Voltage amplifier	Transconductance amplifier	Current amplifier	Transresistance amplifier
Stabilizes...............	A_{vf}	G_{mf}	A_{if}	R_{mf}
Bandwidth..............	Increases	Increases	Increases	Increases
Nonlinear distortion........	Decreases	Decreases	Decreases	Decreases

consider Fig. 17-11. We assume that the feedback network presents no loading on the output of the basic amplifier, which is here considered as a nonideal voltage amplifier. We also assume that there is no forward transmission through the β feedback network, and we investigate the error made because of this assumption.

Voltage Gain and Output Resistance From Fig. 17-11 we have

$$V_o = A_v V_i - I_L R_o \tag{17-8}$$

$$V_i = \frac{R_i}{R_i + R_s} (V_s - V_f) \tag{17-9}$$

Substituting from Eq. (17-9) into Eq. (17-8) and remembering that $V_f = \beta V_o$, we have

$$V_o = \frac{A_v R_i}{R_i + R_s} (V_s - \beta V_o) - I_L R_o$$

$$V_o = \frac{A_{vs} V_s}{1 + A_{vs}\beta} - I_L \frac{R_o}{1 + A_{vs}\beta} \tag{17-10}$$

where

$$A_{vs} \equiv \frac{A_v R_i}{R_i + R_s} \tag{17-11}$$

is the open-circuit voltage amplification, taking the source impedance into account. Note that if $R_s = 0$, $A_{vs} = A_v$. Taking R_s into account, the over-all voltage gain with feedback is

$$A_f \equiv A_{vsf} = \frac{A_{vs}}{1 + A_{vs}\beta} \tag{17-12}$$

Provided that β is independent of the external load R_L, it follows from Eq. (17-10) that the output impedance with feedback is

$$R_{of} = \frac{R_o}{1 + A_{vs}\beta} \tag{17-13}$$

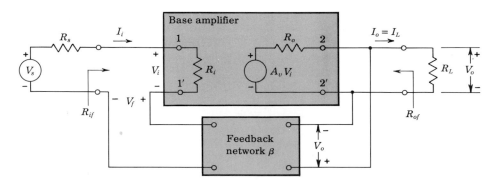

Fig. 17-11 Voltage-series feedback.

For negative feedback, $|1 + A_{vs}\beta| > 1$, and hence $R_{of} < R_o$, in agreement with Table 17-3. Note that the output impedance with feedback depends somewhat on the source resistance R_s because A_{vs} depends upon R_s.

If R_L is considered part of the amplifier instead of an external load, the above equations remain valid, except that A_{vs} is replaced by A_{Vs}, the voltage amplification without feedback, taking both R_s and R_L into account, and R_o is now replaced by the parallel combination of R_o and R_L. If β is a complex function of frequency, then R_{of} is also a complex function of frequency, and is called the output impedance with feedback Z_{of}.

If $|A_{vs}\beta| \gg 1$, then $A_{vsf} \approx 1/\beta$, and hence the voltage gain is stabilized, in agreement with Table 17-3.

Input Resistance The input resistance without feedback R_i is defined by $R_i \equiv V_i/I_i$, where I_i is the input current. The input resistance with feedback is defined by

$$R_{if} \equiv \frac{V_s}{I_i} - R_s \tag{17-14}$$

Referring to Fig. 17-11, we have

$$V_s = I_i(R_s + R_i) + V_f \tag{17-15}$$

$$V_f = \beta V_o = \beta \frac{A_v R_L V_i}{R_L + R_o} = \beta A_V R_i I_i \tag{17-16}$$

where

$$A_V = \frac{A_v R_L}{R_L + R_o} \tag{17-17}$$

is the voltage gain, taking the load into account, but with $R_s = 0$. From Eqs. (17-14) to (17-16),

$$R_{if} = R_i + \frac{V_f}{I_i} = R_i(1 + \beta A_V) \tag{17-18}$$

For $|1 + \beta A_V| > 1$, $R_{if} > R_i$, which agrees with Table 17-3. Note that the input impedance with feedback depends somewhat upon the load resistance because A_V is a function of R_L.

Notation The symbols used in this section for the voltage gain of an amplifier *without feedback* are defined as follows:

A_v = open-circuit gain ($R_L = \infty$), with $R_s = 0$
A_{vs} = open-circuit gain ($R_L = \infty$), taking the source resistance into account ($R_s \neq 0$)
A_V = gain taking load resistance into account ($R_L \neq \infty$), with $R_s = 0$
A_{Vs} = gain taking both load and source resistance into account ($R_L \neq \infty$ and $R_s \neq 0$)

If a feedback amplifier is under consideration, an additional subscript f is added to each symbol.   For example,

A_{Vsf} = gain *with feedback* taking both load and source resistances into account

If frequency response is under consideration, the subscripts o, 1, and 2 are added to each symbol to represent *midband, low-frequency,* and *high-frequency* regions, respectively.   For example,

A_{V2} = high-frequency gain (without feedback) taking load resistance into account, with $R_s = 0$

We now show two practical circuits employing voltage-series feedback.

EXAMPLE   Find A_{vf} and R_{of} for the feedback circuit of Fig. 17-12.

Solution   Suppose that in the circuit of Fig. 17-12 we *define* the output terminals to be K and N, so that $V_o = V_{kn}$, and the input terminals to be G and K, so that $V_i = V_{gk}$.   The external signal generator is connected to G and N, so that $V_s = V_{gn}$.   The circuit may now be redrawn as in Fig. 17-13a, which corresponds to Fig. 17-11, with $R_s = 0$.   Independently of whether the resistor R_k is considered a part of the amplifier or an external load, we have a case of voltage feedback in which $\beta = +1$, since $V_f = V_o$.   Let us consider that R_k is an external load, and not a part of the amplifier.   Then $V_o = \mu V_i$.   Since $R_s = 0$, $A_v = A_{vs}$ and we have

$$A_v = \frac{V_o}{V_i} = \frac{V_{kn}}{V_{gk}} = \mu = A_{vs}$$

and $1 + \beta A_v = 1 + \mu$.   The impedance without feedback seen looking to the left between terminals K and N is $r_p + R_p$.   The voltage gain and output impedance with feedback are found from Eqs. (17-12) and (17-13) to be

$$A_{vf} = \frac{\mu}{\mu + 1}$$

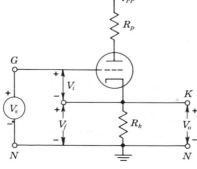

Fig. 17-12 Amplifier with plate and cathode resistors.

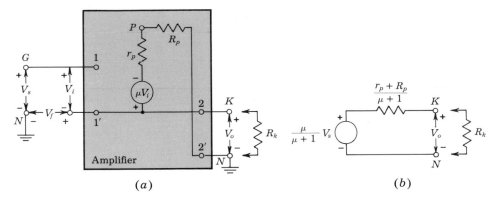

Fig. 17-13 (a) Circuit of Fig. 17-12 redrawn as a voltage-series feedback amplifier. (b) Equivalent circuit with respect to output terminals between cathode and ground.

and

$$R_{of} = \frac{r_p + R_p}{\mu + 1}$$

The equivalent circuit is as indicated in Fig. 17-13b and is the circuit "looking into the cathode" discussed in Sec. 8-8.

We have seen above that voltage-series feedback greatly improves a nonideal voltage amplifier. These results are of particular importance with a transistor amplifier because transistor amplifiers have fairly low input resistance and large output resistance (they are nonideal current amplifiers). It thus becomes possible, using voltage-series feedback, to convert a transistor amplifier into a voltage amplifier having a high input resistance and a low output resistance.

EXAMPLE Find (a) the voltage gain with feedback A_{Vsf}, taking load and source resistances into account, (b) R_{if}, and (c) R_{of} for the feedback circuit of Fig. 17-14a.

Solution a. If we use the simplified CE hybrid model to represent the transistor, we can draw the approximate small-signal equivalent circuit shown in Fig. 17-14b. The voltage gain A_{Vs} without feedback is obtained by connecting the grounded side of V_s to E. With this connection,

$$V_s = (R_s + h_{ie})I_i \qquad V_o = h_{fe}R_eI_i$$

and

$$A_{Vs} \equiv \frac{V_o}{V_s} = \frac{h_{fe}R_e}{R_s + h_{ie}} \tag{17-19}$$

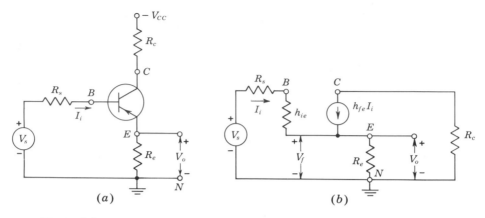

Fig. 17-14 (a) Emitter-follower amplifier circuit. (b) Approximate small-signal equivalent circuit.

In this circuit we have a case of voltage-series feedback in which $\beta = +1$, since $V_f = V_o$. Using Eq. (17-12), we obtain

$$A_{Vsf} = \frac{A_{Vs}}{1 + A_{Vs}\beta} = \frac{\dfrac{h_{fe}R_e}{R_s + h_{ie}}}{1 + \dfrac{h_{fe}R_e}{R_s + h_{ie}}} = \frac{h_{fe}R_e}{R_s + h_{ie} + h_{fe}R_e}$$

b. From Eq. (17-19), with $R_s = 0$, we have $A_V = h_{fe}R_e/h_{ie}$ and

$$R_{if} = R_i(1 + \beta A_V) = h_{ie}\left(1 + h_{fe}\frac{R_e}{h_{ie}}\right) = h_{ie} + h_{fe}R_e$$

c. The output impedance without feedback is $R_o = V/I$, where V and I refer to the open-circuit output voltage and the short-circuit output current of the amplifier without feedback, that is, with the grounded side of V_s in Fig. 17-14b connected to E. Since

$$V = \lim_{R_e \to \infty} V_o = \lim_{R_e \to \infty} \frac{h_{fe}R_e V_s}{R_s + h_{ie}}$$

and

$$I = \frac{h_{fe}V_s}{R_s + h_{ie}}$$

then $R_o = V/I = \lim_{R_e \to \infty} R_e$. Hence, the output resistance without feedback is infinite. This result should be evident since our model of the transistor is that of a current source. From Eq. (17-13) the output resistance with feedback is

$$R_{of} = \frac{R_o}{1 + A_{vs}\beta} = \frac{\lim_{R_e \to \infty} R_e}{1 + \beta \lim_{R_e \to \infty} A_{Vs}} = \lim_{R_e \to \infty} \frac{R_e}{1 + \dfrac{h_{fe}R_e}{R_s + h_{ie}}}$$

where we have used Eq. (17-19) and the fact that $\beta = 1$.   Finally,

$$R_{of} = \frac{R_s + h_{ie}}{h_{fe}} \tag{17-20}$$

The foregoing expressions for A_{vsf}, R_{if}, and R_{of} are based on the assumption of zero forward transmission through the feedback network.   Since there is such forward transmission, these expressions are only approximately true.   In this example we have in effect neglected the base current which flows in R_e compared with the collector current.   The more exact answers are obtained in Sec. 12-5, and they differ from those given above only in that h_{fe} must be replaced by $h_{fe} + 1$.

Effect of Feedback on Amplifier Bandwidth[4,6]   From Eq. (17-12), with $R_s = 0$ and taking R_L into account, we see that if $|\beta A_V| \gg 1$, then

$$A_{Vf} \approx \frac{A_V}{\beta A_V} = \frac{1}{\beta} \tag{17-21}$$

and from this result we concluded that the voltage gain may be made to depend entirely on the feedback network.   However, it is now important to consider the fact that even if β is constant, the voltage gain A_V is not, since it depends on frequency.   This means that at certain high or low frequencies $|\beta A_V|$ will not be much larger than unity, and hence Eq. (17-21) will not be valid.   In order to study the effect of voltage-series feedback on the bandwidth of the amplifier, we refer to the circuit of Fig. 17-15.   It should be pointed out that this particular circuit suffers from the disadvantage that the input-signal voltage V_s must be isolated from ground.   Since usually one terminal of a signal source is grounded, the circuit is of little practical importance.   Figure 17-15 may be modified to include a transformer to couple either the signal or the feedback voltage into the input circuit.   With such a connection the limited frequency response of the transformer must be taken into account.

A fraction β (real and positive) of the output voltage from the single-

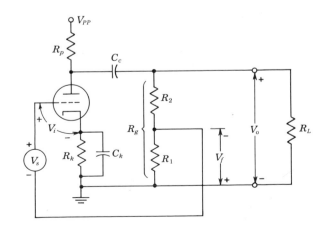

Fig. 17-15 Voltage-series feedback applied to a single-stage RC-coupled amplifier.

stage RC-coupled amplifier is fed back to the input circuit, as indicated in Fig. 17-15. (We assume that C_k is arbitrarily large, so that the self-biasing arrangement in the cathode circuit introduces no frequency distortion.)

The high-frequency voltage gain A_{V2} without feedback is given by Eq. (16-5):

$$A_{V2} = \frac{A_{Vo}}{1 + j(f/f_2)}$$

where A_{Vo} (real and negative) is the midband gain without feedback. The gain with feedback is given by Eq. (17-12):

$$A_{V2f} = \frac{A_{V2}}{1 + \beta A_{V2}} = \frac{\dfrac{A_{Vo}}{1 + j(f/f_2)}}{1 + \dfrac{\beta A_{Vo}}{1 + j(f/f_2)}}$$

$$= \frac{A_{Vo}}{1 + \beta A_{Vo} + j(f/f_2)}$$

By dividing numerator and denominator by $1 + \beta A_{Vo}$, this equation may be put in the form

$$A_{V2f} = \frac{A_{Vof}}{1 + j(f/f_{2f})}$$

where

$$A_{Vof} \equiv \frac{A_{Vo}}{1 + \beta A_{Vo}} \quad \text{and} \quad f_{2f} \equiv f_2(1 + \beta A_{Vo}) \tag{17-22}$$

We see that the *midband amplification with feedback* A_{Vof} equals the midband amplification without feedback A_{Vo} divided by $1 + \beta A_{Vo}$. Also, the *upper 3-dB frequency with feedback* f_{2f} equals the corresponding 3-dB frequency without feedback f_2 multiplied by the same factor $1 + \beta A_{Vo}$. The gain-frequency product has not been changed by feedback because, from Eqs. (17-22),

$$A_{Vof}f_{2f} = A_{Vo}f_2 \tag{17-23}$$

By starting with Eq. (16-2) for the low-frequency gain of a single RC-coupled stage and proceeding as above, we can show that the *lower 3-dB frequency with feedback* f_{1f} is decreased by the same factor as is the gain, or

$$f_{1f} = \frac{f_1}{1 + A_{Vo}\beta} \tag{17-24}$$

For an audio or video amplifier, $f_2 \gg f_1$, and hence the bandwidth is $f_2 - f_1 \approx f_2$. Under these circumstances, Eq. (17-23) may be interpreted to mean that the gain-bandwidth product is the same with or without feedback. Figure 17-16 is a plot of A_V and A_{Vf} versus frequency.

Equations (17-22) and (17-24) show how the upper and lower 3-dB frequencies are affected by this type of negative feedback. We may obtain a physical feeling of the mechanism by which feedback extends bandwidth

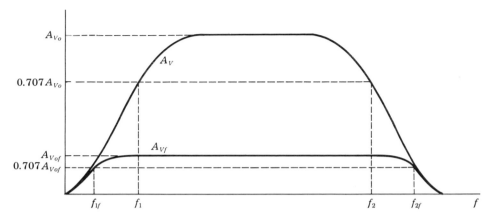

Fig. 17-16 Voltage gain is decreased and bandwidth is increased for an amplifier using voltage-series negative feedback.

by referring to Fig. 17-15. Let us assume that the midband voltage gain $A_{Vo} = -1,000$, $\beta = -0.1$, and $V_s = 0.1$ V. Under these conditions,

$$A_{Vof} = \frac{A_{Vo}}{1 + A_{Vo}\beta} = \frac{-1,000}{1 + 100} = -9.90$$

$$V_o = A_{Vof}V_s = (-9.90)(0.1) = -0.99 \text{ V}$$

$$V_f = \beta V_o = (-0.1)(-0.99) = 0.099 \text{ V}$$

$$V_i = V_s - V_f = 0.1 - 0.099 = 0.001 \text{ V}$$

Note that almost the entire applied signal is canceled (*bucked out*) by the feedback signal, leaving a very small voltage V_i at the input terminals of the amplifier.

Now assume that at some higher frequency the amplifier gain of the amplifier (without feedback) has fallen to half its previous value, so that $A_{V2} = -500$. Then, if V_s remains at 0.1 V,

$$A_{V2f} = \frac{A_{V2}}{1 + A_{V2}\beta} = \frac{-500}{1 + 50} = -9.80$$

$$V_o = A_{V2f}V_s = (-9.80)(0.1) = -0.98 \text{ V}$$

$$V_f = (-0.1)(-0.98) = 0.098 \text{ V}$$

$$V_i = 0.1 - 0.098 = 0.002 \text{ V}$$

Note that although the base amplifier gain has been halved, the amplification with feedback has changed by only 1 percent. In the second case V_i has doubled to compensate for the drop in A_V. There exists a self-regulating action so that, if the open-loop voltage gain falls (as a function of frequency), the feedback voltage also falls. Therefore less of the input voltage is bucked out, permitting more voltage to be applied to the amplifier input, and V_o remains almost constant.

17-6   A VOLTAGE–SERIES FEEDBACK PAIR

Figure 17-17 shows two cascaded stages whose voltage gains are A_{V1} and A_{V2}, respectively.   The output of the second stage is fed back through the feedback network R_1R_2 in opposition to the input signal V_s.   Clearly, then, this is a case of voltage-series negative feedback.   According to Table 17-3, we should expect the input resistance R_i to increase, the output resistance to decrease, and the voltage gain to be stablized.

The circuit of Fig. 17-17a may be redrawn as indicated in Fig. 17-17b so as to correspond to the basic voltage-series feedback configuration of Fig. 17-11. The equivalence of the two circuits in Fig. 17-17 is demonstrated as follows. From Fig. 17-17a

$$V_s = V_{BE} + I'R_1 + IR_1 \qquad I = \frac{V_o - I'R_1}{R_1 + R_2}$$

Combining these two equations yields

$$V_s = V_{BE} + I'R_1 + \frac{R_1 V_o}{R_1 + R_2} - \frac{I'R_1{}^2}{R_1 + R_2}$$

$$= V_{BE} + I'\left(\frac{R_1 R_2}{R_1 + R_2}\right) + \beta V_o$$

where

$$\beta \equiv \frac{R_1}{R_1 + R_2} \qquad\qquad\qquad (17\text{-}25)$$

Note that β is independent of the load.   The above expression for V_s leads to the input circuit of Fig. 17-17b.

The output voltages V_{oa} for Fig. 17-17a and V_{ob} for Fig. 17-17b are respectively given by

$$V_{oa} = I(R_1 + R_2) + I'R_1 \qquad V_{ob} = I(R_1 + R_2)$$

Hence, the two output circuits may be considered to be equivalent provided

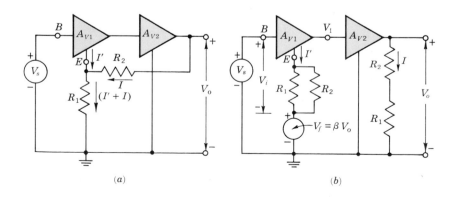

(a)   (b)

Fig. 17-17   (a) Voltage-series feedback pair.   (b) Equivalent circuit.

that $I'R_1 \ll I(R_1 + R_2)$ or

$$\frac{I'}{I} \frac{R_1}{R_1 + R_2} \ll 1 \tag{17-26}$$

This condition is always satisfied for a well-designed amplifier.

Second-collector to First-emitter Feedback Pair   The circuit of Fig. 17-18 shows a two-stage amplifier which makes use of voltage-series feedback by connecting the second collector to the first emitter through the voltage divider R_1R_2.   Capacitors C_1, C_2, C_5, and C_6 are dc blocking capacitors, and capacitors C_3 and C_4 are bypass capacitors for the emitter bias resistors.   All these capacitances represent negligible reactances at the frequencies of operation of this circuit.   For this amplifier the voltage gain A_{Vf} is given approximately by $1/\beta$, and is thus stabilized against temperature changes and transistor replacement.   A more accurate determination of A_{Vf}, as well as a calculation of input and output resistance, is given in the following illustrative problem.

EXAMPLE   Calculate A_{Vf}, R_{of}, and R_{if} for the amplifier of Fig. 17-18.   Assume $R_s = 0$, $h_{fe} = 50$, $h_{ie} = 1.1$ K, $h_{re} = h_{oe} = 0$, and identical transistors.

Solution   The effective load R'_{L1} of transistor $Q1$ is

$$R'_{L1} = 10\|47\|33\|1.1 \text{ K} = 942 \ \Omega$$

From Fig. 17-17b we see that the effective load R'_{L2} of transistor $Q2$ is the collector resistance $R_{c2} = 4.7$ K in parallel with $R_1 + R_2 = 4.8$ K,

$$R'_{L2} - 4.7\|4.8 - 2.37 \text{ K}$$

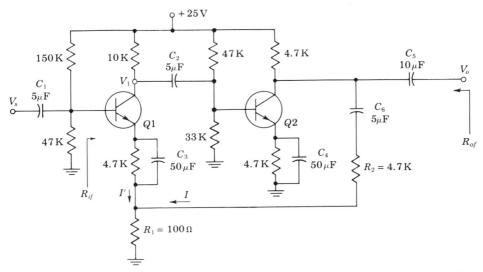

Fig. 17-18   Second-collector to first-emitter feedback pair.   (National Bureau of Standards, Preferred Circuit 201.)

From Fig. 17-17b we see that the effective emitter impedance R_e of $Q1$ is $R_1 \| R_2$, or

$$R_e = R_1 \| R_2 = 0.1 \| 4.7 \text{ K} = .098 \text{ K} = 98 \ \Omega$$

The voltage gain A_{V1} of $Q1$ is from Eq. (12-40) and Fig. 17-17b,

$$A_{V1} \equiv \frac{V_1}{V_i} = \frac{-h_{fe} R'_{L1}}{h_{ie} + (1 + h_{fe}) R_e} = \frac{-50 \times 0.942}{1.1 + (51)(0.098)} = -7.72$$

The voltage gain A_{V2} of $Q2$ is, from Eq. (12-28),

$$A_{V2} \equiv \frac{V_o}{V_1} = -h_{fe} \frac{R'_{L2}}{h_{ie}} = -50 \times \frac{2.37}{1.1} = -108$$

Hence the voltage gain A_V of the two stages in cascade is

$$A_V \equiv \frac{V_o}{V_i} = A_{V1} A_{V2} = 7.72 \times 108 = 834$$

$$\beta = \frac{R_1}{R_1 + R_2} = \frac{100}{4{,}800} = \frac{1}{48} \quad \text{and} \quad A_V \beta = \frac{834}{48} = 17.4$$

Using Eq. (17-12), we obtain

$$A_{Vf} = \frac{834}{1 + 17.4} = 45.4$$

This value is to be compared with the approximate solution (based upon $A_V \to \infty$) given by $A_{Vf} = 1/\beta = 48$.

The output resistance without feedback is $R_o \approx 4.7 \| 4.8 = 2.37$ K. Hence, from Eq. (17-13),

$$R_{of} = \frac{2.37}{1 + 17.4} \text{ K} = 129 \ \Omega$$

The input resistance without feedback is from Eq. (12-39)

$$R_i \approx h_{ie} + (1 + h_{fe}) R_e = 1.1 + (51)(0.098) = 6.1 \text{ K}$$

Hence, from Eq. (17-18),

$$R_{if} = (6.1)(1 + 17.4) = 112 \text{ K}$$

The student should verify that Eq. (17-26) is satisfied.

17-7   CURRENT–SERIES FEEDBACK[7]

In order to investigate the effect of sampling the output current I_o and of returning to the input a voltage proportional to I_o in series opposition to the applied signal V_s, let us consider Fig. 17-19. The basic amplifier has finite and nonzero input and output resistances R_i and R_o and a finite open-circuit voltage gain A_v. The signal-source output resistance is R_s. The output current is sampled by allowing it to develop a voltage drop across a small resistance R.

From Fig. 17-19 we see that $V_f = (-I_o + I_i)R$, and hence the voltage V_f does not depend on I_o alone as required by current-series feedback. How-

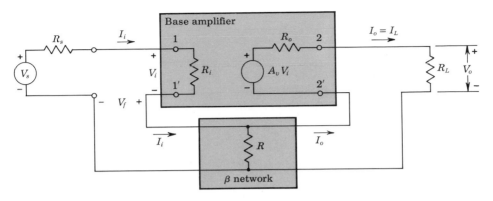

Fig. 17-19   Amplifier with current-series negative feedback.

ever, in the case of a vacuum-tube (or FET) single-stage amplifier which draws no grid (gate) current, $I_i = 0$ and $V_f = -I_oR$. In the case of a common-emitter single-stage amplifier, I_i and I_o represent base and collector currents, respectively. Hence we assume that $I_i \ll I_o$, so that $V_f \approx -I_oR$. Under these circumstances, the forward transmission through the β network is negligible, and Fig. 17-19 approximates a current-series feedback configuration, with $\beta = -R$.

From Eq. (17-6) the transfer gain (the transconductance) with feedback is

$$A_f \equiv G_{mf} \approx \frac{1}{\beta}$$

In this approximate analysis let us assume that the base amplifier of Fig. 17-19 is ideal. Then, since $G_{mf} = I_L/V_s$ and $\beta = -R$,

$$I_L = -\frac{V_s}{R} \tag{17-27}$$

Note that the transconductance with feedback has been stabilized. *The load current is directly proportional to the signal voltage, and this current depends only upon R,* and not upon any other circuit or device parameters.

Voltage Gain and Output Resistance   We shall now analyze the circuit of Fig. 17-19 more accurately by not neglecting I_i compared with I_L. Applying KVL to the output loop yields

$$V_o = A_vV_i - I_L(R_o + R) + I_iR$$

or since $V_i = I_iR_i$,

$$V_o = (A_vR_i + R)I_i - I_L(R_o + R) \tag{17-28}$$

Applying KVL to the input loop gives

$$V_s + I_LR = I_i(R_s + R_i + R) \tag{17-29}$$

Substituting for I_i from Eq. (17-29) into Eq. (17-28) yields

$$V_o = A_{vs}V_s - I_L R_{of} \tag{17-30}$$

where the open-circuit voltage gain, taking the source resistance into account, is

$$A_{vs} \equiv \frac{A_v R_i + R}{R_s + R_i + R} \tag{17-31}$$

and the output resistance with feedback is

$$R_{of} \equiv R_o + R(1 - A_{vs}) \tag{17-32}$$

The load current may be obtained from Eq. (17-30). Substituting $V_o = I_L R_L$ and using Eq. (17-32), we obtain

$$I_L = \frac{A_{vs}V_s}{R_L + R_o + R(1 - A_{vs})} \tag{17-33}$$

If

$$|A_{vs}R| \gg R_L + R_o + R \tag{17-34}$$

then $I_L \approx -V_s/R$, in agreement with Eq. (17-27). Note that condition (17-34) must be satisfied in order that the transconductance of the circuit be stabilized so that the load current depends only upon R and no other parameters of the amplifier. The voltage gain A_{Vsf} is given by

$$A_{Vsf} \equiv \frac{V_o}{V_s} = \frac{I_L R_L}{V_s} \approx -\frac{R_L}{R} \tag{17-35}$$

and hence A_{Vsf} is stable provided that R and R_L are stable resistances.

Input Resistance   The input resistance with feedback R_{if} as defined by Eq. (17-14) is obtained from Eq. (17-29):

$$R_{if} \equiv \frac{V_s}{I_i} - R_s = R_i + R(1 - A_I) \tag{17-36}$$

where the current gain A_I is defined by

$$A_I \equiv \frac{I_L}{I_i} \tag{17-37}$$

Vacuum-tube Amplifier with Unbypassed Cathode Resistance   The results obtained above are applied to the amplifier of Fig. 17-20, which represents either a vacuum-tube or a FET stage. This circuit has the configuration of the current-series feedback amplifier of Fig. 17-19, with

$$R_i = \infty \qquad R = R_k \qquad A_v = -\mu \qquad R_o = r_p \tag{17-38}$$

Hence, from Eqs. (17-31) and (17-32),

$$A_{vs} = -\mu \qquad R_{of} = r_p + (\mu + 1)R_k \tag{17-39}$$

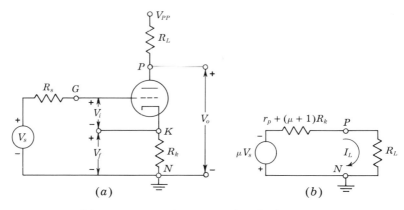

Fig. 17-20 (a) Amplifier with plate and cathode resistors as an
example of current-series feedback. (b) The equivalent circuit from
plate to ground.

The equivalent circuit with respect to the output terminals is given by Fig.
17-20b since KVL applied to this circuit satisfies Eq. (17-30).   This important
result is obtained in Sec. 8-8.

From Eq. (17-36), the input resistance with feedback is infinitely large.

Transistor Stage with Unbypassed Emitter Resistance We examine
next the amplifier of Fig. 17-21a, with the collector resistor R_L and the emitter
resistor R_e. If we assume $h_{re} = 0$, Fig. 17-21b represents the small-signal
model of the transistor between base, emitter, and collector.   In Fig. 17-21c
we replace Norton's form of the output circuit by its Thévenin's equivalent.

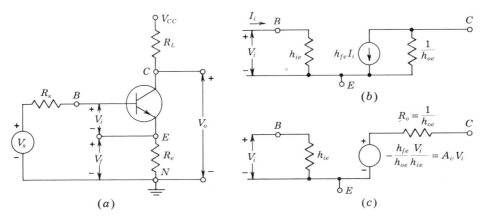

Fig. 17-21 (a) Amplifier with unbypassed emitter resistance as an example of
current-series feedback. (b) The h-parameter model of the transistor, neglecting
h_{re}. (c) The Thévenin's equivalent between C and E in (b).

This amplifier has the configuration of the current-series feedback amplifier of Fig. 17-19, with

$$R_i = h_{ie} \qquad R = R_e \qquad A_v = \frac{-h_{fe}}{h_{oe}h_{ie}} \qquad R_o = \frac{1}{h_{oe}} \tag{17-40}$$

If we assume that the load resistance is small enough so that the current gain A_I may be replaced by the short-circuit current amplification $-h_{fe}$, then Eq. (17-36) for the input impedance with feedback becomes

$$R_{if} = h_{ie} + (1 + h_{fe})R_e \tag{17-41}$$

This expression is identical with Eq. (12-39), derived in Sec. 12-7.

From Eq. (17-31) we obtain

$$A_{vs} = \frac{1}{h_{oe}} \frac{-h_{fe} + h_{oe}R_e}{R_s + h_{ie} + R_e} \tag{17-42}$$

Substituting this expression for A_{vs} into Eq. (17-33), we obtain for the load current

$$I_L = \frac{(-h_{fe} + h_{oe}R_e)V_s}{[1 + h_{oe}(R_e + R_L)](R_s + h_{ie} + R_e) - R_e(-h_{fe} + h_{oe}R_e)} \tag{17-43}$$

If we assume as in Sec. 12-7 that $h_{oe}(R_e + R_L) \ll 1$, then

$$I_L \approx \frac{-h_{fe}V_s}{R_s + h_{ie} + R_e(1 + h_{fe})} \tag{17-44}$$

which is consistent with the equivalent circuit of Fig. 12-11b. Finally, if $h_{fe}R_e \gg R_s + h_{ie} + R_e$, then $I_L \approx V_s/R_e$, and the voltage gain under load is

$$A_{Vsf} = \frac{I_L R_L}{V_s} \approx -\frac{R_L}{R_e} \tag{17-45}$$

in agreement with Eqs. (17-35) and (12-41).

The expression for the output impedance with feedback obtained from Eqs. (17-32), (17-31), and (17-40) is identical with that given in Eq. (12-51), with $h_{re} = 0$.

17-8   CURRENT–SHUNT FEEDBACK

Figure 17-22 shows two transistors in cascade with feedback from the second emitter to the first base through the resistor R'. We now verify that this connection produces negative feedback. The voltage V_{i2} is much larger than V_{i1} because of the voltage gain of Q1. Also, V_{i2} is 180° out of phase with V_{i1}. Because of emitter-follower action, V_{e2} is only slightly smaller than V_{i2}, and these voltages are in phase. Hence V_{e2} is larger in magnitude than V_{i1} and is 180° out of phase with V_{i1}. If the input signal increases so that I_s increases, I_f also increases, and $I_i = I_s - I_f$ is smaller than it would be if there were no feedback. This action is characteristic of *negative* feedback.

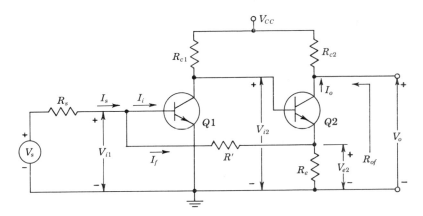

Fig. 17-22   Second-emitter to first-base feedback pair. (The input blocking capacitor and the biasing resistors are not indicated.)

We now show that if $R' \gg R_e$, the configuration of Fig. 17-22 approximates a current-shunt feedback pair. Since $V_{e2} \gg V_{i1}$, then

$$I_f = \frac{V_{i1} - V_{e2}}{R'} \approx - \frac{V_{e2}}{R'} \tag{17-46}$$

If we neglect the base current of $Q2$ compared with the collector current and if $R' \gg R_e$, then $V_{e2} \approx -I_o R_e$, and from Eq. (17-46),

$$I_f \approx \frac{R_e I_o}{R'} = \beta I_o \tag{17-47}$$

where $\beta = R_e/R'$. Since the feedback current is proportional to the output current, this circuit is an example of a current-shunt feedback amplifier. From Table 17-3 we expect the transfer (current) gain A_{if} to be stabilized. From Eqs. (17-6) and (17-47), and assuming $I_s \approx I_f$,

$$A_{if} = \frac{I_o}{I_s} \approx \frac{1}{\beta} = \frac{R'}{R_e} \tag{17-48}$$

and hence we have verified that A_{if} is stable provided that R' and R_e are stable resistances.

From Table 17-3 we expect the input resistance to be low and the output resistance to be high. If we assume that $R_{if} = 0$, then $V_s = I_s R_s$ and the voltage gain with feedback is

$$A_{Vsf} = \frac{V_o}{V_s} = \frac{I_o R_{c2}}{I_s R_s} \approx \frac{R'}{R_e} \frac{R_{c2}}{R_s} \tag{17-49}$$

Note that if R_e, R', R_{c2}, and R_s are stable elements, then A_{Vsf} is stable (independent of the transistor parameters, the temperature, or supply-voltage variations).

Detailed Analysis The feedback amplifier of Fig. 17-22 may be analyzed by examining the effect of resistor R' on the operation of the circuit, using Miller's theorem discussed in Sec. 12-9. From Eqs. (12-62) and (12-63), we note that it is possible to replace R' with two equivalent resistors,

$$R_1 = \frac{R'}{1 - A_V'}$$

and

$$R_2 = \frac{R'}{1 - 1/A_V'}$$

connected as shown in Fig. 17-23 without disturbing the currents and voltages in the circuit. In the expressions for R_1 and R_2, $A_V' \equiv V_{e2}/V_{i1}$ = voltage gain from first base to second emitter (called K in Sec. 12-9).

In most practical cases $-A_V \gg 1$, so that $R_2 \approx R'$. The analysis of the feedback amplifier of Fig. 17-22 may now proceed, using the results given in Table 12-2 applied to the circuit of Fig. 17-23.

EXAMPLE The circuit of Fig. 17-22 has the following parameters: $R_{c1} = 3$ K, $R_{c2} = 500$ Ω, $R_{e2} = 50$ Ω, $R' = R_s = 1.2$ K, $h_{fe} = 50$, $h_{ie} = 1.1$ K, and $1/h_{oe} = 40$ K. Find (a) $A_V' \equiv V_{e2}/V_{i1}$, (b) R_{if}, and also the resistance seen by the source, and (c) A_{Vf}. To provide the desired bias a 15-K resistance is connected from V_{CC} to the first base. Why does this resistor R_3 not affect the values calculated in (a), (b), or (c)?

Solution a. Let us assume that $-A_V' \gg 1$ and then justify this assumption later. Note that the effective emitter resistance R_e' of $Q2$ in Fig. 17-23 is

$$R_e' = R_{e2} \| R' = 50 \| 1,200 \approx 50 \text{ Ω}$$

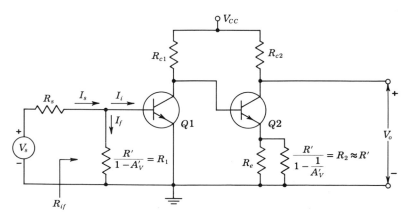

Fig. 17-23 Miller's theorem applied to the feedback pair of Fig. 17-22.

From Table 12-2 the input resistance of $Q2$ is

$$R_{i2} = h_{ie} + (1 + h_{fe})R'_e = 1,100 + (51)(50) = 3,650 \ \Omega = 3.65 \text{ K}$$

The voltage gain *from base to emitter* of $Q2$ is

$$A'_{V2} = 1 - \frac{h_{ie}}{R_{i2}} = 1 - \frac{1.1}{3.65} = 0.70$$

The effective load R'_L of $Q1$ is

$$R'_L = R_{c1}\|R_{i2} = 3\|3.65 = 1.65 \text{ K}$$

The voltage gain *from base to collector* of $Q1$ is

$$A_{V1} = -\frac{h_{fe}R'_L}{h_{ie}} = \frac{-50 \times 1.65}{1.1} = -75.0$$

Hence the voltage gain A'_V from the base of $Q1$ to the emitter of $Q2$ is

$$A'_V = A_{V1}A'_{V2} = -75.0 \times 0.70 = -52.5$$

which justifies our assumption that $-A'_V \gg 1$. Note that the calculation of A'_V is independent of R_3.

    b. From Fig. 17-23,

$$R_1 = \frac{R'}{1 - A'_V} = \frac{1,200}{1 + 52.5} = 22.4 \ \Omega$$

$$R_{if} = R_1\|R_{i1} = R_1\|h_{ie} = 22.4\|1,100 = 22.0 \ \Omega$$

Note that the input impedance is quite small, as predicted. The resistance seen by the signal source is $R_s + R_{if} = 1.22$ K. Since $R_2 = 15$ K is in parallel with $R_{if} = 22.0 \ \Omega$, R_3 has almost no effect on R_{if}.

    c. The voltage gain A_{V2} of $Q2$ *from base to collector* is, from Table 12-2,

$$A_{V2} = -\frac{h_{fe}R_{c2}}{R_{i2}} = \frac{-50 \times 500}{3,650} = -6.85$$

The voltage gain A_V *from the first base to the second collector* is

$$A_V = A_{V1}A_{V2} = (-75.0)(-6.85) = 514 = \frac{V_o}{V_i}$$

The overall voltage gain with feedback A_{Vsf} is given by

$$A_{Vsf} = \frac{V_o}{V_s} = \frac{V_o}{V_i}\frac{V_i}{V_s} = A_V \frac{R_{if}}{R_{if} + R_s} = \frac{(514)(22.0)}{1,220} = 9.3$$

The approximate expression of Eq. (17-49) yields

$$A_{Vsf} = \frac{R'}{R_e}\frac{R_{c2}}{R_s} = \left(\frac{1,200}{50}\right)\left(\frac{500}{1,200}\right) = 10.0$$

which is in error by 7 percent.

17-9   VOLTAGE–SHUNT FEEDBACK[1,7]

Figure 17-24a shows a common-emitter stage with a resistor R' connected from the output to the input.   This configuration is discussed in Sec. 10-3 as a method of stabilizing the operating point of a transistor.   We first obtain an approximate expression for the voltage gain with feedback.

In the circuit of Fig. 17-24a the output voltage V_o is much greater than 180° out of phase with the input voltage V_i.   Hence

$$I_f = \frac{V_i - V_o}{R'} \approx -\frac{V_o}{R'} = \beta V_o \tag{17-50}$$

where $\beta = -1/R'$.   Since the feedback current is proportional to the output voltage, this circuit is an example of a *voltage-shunt feedback amplifier*.   From Table 17-3 we expect the transfer gain (the transresistance) R_{mf} to be stabilized. From Eqs. (17-6) and (17-50), and assuming $I_s \approx I_f$,

$$A_f \equiv R_{mf} \equiv \frac{V_o}{I_s} \approx \frac{1}{\beta} = -R' \tag{17-51}$$

Note that the transresistance equals the feedback resistance from output to input of the transistor and is stable if R' is a stable resistance.

From Table 17-3 we expect both the input and output resistance to be low because of the voltage-shunt feedback.   If we assume that $R_{if} = 0$, then

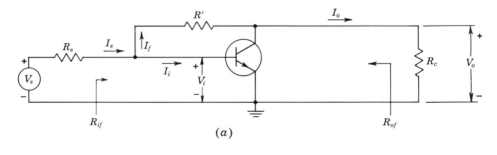

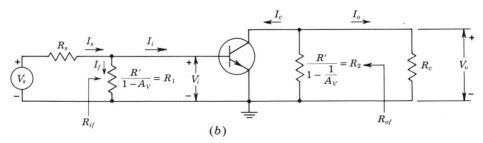

Fig. 17-24   (a) Voltage-shunt negative feedback.   (The supply voltage is not indicated).   (b) Effect of R' on the input and output of the amplifier is found using Miller's theorem.

the voltage gain with feedback is

$$A_{Vsf} = \frac{V_o}{V_s} \approx \frac{V_o}{I_s R_s} = -\frac{R'}{R_s} \tag{17-52}$$

where use is made of Eq. (17-51). Note that if R_f and R_s are stable elements, then A_{Vsf} is stable (independent of the transistor parameters, the temperature, or supply-voltage variations).

Detailed Analysis The feedback amplifier of Fig. 17-24a may be ana-lyzed in a manner similar to that used in the previous section. As shown in Fig. 17-24b, the effect of resistor R' is studied (using Miller's thereom of Sec. 12-9) by replacing R' with resistors $R_1 = R'/(1 - A_V)$ and $R_2 = R'/(1 - 1/A_V)$, where $A_V \equiv V_o/V_i$ is the voltage gain without feedback (but taking the loading of R' into account).

EXAMPLE For the circuit of Fig. 17-24a find (a) A_V, (b) R_{if}, and also the resist-ance seen by V_s, and (c) A_{Vsf}. Assume that $R_c = 4$ K, $R' = 40$ K, $R_s = 10$ K, and the transistor h parameters are those given in Table 11-2 ($h_{ie} = 1.1$ K, $h_{fe} = 50$, and $1/h_{oe} = 40$ K).

Solution a. Let us assume that $|A_V| \gg 1$, so that $R_2 \approx R' = 40$ K. From Fig. 17-24b we see that the equivalent collector resistance R'_L consists of R' and R_c in parallel or $R'_L = 40\|4 = 3.64$ K. With R'_L as the equivalent load, it is clear that the approximate equivalent circuit discussed in Sec. 12-4 is valid, and there-fore we obtain, by inspection of Fig. 17-24b,

$$A'_I = -\frac{I_c}{I_i} = -h_{fe} = -50$$

$$R_i = \frac{V_i}{I_i} = h_{ie} = 1.1 \text{ K}$$

and

$$A_V = \frac{V_o}{V_i} = \frac{A'_I R'_L}{R_i} = -50 \times \frac{3.64}{1.1} = -166$$

Hence our assumption that $|A_V| \gg 1$ is justified.

b. We have from Fig. 17-24b that

$$R_1 = \frac{R'}{1 - A_V} = \frac{40}{167} = 0.24 \text{ K}$$

and

$$R_{if} = h_{ie} \| R_1 = \frac{(1.1)(0.24)}{1.34} = 0.20 \text{ K} = 200 \ \Omega$$

Note that the input impedance is quite small, as predicted. The resistance as seen by the signal source V_s is $R_s + R_{if} = 10.2$ K.

c. The overall voltage gain is given by Eq. (11-36), or

$$A_{Vsf} = A_V \frac{R_{if}}{R_s + R_{if}} = -166 \times \frac{0.20}{10.20} = -3.26$$

The approximate expression of Eq. (17-52) yields

$$A_{Vsf} = -\frac{R'}{R_s} = -\frac{40}{10} = -4$$

which is about 19 percent in error.

Output Resistance   It is important to point out that the circuit of Fig. 17-24b cannot be used to compute R_{of} as equal to $R_2 \| (1/h_{oe})$, since R_{of} is independent of R_c, but $R_2 = R'/(1 - 1/A_V)$, and hence depends on R_c. The circuit of Fig. 17-24b is valid only for signal transmission from left to right. This circuit could still be used to find R_{of} as the ratio of the open-circuit voltage to the short-circuit current across the output terminals. It is more convenient, however, to find R_{of} by setting $V_s = 0$ and driving the amplifier from the output with a source V, as shown in Fig. 17-25, where we assume that $h_{re} = 0$. We find for the output conductance $Y_{of} = 1/R_{of}$ (Prob. 17-20)

$$Y_{of} = \frac{I}{V} = h_{oe} + \frac{1}{R' + R_s\|h_{ie}}\left(1 + h_{fe}\frac{R_s}{R_s + h_{ie}}\right) \qquad (17\text{-}53)$$

Since the output conductance is increased above the value h_{oe} without feedback, the output resistance is decreased below $1/h_{oe} = 40$ K. Using the parameter values in the above example, we find $R_{of} = 870 \ \Omega$.

17-10   THE OPERATIONAL AMPLIFIER

An operational amplifier is a special type of voltage-shunt feedback amplifier of great importance, particularly in electronic analog computers. It can be made to perform many mathematical functions, such as sign changing, scale changing, phase shifting, addition, integration, and differentiation.

The schematic diagram of the inverting-type (A_v negative) operational amplifier is shown in Fig. 17-26a, and the equivalent circuit is given in Fig.

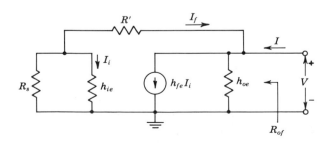

Fig. 17-25   Equivalent circuit for the calculation of the output resistance R_{of} of the voltage-shunt amplifier of Fig. 17-24a.

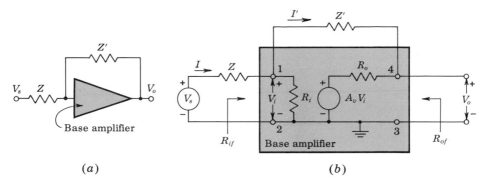

Fig. 17-26 (a) Schematic diagram and (b) equivalent circuit of an operational amplifier. The open-circuit voltage gain A_v is negative.

17-26b. The amplifier differs from the amplifier treated in the previous section only in the fact that it makes use of *a very high gain direct-coupled base amplifier* between terminals 1, 2, 3, and 4. Almost always the base amplifier consists of several common-cathode, common-emitter, or common-source stages in cascade. The input terminal is the grid, the base, or the gate. The output is usually taken from the plate, collector, or drain. Hence this type of feedback is sometimes called collector-to-base, grid-to-plate, or drain-to-gate feedback. Because of their small size, low-power consumption, and long life, transistors and/or FETs are almost exclusively used in operational amplifiers.[8] The feedback connection between amplifier output and input is an impedance Z', and the source is connected to the amplifier through an impedance Z.

Differential Operational Amplifier   The circuit shown in Fig. 17-27a and b represents an operational amplifier with differential input and differential output. The configuration most commonly used for this amplifier is a cascade of two differential amplifier circuits such as that described in Sec. 12-12. This arrangement fulfills the requirement for a high-gain direct-coupled base amplifier, and is readily adapted to integrated-circuit construction techniques.

In this chapter we analyze the single-input type of operational amplifier, and we examine in Probs. 17-28 and 17-29 the differential operational amplifier.

Ideal Operational Amplifier   An equivalent circuit of the operational amplifier obtained by using Miller's theorem (Sec. 12-9) is shown in Fig. 17-28. An ideal model of the operational amplifier consists of a base amplifier with infinite voltage gain, 180° phase shift between input and output, infinite bandwidth, and zero offset voltage (the output voltage is zero when the input voltage is zero). The input impedance for such an amplifier is $Z'/(1 - A_V) = 0$. Proceeding as in the foregoing section, we obtain for the transresistance (now more properly called the *transimpedance*) $R_m = -Z'$, and for the voltage gain

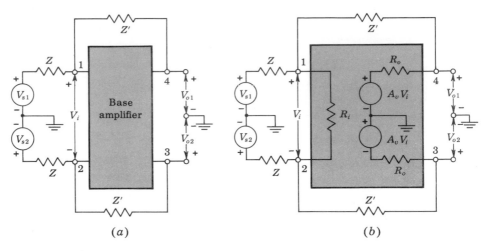

(a)   (b)

Fig. 17-27 (a) Schematic diagram and (b) equivalent circuit of a differential operational amplifier. Note that A_v is negative.

with feedback

$$A_{Vf} = \frac{V_o}{V_s} = -\frac{Z'}{Z} \tag{17-54}$$

corresponding to Eq. (17-52). Since the overall voltage gain is independent of the amplifier and depends only upon the two impedances Z and Z', it is clear that the gain has been stabilized.

The operation of the circuit may now be described in the following terms: At the input to the amplifier proper there exists a virtual short circuit or virtual ground. The term "virtual" is used to imply that, although the feedback from output to input through Z' serves to keep the voltage V_i at zero, no current actually flows through this short. The situation is depicted in Fig. 17-29, where the virtual ground is represented by the heavy double-headed arrow. The current furnished by the generator V_s continues past

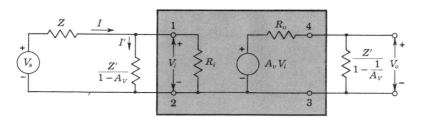

Fig. 17-28 An equivalent circuit of the operational amplifier. Note that $A_V \equiv V_o/V_i$.

Fig. 17-29 Virtual ground in the operational amplifier.

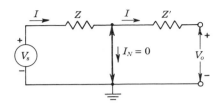

this virtual short through the impedance Z'. Hence $I = V_s/Z$, and

$$A_{Vf} = \frac{V_o}{V_s} = -\frac{IZ'}{V_s} = -\frac{Z'}{Z} \tag{17-55}$$

in agreement with Eq. (17-54). Of course, Fig. 17-29 does not represent a physical circuit, but it is a convenient mnemonic aid from which to calculate the output voltage for a given input signal.

Practical Operational Amplifier Equation (17-54) is valid only if $A_V \equiv V_o/V_i$ is infinite. It is sometimes important to consider the effect of a finite voltage gain. If A_{Vf} is calculated from Fig. 17-28, we obtain the following exact expression:

$$A_{Vf} = \frac{-Y}{Y' - (1/A_V)(Y' + Y + Y_i)} \tag{17-56}$$

where the Y's are the admittances corresponding to the Z's (for example, $Y' = 1/Z'$). Note that, as $A_V \to \infty$,

$$A_{Vf} = -\frac{Y}{Y'} = -\frac{Z'}{Z}$$

in agreement with Eq. (17-55).

17-11   BASIC USES OF OPERATIONAL AMPLIFIERS[9]

An operational amplifier may be used to perform many mathematical operations. This feature accounts for the name which has been assigned to this type of amplifier configuration. Among the basic configurations are the following.

Sign Changer, or Inverter If $Z = Z'$, then $A_{Vf} = -1$, and the sign of the input signal has been changed. Hence such a circuit acts as a phase inverter. If two such amplifiers are connected in cascade, the output from the second stage equals the signal input without change of sign. Hence the outputs from the two stages are equal in magnitude but opposite in phase, and such a system is an excellent paraphase amplifier.

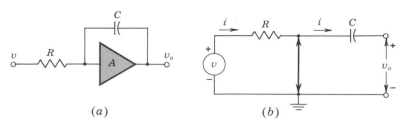

(a)   (b)

Fig. 17-30   (a) Operational integrator; (b) equivalent circuit.

Scale Changer   If the ratio $Z'/Z = k$, a real constant, then $A_{Vf} = -k$, and the scale has been multiplied by a factor $-k$.   Usually, in such a case of multiplication by a constant, -1 or $-k$, Z and Z' are selected as resistors.

Phase Shifter   Assume that Z and Z' are equal in magnitude but differ in angle.   Then the operational amplifier shifts the phase of a sinusoidal input voltage while at the same time preserving its amplitude.   Any phase shift from 0 to 360° (or $\pm 180°$) may be obtained.

Integrator   If $Z = R$ and a capacitor C is used for Z', as in Fig. 17-30, we can show that the circuit performs the mathematical operation of integration.   The input need not be sinusoidal, and hence is represented by the lowercase symbol $v = v(t)$.   (The subscript s is now omitted, for simplicity.)   Correspondingly, the current as a function of time is designated by $i = i(t)$.   In Fig. 17-30b (analogous to Fig. 17-29), the double-headed arrow represents a virtual ground.   Hence $i = v/R$, and

$$v_o = -\frac{1}{C} \int i \, dt = -\frac{1}{RC} \int v \, dt \tag{17-57}$$

The amplifier therefore provides an output voltage proportional to the integral of the input voltage.

If the input voltage is a constant, $v = V$, then the output will be a ramp, $v_o = -Vt/RC$.   Such an integrator makes an excellent sweep circuit for a cathode-ray-tube oscilloscope, and is called a *Miller integrator*, or *Miller sweep*.[10]

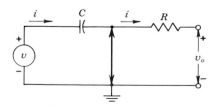

Fig. 17-31   Equivalent circuit of the operational differentiator.

Fig. 17-32 Operational adder, or summing amplifier.

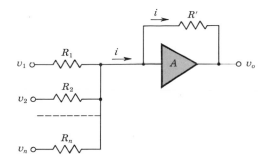

Differentiator If Z is a capacitor C and if $Z' = R$, then we see from the equivalent circuit of Fig. 17-31 that $i = C\, dv/dt$ and

$$v_o = -Ri = -RC\frac{dv}{dt} \tag{17-58}$$

Hence the output is proportional to the time derivative of the input.

Adder, or Summing Amplifier The arrangement of Fig. 17-32 may be used to obtain an output which is a linear combination of a number of input signals. Here

$$i = \frac{v_1}{R_1} + \frac{v_2}{R_2} + \cdots + \frac{v_n}{R_n}$$

and

$$v_o = -R'i = -\left(\frac{R'}{R_1}v_1 + \frac{R'}{R_2}v_2 + \cdots + \frac{R'}{R_n}v_n\right) \tag{17-59}$$

If $R_1 = R_2 = \cdots = R_n$, then

$$v_o = -\frac{R'}{R_1}(v_1 + v_2 + \cdots + v_n) \tag{17-60}$$

and the output is proportional to the sum of the inputs. In the more general case of Eq. (17-59), the scale of each input signal may be adjusted before adding.

Many other methods may of course be used to combine signals. The present method has the advantage that it may be extended to a very large number of inputs requiring only one additional resistor for each additional input. The result depends, in the limiting case of large amplifier gain, only on the resistors involved, and because of the virtual ground, there is a minimum of interaction between input sources.

If in Fig. 17-32 the resistor R' is replaced by a capacitor C, the circuit will simultaneously integrate and add. The output will be given by

$$v_o = -\frac{1}{C}\int i\, dt = -\frac{1}{CR_1}\int v_1\, dt \cdots - \frac{1}{CR_n}\int v_n\, dt \tag{17-61}$$

The General Case   In the important cases considered above, Z and Z' have been simple elements such as a single R or C.   In general, they may be any series or parallel combinations of R, L, or C.   Using the methods of operational calculus, or Laplace transform analysis, Z and Z' can be written in their operational form as $Z(s)$ and $Z'(s)$, where s is the complex-frequency variable.   In this notation the reactance of an inductor is written formally as Ls and that of a capacitor as $1/sC$.   The current $I(s)$ is then $V(s)/Z(s)$, and the output is

$$V_o(s) = -\frac{Z'(s)}{Z(s)} V(s) \tag{17-62}$$

The amplifier thus solves this operational equation.

17-12   ELECTRONIC ANALOG COMPUTATION[9]

The operational amplifier is the fundamental building block in an electronic analog computer.   As an illustration, let us consider how to program the differential equation

$$\frac{d^2v}{dt^2} + K_1 \frac{dv}{dt} + K_2 v - v_1 = 0 \tag{17-63}$$

where v_1 is a given function of time, and K_1 and K_2 are real positive constants.

We begin by assuming that d^2v/dt^2 is available in the form of a voltage. Then, by means of an integrator, a voltage proportional to dv/dt is obtained.   A second integrator gives a voltage proportional to v.   Then an adder (and scale changer) gives $-K_1(dv/dt) - K_2 v + v_1$.   From the differential equation (17-63) this equals d^2v/dt^2, and hence the output of this summing amplifier is fed to the terminal, where we had assumed that d^2v/dt^2 was available in the first place.

The procedure outlined above is carried out in Fig. 17-33.   The voltage d^2v/dt^2 is assumed to be available at an input terminal.   The integrator (1) has a time constant $RC = 1$ sec, and hence its output at terminal 1 is $-dv/dt$. This voltage is fed to a similar integrator (2), and the voltage at terminal 2 is $+v$.   The voltage at terminal 1 is fed to the inverter and scale changer (3), and its output at terminal 3 is $+K_1(dv/dt)$.   This same operational amplifier (3) is used as an adder.   Hence, if the given voltage $v_1(t)$ is also fed into it as shown, the output at terminal 3 also contains the term $-v_1$, or the net output is $+K_1(dv/dt) - v_1$.   Scale changer-adder (4) is fed from terminals 2 and 3, and hence delivers a resultant voltage $-K_2v - K_1(dv/dt) + v_1$ at terminal 4.   By Eq. (17-63) this must equal d^2v/dt^2, which is the voltage that was assumed to exist at the input terminal.   Hence the computer is completed by connecting terminal 4 to the input terminal.   (This last step is omitted from Fig. 17-33 for the sake of clarity of explanation.)

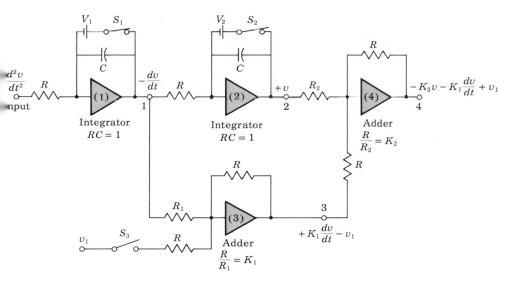

Fig. 17-33 A block diagram of an electronic analog computer. At $t = 0$, S_1 and S_2 are opened and S_3 is closed.

The specified initial conditions (the values of dv/dt and v at $t = 0$) must now be inserted into the computer. We note that the voltages at terminals 1 and 2 in Fig. 17-33 are proportional to dv/dt and v, respectively. Because of the virtual ground at the input of an operational amplifier, the voltage across the capacitor C of an integrator equals the output voltage. Hence initial conditions are taken care of by applying the correct voltages V_1 and V_2 across the capacitors in integrators 1 and 2, respectively.

The solution is obtained by opening switches S_1 and S_2 and simultaneously closing S_3 (by means of relays) at $t = 0$ and observing the waveform at terminal 2. If the derivative dv/dt is also desired, its waveform is available at terminal 1. The indicator may be a cathode-ray tube (with a triggered sweep), a recorder, or, for qualitative analysis with slowly varying quantities, a high-impedance voltmeter.

The solution of Eq. (17-63) can also be obtained with a computer which contains differentiators instead of integrators. However, integrators are almost invariably preferred over differentiators in analog-computer applications, for the following reasons: Since the gain of an integrator decreases with frequency whereas the gain of a differentiator increases nominally linearly with frequency, it is easier to stabilize the former than the latter with respect to spurious oscillations. As a result of its limited bandwidth, an integrator is less sensitive to noise voltages than a differentiator. Further, if the input waveform changes very rapidly, the amplifier of a differentiator may overload. Finally, as a matter of practice, it is very convenient to introduce initial conditions in an integrator.

17-13   FEEDBACK AND STABILITY[11]

Negative feedback for which $|1 + A\beta| > 1$ has been considered in some detail in the foregoing sections. If $|1 + A\beta| < 1$, then the feedback is termed *positive*, or *regenerative*. Under these circumstances, the resultant transfer gain A_f will be greater than A, the nominal gain without feedback, since $|A_f| = |A|/|1 + A\beta| > |A|$. Regeneration as an effective means of increasing the amplification of an amplifier was first suggested by Armstrong.[12] Because of the reduced stability of an amplifier with positive feedback, this method is seldom used.

To illustrate the instability in an amplifier with positive feedback, consider the following situation: No signal is applied, but because of some transient disturbance a voltage V_o appears at the output terminals. A portion of this voltage $-\beta V_o$ will be fed back to the input circuit and will appear in the output as an increased voltage $-A\beta V_o$. If this term just equals V_o, then the spurious output has regenerated itself. In other words, if $-A\beta V_o = V_o$ (that is, if $-A\beta = 1$), the amplifier will oscillate (Sec. 17-15). Hence, if an attempt is made to obtain large gain by making $|A\beta|$ almost equal to unity, there is the possibility that the amplifier may break out into spontaneous oscillation. This would occur if, because of variation in supply voltages, aging of transistors or tubes, etc., $-A\beta$ becomes equal to unity. There is little point in attempting to achieve amplification at the expense of stability. In fact, because of all the advantages enumerated in Sec. 17-2, feedback in amplifiers is almost always negative. However, combinations of positive and negative feedback are used.

The Condition for Stability   If an amplifier is designed to have negative feedback in a particular frequency range but breaks out into oscillation at some high or low frequency, it is useless as an amplifier. Hence, in the design of a feedback amplifier, it must be ascertained that the circuit is stable at *all* frequencies, and not merely over the frequency range of interest. In the sense used here, the system is stable if a transient disturbance results in a response which dies out. A system is unstable if a transient disturbance persists indefinitely or increases until it is limited only by some nonlinearity in the circuit. Thus the question of stability may be considered to involve a study of the transient response of the system. If Laplace transform notation is used, the transfer function $V_o/V_s = A_f$ is a function of the complex frequency $s = \sigma + j\omega$. The poles of the transfer function determine the transient behavior of the network. If a pole exists with a positive value of σ, this will result in a disturbance increasing exponentially with time. Hence the condition which must be satisfied, if a system is to be stable, is that the poles of the transfer function must all lie in the left-hand half of the complex-frequency plane. If the system without feedback is stable, the poles of A do lie in the left-hand half plane. It follows from Eq. (17-2), therefore, that *the stability condition requires that the zeros of* $1 + A\beta$ *all lie in the left-hand half of the complex-frequency plane.*

The Nyquist Criterion   Nyquist[13] has obtained an alternative but equivalent condition for stability which may be expressed in terms of the steady-state, or frequency-response, characteristic.   It is given here without proof: Since the product $A\beta$ is a complex number, it may be represented as a point in the complex plane, the real component being plotted along the X axis, and the j component along the Y axis.   Furthermore, $A\beta$ is a function of frequency. Consequently, points in the complex plane are obtained for the values of $A\beta$ corresponding to all values of f from zero to $+\infty$.   The locus of all these points forms a closed curve.   The criterion of Nyquist is that *the amplifier is unstable if this curve encloses the point $-1 + j0$, and the amplifier is stable if the curve does not enclose this point.*

The criterion for positive or negative feedback may also be represented in the complex plane.   From Fig. 17-34 we see that $|1 + A\beta| = 1$ represents a circle of unit radius, with its center at the point $-1 + j0$.   If, for any frequency, $A\beta$ extends outside this circle, the feedback is negative, since then $|1 + A\beta| > 1$. If, however, $A\beta$ lies within this circle, then $|1 + A\beta| < 1$, and the feedback is positive.   In the latter case the system will not oscillate unless Nyquist's criterion is satisfied.

Illustrations   As a first application of the criterion of stability, consider one stage of a simple RC-coupled vacuum-tube amplifier with voltage-series feedback.   The analysis of this circuit in Secs. 16-5 and 16-6 shows that the nominal gain A is real and negative (a phase angle of 180°) over most of the audio range.   For the high and low frequencies, it is found that the gain falls to zero, and the phase approaches $\perp 90°$.   If the voltage feedback factor β is independent of the frequency, then $A\beta$ varies as A.   The locus of $A\beta$ for all frequencies when plotted in the complex plane can be shown to be a circle plotted as indicated in Fig. 17-35.   It should be noted that under these circumstances this curve is simply a polar plot of the gain A of the circuit. Furthermore, since this curve does not enclose the point $-1 + j0$, the amplifier is stable and the feedback is negative for all frequencies.   Alternatively, it is noted from the diagram that $|1 + A\beta| > 1$ for all frequencies, which is the condition for negative feedback.

As a second specific illustration, suppose that the polar plot of a given

Fig. 17-34   The locus of $|1 + A\beta| = 1$ is a circle of unit radius, with its center at $-1 + j0$.   If the vector $A\beta$ ends in the shaded region, the feedback is positive.

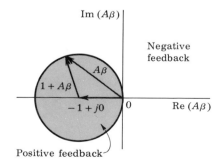

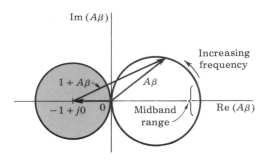

Fig. 17-35 For an *RC*-coupled amplifier, the locus (for all values of frequency) of $A\beta$ in the complex $A\beta$ plane is a circle.

amplifier has the form illustrated in Fig. 17-36. The feedback is negative for this amplifier in the frequency range from 0 to f_1. Positive feedback exists in the frequency range from f_1 to ∞. Note, however, that the locus of $A\beta$ does not enclose the point $-1 + j0$. Hence, according to the Nyquist criterion, oscillations will not occur.

17-14   GAIN AND PHASE MARGINS

In the preceding section, we examine two criteria for determining whether a feedback amplifier is stable or unstable. Often it is difficult to apply either of the above conditions for stability to a practical amplifier. It should be clear from the foregoing discussion that *no oscillations are possible if the magnitude of the loop gain* $|A\beta|$ *is less than unity when its phase angle is* 180°. This condition is sought for in practice to ensure that the amplifier will be stable.

Consider, for example, a three-stage *RC*-coupled vacuum-tube amplifier with voltage-series feedback as in Fig. 17-15. There is a definite maximum value of the feedback fraction $-\beta = R_1/R_g$ allowable for stable operation.[14] To see this, note that if all capacitors are disregarded, there is 180° phase shift in each stage, and 540°, or equivalently, 180°, for the three stages. At high frequencies there is an additional phase shift due to the shunting capacitances, and at the frequency for which the phase shift per stage is 60°, the total phase shift around the loop is zero. If the gain at this frequency is called A_{60}, then β must be chosen such that $A_{60}\beta$ is less than unity, if the possibility of oscillations is to be avoided. Similarly, because of the phase shift introduced

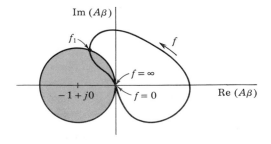

Fig. 17-36 The locus of $A\beta$ in the complex $A\beta$ plane for a circuit which exhibits negative feedback for low frequencies and positive feedback for high frequencies.

by the blocking capacitors, there is a low frequency for which the phase shift per stage is also 60°, and hence there is the possibility of oscillation at this low frequency also, unless the maximum value of β is restricted as outlined above.

It should now be apparent that instead of plotting the product $A\beta$ in the complex plane, it is more convenient to plot the magnitude, usually in decibels, and also the phase of $A\beta$ as a function of frequency. These curves are known as *Bode plots*. If we can show that $|A\beta|$ is less than unity when the phase angle of $A\beta$ is 180°, the closed-loop amplifier will be stable.

Gain Margin The gain margin is defined as the value of $|A\beta|$ in decibels at the frequency at which the phase angle of $A\beta$ is 180°. If the gain margin is negative, this gives the decibel rise in open-loop gain, which is theoretically permissible without oscillation. If the gain margin is positive, the amplifier is potentially unstable.

Phase Margin The phase margin is 180° minus the magnitude of the angle of $A\beta$ at the frequency at which $|A\beta|$ is unity or has a value of zero decibels. The magnitudes of these quantities give an indication of how stable an amplifier is. For example, a linear amplifier of good stability requires gain and phase margins of at least 10 dB and 50°, respectively. These definitions are illustrated in Fig. 17-37.

17-15   SINUSOIDAL OSCILLATORS

Many different circuit configurations deliver an essentially sinusoidal output waveform even without input-signal excitation. The basic principles govern-

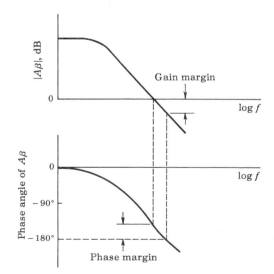

Fig. 17-37 Bode plots relating to the definitions of gain and phase margins.

ing all these oscillators are investigated. In addition to determining the conditions required for oscillation to take place, the frequency and amplitude stability are also studied.

Figure 17-38 shows an amplifier, a feedback network, and an input mixing circuit not yet connected to form a closed loop. The amplifier provides an output signal x_o as a consequence of the external signal x_s applied directly to the amplifier input terminal. The output of the feedback network is $x_f = \beta x_o = A\beta x_s$, and the output of the mixing circuit (which is now simply an inverter) is

$$x_f' = -x_f = -A\beta x_s$$

Suppose it should happen that matters are adjusted in such a way that the signal x_f' is *identically* equal to the externally applied input signal x_s. Since the amplifier has no means of distinguishing the source of the input signal applied to it, it would appear that, if the external source were removed and if terminal 2 were connected to terminal 1, the amplifier would continue to provide the same output signal x_o as before. Note, of course, that the statement $x_f' = x_s$ means that the instantaneous values of x_f' and x_s are exactly equal at all times. Note also that, since in the above discussion no restriction was made on the waveform, it need not be sinusoidal. The amplifier need not be linear, and the waveshape need not preserve its form as it is transmitted through the amplifier, provided only that the signal x_f' has the waveform and frequency of the input signal x_s. The condition $x_f' = x_s$ is equivalent to $-A\beta = 1$, or the *loop gain must equal unity*.

The Barkhausen Criterion We assume in this discussion of oscillators that the entire circuit operates linearly and that the amplifier or feedback network or both contain reactive elements. Under such circumstances, the only periodic waveform which will preserve its form is the sinusoid. For a sinusoidal waveform the condition $x_s = x_f'$ is equivalent to the condition that the *amplitude, phase,* and *frequency* of x_s and x_f' be identical. Since the phase shift introduced in a signal in being transmitted through a reactive network is invariably a function of the frequency, we have the following important principle:

The frequency at which a sinusoidal oscillator will operate is the frequency

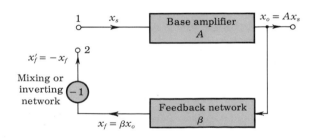

Fig. 17-38 An amplifier with transfer gain A and feedback network β not yet connected to form a closed loop. (Compare with Figs. 17-8 and 17-9.)

*for which the total phase shift introduced, as a signal proceeds from the input
terminals, through the amplifier and feedback network, and back again to the input,
is precisely zero (or, of course, an integral multiple of 2π). Stated more simply,
the frequency of a sinusoidal oscillator is determined by the condition that the
loop phase shift is zero.*

Although other principles may be formulated which may serve equally to
determine the frequency, these other principles may always be shown to be
identical with that stated above. It might be noted parenthetically that it is
not inconceivable that the above condition might be satisfied for more than a
single frequency. In such a contingency there is the possibility of simultaneous
oscillations at several frequencies or an oscillation at a single one of the allowed
frequencies.

The condition given above determines the frequency, provided that the
circuit will oscillate at all. Another condition which must clearly be met is
that the magnitude of x_s and x'_f must be identical. This condition is then
embodied in the following principle:

*Oscillations will not be sustained if, at the oscillator frequency, the magnitude
of the product of the transfer gain of the amplifier and the magnitude of the feedback
factor of the feedback network (the magnitude of the loop gain) is less than unity.*

The condition of *unity loop gain* $-A\beta = 1$ is called the *Barkhausen
criterion*. This condition implies, of course, both that $|A\beta| = 1$ and that the
phase of $-A\beta$ is zero. The above principles are consistent with the feedback
formula $A_f = A/(1 + \beta A)$. For if $-\beta A = 1$, then $A_f \to \infty$, which may be
interpreted to mean that there exists an output voltage even in the absence of
an externally applied signal voltage.

Practical Considerations Referring to Fig. 17-8, it appears that if
$|\beta A|$ at the oscillator frequency is precisely unity, then, with the feedback
signal connected to the input terminals, the removal of the external generator
will make no difference. If $|\beta A|$ is less than unity, the removal of the external
generator will result in a cessation of oscillations. But now suppose that $|\beta A|$
is greater than unity. Then, for example, a 1-V signal appearing initially at
the input terminals will, after a trip around the loop and back to the input
terminals, appear there with an amplitude larger than 1 V. This larger voltage
will then reappear as a still larger voltage, and so on. It seems, then, that
if $|\beta A|$ is larger than unity, the amplitude of the oscillations will continue to
increase without limit. But, of course, such an increase in the amplitude can
continue only as long as it is not limited by the onset of nonlinearity of operation in the active devices associated with the amplifier. Such a nonlinearity
becomes more marked as the amplitude of oscillation increases. This onset
of nonlinearity to limit the amplitude of oscillation is an essential feature of
the operation of all practical oscillators, as the following considerations will
show: The condition $|\beta A| = 1$ does not give a range of acceptable values of
$|\beta A|$, but rather a single and precise value. Now suppose that initially it
were even possible to satisfy this condition. Then, because circuit components

and, more importantly, vacuum tubes and transistors change characteristics (drift) with age, temperature, voltage, etc., it is clear that if the entire oscillator is left to itself, in a very short time $|\beta A|$ will become either less or larger than unity. In the former case the oscillation simply stops, and in the latter case we are back to the point of requiring nonlinearity to limit the amplitude. An oscillator in which the loop gain is exactly unity is an abstraction completely unrealizable in practice. It is accordingly necessary, in the adjustment of a practical oscillator, always to arrange to have $|\beta A|$ somewhat larger (say 5 percent) than unity in order to ensure that, with incidental variations in transistor, tube, and circuit parameters, $|\beta A|$ shall not fall below unity. While the first two principles stated above must be satisfied on purely theoretical grounds, we may add a third general principle dictated by practical considerations, i.e.:

In every practical oscillator the loop gain is slightly larger than unity, and the amplitude of the oscillations is limited by the onset of nonlinearity.

The treatment of oscillators, taking into account the nonlinearity, is very difficult on account of the innate perverseness of nonlinearities generally. In many cases the extension into the range of nonlinear operation is small, and we simply neglect these nonlinearities altogether.

17-16   THE PHASE–SHIFT OSCILLATOR[15]

We select the so-called *phase-shift oscillator* (Fig. 17-39) as a first example because it exemplifies very simply the principles set forth above. Here a FET (or vacuum-tube) amplifier of conventional design is followed by three cascaded arrangements of a capacitor C and a resistor R, the output of the last RC combination being returned to the gate. If the loading of the phase-shift network on the amplifier can be neglected, the amplifier shifts by 180° the phase of any voltage which appears on the gate, and the network of resistors and capacitors shifts the phase by an additional amount. At some frequency

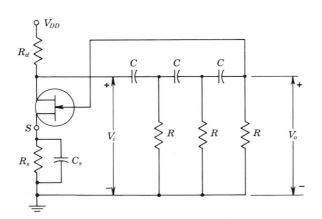

Fig. 17-39 A FET phase-shift oscillator.

the phase shift introduced by the RC network will be precisely 180°, and at this frequency the total phase shift from the gate around the circuit and back to the gate will be exactly zero. This particular frequency will be the one at which the circuit will oscillate provided that the magnitude of the amplification is sufficiently large.

From classical network analysis we find for the transfer function of the RC network, which is also the (negative of the) feedback factor,

$$-\beta = \frac{V_o}{V_i} = \frac{1}{1 - 5\alpha^2 - j(6\alpha - \alpha^3)} \tag{17-64}$$

where $\alpha \equiv 1/\omega RC$. The phase shift of V_o/V_i is 180° for $\alpha^2 = 6$ or $f = 1/(2\pi RC\sqrt{6})$. At that frequency of oscillation $\beta = +\frac{1}{29}$. In order that $|\beta A|$ shall not be less than unity, it is required that $|A|$ be at least 29. Hence a FET or tube with $\mu < 29$ cannot be made to oscillate in such a circuit.

It should be pointed out that it is not always necessary to make use of an amplifier with transfer gain $|A| > 1$ to satisfy the Barkhausen criterion. It is only necessary that $|\beta A| > 1$. Passive network structures exist for which the transfer function $|\beta|$ is greater than unity at some particular frequency. In Prob. 17-55 we show an oscillator circuit consisting of a source follower and the RC circuit of Fig. 17-39 appropriately connected.

Transistor Phase-shift Oscillator If a transistor were used for the active element in Fig. 17-39, the output R of the feedback network would be shunted by the relatively low input resistance of the transistor. Hence, instead of employing voltage-series feedback as in Fig. 17-39, we use voltage-shunt feedback for a transistor phase-shift oscillator as indicated in Fig. 17-40a. For the circuit we assume that $h_{oe}R_c \leq 0.1$, so that we may use the approximate

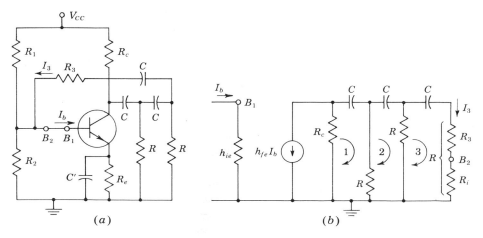

Fig. 17-40 (a) Transistor phase-shift oscillator. (b) The Norton's equivalent circuit for this oscillator.

hybrid model to characterize the small-signal behavior of the transistor, as in Fig. 17-40b. The resistor $R_3 = R - R_i$, where $R_i \approx h_{ie}$ is the input resistance of the transistor. This choice makes the three RC sections of the phase-shifting network alike and simplifies the calculations. We assume that the biasing resistors R_1, R_2, and R_e have no effect on the signal operation and neglect these in the following analysis.

Since the signals x_s and x_f represent currents in the circuit of Fig. 17-40, we must evaluate the current gain around the loop. Hence we imagine the loop broken at the base between B_1 and B_2, but in order not to change the loading on the feedback network, we place R_i from B_2 to ground. If we assume a current I_b to enter the base at B_1, the loop current gain equals I_3/I_b, and is found by writing Kirchhoff's voltage equation for the three meshes (Prob. 17-56). The Barkhausen condition that the phase of I_3/I_b must equal zero leads to the following expression for the frequency of oscillation:

$$f = \frac{1}{2\pi RC} \frac{1}{\sqrt{6 + 4k}} \tag{17-65}$$

where $k \equiv R_c/R$. The requirement that the magnitude of I_3/I_b must exceed unity in order for oscillations to start leads to the inequality

$$h_{fe} > 4k + 23 + \frac{29}{k} \tag{17-66}$$

The value of k which gives the minimum h_{fe} turns out to be 2.7, and for this optimum value of R_c/R, we find $h_{fe} = 44.5$. A transistor with a small-signal common-emitter short-circuit current gain less than 44.5 cannot be used in this phase-shift oscillator.

Variable-frequency Operation The phase-shift oscillator is particularly suited to the range of frequencies from several hertz to several hundred kilohertz, and so includes the range of audio frequencies. At frequencies in the megahertz range, it has no marked advantage over circuits (discussed in the following sections) employing tuned LC networks. The frequency of oscillation may be varied by changing any of the impedance elements in the phase-shifting network. For variations of frequency over a large range, the three capacitors are usually varied simultaneously. Such a variation keeps the input impedance to the phase-shifting network constant (Prob. 17-48) and also keeps constant the magnitude of β and $A\beta$. Hence the amplitude of oscillation will not be affected as the frequency is adjusted. The phase-shift oscillator is operated in class A in order to keep distortion to a minimum.

17-17   RESONANT–CIRCUIT OSCILLATORS

Figure 17-41 shows the *tuned-plate oscillator* in which a resonant circuit is used to determine the frequency. Other oscillators of this type are considered in Sec. 17-19. In Fig. 17-41a, r represents a resistance in series with the plate

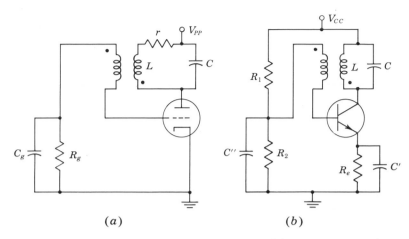

Fig. 17-41 A resonant-circuit oscillator using (a) a vacuum tube (or FET) and (b) a bipolar transistor.

winding (of inductance L) in order to account for the losses in the transformer. If these losses are negligible, so that r can be neglected, then at the frequency $\omega = 1/\sqrt{LC}$, the impedance of the resonant circuit is arbitrarily large and purely resistive. In this case the voltage drop across the inductor from plate to ground is precisely 180° out of phase with the applied input voltage to the vacuum tube, independently of the size of the tube plate resistance. If the direction of the winding of the secondary of the transformer (connected to the grid) is such as to introduce an additional phase shift of 180° (it is assumed that the secondary is not loaded), the total loop phase shift is exactly zero. At this frequency, then, the phase-shift condition for oscillation will have been satisfied. Again, since the transformer is considered to be unloaded, the ratio of the amplitude of the secondary to the primary voltage is M/L, where M is the mutual inductance. Since $A = -\mu$ for an amplifier with an infinite load impedance, the condition $-\beta A = 1$ is equivalent to $\mu = L/M$. More exactly, taking into account the finite size of the resistance r, we find

$$\omega^2 = \frac{1}{LC}\left(1 + \frac{r}{r_p}\right) \tag{17-67}$$

as the frequency-determining condition and

$$g_m = \frac{\mu r C}{\mu M - L} \tag{17-68}$$

as the condition which is equivalent to $-\beta A = 1$.

Note that there is no a priori connection between the oscillation frequency and the steady-state "resonance" frequency. The frequency of oscillation is determined solely by the consideration that the loop phase shift is zero. In this sense, the suggestive near agreement of the frequency of the oscillator and the frequency of a natural oscillation or steady-state resonance is to be considered, superficially at least, as a pure coincidence. In the light of these last remarks it appears, too, that the designation of the oscillator of Sec. 17-16 as a "phase-shift oscillator," as opposed to the present designation, "resonant-circuit oscillator," is entirely artificial. All oscillators, those discussed above as well as those to be considered below, could be called phase-shift oscillators.

Self-bias and Amplitude Stabilization The bias for a resonant-circuit oscillator is obtained from an $R_g C_g$ parallel combination in series with the grid, as in Fig. 17-41a. The grid and cathode of the tube act as a rectifier, and if the $R_g C_g$ time constant is large compared with one period, the grid leak capacitor will charge up essentially to the peak grid swing. This voltage across C_g acts as the bias, and the grid is therefore driven slightly positive only for a short interval at the peak of the swing. The voltage at the grid is a large sinusoid, and since its peak value is approximately at ground potential, we say that the grid is "clamped" to ground. Since the grid base of the tube is traversed in a small fraction of one cycle, the operation is class C.

When the circuit is first energized, the grid bias is zero and the tube operates with a large g_m, one greater than that given by Eq. (17-68). The loop gain is therefore greater than unity, and the amplitude of oscillation starts to grow. As it does so, grid current is drawn, clamping takes place, and the bias automatically adjusts itself so that its magnitude equals the peak value of the grid voltage. As the bias becomes more negative, the value of g_m decreases, and finally, the amplitude stabilizes itself at that value for which the loop gain for the fundamental is reduced to unity. Since the operation is class C, the use of the linear equivalent circuit is at best a rough approximation. In view of the foregoing discussion, the value of g_m in Eq. (17-68) may be considered to be the minimum value required at zero bias in order for oscillations to start. It may also be interpreted as the average value of transconductance which determines the amplitude of oscillation.

A Transistor Tuned-collector Oscillator The transistor circuit of Fig. 17-41b is analogous to the tube oscillator of Fig. 17-41a. The quiescent bias is determined by R_1, R_2, and R_e (Sec. 10-4). If R_1 were omitted, then initially the transistor currents would be zero, g_m would be zero, and the circuit would not oscillate. With R_1 in place, the transistor is biased in its active region, oscillations build up, and the dynamic self-bias is obtained from the $R_2 C''$ combination due to the flow of base current. As explained above, this action results in class C operation.

17-18   A GENERAL FORM OF OSCILLATOR CIRCUIT

Many radio-frequency oscillator circuits fall into the general form shown in Fig. 17-42a. The active device may be a bipolar transistor or a vacuum

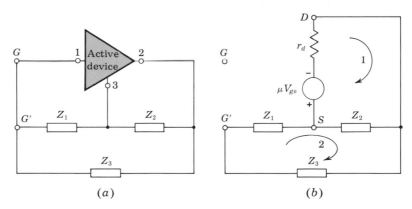

Fig. 17-42 (a) The basic configuration for many resonant-circuit oscillators. (b) The linear equivalent circuit using a FET.

tube or a FET. In the analysis that follows we assume an active device with infinite input resistance such as a FET or a vacuum tube. Figure 17-42b shows the linear equivalent circuit of Fig. 17-42a using a FET.

The Loop Gain The value of $-A\beta$ will be obtained by two different methods. First, we consider the circuit of Fig. 17-42a to be a feedback amplifier with output taken from terminals 2 and 3 (D and S) and with input terminals 1 and 3 (G and S). The load impedance Z_L consists of Z_2 in parallel with the series combination of Z_1 and Z_3. The gain without feedback is $A = -\mu Z_L/(Z_L + r_d)$. The feedback factor is $\beta = -Z_1/(Z_1 + Z_3)$. The loop gain is found to be

$$-A\beta = \frac{-\mu Z_1 Z_2}{r_d(Z_1 + Z_2 + Z_3) + Z_2(Z_1 + Z_3)} \tag{17-69}$$

A second approach is to assume an input voltage V_{gs} between gate and source but with the junction point G' of Z_1 and Z_3 not connected to the gate G. The loop gain is then the voltage developed across Z_1 divided by V_{gs}. The loop-voltage equations for Fig. 17-42b are

$$\mu V_{gs} + I_1(r_d + Z_2) - I_2 Z_2 = 0 \tag{17-70a}$$

and

$$-I_1 Z_2 + I_2(Z_1 + Z_2 + Z_3) = 0 \tag{17-70b}$$

The loop gain is defined by $V_{g's}/V_{gs} = I_2 Z_1/V_{gs}$, and solving for I_2 from Eqs. (17-70a) and (17-70b) gives the result, Eq. (17-69).

Reactive Elements Z_1, Z_2, and Z_3 If the impedances are pure reactances (either inductive or capacitive), then $Z_1 = jX_1$, $Z_2 = jX_2$, and $Z_3 = jX_3$. For an inductor, $X = \omega L$, and for a capacitor, $X = -1/\omega C$. Then

$$-A\beta = \frac{+\mu X_1 X_2}{jr_d(X_1 + X_2 + X_3) - X_2(X_1 + X_3)} \tag{17-71}$$

In order for the loop gain to be real (zero phase shift),

$$X_1 + X_2 + X_3 = 0 \tag{17-72}$$

and

$$-A\beta = \frac{\mu X_1 X_2}{-X_2(X_1 + X_3)} = \frac{-\mu X_1}{X_1 + X_3} \tag{17-73}$$

From Eq. (17-72) we see that the circuit will oscillate at the resonant frequency of the series combination of X_1, X_2, and X_3.

Using Eq. (17-72) in Eq. (17-73) yields

$$-A\beta = \frac{+\mu X_1}{X_2} \tag{17-74}$$

Since $-A\beta$ must be positive and at least unity in magnitude, then X_1 and X_2 must have the same sign. In other words, they must be the same kind of reactance, either both inductive or both capacitive. Then, from Eq. (17-72), $X_3 = -(X_1 + X_2)$ must be inductive if X_1 and X_2 are capacitive, or vice versa.

If X_1 and X_2 are capacitors and X_3 is an inductor, the circuit is called a *Colpitts oscillator*. If X_1 and X_2 are inductors and X_3 is a capacitor, the circuit is called a *Hartley oscillator*. In this latter case, there may be mutual coupling between X_1 and X_2 (and the above equations will then not apply). If X_1 and X_2 are tuned circuits and X_3 represents the gate-to-drain (grid-to-plate) interelectrode capacitance, the circuit is called a *tuned-drain tuned-gate oscillator* (*tuned-plate tuned-grid oscillator*). The foregoing theory indicates that both gate and drain circuits must be tuned to the inductive side of resonance.

Practical Considerations   One form of a Hartley oscillator is shown in Fig. 17-43a. The supply voltage is applied to the plate through the inductor L, whose reactance is high compared with X_2. The capacitor C has a low

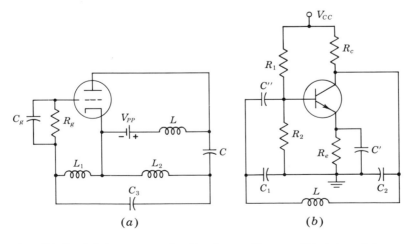

(a)   (b)

Fig. 17-43   (a) A vacuum-tube Hartley oscillator.   (b) A transistor Colpitts oscillator.

reactance at the frequency of oscillation. At zero frequency, however, it acts as an open circuit. Without this capacitor the supply voltage would be short-circuited by L in series with L_2. The parallel combination of C_g and R_g acts to supply the bias. The circuit operates in class C, and the grid current charges up C_g, as explained in Sec. 17-17.

A modified form of Hartley circuit employs mutual coupling between L_1 and L_2 and places C_3 in parallel with L_2.

Transistor versions of all the above types of LC oscillators are possible. As an example, a transistor Colpitts oscillator is indicated in Fig. 17-43b. Qualitatively, this circuit operates in the manner described above. However, the detailed analysis of a transistor oscillator circuit is much more difficult than that of a tube or FET circuit, for two fundamental reasons. First, the low input impedance of the transistor shunts Z_1 in Fig. 17-42a, and hence complicates the expressions for the loop gain given above. Second, if the oscillation frequency is beyond the audio range, the simple low-frequency h-parameter model employed in Fig. 17-40b is no longer valid. Under these circumstances the more complicated high-frequency hybrid-π model of Fig. 13-5 must be used.

17-19   CRYSTAL OSCILLATORS

If a piezoelectric crystal, usually quartz, has electrodes plated on opposite faces and if a potential is applied between these electrodes, forces will be exerted on the bound charges within the crystal. If this device is properly mounted, deformations take place within the crystal, and an electromechanical system is formed which will vibrate when properly excited. The resonant frequency and the Q depend upon the crystal dimensions, how the surfaces are oriented with respect to its axes, and how the device is mounted.[16] Frequencies ranging from a few kilohertz to a few megahertz and Q's in the range from several thousand to several hundred thousand are commercially available. These extraordinarily high values of Q and the fact that the characteristics of quartz are extremely stable with respect to time and temperature account for the exceptional frequency stability of oscillators incorporating crystals (Sec. 17-20).

The electrical equivalent circuit of a crystal is indicated in Fig. 17-44. The inductor L, capacitor C, and resistor R are the analogs of the mass, the compliance (the reciprocal of the spring constant), and the viscous-damping factor of the mechanical system. Typical values[5] for a 90-kHz crystal are $L = 137$ H, $C = 0.0235$ pF, and $R = 15$ K, corresponding to $Q = 5,500$. The dimensions of such a crystal are 30 by 4 by 1.5 mm. Since C' represents the electrostatic capacitance between electrodes with the crystal as a dielectric, its magnitude (~ 3.5 pF) is very much larger than C.

If we neglect the resistance R, the impedance of the crystal is a reactance jX whose dependence upon frequency is given by

$$jX = -\frac{j}{\omega C'}\frac{\omega^2 - \omega_s^2}{\omega^2 - \omega_p^2} \tag{17-75}$$

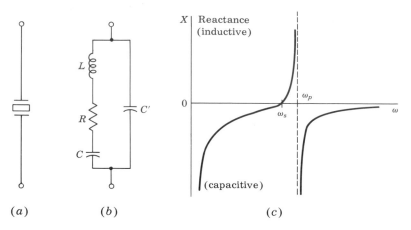

(a)   (b)   (c)

Fig. 17-44 A piezoelectric crystal. (a) Symbol. (b) Electrical model.
(c) The reactance function (if $R = 0$).

where $\omega_s{}^2 = 1/LC$ is the series resonant frequency (the zero impedance frequency), and $\omega_p{}^2 = (1/L)(1/C + 1/C')$ is the parallel resonant frequency (the infinite impedance frequency). Since $C' \gg C$, then $\omega_p \approx \omega_s$. For the crystal whose parameters are specified above, the parallel frequency is only three-tenths of 1 percent higher than the series frequency. For $\omega_s < \omega < \omega_p$, the reactance is inductive, and outside this range it is capacitive, as indicated in Fig. 17-44c.

A variety of crystal-oscillator circuits is possible. If in the basic configuration of Fig. 17-42a a crystal is used for Z_1, a tuned LC combination for Z_2, and the capacitance C_{dg} between drain and gate for Z_3, the resulting circuit is as indicated in Fig. 17-45. From the theory given in the preceding section, the crystal reactance, as well as that of the LC network, must be inductive. In order for the loop gain to be greater than unity, we see from Eq. (17-74)

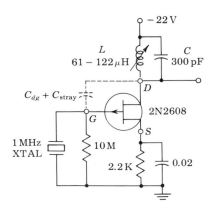

Fig. 17-45 A 1-MHz FET crystal oscillator.
(Courtesy of Siliconix Co.)

that X_1 cannot be too small.   Hence the circuit will oscillate at a frequency which lies between ω_s and ω_p but close to the parallel-resonance value.   Since $\omega_p \approx \omega_s$, the oscillator frequency is essentially determined by the crystal, and not by the rest of the circuit.   Figure 17-45 is the crystal version of the tuned-drain tuned-gate oscillator.

17-20   FREQUENCY STABILITY

An oscillator having initially been set at a particular frequency will invariably not maintain its initial frequency, but will instead drift and wander about in frequency, sometimes uniformly in one direction, sometimes quite erratically. The *frequency stability* of an oscillator is a measure of its ability to maintain as nearly a fixed frequency as possible over as long a time interval as possible. These deviations of frequency arise because the values of the circuit features, on which the oscillator frequency depends, do not remain constant in time. (We use here the term "circuit features" to include circuit components, transistor parameters, supply voltages, stray capacitances, etc.)   Accordingly, an obvious but clearly useless solution of the problem of making a frequency-stable oscillator is to keep constant all the circuit features.   In the first place, the number of circuit features is very large, in general; second, some of the circuit features, such as transistor parameters, are inherently unstable and extremely difficult to keep constant; and third, it is hard enough to know where stray circuit elements and couplings are located and how to estimate their magnitudes without having to devise schemes to maintain them constant.

But, we recognize also that in every oscillator circuit there are a relatively few circuit features on which the frequency is sensitively dependent, whereas the frequency dependence of the far larger number of remaining features is comparatively slight.   For example, in the circuit of Fig. 17-39, the frequency is for the most part determined by R and C, and the other features of the circuit affect the frequency to a much smaller extent.   We shall then have taken a long step in the direction toward frequency stability if we take pains to ensure the stability, at least, of these relatively few passive elements which influence the frequency markedly.   The principal cause of drift in these is the variation of temperature.   Measures for maintaining the temperature constant and for balancing the temperature-induced variation in one such element against that in another can be taken.[17]

Stability Criterion   *If in an oscillator there exists one set of elements which has the property that at the oscillation frequency these components introduce a large variation of phase θ with frequency, then $d\theta/d\omega$ serves as a measure of the independence of the frequency of all other features of the circuit.   The frequency stability improves as $d\theta/d\omega$ increases.   In the limit, as $d\theta/d\omega$ becomes infinite, the oscillator frequency depends only on this set of elements and becomes completely independent of all other features of the circuit.*

The proof of the foregoing principle is almost self-evident, and is readily arrived at from the following considerations: Suppose that a variation takes place in some one feature of the oscillator *other than one of the components of the set of elements described above.* Then, if initially the phase condition for oscillation was satisfied at the frequency of oscillation, it will, in general, no longer be satisfied after the alteration of the circuit feature. The frequency must accordingly shift in order once again to restore the loop phase shift to the exact value zero. If, however, there is a set of elements which, at the nominal oscillator frequency, produces a large phase shift for a small frequency change (that is, $d\theta/d\omega$ large), it is clear that the frequency shift required to restore the circuital phase shift to zero need be only very small.

In a parallel-resonant circuit the impedance changes from an inductive to a capacitive reactance as the frequency is increased through the resonant point. If the Q is infinite (an ideal inductor with zero series resistance), this change in phase is abrupt, $d\theta/d\omega \to \infty$, because the phase changes abruptly from -90 to $+90°$. Hence a tuned-circuit oscillator will have excellent frequency stability provided that Q is sufficiently high and that L and C are stable (independent of temperature, current, etc.).

These ideas about tuned-circuit oscillators can be carried over to account for the exceptional frequency stability of crystal oscillators. From Fig. 17-44c we see that for a crystal with infinite Q the phase changes discontinuously from -90 to $+90°$ as the frequency passes through ω_s and then abruptly back again from $+90$ to $-90°$ as ω passes through ω_p. Of course, infinite Q is unattainable, but since commercially available crystals have values of Q of tens or hundreds of thousands, very large values of $d\theta/d\omega$ are realizable. Hence, if a crystal is incorporated into a circuit (such as that of Fig. 17-45), an oscillator is obtained whose frequency depends essentially upon the crystal itself and nothing else. The crystal frequency does, however, still depend somewhat on the temperature, and regulated-temperature ovens must be employed where the highest stability is required.

To compare the frequency stability of two different types of oscillators, $d\theta/d\omega$ is evaluated for each at the operating frequency. The circuit giving the larger value of $d\theta/d\omega$ has the more stable oscillator frequency.

17-21   NEGATIVE RESISTANCE IN OSCILLATORS

Our study of oscillators thus far has been based on a steady-state analysis, the Barkhausen criterion. It is instructive to consider an alternative, but usually much more complicated, approach based on a transient analysis. In this method the oscillator is replaced by its linear equivalent circuit, and the differential equations are written for the resultant network. The solution for the output voltage (or for one of the mesh currents) will be of the form $Ke^{\sigma t} \sin(\omega t + \varphi)$, where $s = \sigma \pm j\omega$ are the roots of the characteristic equation (s is also the complex-frequency, or the Laplace transform, variable). The symbols K and φ are constants of integration. Since the excitation to an oscillator is zero, then in order for an output to build up, it is necessary that σ be a positive number. If σ were negative, any spurious voltage introduced into the circuit would quickly be damped out. If σ is positive, this spurious signal will cause the output amplitude to increase exponentially with time provided that the system remains linear. However, as we have already emphasized, the oscillator must enter a nonlinear region as its amplitude grows. As it does so, σ must decrease, and when the stable amplitude is reached, $\sigma = 0$, so that the steady-state output is given by $K \sin(\omega t + \varphi)$.

A transient excited in a circuit containing resistance must die down with time because of the losses in the resistor. Hence an interesting interpretation of the fact that the amplitude first builds up in an oscillator is that, during this process, the circuit exhibits a *negative* resistance. In order to carry this concept further, consider the parallel RLC circuit of Fig. 17-46, with no external excitation. The differential equation for the voltage v across this combination is

$$LC \frac{d^2v}{dt^2} + \frac{L}{R}\frac{dv}{dt} + v = 0 \tag{17-76}$$

For this equation we find

$$\sigma = -\frac{1}{2RC} \qquad \omega^2 = \frac{1}{LC} - \frac{1}{4R^2C^2} \tag{17-77}$$

Hence, in order for σ to be positive (for a positive C), it is necessary that R be negative. In an oscillator circuit R is not a constant, but as the amplitude builds up, the device enters its nonlinear region and $R \to \infty$, $\sigma \to 0$, and $\omega^2 \to 1/LC$.

On the basis of this discussion, we can conclude that *all* oscillators might be called "negative-resistance oscillators." This classification is no more useful than it is to designate all oscillators "phase-shift oscillators" because the Barkhausen condition requires that the steady-state phase shift around the loop be zero. Perhaps the term "negative-resistance oscillator" should be reserved for use in connection with a two-terminal device which, because of its internal physics, exhibits a negative resistance. One such device is the tunnel diode whose volt-ampere characteristic is given in Fig. 6-21. We see that over a portion of the characteristic the current decreases as the voltage increases, and hence this device exhibits negative resistance. If a circuit consisting of a resistor R_1, a capacitor C, and an inductor L in parallel is connected across the device whose negative resistance has a magnitude R_2, the circuit of Fig. 17-46 results, where R represents R_1 and R_2 in parallel and

Fig. 17-46   A parallel RLC circuit.

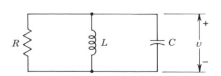

hence is given by

$$R = \frac{-R_1 R_2}{R_1 - R_2} \tag{17-78}$$

If $R_1 > R_2$, then R is negative and oscillations can build up. The amplitude increases until the nonlinear portion of the volt-ampere characteristics is reached. The steady-state output is obtained when the average value of R_2 has increased so that it equals R_1. Under these circumstances $R = \infty$, $\sigma = 0$, and the frequency is given by $f = 1/(2\pi \sqrt{LC})$.

REFERENCES

1. Jennings, R. R.: Negative Feedback in Voltage Amplifiers, *Electro-technol.* (*New York*), vol. 70, pp. 80–83, December, 1962.
   Jennings, R. R.: Negative Feedback in Current Amplifier, *ibid.*, vol. 72, pp. 100–103, July, 1963.
   Jennings, R. R.: Negative Feedback in Transconductance and Transresistance Amplifiers, *ibid.*, vol. 74, pp. 37–41, July, 1964.

2. Bode, H. W.: "Network Analysis and Feedback Amplifier Design," D. Van Nostrand Company, Inc., Princeton, N.J., 1945.

3. Mulligan, J. H., Jr.: Signal Transmission in Nonreciprocal Systems, *Proc. Symp. Adaptive Networks and Feedback Systems*, Polytechnic Institute of Brooklyn, N.Y., vol. 10, p. 129, 1960.

4. Uzunoglu, V.: "Semiconductor Network Analysis and Design," chap. 8, McGraw-Hill Book Company, New York, 1964.
   Ghausi, M. S.: "Principles and Design of Linear Active Circuits," chap. 4, McGraw-Hill Book Company, New York, 1965.
   Thornton, R. D., et al.: "Multistage Transistor Circuits," Semiconductor Electronics Education Committee, vol. 5, chap. 3, John Wiley & Sons, Inc., New York, 1965.
   Hakim, S. S.: "Junction Transistor Circuit Analysis," John Wiley & Sons, Inc., New York, 1962.

5. Uzunoglu, V.: Feedback and Impedance Levels in Transistor Circuits, *Electron Equipment Eng.*, July, 1962, pp. 42–43.
   Blecher, F. H.: Design Principles for Single Loop Transistor Feedback Amplifiers, *IRE Trans. Circuit Theory*, vol. CT-4, p. 145, September, 1957.
   Blackman, R. B.: Effect of Feedback on Impedance, *Bell System Tech. J.*, vol. 22, no. 3, p. 269, October, 1943.

6. Waldauer, F. D.: Wide-band Feedback Amplifiers, *IRE Trans. Circuit Theory*, vol. CT-4, pp. 178–190, September, 1957.
   Hakim, S. S.: Open and Closed Loop Response of Feedback Amplifiers, *Electron. Eng.*, October, 1962, pp. 682–687.

7. Gibbons, J. F.: "Semiconductor Electronics," chap. 14, McGraw-Hill Book Company, New York, 1966.

8. Blecher, F. H.: Transistor Circuits for Analog and Digital Systems, *Bell System Tech. J.*, vol. 35, pp. 295–332, March, 1956.

9. Korn, G. A., and T. M. Korn: Electronic Analog and Hybrid Computers, McGraw-Hill Book Company, New York, 1964.

10. Millman, J., and H. Taub: "Pulse, Digital, and Switching Waveforms," pp. 536–538, McGraw-Hill Book Company, New York, 1965.

11. Terman, F. E.: Feedback Amplifier Design, *Electronics*, vol. 10, pp. 12–15, January, 1937.

12. Armstrong, E. H.: Some Recent Developments in the Audion Receiver, *Proc. IRE*, vol. 3, pp. 215–247, September, 1915.

13. Nyquist, H.: Regeneration Theory, *Bell System Tech. J.*, vol. 11, pp. 126–147, January, 1932.

14. Arguimbau, L. B., and R. B. Adler: "Vacuum-tube Circuits and Transistors," John Wiley & Sons, Inc., New York, 1956.

15. Sherr, S.: Generalized Equations for R-C Phase-shift Oscillators, *Proc. IRE*, vol. 42, pp. 1169–1172, July, 1954.

16. Fair, Z. E.: Piezoelectric Crystals in Oscillator Circuits, *Bell System Tech. J.*, vol. 24, pp. 161–216, April, 1945.

17. Chance, B., et al.: "Waveforms," Radiation Laboratory Series, vol. 19, pp. 128–131, McGraw-Hill Book Company, New York, 1949.

18 / LARGE-SIGNAL AMPLIFIERS

An amplifying system usually consists of several stages in cascade. The input and intermediate stages operate in a small-signal class A mode. Their function is to amplify the small input excitation to a value large enough to drive the final device. This output stage feeds a transducer such as a cathode-ray tube, a loudspeaker, a servomotor, etc., and hence must be capable of delivering a large voltage or current swing or an appreciable amount of power. This chapter considers such large-signal amplifiers.

Each active device in the small-signal stages is replaced by a linear model, and the overall response is determined by linear circuit analysis, as in Chaps. 8 and 12. In the final stage, however, the output voltage and current swings are so large that the transistor or tube cannot be represented by a linear model, and the analysis must be performed graphically, using the experimentally determined device output characteristics. It is now found that a new type of distortion, due to the device nonlinearity, manifests itself by introducing frequency components into the output which are not present in the input signal.

Only large-signal audio-frequency amplifiers are considered in this chapter. Particular emphasis is placed on the types of circuit used and calculations of the distortion components, the power output, and the efficiency. Bias-stabilization techniques and thermal-runaway considerations are very important with power amplifiers. These topics are discussed in Chap. 10, and hence they are not considered here.

18-1   CLASS A LARGE–SIGNAL AMPLIFIERS

A simple transistor amplifier that supplies power to a pure resistance load R_L is indicated in Fig. 18-1a, and the corresponding tube circuit in

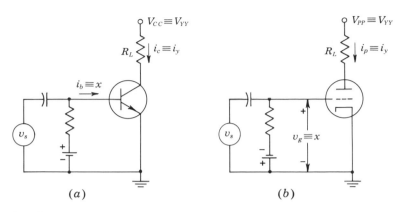

Fig. 18-1 The schematic wiring diagram of a simple series-fed amplifier with (a) a transistor and (b) a tube.

Fig. 18-1b. The general analysis of both circuits (or similar configurations with a FET or a pentode) is identical, and is made simultaneously by choosing appropriate notation. The input excitation is designated by the symbol x, which represents base current if a transistor is under consideration, grid voltage if the active device is a tube, or gate voltage if a FET is used. The output circuit is identified by the subscript y. Thus, using the notation in Table 9-1, I_Y represents quiescent collector, plate, or drain current; i_Y gives the total instantaneous collector, plate, or drain current; v_y designates the instantaneous variation from the quiescent value of the collector, plate, or drain voltage; etc.

Let us assume that the static output characteristics are equidistant for equal increments of input excitation, as indicated in Fig. 18-2. Then, if the

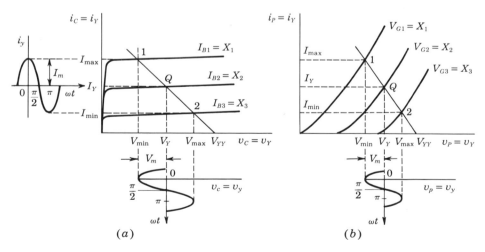

Fig. 18-2 The output characteristics and the current and voltage waveforms for a series-fed load for (a) a transistor or (b) a triode amplifier. Compare with Fig. 7-18.

input signal is a sinusoid, the output current and voltage are also sinusoidal, as shown. Under these circumstances the nonlinear distortion is negligible, and the power output may be found graphically as follows:

$$P = V_y I_y = I_y^2 R_L \tag{18-1}$$

where V_y and I_y are the rms output voltage and current, respectively, and R_L is the load resistance. The numerical values of V_y and I_y can be determined graphically in terms of the maximum and minimum voltage and current swings, as indicated in Fig. 18-2. If I_m (V_m) represents the peak sinusoidal current (voltage) swing, it is seen that

$$I_y = \frac{I_m}{\sqrt{2}} = \frac{I_{max} - I_{min}}{2\sqrt{2}} \tag{18-2}$$

and

$$V_y = \frac{V_m}{\sqrt{2}} = \frac{V_{max} - V_{min}}{2\sqrt{2}} \tag{18-3}$$

so that the power becomes

$$P = \frac{V_m I_m}{2} = \frac{I_m^2 R_L}{2} = \frac{V_m^2}{2R_L} \tag{18-4}$$

which may also be written in the form

$$P = \frac{(V_{max} - V_{min})(I_{max} - I_{min})}{8} \tag{18-5}$$

This equation allows the output power to be calculated very simply. All that is necessary is to plot the load line on the volt-ampere characteristics of the device and to read off the values of V_{max}, V_{min}, I_{max}, and I_{min}.

18-2   SECOND–HARMONIC DISTORTION

In the preceding section the active device is idealized as a perfectly linear device. In general, however, the dynamic transfer characteristic (Sec. 7-11) is not a straight line. This nonlinearity arises because the static output characteristics are not equidistant straight lines for constant increments of input excitation. If the dynamic curve is nonlinear over the operating range, the waveform of the output voltage differs from that of the input signal. Distortion of this type is called *nonlinear*, or *amplitude*, *distortion*.

In order to investigate the magnitude of this distortion we assume that the dynamic curve with respect to the quiescent point Q can be represented by a parabola rather than a straight line. Thus, instead of relating the alternating output current i_y with the input excitation x by the equation $i_y = Gx$ resulting from a linear circuit, we assume that the relationship between i_y and x is given more accurately by the expression

$$i_y = G_1 x + G_2 x^2 \tag{18-6}$$

where the G's are constants. Actually, these two terms are the beginning of a power-series expansion of i_y as a function of x.

If the input waveform is sinusoidal and of the form

$$x = X_m \cos \omega t \tag{18-7}$$

the substitution of this expression in Eq. (18-6) leads to

$$i_y = G_1 X_m \cos \omega t + G_2 X_m{}^2 \cos^2 \omega t$$

Since $\cos^2 \omega t = \frac{1}{2} + \frac{1}{2} \cos 2\omega t$, the expression for the instantaneous total current i_Y reduces to the form

$$i_Y = I_Y + i_y = I_Y + B_o + B_1 \cos \omega t + B_2 \cos 2\omega t \tag{18-8}$$

where the B's are constants which may be evaluated in terms of the G's. The physical meaning of this equation is evident. It shows that the application of a sinusoidal signal on a parabolic dynamic characteristic results in an output current which contains, in addition to a term of the same frequency as the input, a second-harmonic term, and also a constant current. This constant term B_o adds to the original dc value I_Y to yield a total dc component of current $I_Y + B_o$. *Parabolic nonlinear distortion introduces into the output a component whose frequency is twice that of the sinusoidal input excitation. Also, since a sinusoidal input signal changes the average value of the output current, rectification takes place.*

The amplitudes B_o, B_1, and B_2 for a given load resistor are readily determined from either the static or the dynamic characteristics. We observe from Fig. 18-2 that

$$\text{When } \omega t = 0: \quad i_Y = I_{\max}$$

$$\text{When } \omega t = \frac{\pi}{2}: \quad i_Y = I_Y \tag{18-9}$$

$$\text{When } \omega t = \pi: \quad i_Y = I_{\min}$$

By substituting these values in Eq. (18-8), there results

$$I_{\max} = I_Y + B_o + B_1 + B_2$$

$$I_Y = I_Y + B_o - B_2 \tag{18-10}$$

$$I_{\min} = I_Y + B_o - B_1 + B_2$$

This set of three equations determines the three unknowns B_o, B_1, and B_2. It follows from the second of this group that

$$B_o = B_2 \tag{18-11}$$

By subtracting the third equation from the first, there results

$$B_1 = \frac{I_{\max} - I_{\min}}{2} \tag{18-12}$$

With this value of B_1, the value for B_2 may be evaluated from either the first or the last of Eqs. (18-10) as

$$B_2 = B_o = \frac{I_{max} + I_{min} - 2I_Y}{4} \tag{18-13}$$

The second-harmonic distortion, D_2, is defined as

$$D_2 \equiv \frac{|B_2|}{|B_1|} \tag{18-14}$$

(To find the percent second-harmonic distortion, D_2 is multiplied by 100.) The quantities I_{max}, I_{min}, and I_Y appearing in these equations are obtained directly from the characteristic curves of the transistor, tube, or FET and the load line.

If the dynamic characteristic is given by the parabolic form (18-6) and if the input contains two frequencies ω_1 and ω_2, then the output will consist of a dc term and sinusoidal components of frequencies ω_1, ω_2, $2\omega_1$, $2\omega_2$, $\omega_1 + \omega_2$, and $\omega_1 - \omega_2$ (Prob. 18-1). The sum and difference frequencies are called *intermodulation*, or *combination*, frequencies.

18-3   HIGHER–ORDER HARMONIC GENERATION

The analysis of the previous section assumes a parabolic dynamic characteristic. This approximation is usually valid for amplifiers where the swing is small. For a power amplifier with a large input swing, however, it is necessary to express the dynamic transfer curve with respect to the Q point by a power series of the form

$$i_y = G_1 x + G_2 x^2 + G_3 x^3 + G_4 x^4 + \cdots \tag{18-15}$$

If we assume that the input wave is a simple cosine function of time, of the form in Eq. (18-7), then the output current will be given by

$$i_Y = I_Y + B_o + B_1 \cos \omega t + B_2 \cos 2\omega t + B_3 \cos 3\omega t + \cdots \tag{18-16}$$

This equation results when Eq. (18-7) is inserted in Eq. (18-15) and the proper trigonometric transformations are made.

That the output-current waveform must be expressible by a relationship of this form is made evident from an inspection of Fig. 18-2. It is observed from this figure that the output-current curve must possess *zero-axis symmetry*, or that the current is an *even* function of time. Expressed mathematically, $i(\omega t) = i(-\omega t)$. Physically, it means that the waveshape for every quarter cycle of the output-current curve as the operating point moves from point Q to point 1 is similar to the shape of the curve that is obtained as the operating point moves back from point 1 to point Q. Similarly, the waveshape of the current generated by the operating point as it moves from point Q to point 2 is symmetrical with that generated as it moves from point 2 back to point Q. These conditions are true regardless of the curvature of the characteristics. Since i_Y is an even function of time, the Fourier series in Eq. (18-16), representing a periodic function possessing this symmetry, contains only cosine terms. (If any sine terms were present, they would destroy the symmetry since they are *odd*, and not *even*, functions of time.)

If we assume, as is frequently done in the literature, that the excitation is a sine instead of a cosine function of time, the resulting output current is no longer expressed by a series of cosine terms only. Though a sine function differs from a cosine function in the shift of the time axis by an amount $\omega t = \pi/2$, nevertheless such a shift destroys the above-noted zero-axis symmetry. It is found in this case that the Fourier series representing the output current contains odd sine components and even cosine components.

Calculation of Fourier Components Any one of a number of methods[1] may be used in order to obtain the coefficients B_o, B_1, B_2, etc. The method due to Espley, which is simply an extension of the procedure of the last section, is described here. It is assumed in the foregoing section that only three terms, B_o, B_1, and B_2, of the Fourier series are different from zero. These three components are evaluated in terms of the three measured currents, I_{max}, I_{min}, and I_Y. As the next approximation, it is assumed that only five terms, B_o, D_1, D_2, B_3, and B_4, exist in the resulting Fourier series. In order to evaluate these five coefficients, the values of the currents at five different values of x are needed. These are chosen at equal intervals in input swing. Thus I_{max}, $I_{\frac{1}{2}}$, I_Y, $I_{-\frac{1}{2}}$, and I_{min} correspond, respectively, to the following values of x: the maximum positive value, one-half the maximum positive value, zero, one-half the maximum negative value, and the maximum negative value. These values are illustrated in Fig. 18-3.

Assuming an input signal of the form $x = X_m \cos \omega t$ as illustrated, then

$$\text{When } \omega t = 0: \quad i_Y = I_{max}$$

$$\text{When } \omega t = \frac{\pi}{3}: \quad i_Y = I_{\frac{1}{2}}$$

$$\text{When } \omega t = \frac{\pi}{2}: \quad i_Y = I_Y \qquad\qquad (18\text{-}17)$$

$$\text{When } \omega t = \frac{2\pi}{3}: \quad i_Y = I_{-\frac{1}{2}}$$

$$\text{When } \omega t = \pi: \quad i_Y = I_{min}$$

By combining these conditions with Eq. (18-16), five equations containing

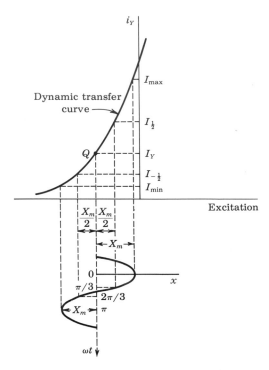

Fig. 18-3 The values of signal excitation and the corresponding values of output current used in the five-point schedule for determining the Fourier components B_0, B_1, B_2, B_3, and B_4 of the current.

five unknowns are obtained.   The solution of these equations yields

$$B_o = \tfrac{1}{6}(I_{\max} + 2I_{\frac{1}{2}} + 2I_{-\frac{1}{2}} + I_{\min}) - I_Y$$

$$B_1 = \tfrac{1}{3}(I_{\max} + I_{\frac{1}{2}} - I_{-\frac{1}{2}} - I_{\min})$$

$$B_2 = \tfrac{1}{4}(I_{\max} - 2I_Y + I_{\min}) \tag{18-18}$$

$$B_3 = \tfrac{1}{6}(I_{\max} - 2I_{\frac{1}{2}} + 2I_{-\frac{1}{2}} - I_{\min})$$

$$B_4 = \tfrac{1}{12}(I_{\max} - 4I_{\frac{1}{2}} + 6I_Y - 4I_{-\frac{1}{2}} + I_{\min})$$

The harmonic distortion is defined as

$$D_2 \equiv \frac{|B_2|}{|B_1|} \qquad D_3 \equiv \frac{|B_3|}{|B_1|} \qquad D_4 \equiv \frac{|B_4|}{|B_1|} \tag{18-19}$$

where D_s ($s = 2, 3, 4, \ldots$) represents the distortion of the sth harmonic.

Power Output   If the distortion is not negligible, the power delivered at the fundamental frequency is

$$P_1 = \frac{B_1{}^2 R_L}{2} \tag{18-20}$$

However, the total power output is

$$P = (B_1{}^2 + B_2{}^2 + B_3{}^2 + \cdots) \frac{R_L}{2} = (1 + D_2{}^2 + D_3{}^2 + \cdots)P_1$$

or

$$P = (1 + D^2)P_1 \tag{18-21}$$

where *the total distortion*, or *distortion factor*, is defined as

$$D \equiv \sqrt{D_2{}^2 + D_3{}^2 + D_4{}^2 + \cdots} \tag{18-22}$$

If the total distortion is 10 percent of the fundamental, then

$$P = [1 + (0.1)^2]P_1 = 1.01P_1$$

The total power output is only 1 percent higher than the fundamental power when the distortion is 10 percent. Hence little error is made in using only the fundamental term P_1 in calculating the power output. Considerable error may be made, however, if Eq. (18-5), rather than Eq. (18-20), is used to calculate the power. The former is based on the assumption that the fundamental component B_1 may be calculated from Eq. (18-12) rather than from the more accurate formula (18-18).

In passing, it should be noted that the total harmonic distortion is not necessarily indicative of the discomfort to someone listening to music. Usually, the same amount of distortion is more irritating, the higher the order of the harmonic frequency.

18-4   THE TRANSFORMER COUPLED AUDIO POWER AMPLIFIER

If the load resistance is connected directly in the output circuit of the power stage, as shown in Fig. 18-1, the quiescent current passes through this resistance. This current represents a considerable waste of power, since it does not contribute to the ac (signal) component of power. Furthermore, it is generally inadvisable to pass the dc component of current through the output device, for example, the voice coil of a loudspeaker. For these reasons an arrangement using an output transformer is usually employed, as in Fig. 18-4. Although the input circuit also contains a transformer, it is possible to feed the excitation to the power stage through an RC coupling, particularly if the active device is a tube or a FET which requires very little driving power.

Impedance Matching   In order to transfer a significant amount of power to a load such as a loudspeaker with a voice-coil impedance of 5 to 15 Ω, it is necessary to use an output matching transformer. This follows from the fact that the internal device resistance may be very much higher than that of the speaker, and so most of the power generated would be lost in the active device.

The impedance-matching properties of an ideal transformer follow from the simple transformer relations

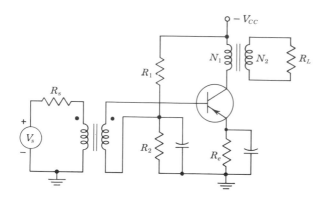

Fig. 18-4 A transformer-coupled transistor output stage.

$$V_1 = \frac{N_1}{N_2} V_2 \quad \text{and} \quad I_1 = \frac{N_2}{N_1} I_2 \tag{18-23}$$

where V_1 (V_2) = primary (secondary) voltage
$\quad$ I_1 (I_2) = primary (secondary) current
$\quad$ N_1 (N_2) = number of primary (secondary) turns
When $N_2 < N_1$, these equations show that the transformer reduces the voltage in proportion to the turns ratio $n = N_2/N_1$ and steps the current up in the same ratio. The ratio of these equations yields

$$\frac{V_1}{I_1} = \frac{1}{n^2} \frac{V_2}{I_2}$$

Since, however, V_1/I_1 represents the effective input resistance R'_L, whereas V_2/I_2 is the output resistance R_L, then

$$R'_L = \frac{1}{n^2} R_L \tag{18-24}$$

Maximum Power Output A practical problem is to find the transformer turns ratio n (for a given value of R_L) in order that the power output be a maximum for a small allowable distortion. This problem is solved graphically as follows: First the quiescent operating point Q is located, taking into consideration the bounds discussed in Sec. 10-1 and indicated in Fig. 10-2. The quiescent current is $I_C = P_C/V_C$, where P_C is the value of collector dissipation specified by the manufacturer, and V_C is a value of quiescent collector voltage which locates Q somewhere near the center of the V_{CE} scale. The choice of V_C is somewhat arbitrary, but is subject to the restriction that V_{CE} must be less than $V_C(\text{max})$ even if the transistor is driven to cutoff. For the transistor whose characteristics are plotted in Fig. 18-5, the manufacturer specifies $P_C = 10$ W and $V_{CE}(\text{max}) = 30$ V. A reasonable quiescent point Q is $V_C = -7.5$ V and $I_C = -1.1$ A. A static load line passing through this Q point with a slope corresponding to the small transformer dc primary resist-

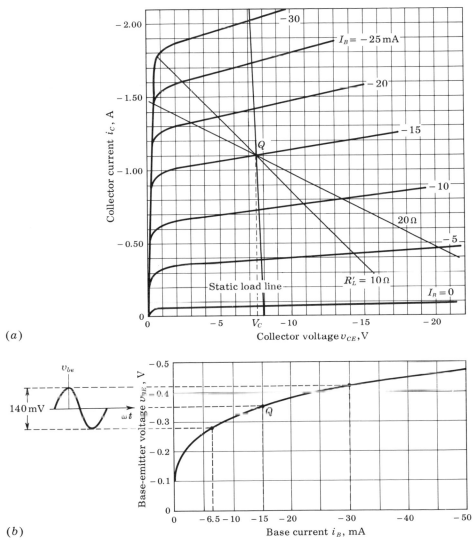

(a)

(b)

Fig. 18-5 (a) The collector characteristics for a power transistor. A static load line for a transformer-coupled load is indicated. Also shown are load lines for dynamic resistances of 10 and 20 Ω. (b) The input characteristic.

ance plus the small value of R_e is shown in Fig. 18-5a.   The intersection of this line with the voltage axis gives the required power-supply voltage V_{CC}.

The base current at the Q point is seen to be -15 mA.   If we were to drive the transistor too close to cutoff, an unacceptable amount of distortion would result.   Hence the peak-to-peak voltage swing v_{be} is limited to 140 mV.   We are here assuming that the input transformer in Fig. 18-4 represents voltage

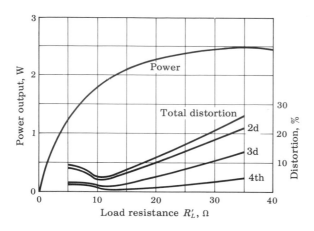

drive for the power transistor and that the source resistance R_s reflected into the secondary circuit of the input transformer is negligible. From the input characteristic of Fig. 18-5b we see that the corresponding base current extremes are $I_{b,\max} = -30$ mA and $I_{b,\min} = -6.5$ mA. Note that the input current swing is not symmetric with respect to the quiescent point $I_B = -15$ mA. In Sec. 9-13 we show that the nonsymmetric base current swing compensates for the nonsymmetric collector voltage swing, and thus we have less distortion with voltage drive than with current drive. If the effect of R_s is not negligible, the input characteristic of Fig. 18-5b must be modified by constructing the dynamic input characteristic corresponding to the given R_s, as discussed in Sec. 4-9 and Fig. 4-8.

A series of load lines are drawn through Q for different values of R'_L. The two indicated in Fig. 18-5a correspond to $R'_L = 10$ and $20\ \Omega$. For each such load line the dynamic transfer characteristic of Fig. 18-3 is constructed using Fig. 18-5a and b, and the output power and distortion are calculated using the formulas in Sec. 18-3. For example, we see from Fig. 18-5b that when the input excitation voltage is at its maximum, the base current is $I_B = -30$ mA, and from Fig. 18-5a and the $R'_L = 20\ \Omega$ load line, the maximum collector current is $I_{C,\max} = -1.45$ A. Similarly, we obtain the value $I_{C\frac{1}{2}} = -1.35$ A by noting from Fig. 18-5b that $I_b = -21$ mA when the input excitation voltage is at half its positive swing, or 35 mV above the Q point. The intersection of the load line $R'_L = 20\ \Omega$ with the $I_b = -21$ mA base current line in Fig. 18-5a results in $I_{C\frac{1}{2}} = -1.35$ A. The results of such calculations are plotted in Fig. 18-6.

For R'_L very small, the voltage swing, and hence the power output P, approach zero. For R'_L very large, the current swing is small, and again P approaches zero. Therefore, in Fig. 18-6 the plot of P versus R'_L has a maximum. Note also that this maximum is quite broad. By choosing $R'_L = 15\ \Omega$, a total distortion of less than 10 percent is obtained with a power output of 2.1 W, a value which is only 20 percent less than 2.5 W, the peak power possible.

18-5   POWER AMPLIFIERS USING TUBES[2]

The discussion of the preceding section is applicable to a triode, beam power tube, or pentode, as well as to a transistor.   A power pentode or beam tube is capable of delivering a large amount of power with a small grid swing (high power sensitivity), at a high efficiency, and with low distortion.   Under ordinary conditions of operation of a triode, the second harmonic is the principal component of distortion.   It is shown below that it is possible to eliminate completely, by the proper choice of the load resistance, the second-harmonic distortion component in a multielectrode tube.   The third-order distortion term is then the most important.

Zero Second-harmonic Distortion   Consider the pentode whose characteristics are indicated in Fig. 18-7, operating at the Q point $V_P = 200$ V and $V_G = -15$ V.   In this figure are shown three load lines corresponding to load resistances of 3, 5.5, and 8 K.   Suppose that a signal voltage having a peak value of 15 V is impressed on the grid.   The grid will then swing from 0 to -30 V.   Oscillograms of the output-*current* waveforms reveal the following characteristics: The waveform closely resembles a sine wave for the case $R_L' = 5.5$ K.   For $R_L' = 8$ K, the upper half of the wave is decidedly smaller than the lower loop, whereas for $R_L' = 3$ K, the upper half is larger.   The lower half of the current wave is identical for all three resistances.

An inspection of the static characteristics reveals the reason for these results.   The bottom half of the wave is obtained as the grid swings from -15 to -30 V.   At the quiescent point (-15 V) the current is the same for all three loads.   At   30 V the current is still practically the same for all loads, for this characteristic is approximately a horizontal line, as seen in Fig. 18-7. Consequently, the lower halves of the current waves are almost identical for the three loads.

The upper loop of the output-current wave is obtained as the grid swings from -15 V to zero.   Since the characteristic for $V_G = 0$ is a rapidly varying one in the region of low values of v_P, the peak current depends critically upon the point of intersection of the load line with this characteristic.   For low resistances the point of intersection will be on the upper portion of the $V_G = 0$

Fig. 18-7   The plate characteristics for a power pentode.   Dynamic load lines are shown for resistances of 3, 5.5, and 8 K passing through the Q point (200 V, 37 mA).

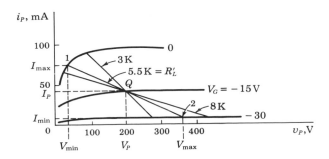

curve, resulting in a peaked output wave. For high resistances, the point of intersection will be on the rapidly falling portion of this curve, and gives rise to a flat-topped curve.

The choice of $R'_L = 5.5$ K was determined by the requirement that the second-harmonic distortion be zero. From Eqs. (18-18),

$$B_2 = \tfrac{1}{4}(I_{max} - 2I_P + I_{min})$$

and I_{max} must equal $2I_P - I_{min}$ in order that $B_2 = 0$. It is found from Fig. 18-7 that I_P, under the prescribed conditions of operation, is equal to 37 mA. Also, I_{min} (corresponding to $V_G = -30$ V) is substantially independent of the load line, and is found to be 7 mA. Hence

$$I_{max} = 2 \times 37 - 7 = 67 \text{ mA}$$

The corresponding value of $v_P = V_{min}$ is 35 V. It follows that

$$R'_L = \frac{200 - 35}{67 - 37} = 5.5 \text{ K}$$

The other two values of load resistance were arbitrarily chosen in order to illustrate the distortion.

With current excitation, it is *not* possible to eliminate second-harmonic distortion in a transistor. The plate characteristics of a pentode become more widely spaced (Fig. 18-7) as the grid voltage increases because g_m increases with increasing current. It is this feature of the output curves which makes possible a choice of R'_L to give zero second-harmonic distortion. On the other hand, the collector characteristics of a transistor crowd together at the higher currents because h_{FE} decreases with increasing current for large currents (Fig. 9-12). With such a bunching of the curves at high currents it is not possible (with a base current swing which is symmetrical about the Q point) to find a load for which $I_{max} - I_C = I_C - I_{min}$, the necessary condition for $B_2 = 0$. With voltage drive, the second-harmonic distortion in a transistor may be minimized by the proper choice of load (Fig. 18-6). If two identical devices (transistors or tubes) are used in a *push-pull configuration* (Sec. 18-8), then the second-harmonic distortion may be eliminated completely.

Beam Power Amplifier The power output and harmonic distortion for a 6L6 beam power tube operating at the quiescent point $V_P = V_{G2} = 250$ V and a plate dissipation of 19 W are shown in Fig. 18-8. We see that the maximum in the power-output curve is quite broad. For example, it is possible to obtain at least 6.5 W of output power with less than 10 percent distortion for any load resistance in the range from 2.5 to 4.5 K. Note that the optimum value of R'_L for a beam power tube or a pentode is a small fraction of the plate resistance (22.5 K for the 6L6), whereas for a triode the optimum value of R'_L turns out to be several times r_p.

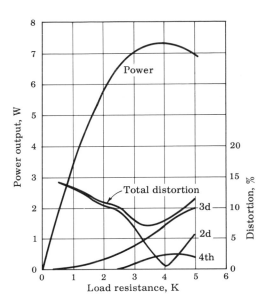

Fig. 18-8   Power output and distortion of a 6L6 beam tube as a function of load resistance. (Operating conditions: $V_P = V_{G2} = 250$ V, $I_P = 72$ mA, and $V_{G1} = -14$ V.)

18-6   SHIFT OF DYNAMIC LOAD LINE

The analysis which is given in Secs. 18-4 and 18-5 must be corrected slightly if an appreciable change in direct current occurs because of rectification caused by the nonlinearity of the dynamic characteristic. Consider Fig. 18-9, on which are indicated the static and dynamic load lines of a pentode or a transistor working into a transformer-coupled resistive load. Point Q is the quiescent point if there is no rectification. If a calculation reveals that $B_o \neq 0$, then it is no longer valid to draw the dynamic load line through the point Q. Instead, it must now pass through some other point D of the static load line. The new dynamic load line $D'DD''$ is drawn parallel to the original dynamic line through the point D. The new "quiescent" point Q' is located on the quiescent excitation curve X, and the corresponding quiescent current is I'_Y. The point D must be determined by trial and error.[3]   The correct location is that for

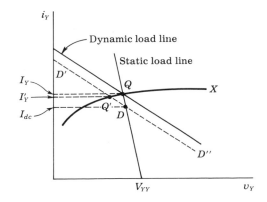

Fig. 18-9   The operating point shifts when rectification occurs because of a nonlinear dynamic curve.

which $I_{dc} = I'_Y + B'_o$. The component B'_o due to rectification may be either positive or negative.

18-7   EFFICIENCY

The various components of power in an amplifier circuit are now examined. Suppose that the stage is supplying power to a pure resistance load. The average power input from the dc supply is $V_{YY}I_Y$. The power absorbed by the output circuit is $I_Y{}^2R_1 + I_yV_y$, where I_y and V_y are the rms output current and voltage, respectively, and where R_1 is the *static* load resistance. If P_D denotes the average power dissipated by the active device, then, in accordance with the principle of the conservation of energy,

$$V_{YY}I_Y = I_Y{}^2R_1 + I_yV_y + P_D \tag{18-25}$$

Since, however,

$$V_{YY} = V_Y + I_YR_1$$

P_D may be written in the form

$$P_D = V_YI_Y - V_yI_y \tag{18-26}$$

If the load is not a pure resistance, V_yI_y must be replaced by $V_yI_y \cos \theta$, where $\cos \theta$ is the power factor of the load.

Equation (18-26) expresses the amount of power that must be dissipated by the active device. It represents the kinetic energy of the electrons which is converted into heat upon bombardment of the collector or plate by these electrons. If the ac power output is zero, i.e., if no applied signal exists, then P_D has its maximum value of V_YI_Y. Otherwise, the heating of the device is reduced by the amount of the ac power converted by the stage and supplied to the load. Hence a device is cooler when delivering power to a load than when there is no such ac power transfer. Obviously, then, the maximum dissipation is determined by the zero-excitation value.

Conversion Efficiency A measure of the ability of an active device to convert the dc power of the supply into the ac (signal) power delivered to the load is called the *conversion efficiency*, or *theoretical efficiency*. This figure of merit, designated η, is also called the *collector-circuit efficiency* for a transistor amplifier and the *plate-circuit* efficiency for a tube stage. By definition, the percentage efficiency is

$$\eta \equiv \frac{\text{signal power delivered to load}}{\text{dc power supplied to output circuit}} \times 100\% \tag{18-27}$$

In general,

$$\eta = \frac{\frac{1}{2}B_1{}^2R'_L}{V_{YY}(I_Y + B_o)} \times 100\% \tag{18-28}$$

If the distortion components are negligible, then

$$\eta = \frac{\frac{1}{2}V_m I_m}{V_{YY}I_Y} \times 100\% = 50\,\frac{V_m I_m}{V_{YY}I_Y}\,\% \qquad (18\text{-}29)$$

The collector-circuit efficiency differs from the overall efficiency because the power taken by the base is not included in the denominator of Eq. (18-28). For a tube the overall efficiency must include the grid power, the cathode-heating power, and (for a pentode) the screen power.

Maximum Value of Efficiency It is possible to obtain an approximate expression for η if certain idealizations are made in the characteristic curves. These assumptions, of course, introduce errors in the analysis. However, the results permit a rapid estimate to be made of the numerical value of η and, in particular, furnish an upper limit for this figure of merit. It is assumed that the static curves are equally spaced in the region of the load line for equal increments in excitation (grid voltage or base current). Thus, in Fig. 18-10, the distance from 1 to Q is the same as that from Q to 2. It is also assumed that the excitation is such as to give zero minimum current. The construction in Fig. 18-10 may be used to analyze either a series-fed or a transformer-fed load. The only difference between the two circuits is that the supply voltage V_{YY} equals $V_{\max}$ in the series-fed case, whereas V_{YY} is equal to the quiescent voltage V_Y (on the assumption that the static dc drop is negligible) in the transformer-coupled amplifier. The reader should compare Fig. 18-10 with Figs. 18-2, 18-5, and 18-7.

Under the foregoing idealized conditions,

$$I_Y = I_m \qquad \text{and} \qquad V_m = \frac{V_{\max} - V_{\min}}{2}$$

so that Eq. (18-29) becomes

$$\eta = \frac{25(V_{\max} - V_{\min})}{V_{YY}}\,\% \qquad (18\text{-}30)$$

The type of coupling used must now be taken into account. For the series-fed

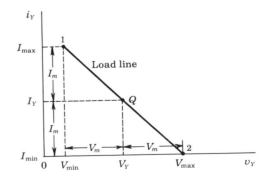

Fig. 18-10 Pertaining to the calculation of the conversion efficiency of an ideal distortionless amplifier.

load, $V_{YY} = V_{max}$, and

$$\eta = \frac{25(V_{max} - V_{min})}{V_{max}} \% \tag{18-31}$$

This result indicates that the upper limit of the conversion efficiency is 25 percent, and even this low value is approached only if V_{min} is negligible compared with V_{max}.

If the load is coupled to the stage through a transformer, then

$$V_{YY} = V_Y = \frac{V_{max} + V_{min}}{2}$$

and Eq. (18-30) reduces to

$$\eta = 50 \frac{V_{max} - V_{min}}{V_{max} + V_{min}} \% \tag{18-32}$$

This result shows that the upper limit of the theoretical efficiency for a transformer-coupled power amplifier is 50 percent, or twice that of the series-fed circuit. For a transistor amplifier V_{min} occurs near the saturation region, and hence $V_{min} \ll V_{max}$, and the collector-circuit efficiency may approach the upper limit of 50 percent. For beam power tubes operating near the peak of the power curve, $\eta \approx 40$ percent. Finally, for a triode, where V_{min} is usually not negligible compared with V_{max}, a value of η of less than 30 percent may be expected.

The numerical value of the conversion efficiency must be calculated from Eq. (18-28). The use of Eqs. (18-31) and (18-32) may lead to large errors in η since these equations are derived using the highly idealized conditions indicated in Fig. 18-10.

18-8   PUSH–PULL AMPLIFIERS[4]

A great deal of the distortion introduced by the nonlinearity of the dynamic transfer characteristic may be eliminated by the circuit shown in Fig. 18-11, know as a *push-pull configuration*. In the circuit the excitation is introduced through a center-tapped transformer. Thus, when the signal on transistor $Q1$ is positive, the signal on $Q2$ is negative by an equal amount. Any other circuit that provides two equal voltages which differ in phase by 180° may be used in place of the input transformer.

Although the active devices are indicated as transistors in Fig. 18-11, FETs, triodes, beam power tubes, etc., may also be used in this push-pull arrangement. And the discussion to follow applies equally well regardless of the particular power device employed.

Consider an input signal (base current) of the form $x_1 = X_m \cos \omega t$ applied to $Q1$. The output current of this transistor is given by Eq. (18-16) and is repeated here for convenience:

$$i_1 = I_C + B_o + B_1 \cos \omega t + B_2 \cos 2\omega t + B_3 \cos 3\omega t + \cdots \tag{18-33}$$

The corresponding input signal to $Q2$ is

$$x_2 = -x_1 = X_m \cos (\omega t + \pi)$$

The output current of this transistor is obtained by replacing ωt by $\omega t + \pi$ in the expression for i_1. That is,

$$i_2(\omega t) = i_1(\omega t + \pi) \tag{18-34}$$

whence

$$i_2 = I_C + B_o + B_1 \cos (\omega t + \pi) + B_2 \cos 2(\omega t + \pi) + \cdot \cdot \cdot$$

which is

$$i_2 = I_C + B_o - B_1 \cos \omega t + B_2 \cos 2\omega t - B_3 \cos 3\omega t + \cdot \cdot \cdot$$
$$\tag{18-35}$$

As illustrated in Fig. 18-11, the current i_1 and i_2 are in opposite directions through the output-transformer primary windings. The total output current is then proportional to the difference between the collector currents in the two transistors. That is,

$$i = k(i_1 - i_2) = 2k(B_1 \cos \omega t + B_3 \cos 3\omega t + \cdot \cdot \cdot) \tag{18-36}$$

This expression shows that a push-pull circuit will balance out all even harmonics in the output and will leave the third-harmonic term as the principal source of distortion. This conclusion was reached on the assumption that the two transistors are identical. If their characteristics differ appreciably, the appearance of even harmonics must be expected.

The fact that the output current contains no even-harmonic terms means that the push-pull system possesses "half-wave," or "mirror," symmetry, in addition to the zero-axis symmetry. Half-wave symmetry requires that the bottom loop of the wave, when shifted 180° along the axis, will be the mirror image of the top loop. The condition of mirror symmetry is represented

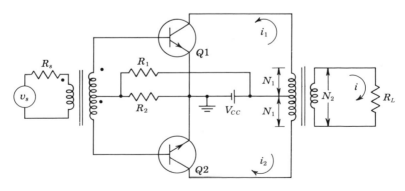

Fig. 18-11   Two transistors in a push-pull arrangement.

mathematically by the relation

$$i(\omega t) = -i(\omega t + \pi) \tag{18-37}$$

If $\omega t + \pi$ is substituted for ωt in Eq. (18-36), it will be seen that Eq. (18-37) is satisfied.

Advantages of a Push-Pull System Because no even harmonics are present in the output of a push-pull amplifier, such a circuit will give more output per active device for a given amount of distortion. For the same reason, a push-pull arrangement may be used to obtain less distortion for a given power output per transistor.

Another feature of the push-pull system is evident from an inspection of Fig. 18-11. It is noticed that the dc components of the collector current oppose each other magnetically in the transformer core. This eliminates any tendency toward core saturation and consequent nonlinear distortion that might arise from the curvature of the transformer magnetization curve. Another advantage of this system is that the effects of ripple voltages that may be contained in the power supply because of inadequate filtering will be balanced out. This cancellation results because the currents produced by this ripple voltage are in opposite directions in the transformer winding, and so will not appear in the load. Of course, the power-supply hum will also act on the voltage-amplifier stages, and so will be part of the input to the power stage. This hum will not be eliminated by the push-pull circuit.

18-9 CLASS B AMPLIFIERS[5]

The circuit for the class B push-pull system is the same as that for the class A system except that the devices are biased approximately at cutoff. The transistor circuit of Fig. 18-11 operates class B if $R_2 = 0$ because a transistor is essentially at cutoff if the base is shorted to the emitter (Sec. 9-15). The advantages of class B as compared with class A operation are the following: It is possible to obtain greater power output, the efficiency is higher, and there is negligible power loss at no signal. For these reasons, in systems where the power supply is limited, such as those operating from solar cells or a battery, the output power is usually delivered through a push-pull class B transistor circuit. The disadvantages are that the harmonic distortion is higher, self-bias cannot be used, and the supply voltages must have good regulation.

Power Considerations In order to investigate the conversion efficiency of the system, it is assumed, as in Sec. 18-7, that the output characteristics are equally spaced for equal intervals of excitation, so that the dynamic transfer curve is a straight line. It is also assumed that the minimum current is zero. The graphical construction from which to determine the output-current and voltage waveshapes for a single transistor operating as a class B stage is indicated in Fig. 18-12. Note that for a sinusoidal excitation the output is sinusoidal during one-half of each period and is zero during the second half cycle. The effective load resistance is $R'_L = (N_1/N_2)^2 R_L$. This expression for R'_L is the same as that in Eq. (18-24), where now N_1 represents the number of primary turns to the center tap (Fig. 18-11).

The waveforms illustrated in Fig. 18-12 represent one transistor $Q1$ only. The output of $Q2$ is, of course, a series of sine loop pulses that are 180° out of phase with those of $Q1$. The load current, which is proportional to the difference between the two collector currents, is therefore a perfect sine wave for the ideal conditions assumed. The power output is

$$P = \frac{I_m V_m}{2} = \frac{I_m}{2}(V_{CC} - V_{min}) \qquad (18\text{-}38)$$

The corresponding direct collector current in each transistor under load is the average value of the half sine loop of Fig. 18-12. Since $I_{dc} = I_m/\pi$ for this waveform, the dc input power from the supply is

$$P_i = 2\frac{I_m V_{CC}}{\pi} \qquad (18\text{-}39)$$

The factor 2 in this expression arises because two transistors are used in the push-pull system.

Taking the ratio of Eqs. (18-38) and (18-39), we obtain for the collector-

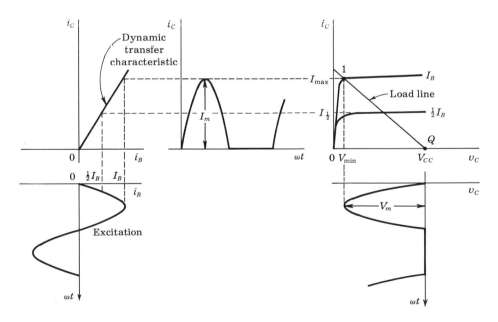

Fig. 18-12 Graphical construction for determining the output waveforms of a single class B transistor stage.

circuit efficiency

$$\eta \equiv \frac{P}{P_i} \times 100 = \frac{\pi}{4} \frac{V_m}{V_{CC}} = \frac{\pi}{4} \left(1 - \frac{V_{min}}{V_{CC}} \right) \times 100\% \qquad (18\text{-}40)$$

This expression shows that the maximum possible conversion efficiency is $25\pi = 78.5$ percent for a class B system compared with 50 percent for class A operation. For a transistor circuit where $V_{min} \ll V_{CC}$, it is possible to approach this upper limit of efficiency. This large value of η results from the fact that there is no current in a class B system if there is no excitation, whereas there is a drain from the power supply in a class A system even at zero signal. We also note that in a class B amplifier the dissipation at the collectors is zero in the quiescent state and increases with excitation, whereas the heating of the collectors of a class A system is a maximum at zero input and decreases as the signal increases. Since the direct current increases with signal in a class B amplifier, the power supply must have good regulation.

The collector dissipation P_C (in both transistors) is the difference between the power input to the collector circuit and the power delivered to the load. Since $I_m = V_m/R'_L$,

$$P_C = P_i - P = \frac{2}{\pi} \frac{V_{CC}V_m}{R'_L} - \frac{V_m{}^2}{2R'_L} \qquad (18\text{-}41)$$

This equation shows that the collector dissipation is zero at no signal ($V_m = 0$), rises as V_m increases, and passes through a maximum at $V_m = 2V_{CC}/\pi$ (Prob. 18-23). The peak dissipation is found to be

$$P_C(\text{max}) = \frac{2V_{CC}{}^2}{\pi^2 R'_L} \qquad (18\text{-}42)$$

The maximum power which can be delivered is obtained for $V_m = V_{CC}$ (if $V_{min} = 0$), or

$$P(\text{max}) = \frac{V_{CC}{}^2}{2R'_L} \qquad (18\text{-}43)$$

Hence

$$P_C(\text{max}) = \frac{4}{\pi^2} P(\text{max}) \approx 0.4P(\text{max}) \qquad (18\text{-}44)$$

If, for example, we wish to deliver 10 W from a class B push-pull amplifier, then $P_C(\text{max}) = 4$ W, or we must select transistors which have collector dissipations of approximately 2 W each. In other words, we can obtain a push-pull output of five times the specified power dissipation of a single transistor. On the other hand, if we paralleled two transistors and operated them class A to obtain 10 W out, the collector dissipation of each transistor would have to be at least 10 W (assuming 50 percent efficiency). And at no excitation there would be a steady loss of 10 W in each transistor, whereas in class B the standby (no-signal) dissipation is zero. This example clearly indicates the superiority of the push-pull over the parallel configuration.

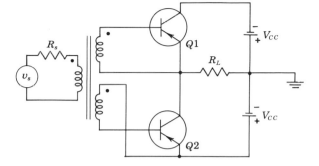

Fig. 18-13 A class B push-pull circuit which does not use an output transformer.

Distortion The output of a push-pull system always possesses mirror symmetry (Sec. 18-8), so that $I_Y = I_C = 0$, $I_{max} = -I_{min}$, and $I_{\frac{1}{2}} = -I_{-\frac{1}{2}}$. Under these circumstances, Eqs. (18-18) reduce to

$$B_o = B_2 = B_4 = 0 \qquad B_1 = \tfrac{2}{3}(I_{max} + I_{\frac{1}{2}}) \qquad B_3 = \tfrac{1}{3}(I_{max} - 2I_{\frac{1}{2}})$$

$$(18\text{-}45)$$

Note that there is no even-harmonic distortion. The principal contribution to distortion is the third harmonic, given by $D_3 = |B_3|/|B_1|$. The values I_{max} and $I_{\frac{1}{2}}$ are found as follows: A load line corresponding to $R'_L = (N_1/N_2)^2 R_L$ is drawn on the collector characteristics through the point $I_C = 0$ and $V_{CE} = V_{CC}$. If the peak base current is I_B, then the intersection of the load line with the I_B curve is I_{max} and with the $I_B/2$ characteristic is $I_{\frac{1}{2}}$, as indicated in Fig. 18-12.

The power output, taking distortion into account, is

$$P = (1 + D_3{}^2)\frac{B_1{}^2 R'_L}{2} \qquad\qquad (18\text{-}46)$$

Special Circuits[6] A class B configuration which dispenses with the output transformer is shown in Fig. 18-13. This arrangement requires a power supply whose center tap is grounded, a condition which is not difficult to obtain with batteries.

A circuit which requires neither an output nor an input transformer is shown in Fig. 18-14. This arrangement uses transistors having complementary symmetry (one n-p-n and one p-n-p type), and hence there is no vacuum-

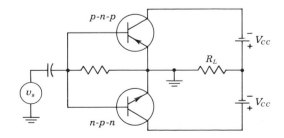

Fig. 18-14 A push-pull circuit using transistors having complementary symmetry.

tube counterpart of this circuit. The difficulty with the circuit is that of obtaining matched complementary transistors. If there is an unbalance in the characteristics of the two transistors in Fig. 18-14 (or also in Figs. 18-11 and 18-13), then considerable distortion will be introduced; even harmonics will no longer be canceled. Very often negative feedback is used in power amplifiers to reduce nonlinear distortion. In Fig. 18-14 the power supply "floats" with respect to ground. (Neither side of the power supply is grounded.)

18-10   CLASS AB OPERATION

In addition to the distortion introduced by not using matched transistors and that due to the nonlinearity of the collector characteristics, there is one more source of distortion, that caused by nonlinearity of the input characteristic. As pointed out in Sec. 9-15 and Fig. 9-20, no appreciable base current flows until the emitter junction is forward-biased by the cutin voltage V_γ, which is 0.1 V for germanium and 0.5 V for silicon (Table 9-2). Under these circumstances a sinusoidal base-voltage excitation will not result in a sinusoidal output current.

The distortion caused by the nonlinear transistor input characteristic is indicated in Fig. 18-15. The i_B-v_B curve for each transistor is drawn, and

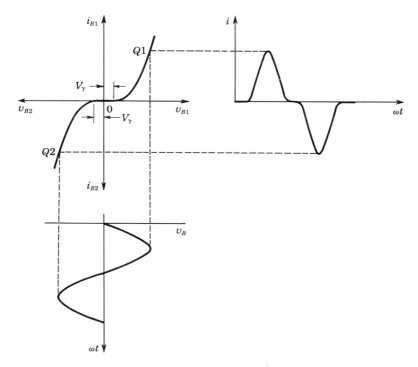

Fig. 18-15 Crossover distortion.

the construction used to obtain the output current (assumed proportional to the base current) is shown.   In the region of small currents (for $v_B < V_\gamma$) the output is much smaller than it would be if the response were linear.   This effect is called *crossover distortion*.   Such distortion would not occur if the driver were a true current generator, in other words, if the base current (rather than the base voltage) were sinusoidal.

In order to minimize crossover distortion, the transistors must operate in a class AB mode, where a small standby current flows at zero excitation.   In the circuit of Fig. 18-11, the voltage drop across R_2 is adjusted to be approximately equal to V_γ.   Class AB operation results in less distortion than class B, but the price which must be paid for this improvement is a loss in efficiency and a waste of standby power.   The calculations of the distortion components in a class AB or class A push-pull amplifier due to the nonlinearity of the collector characteristics is somewhat involved since it requires the construction of composite output curves for the pair of transistors.[7]

REFERENCES

1. Espley, D. C.: The Calculation of Harmonic Production in Thermionic Valves with Resistive Loads, *Proc. IRE*, vol. 21, pp. 1439–1446, October, 1933.
   Chaffee, E. L.: A Simplified Harmonic Analysis, *Rev. Sci. Instr.*, vol. 7, pp. 384–389, October, 1936.
   Block, A.: Distortion in Valves with Resistive Loads, *Wireless Eng.*, vol. 16, pp. 592–596, December, 1939.

2. Nottingham, W. B.: Optimum Conditions for Maximum Power in Class A Amplifiers, *Proc. IRE*, vol. 29, pp. 620–623, December, 1941.

3. Kilgour, C. E.: Graphical Analysis of Output Tube Performance, *Proc. IRE*, vol. 19, pp. 42–50, January, 1931.
   Millman, J.: "Vacuum-tube and Semiconductor Electronics," p. 419, McGraw-Hill Book Company, New York, 1958.

4. Langsford Smith, F., and A. R. Cheaterman: Ultra Linear Amplifiers, *Radiotronics*, vol. 20, nos. 5–7, May–July, 1955.

5. Gordon, M.: Class B Audio Frequency Amplification, *Wireless Eng.*, vol. 16, pp. 457–459, September, 1939.
   Woll, H. J.: Low-frequency Amplifiers, in L. P. Hunter (ed.), "Handbook of Semiconductor Electronics," 2d ed., chap. 11, McGraw-Hill Book Company, New York, 1962.
   Lo, A. W., et al.: "Transistor Electronics." pp. 197–224, Prentice-Hall, Inc., Englewood Cliffs, N.J., 1956.

6. Lohman, R. D.: Complementary Symmetry Transistor Circuits, *Electronics*, vol. 26, pp. 140–143, September, 1953.

7. Millman, J.: Ref. 3, pp. 424–430.

19/PHOTOELECTRIC DEVICES

The liberation of electrons from matter under the influence of light is known as the *photoelectric effect*, first observed by Hertz in 1887. Today, many commercial devices are based on this discovery.

The photoelectric effect includes (1) the liberation of electrons from a metallic surface, and (2) the generation of hole-electron pairs in semiconductors when these solids are subjected to radiation. The first phenomenon is called the *photoemissive effect* and is exploited in vacuum and gas phototubes. Photoeffects in semiconductors may be subdivided into two types: (1) the *photoconductive effect;* i.e., the electrical conductivity of a semiconductor bar depends upon the light intensity; and (2) the *junction photoeffect;* i.e., the current across a reverse-biased *p-n* junction is determined by the intensity of the illumination. If the *p-n* junction is open-circuited, an emf is generated. This latter phenomenon is called the *photovoltaic effect.*

This chapter discusses photoelectric theory, considers practical photodevices, and shows how these are used in a circuit.

19-1   PHOTOEMISSIVITY

Using the experimental arrangement indicated in Fig. 19-1, the following characteristics of the photoemissive effect are obtained:[1]

1. The photoelectrons liberated from the photosensitive surface possess a range of initial velocities. However, a definite negative potential when applied between the collector and the emitting surface will retard the fastest-moving electrons. This indicates that the emitted electrons are liberated with all velocities from zero to a definite maximum value v_{max}. The maximum velocity of the emitted electrons

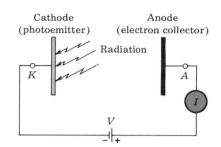

Fig. 19-1 The photoelectric current I is measured as a function of the voltage V between photoemitter and collector.

is given by the relation

$$\tfrac{1}{2}mv_{\text{max}}^2 = eV_r \tag{19-1}$$

where V_r is the retarding potential, in volts, necessary to reduce the photocurrent to zero. As the accelerating potential is increased, the number of electrons to the collector increases until saturation occurs. In Fig. 19-2a are plotted curves showing the variation of photocurrent I versus anode potential V with the light intensity j as a parameter. These curves indicate that V_r, and hence v_{max}, are independent of the light intensity.

2. If the photoelectric current is measured as a function of the anode potential for different light frequencies f and equal intensities of the incident light, the results[2] obtained are essentially those illustrated in Fig. 19-2b. It is observed that the greater the frequency of the incident light, the greater must be the retarding potential to reduce the photocurrent to zero. This means, of course, that the maximum velocity of emission of the photoelectrons increases with the frequency of the incident light. Experimentally, it is found that a linear relationship exists between V_r and f.

The experimental facts 1 and 2 may be summarized in the statement that the *maximum energy of the electrons liberated photoelectrically is independent of the light intensity but varies linearly with the frequency of the incident light.*

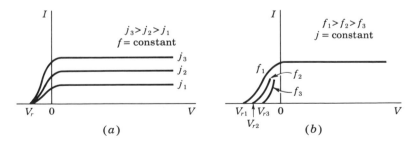

(a)   (b)

Fig. 19-2 Photocurrent vs. anode voltage. (a) With light intensity j as a parameter. The frequency f of the incident light is a constant. (b) With the frequency of incident light as a parameter. The light intensity is a constant.

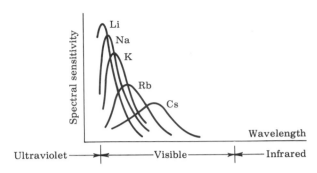

Fig. 19-3 Spectral sensitivity as a function of wavelength for the alkali metals. (E. F. Seiler, *Astrophys. J.*, vol. 52, p. 129, 1920.)

3. If the saturation current is plotted as a function of the light intensity, we find that the photoelectric current is directly proportional to the intensity of the light.

4. The foregoing photoelectric characteristics are practically independent of temperature, within wide ranges of temperature.

5. The electrons are emitted immediately upon the exposure of the surface to light. The time lag has been determined experimentally[3] to be less than 3 nsec.

6. Photoelectric cells are selective devices. This means that a given intensity of light of one wavelength, say red light, will not liberate the same number of electrons as an equal intensity of light of another wavelength, say blue light. That is, the photoelectric yield, defined as the photocurrent (in amperes) per watt of incident light, depends upon the frequency of the light. Alternative designations of the term "photoelectric yield" to be found in the literature are *spectral response, quantum yield, spectral sensitivity, specific photosensitivity, and current-wavelength characteristic.* The relative response curves for the alkali metals are shown in Fig. 19-3.

Curves of these types are obtained experimentally in the following way: Light from an incandescent source is passed through the prism of a monochromator for dispersion, a narrow band of wavelengths being selected by means of an appropriately placed slit system. The current given by the photoelectric surface when exposed to the light passing through the system of slits is noted. The current given by a blackened thermopile when exposed to the same light is also noted. The ratio of these two readings is plotted vs. the wavelength of the incident light. Blackened thermopiles are used because they absorb all radiation incident upon them equally, regardless of the wavelength. This procedure permits a measure of the energy contained in any part of the spectrum to be made. An automatic spectral-sensitivity-curve tracer has been designed for obtaining these curves quickly with the aid of a cathode-ray tube.[4]

19-2   PHOTOELECTRIC THEORY

The foregoing experimental facts find their explanation in the electronic theory of metals and in the light-quantum hypothesis of Planck. As discussed in

Sec. 2-3, Planck made the fundamental assumption that radiant energy is not continuous, but can exist only in discrete quantities called *quanta*, or *photons*. Bohr used this same theory of photons to explain the spectra of atoms (Sec. 2-1). Einstein applied the same hypothesis to explain photo-emission, as we now demonstrate. Planck's basic assumption is that, *associated with light of frequency f (hertz) are a number of photons, each of which has an energy hf (joules)*, where h (joule-seconds) is called *Planck's constant* (Appendix A). The greater the intensity of the light, the larger the number of photons present, but the energy of each photon remains unchanged. Of course, if the light beam is heterogeneous rather than monochromatic, the energy of the photons therewith associated will vary and will depend upon the frequency.

Einstein Equation If monochromatic light of frequency f falls upon a metal whose work function is E_W (electron volts), corresponding to U_W (joules), the velocity of the emitted electron is, according to Einstein,[5]

$$\tfrac{1}{2}mv^2 \leq hf - U_W \tag{19-2}$$

The significance of this equation becomes apparent if the electronic theory of matter is taken into consideration. Since photoelectric devices are operated at low (room) temperature, the completely degenerate distribution function must be employed. Figure 19-4 shows the energy distribution function at low temperatures, and also the potential-energy barrier at the surface of the metal (Fig. 3-14).

Figure 19-4 indicates that the electrons within the metal exist in energy levels ranging from zero to a maximum energy given by the Fermi level E_F eV, but none has energies greater than this value. If an electron possessing the Fermi energy receives the photon of light energy hf and travels normal to the surface of the metal, the kinetic energy that it will have, upon escaping from the metal, will be $hf - U_W$ (joules). This follows from the significance of the work function U_W, which is the minimum energy that must be supplied at 0°K in order to permit the fastest-moving surface-directed electron just to surmount the potential-energy barrier at the surface of the metal and to escape.

Since some of the electrons which have energies less than the Fermi level may absorb the incident photons, an energy greater in magnitude than U_W

Fig. 19-4 Energy-level diagram for the free electrons within a metal. The potential-energy barrier at the surface of the metal is also shown.

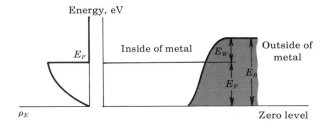

will be expended when they escape. This fact explains the inequality of Eq. (19-2).

According to Eq. (19-2), the retarding potential V_r that will just repel the fastest-moving electron is given by

$$eV_r = \tfrac{1}{2}mv_{\max}^2 = hf - U_W \tag{19-3}$$

which is in agreement with the experimental facts 1 and 2 of Sec. 19-1. This result shows that the maximum energy of the escaping electrons varies linearly with the frequency and is independent of the light intensity. The latter condition follows from the fact that the intensity of the incident light does not enter into this expression. Equation (19-3) was verified experimentally by Millikan.[6] He plotted retarding voltage vs. frequency and obtained a straight line. The slope of this line gives the value of the ratio h/e. The value of this ratio found by this method agrees very well with that from other experiments. The intercept of the Einstein line with the V_r axis gives U_W/e (provided that corrections are made for contact difference of potential). The value of the work function obtained photoelectrically agrees well with that measured thermionically for the same emitter.

The fact that the photoelectric current is strictly proportional to the light intensity is readily explained. A greater light intensity merely denotes the presence of a larger number of photons. Further, since each photon is equally effective in ejecting electrons, the number of electrons per second ejected must be proportional to the light intensity.

Threshold Wavelength The minimum frequency of light, known as the *threshold frequency* f_c, that can be used to cause photoelectric emission can be found from Eq. (19-3) by setting the velocity equal to zero. The result is

$$f_c = \frac{U_W}{h} \tag{19-4}$$

The corresponding wavelength, known as the *long-wavelength limit*, or the *threshold wavelength*, or the *cutoff wavelength* λ_c (meters) beyond which photoelectric emission cannot take place, is

$$\lambda_c = \frac{c}{f_c} = \frac{ch}{U_W}$$

If the work function U_W in joules is converted to E_W in electron volts and if the wavelength λ_c is expressed in angstrom units, Å (Appendix B), we obtain

$$\lambda_c = \frac{12,400}{E_W} \tag{19-5}$$

For response over the entire visible region, 3,800 to 7,600 Å, the work function of the photosensitive surface must be less than 1.63 V. This statement follows directly from Eq. (19-5).

EXAMPLE A tungsten surface having a work function of 4.52 eV is irradiated with the mercury line, 2,537 Å. What is the maximum speed of the emitted electrons?

Solution The electron-volt equivalent of the energy of the incident photons is $12,400/2,537 = 4.88$ eV. According to the Einstein equation, the maximum energy of the emitted electrons is

$$4.88 - 4.52 = 0.36 \text{ eV}$$

From Eq. (1-13) the corresponding velocity is

$$v_{\max} = 5.93 \times 10^5 \sqrt{0.36} = 3.56 \times 10^5 \text{ m/sec}$$

If it is remembered that the distribution function of electrons in metals varies very little with temperature, then fact 4 of Sec. 19-1 is evident. Strictly speaking, however, the totally degenerate distribution function applies only at the temperature 0°K. At room temperature, therefore, a few electrons will have emission velocities greater than those predicted by Eq. (19-3). Hence no absolutely sharp long-wavelength limit exists for any substance, since the curves, such as those of Fig. 19-1, approach the axis asymptotically. Fowler[7] investigated this matter theoretically, and this theory provides a method of determining the photoelectric work function independent of the temperature of the surface. For most practical purposes the use of the completely degenerate distribution function even at room temperature is quite reasonable. Hence it is justifiable to consider cutoff to occur sharply for frequencies below the critical value f_c.

Spectral Response A qualitative explanation for the shapes of the curves of Fig. 19-3 is readily found. There can be no response for frequencies below f_c; hence cutoff occurs at the point $f = f_c$. As f increases above f_c, the energy of the incident photon hf increases, and some electrons in levels below the maximum energy state are permitted to escape. As a result, the response increases as the frequency increases, or correspondingly, as the wavelength decreases. However, a point of maximum response must exist. This conclusion follows from the fact that if the energy of the light is U (joules), the number of photons in the light beam is U/hf. The photocurrent must decrease as f increases because of the decreased number of photons present and because, as f increases, other photon-absorption processes occur which do not lead to emission. A second peak is sometimes found to occur at the short wavelengths. A complete quantitative explanation for the shapes of these curves has not yet been given.

19-3   DEFINITIONS OF SOME RADIATION TERMS

A beam of light which strikes a surface consists of a stream of photons. If we know the number of photons per second striking the surface and in addition the energy of each photon in joules, we can calculate the *radiant flux*, which gives the number of joules per second, or the power in watts of the beam.

Irradiation is defined as the total radiant power density incident upon a receiving surface in milliwatts per square centimeter. The concept of *illumination* is based on the ability of the human eye to see different wavelengths of radiation. Figure 19-5a shows a plot of the relative spectral response of the human eye of a so-called standard observer, and is referred to as the *standard luminosity* curve. From this curve it can be seen that the human eye responds to light between 0.38 and 0.76 μ and has a maximum response at a wavelength of 0.55 μ, where μ denotes the micron (Appendix B). If a white surface is illuminated with the same intensity light at 0.55 and 0.61 μ, respectively, only half the brightness will be seen at 0.61 μ as at 0.55 μ. Also, note that the response is extremely small outside the range 0.4 to 0.7 μ (4,000 to 7,000 Å).

A radiant power density which is weighted in proportion to the standard luminosity curve is called *illumination*. The unit of luminous flux is called

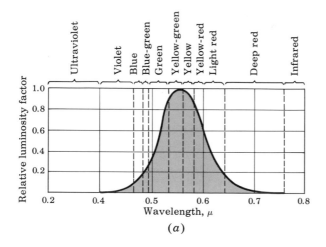

(a)

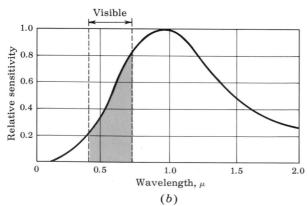

(b)

Fig. 19-5 (a) The standard luminosity curve for the eye; (b) the relative response curve for an incandescent lamp at 2900°K. (Courtesy of Texas Instruments, Inc.)

the *lumen*.   The lumen is defined so that 1 W of light at $\lambda = 0.55\,\mu$ is equal to 680 lumens.   Conversely, 1 lumen = 0.0016 W for yellow-green light.   From the standard luminosity curve we see that 1 W of light at 0.61 μ is equal to 340 lumens.   One *candlepower* corresponds to a total light flux of 4π lumens. One lumen per square foot is called the *foot-candle*.

Figure 19-5b shows the relative spectral distribution of a tungsten light source operating at a temperature of 2900°K.   In order to compute the illumination from this source, the spectral response of the light source (at a given wavelength) is multiplied by the ordinate of the standard luminosity curve (at the same λ), and the area under the product curve is obtained.

19-4   PHOTOTUBES

The essential elements of a phototube are a sensitive cathode surface of large area and a collecting electrode, contained in a glass bulb.   Many of the present-day phototubes consist of a semicylindrical metallic cathode on which the photosensitive substance has been evaporated.   The anode is a straight wire that is practically coaxial with the cathode.

Volt-Ampere Characteristics   The curves for a vacuum phototube are shown in Fig. 19-6a.   The current that exists at zero accelerating potential results from the initial velocities of the electrons.   Note that a retarding potential must be applied in order to reduce the current to zero.

As the anode-cathode potential is increased, the current to the anode increases very rapidly at first, the nonsaturation resulting from the possible space-charge effects, and also from the fact that some electrons are missing the wire anode on their journey from the cathode, since the attractive field is small at these low potentials.   The current very soon reaches a saturation

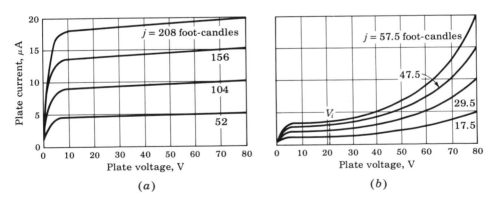

Fig. 19-6   Volt-ampere characteristics with light intensity as a parameter (a) of a vacuum phototube, (b) of a gas-filled phototube.

value, for the field becomes sufficient to attract all the electrons liberated from the cathode under the influence of the incident light. The continued increase in photocurrent as the anode potential is increased results from the more complete collection of the electrons.

By filling the glass envelope with an inert gas, such as neon or argon, at a pressure of the order of 0.5 mm, the current yield for a given intensity of illumination is greatly increased, as illustrated in Fig. 19-6b. The increased current is produced by ionization of the gas for voltages in excess of the ionization potential V_i. The additional electrons generated by ionization give rise to the so-called *Townsend discharge*.[8] It is important never to raise the potential across the tube to the point where a glow discharge occurs, for that will cause cathode sputtering, with a consequent permanent damage to the cathode surface.

Sensitivity Commercial phototubes are now available with photoelectric yields[9] that have peaks in various portions of the radiation spectrum. Figure 19-7 shows the spectral response of the three most common photosurfaces. Surface S-1 consists of a composite silver–cesium oxide–cesium surface. Such a surface is sensitive throughout the entire visible region and has a high sensitivity in the infrared. As a result, this composite surface is used extensively in commercial phototubes. Surface S-3 is a silver–rubidium oxide–rubidium surface which has a sensitivity largely confined to the visible region, although

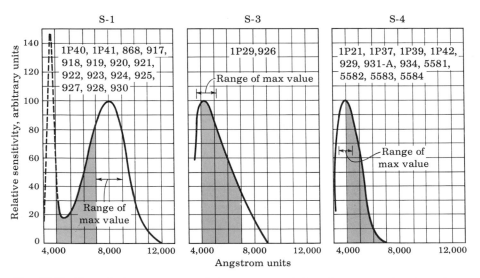

Fig. 19-7 The relative response of three commercial surfaces as a function of wavelength. The phototubes using these surfaces are listed on each diagram. The visible region is shaded. (From V. K. Zworykin and G. A. Ramberg, "Photoelectricity and Its Applications," John Wiley & Sons, Inc., New York, 1949.)

it has its greatest sensitivity in the blue end of the spectrum. Surface S-4 shows the response of an antimony-cesium surface that is very sensitive to the green, blue, and near ultraviolet and is insensitive to red and infrared radiation. The tube has a sensitivity of 120 μA/lumen when daylight is used as the source. When a tungsten lamp, operating at a filament temperature of 2870°K, is the source of light, the sensitivity of the S-1 surface is 20, of the S-3 surface 6.5, and of the S-4 surface 45 μA/lumen.

Practical Considerations It should be kept in mind that the curves shown in this chapter, and also those supplied by the phototube manufacturers, are typical rather than specified for any particular tube type. Large variations may exist in the characteristics of phototubes manufactured under presumably identical conditions. This results from the fact that the number of photoelectrons emitted for a given illumination varies appreciably for even slight changes in the surface preparation of the cathode. For the same reason, it is often found that different portions of the same emitting surface may possess different sensitivities. It is advisable, therefore, to illuminate a large part of the cathode uniformly whenever possible, rather than to focus the light source on only a portion of the photoemissive surface.

In any particular application, careful consideration must be given to the choice of the light source, as well as to the photocell characteristics. For example, it is desirable that the source emit strongly in the frequency range in which the photocell is most sensitive, if large photocurrents are to be obtained.

A gas photocell has greater sensitivity than a comparable vacuum tube. However, the current from the gas-filled device increases more rapidly than the illumination for anode voltages that are higher than the ionization potential of the gas (Fig. 19-6b). This nonlinearity of the current with incident flux must be taken into account in applications using a gas tube.

19-5   APPLICATIONS OF PHOTODEVICES

The basic circuit employing a light-sensitive device is the same for a photoemissive device (Fig. 19-8a) as for a semiconductor device (Fig. 19-8b or c).

As the luminous flux that is incident on the cell varies, the output current changes, and a changing voltage appears across the load resistor R_L. Although the basic circuits are the same, there are three important types of application of phototubes, just as there are with amplifiers: (1) A definite fixed amount of illumination is to be measured. This application involves a dc, or quiescent, value calculation. (2) Rapid variations in light intensity are to be faithfully reproduced. This mode of operation is a small-signal application. (3) A definite large change in light intensity is to be detected. This represents a large-signal or switching-mode application.

The field of photometry and colorimetry offers many examples of the first type of application. In such cases, R_L might simply be the internal resistance

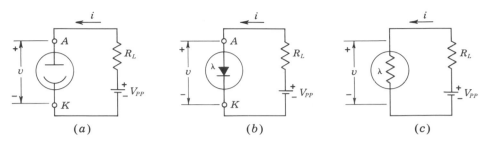

Fig. 19-8 The basic circuit using a photoelectric device consists of a supply voltage V_{PP} in series with the load R_L across the device. The symbol in (a) represents a phototube, in (b) a p-n junction photodiode, and in (c) a photoconductive cell.

of the indicating instrument. If the incident light is too small to be measurable directly, a dc amplifier might be used. In this case, R_L will be the input resistance of the amplifier. The light beam of varying intensity that has been modulated by the sound track of a motion-picture film or by the scanning process in a television tube is of the second class. Applications of the third type are exemplified by ON and OFF circuits. In such cases the phototube is used in conjunction with a relay, so that some circuit is either energized or deenergized when the light intensity exceeds or falls below some preassigned value. Many of the common applications of the "electric eye" belong to this third class. A few illustrations are the counting or sorting of objects on a conveyor belt, the automatic opening of a door as it is approached, devices for the protection of human life, and fire-alarm systems.

Circuit Analysis In order to determine the current that will flow in the circuit of Fig. 19-8 for a given light flux, supply voltage, and load resistance, it is necessary to use the volt-ampere device characteristics. The straight line, expressed by the relation

$$v = V_{PP} - iR_L \tag{19-6}$$

is superposed on this set of static characteristics. This is the same load line that is discussed in connection with the diode rectifier in Sec. 4-9. It is drawn through the point $i = 0$, $v = V_{PP}$, and with a slope determined by the load resistor R_L, as shown in Fig. 19-9.

The intersection of the load line with each volt-ampere curve gives the current output at the value of intensity for which that curve was constructed. In this way a curve of current vs. intensity or flux for each value of load resistance can be found. The curves for $R_L = 1$, 25, and 50 M and $V_{PP} = 250$ V for the RCA 929 vacuum phototube are reproduced in the upper sections of Fig. 19-10. It is noted that these curves are practically linear and almost independent of the load resistance. This result is a consequence of the fact

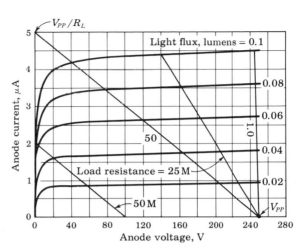

Fig. 19-9 Volt-ampere characteristics of an RCA 929 vacuum phototube. The load lines for $V_{PP} = 250$ V and $R_L = 1.0, 25,$ and 50 M and also the line for $V_{PP} = 100$ V and $R_L = 50$ M are shown. (Courtesy of RCA Manufacturing Co.)

that the volt-ampere characteristics of Fig. 19-9 are essentially horizontal lines that are equally spaced for equal intervals of light flux. Since, for a given light intensity, the plate current is nearly independent of voltage, except for small voltages, *the vacuum photocell may be considered to be a constant-current generator.* This characteristic is made use of in certain applications.

If the load resistance is too high, or if the plate supply voltage is low, the load line will intersect the volt-ampere curves for the higher intensities in the region near the origin, where the curves are close together. Under these circumstances, a curve of current vs. light flux will no longer be linear. In fact, it will show a *saturation* value, as indicated by the lower curve in Fig. 19-10, and *bottoming* is said to have taken place. This expression arises from the fact that the tube voltage remains at the bottom of the characteristic (approximately zero voltage), although the excitation is increased. Where modulated light is to be translated into proportional electrical voltages, this condition is to be avoided. However, such a characteristic may be highly desirable in certain special applications.

The analysis of a circuit containing a semiconductor device is performed

Fig. 19-10 Photocurrent as a function of light flux (dynamic curves). The upper (linear) characteristics are for $V_{PP} = 250$ V, and the lower (nonlinear) curve is for $V_{PP} = 100$V.

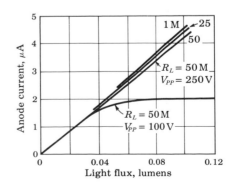

in exactly the same manner as described above. The volt-ampere characteristics of such cells must, of course, be used in this analysis. These characteristics are obtained later in this chapter.

19-6   MULTIPLIER PHOTOTUBES

Very weak light intensities must be measured in many applications, such as nuclear-radiation detection, television pickup devices, colorimetry, astronomy, and many industrial processes. A very sensitive device suitable for such applications is obtained by amplifying the current from a photoelectric surface by means of secondary emission.

The principle of operation of a photomultiplier tube is illustrated in Fig. 19-11. Light impinges upon the cathode and emits photoelectrons which are directed toward a plate A called a *dynode*. Upon collision with A, secondary electrons are liberated. These, in turn, travel to dynode B, where more secondary electrons are released. The charges leaving B are directed toward the next plate (if more are included), and the electrons from the last dynode are finally collected by the anode. If the ratio of the number of secondary to primary electrons is δ, and if there are n dynodes, the current at the collector is

$$i = i_o \delta^n \tag{19-7}$$

where i_o is the initial current at the photocathode. The overall current gain is δ^n.

One of the earliest photomultiplier tubes[10] employed a configuration of perpendicular electric and magnetic fields both to focus and to direct the beam from dynode to dynode. In Fig. 19-11 the magnetic field is perpendicular to the plane of the paper, and the electrons move in practically cycloidal paths, as shown. However, if an electron starts from rest at the cathode, it will have zero velocity when it reaches the first dynode. Under these circumstances, the electrons from the cathode could cause no secondary emission at this emitter. For this reason, an additional potential gradient must exist from the cathode to the first dynode and from the first to the second emitter, etc. The addition of this field distorts the original field, making an exact determination of the paths of the particles very difficult. The effect of the initial velocities is to cause a slight defocusing of the beam in passing from

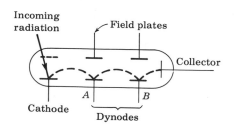

Fig. 19-11 The approximate cycloidal path in a magnetic secondary-emission electron multiplier. The magnetic field is perpendicular to the plane of the paper.

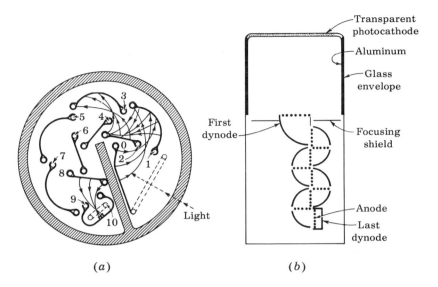

(a)   (b)

Fig. 19-12 (a) A circular photomultiplier. (Courtesy of Radio Corporation of America.) (b) A linear photomultiplier. (Courtesy of A. B. Du Mont Laboratories, Inc.)

one emitter to the next. This deforming imposes a practical limitation upon the number of emitters that may be used, and so upon the subsequent gain of the unit.

Because of the need for a magnetic field as well as an electric field, a great deal of attention has been given to the development of electrostatic secondary-emission multipliers. These use no magnetic field, but the shapes and the orientations of the electrodes are such that the electrons pass progressively from one dynode to the next. Two different types of electrostatic multipliers are illustrated in Fig. 19-12.

The RCA type 931-A tube with nine dynodes has a current amplification of 200,000 and a sensitivity of 2 A/lumen. This tube is about the size of a small receiving tube. The Du Mont tube uses an end window with a semitransparent cesium-antimony photoemissive surface. Light impinges on one side, and the photoelectrons emitted from the other side are focused onto the first dynode by means of the focusing shield. The box-type dynodes are in the shape of one-fourth of a "pill box," as indicated in Fig. 19-13. The secondary-

Fig. 19-13 Box-type dynodes. The sketch is drawn assuming $\delta = 2$.

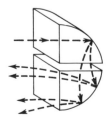

emission surfaces are of silver-magnesium, for which δ equals about 3 or 4 at the recommended operating voltages. Tubes with photocathode diameters ranging from $\frac{3}{4}$ to 14 in. are available, and most of these are built with 10 secondary emitters. The dynode voltages (100 to 150 V per stage) are obtained by means of a resistive divider arrangement from a high-voltage power supply. With these Du Mont multiplier phototubes it is possible to obtain a current amplification of 3,000,000 and a sensitivity of 100 A/lumen.

19-7 PHOTOCONDUCTIVITY[11,12]

If radiation falls upon a semiconductor, its conductivity increases. This *photoconductive effect* is explained as follows: The conductivity of a material is proportional to the concentration of charge carriers present, as indicated in Eq. (5-1). Radiant energy supplied to the semiconductor causes covalent bonds to be broken, and hole-electron pairs in excess of those generated thermally are created. These increased current carriers decrease the resistance of the material, and hence such a device is called a *photoresistor*, or *photoconductor*. For a light-intensity change of 100 ft-c the resistance of a commercial photoconductor may change by several kilohms.

In Fig. 19-14 we show the energy diagram of a semiconductor having both acceptor and donor impurities. If photons of sufficient energies illuminate this specimen, the following transitions are possible: An electron-hole pair can be created by a high-energy photon, in what is called *intrinsic excitation;* a photon may excite a donor electron into the conduction band; or a valence electron may go into an acceptor state. The last two transitions are known as *impurity excitations*. Since the density of states in the conduction and valence bands greatly exceeds the density of impurity states, photoconductivity is due principally to intrinsic excitation.

Spectral Response The minimum energy of a photon required for intrinsic excitation is the forbidden-gap energy E_G (electron volts) of the

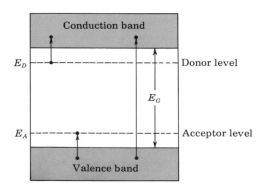

Fig. 19-14 Photoexcitation in semiconductors.

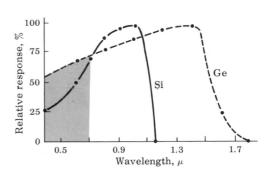

Fig. 19-15 Relative spectral response of Si and Ge. (Courtesy of Texas Instruments, Inc.)

semiconductor material. The long-wavelength threshold of the material is defined as the wavelength corresponding to the energy gap E_G, and is given by Eq. (19-5), namely,

$$\lambda_c = \frac{1.24}{E_G} \tag{19-8}$$

if λ_c is expressed in microns. For Si, $E_G = 1.1$ eV and $\lambda_c = 1.13\ \mu$, whereas for Ge, $E_G = 0.72$ eV and $\lambda_c = 1.73\ \mu$ at room temperature (Table 5-1).

The spectral-sensitivity curves for Si and Ge are plotted in Fig. 19-15 and are similar in shape to those given in Fig. 19-3 for a metal. Note that the long-wavelength limit is slightly greater than the values of λ_c calculated above, because of the impurity excitations. As the wavelength is decreased ($\lambda < \lambda_c$ or $f > f_c$), the response increases and reaches a maximum.

The Photoconductive Current The carriers generated by photoexcitation will move under the influence of an applied field. If they survive recombination, they will reach the ohmic contacts at the ends of the semiconductor bar, and thus they will constitute the device current. This current may be calculated if we know the rate P_r at which carriers are produced by light, and the average lifetime τ of the newly created carriers. The steady-state photocurrent is then given by

$$i = \frac{eP_r\tau}{T_t} \tag{19-9}$$

where T_t is the average transit time for carriers to reach the ohmic contacts.

Commercial Photoconductive Cells The photoconducting device with the widest application is the cadmium sulfide cell. The sensitive area of this device consists of a layer of chemically deposited CdS, which may contain a small amount of silver, antimony, or indium impurities. Figure 19-16 shows the relationship between illumination and resistance for six different CdS photoconductors. In absolute darkness the resistance may be as high as 2 M, and when stimulated with strong light, the resistance may be less than 10 Ω.

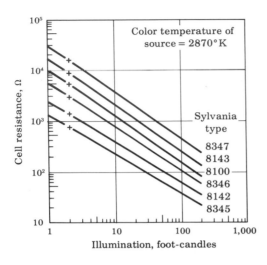

Fig. 19-16 Curve of resistance vs. illumination for commercial CdS. (Courtesy of Sylvania Electric Products, Inc.)

The spectral response of the cadmium sulfide photoconductor is shown in Fig. 19-17. Like the human eye, the response is best over the visible spectrum and tapers off toward the infrared and ultraviolet.

The primary advantages of CdS photoconductors are their high dissipation capability, their excellent sensitivity in the visible spectrum, and their low resistance when stimulated by light. These photoconductors are designed to dissipate safely 300 mW, and can be made to handle safely power levels of several watts. Hence a CdS photoconductor can operate a relay directly, without intermediate amplifier circuits.

Other types of photoconductive devices are available for specific applications. A lead sulfide, PbS, cell has a peak on the sensitivity curve at 2.9 μ, and hence is used for infrared-detection or infrared-absorption measurements. A selenium cell is sensitive throughout the visible, and particularly toward the blue end of the spectrum.

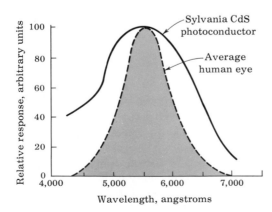

Fig. 19-17 Spectral response of a CdS photoconductor compared with the standard luminosity curve. (Courtesy of Sylvania Electric Products, Inc.)

19-8   THE SEMICONDUCTOR PHOTODIODE[12,13]

If a reverse-biased *p-n* junction is illuminated, the current varies almost linearly with the light flux. This effect is exploited in the semiconductor *photodiode*. This device consists of a *p-n* junction embedded in a clear plastic, as indicated in Fig. 19-18. Radiation is allowed to fall upon one surface across the junction. The remaining sides of the plastic are either painted black or enclosed in a metallic case. The entire unit is extremely small compared with a phototube. The semiconductor photodiode has dimensions of the order of tenths of an inch.

Volt-Ampere Characteristics   If reverse voltages in excess of a few tenths of a volt are applied, an almost constant current (independent of the magnitude of the reverse bias) is obtained. The dark current corresponds to the reverse saturation current due to the thermally generated minority carriers. As explained in Sec. 6-2, these minority carriers "fall down" the potential hill at the junction, whereas this barrier does not allow majority carriers to cross the junction. Now if light falls upon the surface, additional electron-hole pairs are formed. Since the concentration of majority carriers greatly exceeds that of minority carriers, the percent increase in majority carriers is much smaller than the percent increase in minority carriers. Hence it is justifiable to ignore the increase in majority density and to consider the radiation solely as a *minority-carrier injector*. These injected minority carriers (for example, electrons in the *p* side) diffuse to the junction, cross it, and contribute to the current.

From Eq. (6-27) we see that the reverse saturation current I_o in a *p-n* diode is proportional to the concentrations p_{no} and n_{po} of minority carriers in the *n* and *p* region, respectively. If we illuminate a reverse-biased *p-n* junction, the number of new hole-electron pairs is proportional to the number of incident photons. Hence the current under large reverse bias is $I = I_o + I_s$, where I_s, the short-circuit current, is proportional to the light intensity. Hence the volt-ampere characteristic is given by

$$I = I_s + I_o(1 - \epsilon^{V/\eta V_T}) \tag{19-10}$$

where I, I_s, and I_o represent the *magnitude* of the reverse current, and V is

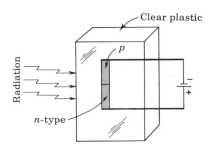

Fig. 19-18   The construction of a semiconductor photodiode.

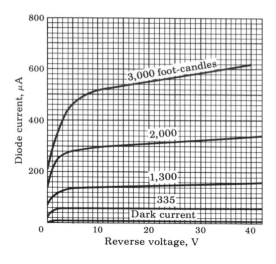

Fig. 19-19   Volt-ampere characteristics for the 1N77 germanium
photodiode.   (Courtesy of
Sylvania Electric Products, Inc.)

positive for a forward voltage and negative for a reverse bias.   The parameter
η is unity for germanium and 2 for silicon, and V_T is the volt equivalent of
temperature defined by Eq. (3-34).

A typical photodiode volt-ampere characteristic is indicated in Fig. 19-19.
The curves (with the exception of the dark-current curve) do not pass through
the origin.   The characteristics in the millivolt range and for positive bias
are discussed in the following section.   The slope of the curves of Fig. 19-19
(for voltages greater than a few volts) corresponds to a dynamic resistance of
the order of a megohm to hundreds of megohms.

Small-signal Model   In view of the foregoing discussion, a model for the
p-n photocell is that indicated in Fig. 19-20.   In Fig. 19-20a an ideal junction
diode is indicated in parallel with a current source which is proportional to
the light intensity.   In Fig. 19-20b it is assumed that the diode is heavily
reverse-biased, and hence that the diode may be replaced by its reverse
resistance R.   The transition capacitance C and ohmic resistance r are also

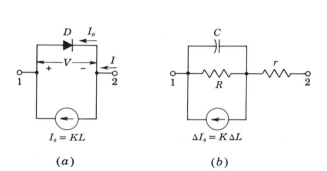

Fig. 19-20   Circuit model
for a p-n photodiode.
In (a) an ideal p-n junction diode D is indicated,
and I_s is the short-circuit
current proportional to
the illumination.   In (b) a
reverse bias is assumed,
and the parasitic ele-
ments C, R, and r are
taken into consideration.

included. The barrier capacitance C, the reverse resistance R, and the bulk ohmic resistance r have the following order of magnitudes:

$$C \approx 10 \text{ pF} \qquad R \approx 50 \text{ M} \qquad r \approx 100 \text{ }\Omega$$

The symbol L represents light flux in lumens, and K is a proportionality constant in the range 10 to 50 mA/lumen. Incidentally, the spectral response of the semiconductor photodiode is the same as that for a photoconductive cell, and is indicated in Fig. 19-15.

Sensitivity with Position of Illumination The current in a reverse-biased semiconductor photodiode depends upon the diffusion of minority carriers to the junction. If the radiation is focused into a small spot far away from the junction, the injected minority carriers can recombine before diffusing to the junction. Hence a much smaller current will result than if the minority carriers were injected near the junction. The photocurrent as a function of the distance from the junction at which the light spot is focused is indicated in Fig. 19-21. The curve is somewhat asymmetrical because of the differences in the diffusion lengths of minority carriers in the p and n sides.

Comparison of Semiconductor and Vacuum Photodiodes Although the characteristics in Fig. 19-19 resemble those of a vacuum tube, there are several important differences between semiconductor and vacuum photodiodes. A comparison between these devices is summarized in Table 19-1. In particular, note that the semiconductor photocell is about 200 times as sensitive as is the vacuum tube to the same illumination (from a tungsten lamp as the light source). The open-circuit operation of the p-n photodiode is discussed in Sec. 19-10.

The p-n photodiode and, particularly, the improved n-p-n version described in the following section find extensive application in high-speed reading of computer punched cards and tapes, light-detection systems, reading of film sound track, light-operated switches, production-line counting of objects which interrupt a light beam, etc.

Fig. 19-21 Sensitivity of a semi-conductor photodiode as a function of the distance of the light spot from the junction.

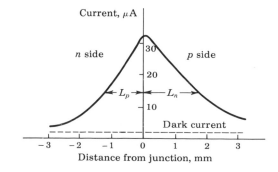

TABLE 19-1   Comparison of vacuum and semiconductor photodiodes

	Vacuum	Semiconductor
Dark current, μA.................	0	20
Temperature coefficient.............	0	I_o doubles every 10°C
Sensitivity, mA/lumen.............	0.045	10
Size...........................	Large (inches)	Small (tenths of inch)
Characteristics..................	Stable	Drift with age
Microphonics....................	Yes	No
Frequency response...............	>100 MHz	<1 MHz
Spectral response................	Depends upon cathode	Fig. 19-15
Short-circuit operation.............	No	Yes
Open-circuit operation.............	No	Yes

19-9   MULTIPLE–JUNCTION PHOTODIODES[12,14]

The n-p-n junction photoconductive cell is a much more sensitive semiconductor photodevice than the p-n photodiode. This cell, also known by the trade name *Photo-duo-diode*, is shown in Fig. 19-22.

The operation of this device can best be understood if we recognize that junction J_1 in Fig. 19-22 is biased slightly in the forward direction, and junction J_2 is biased in the reverse direction. The reader should refer to Fig. 9-2c, which represents potential energy for holes in a p-n-p structure and hence also potential energy for electrons in the n-p-n photocell. The current I consists principally of electrons moving from the left-hand n-type region, over the forward-biased barrier of J_1, into the p-type region, and then over the reverse-biased junction J_2. The main obstacle to this flow is the left-hand barrier. A photon absorbed in the p-type region liberates an electron-hole pair. The electrons will diffuse to either the left or the right junction, and since no barrier to their motion is presented at these junctions, they will leave the p-type region. However, the holes are trapped in the p-type region by the potential-energy hills at junction J_1 and J_2. These trapped holes form a positive space charge in the p-type region which causes an additional forward bias to appear at J_1. The effect on the right-hand junction is to reduce slightly the large reverse

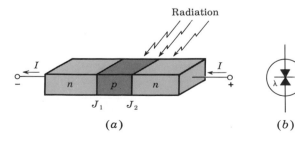

Radiation

I ◀── ── I

n p n

J_1 J_2

(a)   (b)

Fig. 19-22 An n-p-n photodiode. (a) Construction and (b) circuit symbol.

bias across that junction.   The increase in the forward bias of J_1 enhances the flow of electrons from the left-hand n-type material to the right.   For maximum sensitivity the illuminated area should be close to the reverse-biased junction J_2.

The foregoing qualitative discussion indicates that the primary holes liberated photoelectrically act as a trigger, enabling many more electrons to move from left to right.   With proper choice of materials, about 100 times the current (for the same illumination) is collected from the Photo-duo-diode than from the simple p-n photodiode.

Volt-Ampere Characteristics   The basic circuit employing the n-p-n photocell is the same as that given in Fig. 19-8b; namely, the device is connected in series with a load resistor R_L and a supply voltage V_{PP}.   Typical volt-ampere characteristic curves are shown in Fig. 19-23 for a symmetrical n-p-n diffused silicon Photo-duo-diode for different values of illumination intensities.

19-10   THE PHOTOVOLTAIC EFFECT[15,16]

In Fig. 19-19 we see that an almost constant reverse current due to injected minority carriers is collected in the p-n photodiode for large reverse voltages. If the applied voltage is reduced in magnitude, the barrier at the junction is reduced.   This decrease in the potential hill does not affect the minority current (since these particles fall down the barrier), but when the hill is reduced sufficiently, some majority carriers can also cross the junction.   These carriers correspond to a forward current, and hence such a flow will reduce the net (reverse) current.   It is this increase in majority-carrier flow which accounts for the drop in the reverse current near the zero-voltage axis in Fig. 19-19. An expanded view of the origin in this figure is indicated in Fig. 19-24.   (Note

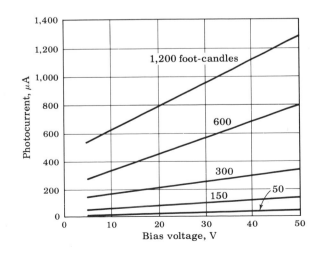

Fig. 19-23   The volt-ampere characteristics of the 1N2175 silicon n-p-n photocell.   Light source is a tungsten filament lamp operated at a color temperature of 2870°K. (Courtesy of Texas Instruments, Inc.)

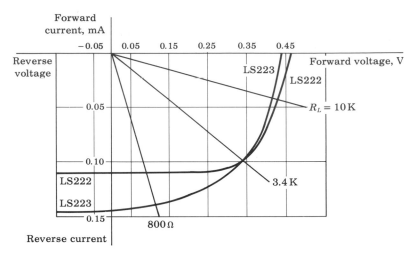

Fig. 19-24 Volt-ampere characteristics for the LS222 and LS223 p-n junction photodiodes at a light intensity of 500 ft-candles. (Courtesy of Texas Instruments, Inc.)

that the first quadrant of Fig. 19-19 corresponds to the third quadrant of Fig. 19-24.)

The Photovoltaic Potential If a forward bias is applied, the potential barrier is lowered, and the majority current increases rapidly. When this majority current equals the minority current, the total current is reduced to zero. The voltage at which zero resultant current is obtained is called the *photovoltaic* potential. Since, certainly, no current flows under open-circuited conditions, the photovoltaic emf is obtained across the open terminals of a *p-n* junction.

An alternative (but of course equivalent) physical explanation of the photovoltaic effect is the following: In Sec. 6-1 we see that the height of the potential barrier at an open-circuited (nonilluminated) *p-n* junction adjusts itself so that the resultant current is zero, the electric field at the junction being in such a direction as to repel the majority carriers. If light falls on the surface, minority carriers are injected, and since these fall down the barrier, the minority current increases. Since under open-circuited conditions the total current must remain zero, the majority current (for example, the hole current in the *p* side) must increase the same amount as the minority current. This rise in majority current is possible only if the retarding field at the junction is reduced. Hence the barrier height is automatically lowered as a result of the radiation. Across the diode terminals there appears a voltage just equal to the amount by which the barrier potential is decreased. This potential is the photovoltaic emf and is of the order of magnitude of 0.5 V for a silicon and 0.1 V for a germanium cell.

The photovoltaic voltage V_{max} corresponds to an open-circuited diode. If $I = 0$ is substituted into Eq. (19-10), we obtain

$$V_{max} = \eta V_T \ln\left(1 + \frac{I_s}{I_o}\right) \tag{19-11}$$

Since, except for very small light intensities, $I_s/I_o \gg 1$, then V_{max} increases logarithmically with I_s, and hence with illumination. Such a logarithmic relationship is obtained experimentally, as indicated in Fig. 19-25a.

Maximum Output Power   If a resistor R_L is placed directly across the diode terminals, the resulting current can be found by drawing a load line corresponding to R_L and passing through the origin, as shown in Fig. 19-24. If $R_L = 0$, then the output voltage V is zero, and for $R_L = \infty$, the output current I is zero. Hence, for these two extreme values of load, the output power is zero. If for each assumed value of R_L the values of V and I are read from Fig. 19-24 and $P = VI$ is plotted versus R_L, we can obtain the *optimum* load resistance to give maximum output power. For the types LS222 and LS223 photovoltaic light sensors, this optimum load is 3.4 K and $P_{max} \approx 34$ μW. When the p-n photodiode is used as an energy converter (to transform radiant energy into electric energy), the optimum load resistance should be used.

The Short-circuit Current   We see from Fig. 19-24 and Eq. (19-10) that a definite (nonzero) current is obtained for zero applied voltage. Hence a junction photocell can be used under short-circuit conditions. As already emphasized, this current I_s is proportional to the light intensity. Such a linear relationship is obtained experimentally, as indicated in Fig. 19-25b.

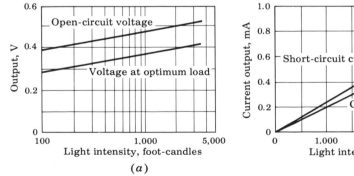
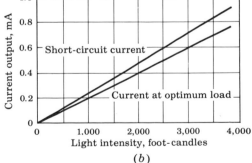

Fig. 19-25   (a) Open-circuit voltage output as function of light intensity, and (b) short-circuit current as function of light intensity, for the LS223 photovoltaic cell. (Courtesy of Texas Instruments, Inc.)

Spectral Response   The spectral sensitivity of a photovoltaic cell depends upon the semiconductor material.   The response for the LS223 cell is essentially that indicated in Fig. 19-15 for silicon.   Such a device has excellent sensitivity over the entire visible range.   Cells of other semiconductor materials have their maximum response outside the visible region.[17]   For example, an indium antimonide photovoltaic diode is most sensitive in the infrared (2 to 5 μ).

Solar-energy Converters[18]   The current drain from a photovoltaic cell may be used to power electronic equipment or, more commonly, to charge auxiliary storage batteries.   Such energy converters using sunlight as the primary energy are called *solar batteries* and are used in satellites like the Telstar. A silicon photovoltaic cell of excellent stability and high ($\sim$14 percent) conversion efficiency[18] is made by diffusing a thin n-type impurity onto a p-type base.   In direct noonday sunlight such a cell generates an open-circuit voltage of approximately 0.6 V.   A report on the research on photovoltaic solar-energy converters made from semiconductors other than silicon is contained in Ref. 16.

REFERENCES

1. Hughes, A. L., and L. A. DuBridge: "Photoelectric Phenomena," McGraw-Hill Book Company, New York, 1932.

2. Richardson, O. W., and K. T. Compton: The Photoelectric Effect, *Phil. Mag.*, vol. 24, pp. 575–594, October, 1912.

3. Lawrence, E. O., and J. W. Beams: The Element of Time in the Photoelectric Effect, *Phys. Rev.*, vol. 32, pp. 478–485, September, 1928.

4. Perkins, T. B.: An Automatic Spectral-sensitivity Curve Tracer, *J. Opt. Soc. Am.*, vol. 29, no. 6, pp. 226–234, 1939.

5. Einstein, A.: Über einen du Erzeugung und Verwandlung des Lichtes betreffenden heuristischen Gesichtspunkt, *Ann. Physik*, vol. 17, no. 4, pp. 132–148, 1905.

6. Millikan, R. A.: A Direct Photoelectric Determination of Planck's h, *Phys. Rev.*, vol. 7, pp. 355–388, March, 1916.

7. Fowler, R. H.: The Analysis of Photoelectric Sensitivity Curves for Clean Metals at Various Temperatures, *Phys. Rev.*, vol. 38, pp. 45–56, July, 1931.
   DuBridge, L. A.: A Further Experimental Test of Fowler's Theory of Photoelectric Emission, *ibid.*, vol. 39, pp. 108–118, January, 1932.

8. Millman, J.: "Vacuum-tube and Semiconductor Electronics," chap. 12, McGraw-Hill Book Company, New York, 1958.

9. Glover, A. M., and R. B. Janes: New High-sensitivity Photosurface, *Electronics*, vol. 13, pp. 26–27, August, 1940.

10. Zworykin, V. K., G. A. Morton, and L. Malter: The Secondary Emission Multiplier: A New Electronic Device, *Proc. IRE*, vol. 21, pp. 351–375, March, 1936.

11. Bube, R. H.: "Photoconductivity of Solids," John Wiley & Sons, Inc., New York, 1960.
    Hunter, L. P.: Photoconductivity and Photovoltaic Cells, in L. P. Hunter (ed.), "Handbook of Semiconductor Electronics," 2d ed., chap. 5, McGraw-Hill Book Company, New York, 1962.

12. Shive, J. N.: "Semiconductor Devices," chaps. 8 and 9, D. Van Nostrand Company, Inc., Princeton, N.J., 1959.

13. Pietenpol, W. J.: P-N Junction Rectifier and Photocell, *Phys. Rev.*, vol. 82, p. 120, 1951.

14. Shive, J. N.: Properties of Germanium Phototransistors, *J. Opt. Soc. Am.*, vol. 39, p. 243, 1953.

15. Rappaport, R.: The Photovoltaic Effect and Its Utilization, *RCA Rev.*, vol. 21, no. 3, pp. 373–397, September, 1959.

16. Loferski, J. J.: Recent Research on Photovoltaic Solar Energy Converters, *Proc. IEEE*, vol. 51, no. 5, pp. 667–674, May, 1963.

17. Loferski, J. J., and J. J. Wysocki: Spectral Response of Photovoltaic Cells, *RCA Rev.*, vol. 22, no. 1, pp. 38–56, March, 1961.

18. Chapin, D. M., C. S. Fuller, and G. L. Pearson: A New Silicon P-N Junction Photocell for Converting Solar Radiation into Electrical Power, *J. Appl. Phys.*, vol. 25, p. 676, 1954.
    Prince, M. B.: Silicon Solar Energy Converters, *J. Appl. Phys.*, vol. 26, p. 534, 1055.
    Prince, M. B., and M. Wolf: New Developments in Silicon Photovoltaic Devices, *J. Brit. IRE*, vol. 18, p. 583, October, 1958.

20/RECTIFIERS AND
POWER SUPPLIES

Almost all electronic circuits require a dc source of power. For portable low-power systems batteries may be used. More frequently, however, electronic equipment is energized by a *power supply*, a piece of equipment which converts the alternating waveform from the power lines into an essentially direct voltage. This process of ac-to-dc conversion is studied in this chapter.

20-1   A HALF–WAVE RECTIFIER

Any electrical device which offers a low resistance to the current in one direction but a high resistance to the current in the opposite direction is called a *rectifier*. Such a device is capable of converting a sinusoidal input waveform, whose average value is zero, into a unidirectional (though not constant) waveform, with a nonzero average component. The basic circuit for half-wave rectification is shown in Fig. 20-1a. The rectifying device is usually a semiconductor diode (or for very high voltages, a vacuum-tube diode). The piecewise linear approximation for the diode is given in Fig. 6-11, and indicates that the device has essentially infinite resistance in the reverse direction (for a voltage v less than the cutin voltage V_γ) and a small and constant resistance R_f in the forward direction (for $v > V_\gamma$). Since in a rectifier circuit the input $v_i = V_m \sin \omega t$ has a peak value V_m which is very large compared with the offset voltage V_γ, we assume in the following discussion that $V_\gamma = 0$. Subject to this idealization of the diode characteristic, the current i in the diode or load R_L is given by

$$i = I_m \sin \alpha \qquad \text{where } 0 \le \alpha \le \pi$$
$$i = 0 \qquad \text{where } \pi \le \alpha \le 2\pi$$

(20-1)

where

$$\alpha \equiv \omega t \qquad I_m \equiv \frac{V_m}{R_f + R_L} \qquad (20\text{-}2)$$

The transformer secondary waveform v_i is shown in Fig. 20-1b, and the rectified current i is pictured in Fig. 20-1c. Note that the output current is unidirectional and has a nonzero average value.

Reading of a DC Ammeter   It is important to know what a measuring instrument, such as a dc ammeter, an ac voltmeter, a wattmeter, etc., will read when inserted into a rectifier circuit. We illustrate below how to calculate what each such meter should indicate.

A dc ammeter is constructed so that the needle deflection indicates the average value of the current passing through it. By definition, the average value of a periodic function is given by the area of one cycle of the curve divided by the base. Expressed mathematically,

$$I_{dc} = \frac{1}{2\pi} \int_0^{2\pi} i \, d\alpha \qquad (20\text{-}3)$$

For the half-wave circuit under consideration, it follows from Eqs. (20-1) that

$$I_{dc} = \frac{1}{2\pi} \int_0^{\pi} I_m \sin \alpha \, d\alpha = \frac{I_m}{\pi} \qquad (20\text{-}4)$$

Note that the upper limit of the integral has been changed from 2π to π since the instantaneous current in the interval from π to 2π is zero and so contributes nothing to the integral.

Reading of an AC Ammeter   An ac ammeter is constructed so that the needle deflection indicates the effective or rms current passing through it. Such a

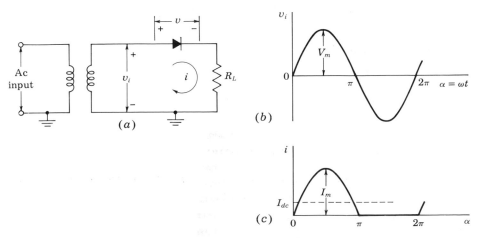

Fig. 20-1   (a) Basic circuit of half-wave rectifier.   **(b)** Transformer sinusoidal secondary voltage v_i.   **(c)** Diode and load current i.

"square-law" instrument may be of the thermocouple type. By definition, the effective or rms value squared of a periodic function of time is given by the area of one cycle of the curve which represents the square of the function, divided by the base. Expressed mathematically,

$$I_{\text{rms}} = \left(\frac{1}{2\pi} \int_0^{2\pi} i^2 \, d\alpha \right)^{\frac{1}{2}} \tag{20-5}$$

By use of Eqs. (20-1), it follows that

$$I_{\text{rms}} = \left(\frac{1}{2\pi} \int_0^{\pi} I_m{}^2 \sin^2 \alpha \, d\alpha \right)^{\frac{1}{2}} = \frac{I_m}{2} \tag{20-6}$$

It should be noted that the rms value of this wave is different from the rms value of a sinusoidal wave $(I_m/\sqrt{2})$.

Reading of a DC Voltmeter *This instrument reads the average value of the voltage across its terminals.* If the voltmeter is across the diode, the instantaneous diode voltage must be plotted, and the area under one cycle of this curve must be found. When the diode is conducting, it has a resistance R_f, and the voltage across it is iR_f. When the device is nonconducting, the current is zero, and from Fig. 20-1a it is seen that the transformer secondary voltage v_i appears across the diode. Thus

$$v = iR_f = I_m R_f \sin \alpha \qquad 0 \leq \alpha \leq \pi$$
$$v = V_m \sin \alpha \qquad \pi \leq \alpha \leq 2\pi \tag{20-7}$$

A plot of the voltage across the rectifier is shown in Fig. 20-2. The reading of the dc voltmeter is

$$V_{\text{dc}} = \frac{1}{2\pi} \left(\int_0^{\pi} I_m R_f \sin \alpha \, d\alpha + \int_{\pi}^{2\pi} V_m \sin \alpha \, d\alpha \right)$$

$$= \frac{1}{\pi} (I_m R_f - V_m) = \frac{1}{\pi} [I_m R_f - I_m (R_f + R_L)]$$

where use has been made of Eqs. (20-2). Hence

$$V_{\text{dc}} = - \frac{I_m R_L}{\pi} \tag{20-8}$$

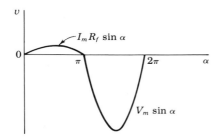

Fig. 20-2 The voltage across the diode in Fig. 20-1.

This result is negative, which means that if the voltmeter is to read upscale, its positive terminal must be connected to the cathode of the diode. Since $I_{dc} = I_m/\pi$, the dc diode voltage is seen to be equal to $-I_{dc}R_L$, or to the negative of the dc voltage across the load resistor. This result is evidently correct because the sum of the dc voltages around the complete circuit must add up to zero.

It should be noted that the voltmeter reading does *not* equal the product of the direct current I_{dc} times the diode resistance R_f. The reason for this is that the tube is a nonlinear device whose resistance is constant (and equals R_f) only when the anode voltage is positive. On the other hand, the dc voltage across the load does equal the product of direct current I_{dc} times the output resistance R_L because the load is a truly constant resistor.

Reading of a Wattmeter *This instrument is built to indicate the average value of the product of the instantaneous current through its current coil and the instantaneous voltage across its potential coil.* Hence the power read by a wattmeter, whose voltage coil is placed across the transformer secondary, is

$$P_i = \frac{1}{2\pi} \int_0^{2\pi} v_i i \, d\alpha \tag{20-9}$$

Since $v_i = i(R_f + R_L)$ for $0 \le \alpha \le \pi$,

$$P_i = \frac{1}{2\pi} \int_0^{\pi} i^2(R_f + R_L) \, d\alpha = \frac{1}{2\pi} \int_0^{\pi} I_m^2 \sin^2 \alpha (R_f + R_L) \, d\alpha$$

The equation may be written, by virtue of Eq. (20-6), as

$$P_i = I_{rms}^2(R_f + R_L) \tag{20-10}$$

This result could have been written down immediately by arguing physically that all the power supplied by the transformer must be used to heat the load and the device resistances.

The above general method of calculating what dc or ac instruments will read in any electronic circuit is *not* restricted to the simple diode rectifier. The waveforms, in general, may be more complicated than those of the simple circuit considered above, but the method is the same. For assistance in the calculations, rough sketches of the curves are made, and the readings of the instruments are obtained from an evaluation of the area under the curve (for a dc instrument) or the area under the squared function (for an ac instrument). If a wattmeter reading is desired, the curve representing the current through its current coil is multiplied by the curve representing the voltage across its potential coil, and the area under the product curve is then evaluated.

Peak Inverse Voltage For each rectifier circuit there is a maximum voltage to which the diode is subjected. This potential is called the *peak inverse voltage*, because it occurs during that part of the cycle when the diode is nonconducting. From Fig. 20-2 it is clear that for the half-wave circuit (without a filter) the peak inverse voltage is V_m, the peak transformer secondary voltage.

Regulation   The variation of dc output voltage as a function of dc load current is called *regulation*.   The percentage regulation is defined as

$$\% \text{ regulation} \equiv \frac{V_{\text{no load}} - V_{\text{full load}}}{V_{\text{full load}}} \times 100\% \tag{20-11}$$

For an ideal power supply the output voltage is independent of the load (the output current) and the percentage regulation is zero.

The variation of V_{dc} with I_{dc} for the half-wave rectifier is obtained as follows: From Eqs. (20-4) and (20-2),

$$I_{\text{dc}} = \frac{I_m}{\pi} = \frac{V_m/\pi}{R_f + R_L} \tag{20-12}$$

Solving Eq. (20-12) for $V_{\text{dc}} = I_{\text{dc}} R_L$, we obtain

$$V_{\text{dc}} = \frac{V_m}{\pi} - I_{\text{dc}} R_f \tag{20-13}$$

This result (which is consistent with Thévenin's theorem) shows that V_{dc} equals V_m/π at no load and that the dc voltage decreases linearly with an increase in dc output current.   The larger the magnitude of the diode forward resistance, the greater is this decrease for a given current change.   Clearly, the effective internal resistance of the power supply is R_f.   In practice, the resistance R_s of the transformer secondary is in series with the diode, and in Eq. (20-13) R_s should be added to R_f.   The best method of estimating the diode resistance is to obtain a regulation plot of V_{dc} versus I_{dc} in the laboratory.   The negative slope of the resulting straight line gives $R_f + R_s$.

As an illustration, consider a 12-V 100-mA supply with $R_f + R_s = 20 \ \Omega$. The no-load voltage is 12 V, the full-load voltage is $12 - (0.1)(20) = 10$ V, and from Eq. (20-11), the percentage regulation is

$$\frac{12 - 10}{10} \times 100 = 20\%$$

Power-supply Specifications   The most important characteristics which must be specified for a power supply are the following:

1. The required output dc voltage
2. The regulation
3. The average and peak currents in each diode
4. The peak inverse voltage of each diode
5. The ripple factor

The first four requirements are considered above, and the fifth is the subject of the following section.

20-2   RIPPLE FACTOR

Although it is the purpose of a rectifier to convert alternating into direct current, the simple circuit considered above does not achieve this. Nor, in fact, do any of the more complicated rectifier circuits have a truly constant output. What is accomplished is the conversion from an alternating current into a unidirectional current, periodically fluctuating components still remaining in the output wave. It is for this reason that filters are frequently used in order to decrease these ac components. A measure of the fluctuating components is given by the *ripple factor r*, which is defined as

$$r \equiv \frac{\text{rms value of alternating components of wave}}{\text{average value of wave}}$$

This may be written

$$r \equiv \frac{I'_{\text{rms}}}{I_{\text{dc}}} = \frac{V'_{\text{rms}}}{V_{\text{dc}}} \tag{20-14}$$

where the terms I'_{rms} and V'_{rms} denote the rms value of the ac components of the current and voltage, respectively.

In order to measure the ripple factor of a given rectifier system experimentally, the measurement of the ripple voltage or the ripple current in the output should be made with instruments that respond to higher than power frequencies, so that the contributions from the higher harmonic terms will be recorded. A capacitor must be used in series with the input to the meter in order to "block" the dc component. This capacitor charges up to the average value of the voltage, and only the ripple components in the wave are recorded by the meter.

An analytical expression for the ripple factor, defined in Eq. (20-14), is possible. By noting that the instantaneous ac component of current is given by

$$i' = i - I_{\text{dc}}$$

then

$$I'_{\text{rms}} \equiv \sqrt{\frac{1}{2\pi} \int_0^{2\pi} (i - I_{\text{dc}})^2 \, d\alpha} = \sqrt{\frac{1}{2\pi} \int_0^{2\pi} (i^2 - 2I_{\text{dc}}i + I_{\text{dc}}^2) \, d\alpha}$$

The first term of the integral becomes, simply, I_{rms}^2 of the total wave. Since $\frac{1}{2\pi} \int_0^{2\pi} i \, d\alpha$ is I_{dc} by definition, the second term under the integral sign is

$$(-2I_{\text{dc}})(I_{\text{dc}}) = -2I_{\text{dc}}^2$$

The rms ripple current then becomes

$$I'_{\text{rms}} = \sqrt{I_{\text{rms}}^2 - 2I_{\text{dc}}^2 + I_{\text{dc}}^2} = \sqrt{I_{\text{rms}}^2 - I_{\text{dc}}^2}$$

By combining this result with Eq. (20-14),

$$r = \frac{\sqrt{I_{rms}^2 - I_{dc}^2}}{I_{dc}} = \sqrt{\left(\frac{I_{rms}}{I_{dc}}\right)^2 - 1} \tag{20-15}$$

This result is independent of the current waveshape and is *not* restricted to a half-wave configuration. In the case of the half-wave rectifier, the ratio

$$\frac{I_{rms}}{I_{dc}} = \frac{I_m/2}{I_m/\pi} = \frac{\pi}{2} = 1.57$$

from Eqs. (20-4) and (20-6). Hence

$$r = \sqrt{1.57^2 - 1} = 1.21 \tag{20-16}$$

This result indicates that the rms ripple voltage exceeds the dc output voltage and shows that the half-wave rectifier is a relatively poor circuit for converting alternating into direct current.

20-3   A FULL–WAVE RECTIFIER

The circuit of a full-wave rectifier is shown in Fig. 20-3a. This circuit is seen to comprise two half-wave circuits which are so connected that conduction takes place through one diode during one half of the power cycle and through the other diode during the second half of the power cycle.

The current to the load, which is the sum of these two currents, has the form shown in Fig. 20-3b. The dc and rms values of the load current in such

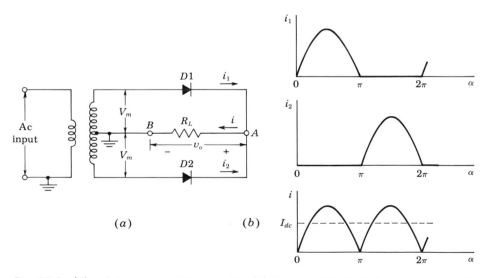

(a)   (b)

Fig. 20-3 (a) A full-wave rectifier circuit. (b) The individual diode currents and the load current i. The output voltage is $v_o = iR_L$.

a system are readily found, from the definitions (20-3) and (20-5), to be

$$I_{dc} = \frac{2I_m}{\pi} \qquad I_{rms} = \frac{I_m}{\sqrt{2}} \tag{20-17}$$

where

$$I_m = \frac{V_m}{R_f + R_L} \tag{20-18}$$

and V_m is the peak transformer secondary voltage from an end to the center tap. Note, by comparing Eqs. (20-4) with (20-17), that the direct current supplied to the load for the full-wave connection is twice that for the half-wave circuit.

A little thought should convince the reader that the input power supplied to the circuit in the full-wave case is given by the same expression as for the half-wave case, viz.,

$$P_i = I_{rms}^2(R_f + R_L) \tag{20-19}$$

Ripple Factor   The required current ratio that appears in the expression for the ripple factor is

$$\frac{I_{rms}}{I_{dc}} = \frac{I_m/\sqrt{2}}{2I_m/\pi} = 1.11$$

The ripple factor for the full-wave circuit is, from Eq. (20-15),

$$r = \sqrt{1.11^2 - 1} = 0.482 \tag{20-20}$$

A comparison of this value with the value given by Eq. (20-16) for the half-wave circuit shows that the ripple factor has dropped from 1.21 in the half-wave case to 0.482 in the present case.

Regulation   The dc output voltage is given by

$$V_{dc} = \frac{2V_m}{\pi} - I_{dc}R_f \tag{20-21}$$

Peak Inverse Voltage   Let us consider the circuit of Fig. 20-3a from the point of view of peak inverse voltage. At the instant of time when the transformer secondary voltage to midpoint is at its peak value V_m, diode $D1$ is conducting and $D2$ is nonconducting. If we apply KVL around the outside loop and neglect the small voltage drop across $D1$, we obtain $2V_m$ for the peak inverse voltage across $D2$. Note that this result is obtained without reference to the nature of the load, which can be a pure resistance R_L or a combination of R_L and some reactive elements which may be introduced to "filter" the ripple. We conclude that, *in a full-wave circuit, independently of the filter used, the peak inverse voltage across each diode is twice the maximum transformer voltage measured from midpoint to either end.*

Semiconductor-junction power diodes are packaged in pairs for full-wave rectification.   Vacuum-tube diodes are also constructed to contain both diodes within a single envelope for use in full-wave rectifier circuits.

20-4   OTHER FULL–WAVE CIRCUITS

A variety of other rectifier circuits find extensive use.   Among these are the bridge circuit, several voltage-doubling circuits, and a number of voltage-multiplying circuits.   The bridge circuit finds application not only for power circuits, but also as a rectifying system in rectifier ac meters for use over a fairly wide range of frequencies.

The Bridge Rectifier   The essentials of the bridge circuit are shown in Fig. 20-4.   In order to understand the action of this circuit, it is necessary only to note that two tubes conduct simultaneously.   For example, during that portion of the cycle when the transformer polarity is that indicated in Fig. 20-4, tubes 1 and 3 are conducting, and current passes from the positive to the negative end of the load.   The conduction path is shown on the figure. During the next half cycle, the transformer voltage reverses its polarity, and tubes 2 and 4 send current through the load in the same direction as during the previous half cycle.

The principal features of the bridge circuit are the following: The currents drawn in both the primary and the secondary of the supply transformer are sinusoidal, and therefore a smaller transformer may be used than for the full-wave circuit of the same output; a transformer without a center tap is used; and each tube has only transformer voltage across it on the inverse cycle.   The bridge circuit is thus suitable for high-voltage applications.   For example, if the output is 10,000 V, the peak inverse voltage across each tube

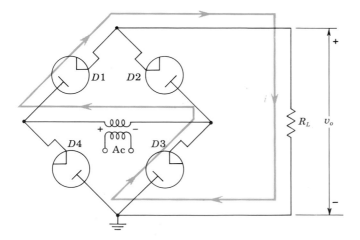

Fig. 20-4 Full-wave bridge circuit.

Fig. 20-5   The rectifier voltmeter.

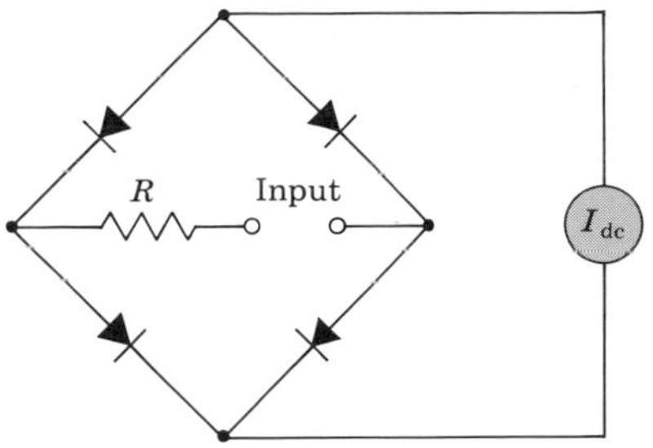

is 10,000 V. However, if a full-wave circuit were used, the peak inverse voltage would be 20,000 V. The transformers supplying the heaters of the tubes must be properly insulated for the high voltage.

The Rectifier Meter This instrument, illustrated in Fig. 20-5, is essentially a bridge-rectifier system, except that semiconductor elements replace the tubes, and of course no transformer is required. Instead, the voltage to be measured is applied through a multiplier resistor R to two corners of the bridge, a dc milliammeter being used as an indicating instrument across the other two corners. Since the dc milliammeter reads average values of current, the meter scale is calibrated to give rms values when a sinusoidal voltage is applied to the input terminals. As a result, this instrument will not read correctly when used with waveforms which contain appreciable harmonics.

Voltage Multipliers A common voltage-doubling circuit, which delivers a dc voltage approximately equal to twice the transformer maximum voltage at no load, is shown in Fig. 20-6. This circuit is operated by alternately charging each of the two capacitors to the transformer peak voltage V_m, current being continually drained from the capacitors through the load. The capacitors also act to smooth out the ripple in the output.

This circuit is characterized by poor regulation unless very large capacitors are used. The inverse voltage across the diodes during the nonconducting cycle is twice the transformer peak voltage. The action of this circuit will be better understood after the capacitor filter is studied in Sec. 20-7.

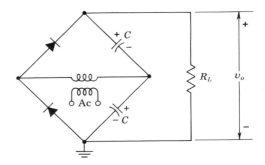

Fig. 20-6   The bridge voltage-doubler circuit. This is the single-phase full-wave bridge circuit of Fig. 20-4 with two capacitors replacing two tubes.

Circuits for obtaining n-fold multiplication,[1] n even or odd, are given in Probs. 20-8 and 20-9.

20-5   THE HARMONIC COMPONENTS IN RECTIFIER CIRCUITS

An analytical representation of the output current wave in a rectifier is obtained by means of a Fourier series.   The result of such an analysis for the half-wave circuit of Fig. 20-1 leads to the following expression for the current waveform:

$$i = I_m \left[\frac{1}{\pi} + \frac{1}{2} \sin \omega t - \frac{2}{\pi} \sum_{k=2,4,6,\ldots} \frac{\cos k\omega t}{(k+1)(k-1)} \right] \qquad (20\text{-}22)$$

The lowest angular frequency present in this expression is that of the primary source of the ac power.   Except for this single term of angular frequency ω, all other terms in the final expression are even harmonics of the power frequency.

The corresponding expression for the output of the full-wave rectifier, illustrated in Fig. 20-3, may be derived from Eq. (20-22).   By recalling that the full-wave circuit consists essentially of two half-wave circuits which are so arranged that one circuit conducts during one half cycle and the second operates during the second half cycle, it is clear that the currents are functionally related by the expression $i_1(\alpha) = i_2(\alpha + \pi)$.   The total load current $i = i_1 + i_2$ attains the form

$$i = I_m \left[\frac{2}{\pi} - \frac{4}{\pi} \sum_{\substack{k \text{ even} \\ k \neq 0}} \frac{\cos k\omega t}{(k+1)(k-1)} \right] \qquad (20\text{-}23)$$

We observe that the fundamental angular frequency ω has been eliminated from the equation, the lowest frequency in the output being 2ω, a second-harmonic term.   This offers a definite advantage in the effectiveness of filtering of the output.   A second desirable feature of the full-wave circuit is the fact that the current pulses in the two halves of the transformer winding are in such directions that the magnetic cycle through which the iron of the core is taken is essentially that of the alternating current.   This eliminates any dc saturation of the transformer core, which would give rise to additional harmonics in the output.

A power supply must provide an essentially ripple-free source of power from an ac line.   It is demonstrated above that the output of a rectifier contains ripple components in addition to a dc term.   Hence it is necessary to include a filter between the rectifier and the load in order to attenuate these ripple components.   In the following sections we make a detailed study of such filters.

Because the rectifier is a nonlinear device, no simple exact method of solution of the power-supply problem exists.   However, for each type of filter used, a reasonable linear approximation is made which allows the circuit to

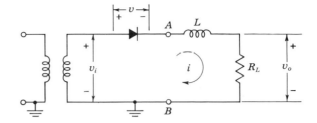

Fig. 20-7 Half-wave rectifier with choke filter.

be analyzed by the usual methods of ac circuit theory.   Hence the results
obtained are not exact, but do represent good engineering approximations.

20-6   INDUCTOR FILTERS

The operation of the inductor filter depends on the fundamental property
of an inductor to oppose any change of current.   As a result, any sudden
changes that might occur in a circuit without an inductor are smoothed out
by the presence of an inductor in the circuit.

Half-wave Rectifier   Suppose that an inductor, or "choke" filter, is connected in series with the load in a half-wave circuit, as illustrated in Fig.
20-7.   For simplicity in the analysis, assume that the diode and choke resistances are negligible.   Then the controlling differential equation for the current
in the circuit during the time that current flows is

$$v_i = V_m \sin \omega t = L \frac{di}{dt} + R_L i \tag{20-24}$$

An exact solution of this differential equation may be obtained subject to the
initial condition that $i = 0$ at $t = 0$.   The solution is valid only as long as it
yields a positive value of current, since the diode can conduct only in one direction.   The time at which the current falls to zero is called the *cutout point.*
The solution is given in Prob. 20-11, and the results are illustrated graphically
in Fig. 20-8, with $\omega L/R_L$ as a parameter.   The effect of changing the inductance
on the waveform of the current is clearly seen.   The simple inductor filter is
seldom used with a half-wave circuit.

**Fig. 20-8   The effect of changing the
inductance on the waveform of the output
circuit in a half-wave rectifier with an
inductor filter.   The load resistance R_L is
assumed constant.**

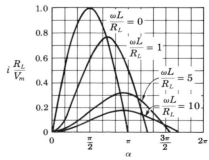

Full-wave Rectifier   Suppose that a choke input filter is applied to the output of a full-wave rectifier.   The circuit is given in Fig. 20-9a.   The load-current waveforms obtained with and without an inductor are shown in Fig. 20-9b.

An exact solution of the circuit differential equation can be obtained (Prob. 20-12).   However, since no cutout occurs in the load current, it is now simpler to proceed by finding an approximate solution.   The results will be sufficiently accurate for most applications and will be in a much more useful form than the exact solution.

The voltage applied to the circuit comprising the load resistor and the inductor filter is that given in Eq. (20-23), with the current replaced by the voltage (I_m is replaced by V_m).   The amplitudes of the ac terms beyond the first are small compared with the amplitude of the first term in the series.   Thus the fourth-harmonic-frequency term is only 20 percent of the second-harmonic term.   Further, since the impedance of the inductor increases with the frequency, better filtering action for the higher-harmonic term results.   It is therefore expected that the waveform in the output will be principally of second-harmonic frequency, and we may neglect all harmonics except the first ac term.   That is, the equivalent circuit of the rectifier under these circumstances is assumed to be that illustrated in Fig. 20-10.   For the sake of simplicity, and because they introduce little error, the diode drop and the diode resistance are neglected in the ripple calculations of this section.   In addition, the resistance and leakage inductance of the transformer and the resistance of the inductor are likewise neglected.

We note that only linear elements exist in the equivalent circuit and that the input voltage consists of a battery $2V_m/\pi$ in series with an ac source whose emf is $(-4V_m/3\pi)\cos 2\omega t$.   The load current will then be, in accordance with elementary circuit theory,

$$i = \frac{2V_m}{\pi R_L} - \frac{4V_m}{3\pi}\frac{\cos(2\omega t - \psi)}{\sqrt{R_L^2 + 4\omega^2 L^2}} \qquad (20\text{-}25)$$

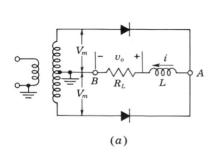

(a)

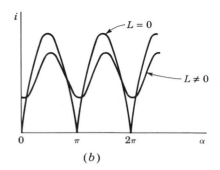

(b)

Fig. 20-9   (a) The schematic wiring diagram of a full-wave choke-input-filtered rectifier.   (b) The load-voltage waveforms for $L = 0$ and $L \neq 0$.

Fig. 20-10 The equivalent circuit of a
full-wave choke-input-filtered rectifier.

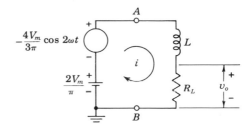

where

$$\tan \psi \equiv \frac{2\omega L}{R_L} \tag{20-26}$$

The load-current curve in Fig. 20-9b is expressed by Eq. (20-25). The load
voltage is $v_o = iR_L$.

The Ripple Factor   From the definition in Eq. (20-14) we have

$$r = \frac{\dfrac{4V_m}{3\pi \sqrt{2}} \dfrac{1}{\sqrt{R_L{}^2 + 4\omega^2 L^2}}}{2V_m/\pi R_L} = \frac{2R_L}{3\sqrt{2}} \frac{1}{\sqrt{R_L{}^2 + 4\omega^2 L^2}}$$

which may be expressed in the form

$$r = \frac{2}{3\sqrt{2}} \frac{1}{\sqrt{1 + 4\omega^2 L^2/R_L{}^2}} \tag{20-27}$$

This expression shows that filtering improves with decreased circuit resistance,
or correspondingly, with increased currents. At no load, $R_L = \infty$, whence
the filtering is poorest, and $r = 2/(3\sqrt{2}) = 0.47$. This result that applies
when no choke is included in the circuit should be compared with Eq. (20-20),
which gives 0.482. The difference arises from the higher-order terms in the
Fourier series that have been neglected in the present calculation.

If the ratio $4\omega^2 L^2/R_L{}^2$ is large compared with unity, the ripple factor
reduces to

$$r = \frac{1}{3\sqrt{2}} \frac{R_L}{\omega L} \tag{20-28}$$

This result shows that at any load the ripple varies inversely as the magnitude
of the inductance. Also, the ripple is smaller for small values of R_L, that is,
for high currents.

Regulation   The dc output voltage is given by

$$V_{\text{dc}} = I_{\text{dc}} R_L = \frac{2V_m}{\pi} = 0.637 V_m = 0.90 V_{\text{rms}} \tag{20-29}$$

where V_{rms} is the transformer secondary voltage measured to the center tap.
Note that, under the assumptions made in the analysis, the output voltage
is a constant, independent of the load; i.e., perfect regulation exists. Because of

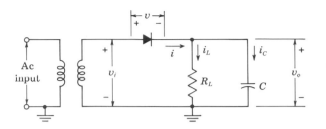

Fig. 20-11 A half-wave capacitor-filtered rectifier.

the effect of the choke resistance, the resistance of the diode, and the resistance of the transformer winding, the foregoing equation represents the output only at no load. The output voltage will decrease as the current increases in accordance with the equation

$$V_{\mathrm{dc}} = \frac{2V_m}{\pi} - I_{\mathrm{dc}}R \qquad (20\text{-}30)$$

where R is the total resistance in the circuit, exclusive of the load.

20-7   CAPACITOR FILTERS[2]

Filtering is frequently effected by shunting the load with a capacitor. The action of this system depends upon the fact that the capacitor stores energy during the conduction period and delivers this energy to the load during the inverse, or nonconducting, period. In this way, the time during which the current passes through the load is prolonged, and the ripple is considerably decreased.

Consider the half-wave capacitive rectifier of Fig. 20-11. Suppose, first, that the load resistor $R_L = \infty$. The capacitor will charge to the potential V_m, the transformer maximum value. Further, the capacitor will maintain this potential, for no path exists by which this charge is permitted to leak off, since the diode will not pass a negative current. The diode resistance is infinite in the inverse direction, and no charge can flow during this portion of the cycle. Consequently, the filtering action is perfect, and the capacitor voltage v_o remains constant at its peak value, as in seen in Fig. 20-12.

The voltage v_o across the capacitor is, of course, the same as the voltage across the load resistor, since the two elements are in parallel. The diode

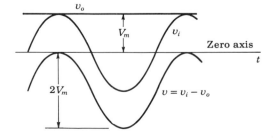

Fig. 20-12 Voltages in a half-wave capacitor-filtered rectifier at no load. The output voltage v_o is a constant, indicating perfect filtering. The diode voltage v is negative for all values of time, and the peak inverse voltage is $2V_m$.

voltage v is given by

$$v = v_i - v_o \tag{20-31}$$

We see from Fig. 20-12 that the diode voltage is always negative and that the peak inverse voltage is twice the transformer maximum. Hence the presence of the capacitor causes the peak inverse voltage to increase from a value equal to the transformer maximum when no capacitor filter is used to a value equal to twice the transformer maximum value when the filter is used.

Suppose, now, that the load resistor R_L is finite. Without the capacitor input filter, the load current and the load voltage during the conduction period will be sinusoidal functions of the time. The inclusion of a capacitor in the circuit results in the capacitor charging in step with the applied voltage. Also, the capacitor must discharge through the load resistor, since the tube will prevent a current in the negative direction. Clearly, the diode acts as a switch which permits charge to flow into the capacitor when the transformer voltage exceeds the capacitor voltage, and then acts to disconnect the power source when the transformer voltage falls below that of the capacitor.

The analysis now proceeds in two steps. First, the conditions during conduction are considered, and then the situation when the diode is nonconducting is investigated.

Diode Conducting If the diode drop is neglected, the transformer voltage is impressed directly across the load. Hence the output voltage is $v_o = V_m \sin \omega t$. The question immediately arises: Over what interval of time is this equation applicable? In other words, over what portion of each cycle does the diode remain conducting? The point at which the diode starts to conduct is called the *cutin point*, and that at which it stops conducting is called the *cutout point*. The latter will first be found in the same manner as that indicated for obtaining the cutout point for a half-wave inductor filter. The expression for the diode current is found, and the instant where this current falls to zero is the cutout time.

The expression for the diode current can be written down directly. Since the transformer voltage is sinusoidal and is impressed directly across R_L and C in parallel, the phasor current I is found by multiplying the phasor voltage V by the complex admittance $1/R_L + j\omega C$. Hence

$$I = \left(\frac{1}{R_L} + j\omega C\right) V$$

$$= \left[\sqrt{\left(\frac{1}{R_L}\right)^2 + \omega^2 C^2} \; \underline{/\tan^{-1} \omega C R_L}\right] V \tag{20-32}$$

Since V has a peak value V_m, then the instantaneous current is

$$i = V_m \sqrt{\omega^2 C^2 + \frac{1}{R_L^2}} \sin(\omega t + \psi) \tag{20-33}$$

where

$$\psi \equiv \tan^{-1} \omega C R_L \tag{20-34}$$

This expression shows that the use of a large capacitance to improve the filtering for a given load R_L is accompanied by a high peak diode current i. The diode current has the form illustrated in Fig. 20-13. For a specified average load current, the diode current will become more peaked, and the conduction period will decrease as the capacitance is made larger.

It is to be emphasized that the use of a capacitor filter may impose serious duty conditions on the rectifying diode, since the average current may be well within the current rating of the diode, and yet the peak current may be excessive.

The cutout time t_1 is found by equating the diode current to zero at this time. Thus, from Eq. (20-33),

$$0 = \sin (\omega t_1 + \psi)$$

or

$$\omega t_1 + \psi = n\pi$$

where n is any positive or negative integer. The value of t_1 indicated in Fig. 20-13 in the first half cycle corresponds to $n = 1$, or

$$\omega t_1 = \pi - \psi = \pi - \tan^{-1} \omega C R_L \tag{20-35}$$

Diode Nonconducting   In the interval between the cutout time t_1 and the cutin time t_2, the diode is effectively out of the circuit, and the capacitor discharges through the load resistor with a time constant $C R_L$. Thus the capacitor voltage (equal to the load voltage) is

$$v_o = A \epsilon^{-t/CR_L} \tag{20-36}$$

To determine the value of the constant A appearing in this expression, it is noted from Fig. 20-13 that at the time $t = t_1$, the cutout time,

$$v_o = v_i = V_m \sin \omega t_1$$

whence

$$A = (V_m \sin \omega t_1) \epsilon^{+t_1/CR_L} \tag{20-37}$$

Equation (20-36) thus attains the form

$$v_o = (V_m \sin \omega t_1) \epsilon^{-(t-t_1)/CR_L} \tag{20-38}$$

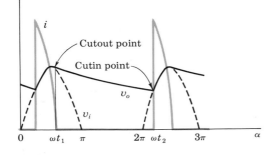

Fig. 20-13   Theoretical sketch of diode current i and output voltage v_o in a half-wave capacitor-filtered rectifier.

Since t_1 is known from Eq. (20-35), v_o can be plotted as a function of time. This exponential curve is indicated in Fig. 20-13, and where it intersects the sine curve $V_m \sin \omega t$ (in the following cycle) is the cutin point t_2. The validity of this statement follows from the fact that at an instant of time greater than t_2, the transformer voltage v_i (the sine curve) is greater than the capacitor voltage v_o (the exponential curve). Since the diode voltage is $v = v_i - v_o$, then v will be positive beyond t_2 and the diode will become conducting. Thus t_2 is the cutin point.

Graphical Solution　　The output voltage consists of a section of the input sine curve followed by an exponential section. The cutin time t_2 cannot be given by an explicit analytic expression, but must be found graphically by the method outlined above.

In principle at least, the foregoing results permit a complete analysis of the capacitor filter to be effected. For given values of ω, R_L, C, and V_m, the diode current is given by Eq. (20-33). If $\alpha \equiv \omega t$, $\alpha_1 \equiv \omega t_1$, and $\alpha_2 \equiv \omega t_2$, the output voltage is given by

$$v_o = V_m \sin \alpha \qquad \text{for } \alpha_2 < \alpha < \alpha_1$$

and by Eq. (20-38), 　　　　　　　　　　　　　　　　　　　　　　　　(20-39)

$$v_o = (V_m \sin \alpha_1)\epsilon^{-(\alpha - \alpha_1)/\omega C R_L} \qquad \text{for } \alpha_1 < \alpha < 2\pi + \alpha_2$$

In these equations α_1 and α_2 represent the cutout and cutin angles *in the first half cycle*, respectively. The cutout angle is found from Eq. (20-35).

The dc output voltage, the ripple factor, the peak diode current, etc., may then be calculated. These quantities can be plotted as functions of the parameters ω, R_L, C, and V_m. Such an analysis is quite involved, but it has been carried out, and the results are given in graphical form.

Full-wave Circuit　　The analysis of a full-wave rectifier with a capacitor filter requires a simple extension of that just made for the half-wave circuit. In Fig. 20-13 a dashed half-sinusoid is added between π and 2π. The cutin point now lies between π and 2π, where the exponential portion of v_o intersects this sinusoid. The cutout point is the same as that found for the half-wave rectifier.

20-8　　APPROXIMATE ANALYSIS OF CAPACITOR FILTERS

It is possible to make several reasonable approximations which permit an analytic solution to the problem. This approximate solution possesses the advantage that it clearly indicates the dependence of the dc output voltage and ripple factor upon the circuit component values. This analysis is sufficiently accurate for most engineering applications.

We assume that the output-voltage waveform for a full-wave circuit with

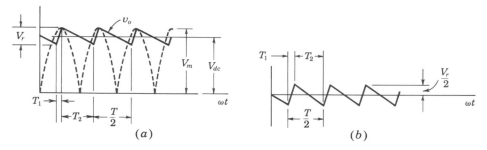

Fig. 20-14 (a) The approximate load-voltage waveform v_o in a full-wave capacitor-filtered rectifier. (b) The ripple waveform.

a capacitor filter may be approximated by a broken curve made up of portions of straight lines, as shown in Fig. 20-14a. The peak value of this wave is V_m, the transformer maximum voltage. If the total capacitor discharge voltage is denoted by V_r, then, from the diagram, the average value of the voltage is

$$V_{dc} = V_m - \frac{V_r}{2} \tag{20-40}$$

The instantaneous ripple voltage is obtained by subtracting V_{dc} from the instantaneous load voltage. This result is indicated in Fig. 20-14b. The rms value of this "triangular wave" is independent of the slopes or lengths of the straight lines and depends only upon the peak value. Calculation of this rms ripple voltage yields

$$V'_{rms} = \frac{V_r}{2\sqrt{3}} \tag{20-41}$$

It is necessary, however, to express V_r as a function of the load current and the capacitance. If T_2 represents the total nonconducting time, the capacitor, when discharging at the constant rate I_{dc}, will lose an amount of charge $I_{dc}T_2$. Hence the change in capacitor voltage is $I_{dc}T_2/C$, or

$$V_r = \frac{I_{dc}T_2}{C} \tag{20-42a}$$

The better the filtering action, the smaller will be the conduction time T_1 and the closer T_2 will approach the time of half a cycle. Hence we assume that $T_2 = T/2 = 1/2f$, where f is the fundamental power-line frequency. Then

$$V_r = \frac{I_{dc}}{2fC} \tag{20-42b}$$

$$r \equiv \frac{V'_{rms}}{V_{dc}} = \frac{I_{dc}}{4\sqrt{3}\,fCV_{dc}} = \frac{1}{4\sqrt{3}\,fCR_L} \tag{20-43}$$

$$V_{dc} = V_m - \frac{I_{dc}}{4fC} \tag{20-44}$$

The ripple is seen to vary inversely with the load resistance and with the capacitance. The effective output resistance R_o of the power supply is given by the factor which multiplies I_{dc} in Eq. (20-44), or $R_o = 1/4fC$. This output resistance varies inversely with capacitance. Hence, in order to keep the ripple low and to ensure good regulation, very large capacitances (of the order of tens of microfarads) must be used. The most common type of capacitor for this rectifier application is the electrolytic capacitor. These capacitors are polarized, and care must be taken to insert them into the circuit with the terminal marked $+$ to the positive side of the output.

The desirable features of rectifiers employing capacitor input filters are the small ripple and the high voltage at light load. The no-load voltage is equal, theoretically, to the maximum transformer voltage. The disadvantages of this system are the relatively poor regulation, the high ripple at large loads, and the peaked currents that the diodes must pass.

An approximate analysis similar to that given above applied to the half-wave circuit shows that the ripple, and also the drop from no load to a given load, are double the values calculated for the full-wave rectifier.

20-9   L–SECTION FILTER

The two types of filtering action considered above may be combined into a single L-section filter. This filter combines the decreasing ripple with increasing load of the series inductor with the increasing ripple with increasing load of the shunt capacitor. Such a filter is illustrated in Fig. 20-15. The inductor offers a high series impedance to the harmonic terms, and the capacitor offers a low shunt impedance to them. The resulting current through the load is smoothed out much more effectively than with either L or C alone in the circuit.

Regulation The dc voltage is readily calculated by taking, for the voltage impressed at the terminals AB of the filter of Fig. 20-15, the first two terms in the Fourier series representation of the output voltage of the rectifier, viz., from Fig. 20-10,

$$v = \frac{2V_m}{\pi} - \frac{4V_m}{3\pi} \cos 2\omega t \qquad (20\text{-}45)$$

Thus the two diodes are replaced by a battery in series with an ac source having twice the power-line frequency. This is the same equivalent circuit that is used in Sec. 20-6 for a full-wave inductor filter. If the resistance in series with the inductance is neglected, the dc output voltage equals the dc input voltage, or

$$V_{dc} = \frac{2V_m}{\pi}$$

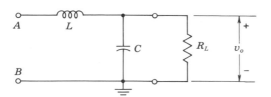

Fig. 20-15 An L-section filter.

If the sum of the diode, transformer, and choke resistances is R, then

$$V_{dc} = \frac{2V_m}{\pi} - I_{dc}R \qquad (20\text{-}46)$$

The Ripple Factor Since the object of the filter is to suppress the harmonic components in the system, the reactance of the choke must be large compared with the combined parallel impedance of capacitor and resistor. The latter combination is kept small by making the reactance of the capacitor much smaller than the resistance of the load. Very little error is introduced, therefore, by assuming that the entire alternating current passes through the capacitor and none through the resistor. Under these conditions the net impedance across AB is approximately $X_L = 2\omega L$, the reactance of the inductor at the second-harmonic frequency. The alternating current through the circuit is

$$I'_{rms} = \frac{4V_m}{3\sqrt{2}\,\pi}\frac{1}{X_L} = \frac{\sqrt{2}}{3} V_{dc}\frac{1}{X_L} \qquad (20\text{-}47)$$

where the resistance R in Eq. (20-46) has been neglected. The ac voltage across the load (the ripple voltage) is the voltage across the capacitor. This is

$$V'_{rms} = I'_{rms}X_C = \frac{\sqrt{2}}{3} V_{dc}\frac{X_C}{X_L} \qquad (20\text{-}48)$$

where $X_C = 1/2\omega C$ is the reactance of the capacitor at the second-harmonic frequency. The ripple factor is then given by

$$r = \frac{V'_{rms}}{V_{dc}} = \frac{\sqrt{2}}{3}\frac{X_C}{X_L} = \frac{\sqrt{2}}{3}\frac{1}{2\omega C}\frac{1}{2\omega L} \qquad (20\text{-}49)$$

which is, at 60 Hz,

$$r = \frac{0.83}{LC} \qquad (20\text{-}50)$$

with C in microfarads and L in henrys.

It is noticed that the effect of combining the decreasing ripple arising with a simple inductor filter and the increasing ripple arising with a simple capacitor filter for increasing loads is *a constant ripple independent of load.*

The Critical Inductance The foregoing analysis assumes that a current flows through the circuit at all times. If any cutout points of the type discussed in the previous section exist, this analysis is no longer valid. Consider the conditions that exist when no inductor is used. As already found, current will flow in the diode circuit for a small portion of the cycle, and the capacitor will become charged to the peak transformer voltage in each cycle. Suppose that a small inductance is now inserted in the line. Although the time over which diode current will exist will be somewhat lengthened, cutout may still occur. As the value of the inductance is increased, a value will be reached for which the diode circuit supplies current to the load continuously, and no cutout occurs. This value of inductance is referred to as the *critical inductance* L_c. Under these circumstances, each diode conducts for one-half of the cycle, and the input voltage to the filter circuit has the form given by Eq. (20-45). It is only under these circumstances that the above-developed L-section filter theory is applicable.

Referring to Fig. 20-16, we see that, if the rectifier is to pass current throughout the entire cycle, the peak $\sqrt{2}\,I'_{\text{rms}}$ of the ac component of the current must not exceed the direct current, $I_{\text{dc}} = V_{\text{dc}}/R_L$. Therefore, for the diode current to exist during the entire cycle, it is necessary that

$$\frac{V_{\text{dc}}}{R_L} \geq \sqrt{2}\,I'_{\text{rms}} = \frac{2V_{\text{dc}}}{3}\frac{1}{X_L}$$

where use has been made of Eq. (20-47). Hence

$$X_L \geq \frac{2R_L}{3} \tag{20-51}$$

and the value for the critical inductance is given by

$$L_c = \frac{R_L}{3\omega} \tag{20-52}$$

For a 60-Hz input frequency, this becomes

$$L_c = \frac{R_L}{1,130} \tag{20-53}$$

where R_L is expressed in ohms and L_c is in henrys.

It must be remembered that these values of critical inductance have been based not upon the true input voltage, but rather upon an approximate voltage made up of the dc term and the first ac harmonic term in the Fourier series of

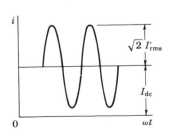

Fig. 20-16 The diode current in a full-wave circuit when an L-section filter is used.

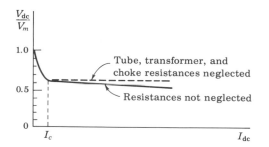

Fig. 20-17 The regulation curve of a rectifier with an L-section filter.

the true input voltage. It is shown in Sec. 20-6 that this approximation introduces very little error in the calculation of the ripple factor. However, the neglect of the higher harmonic terms introduces an appreciable error in the calculation of the critical inductance.† It is advisable for conservative design to increase the values of L_c calculated from Eq. (20-52) by about 25 percent.

The effect of the cutout is illustrated in Fig. 20-17, which shows a regulation curve of the system for constant L and a varying load current. Clearly, when the current is zero (R_L is infinite) the filter is of the simple capacitor type, and the output voltage is V_m. With increasing load current, the voltage falls, until at $I = I_c$ (the current at which $L = L_c$) the output potential is that corresponding to the simple L filter with no cutout, or $0.636V_m$. For values of I greater than I_c, the change in potential results from the effects of the resistances of the various elements of the circuit.

Design Considerations It is not possible to satisfy the conditions of Eq. (20-51) for all values of load, since at no load this would require an infinite inductance. If good voltage regulation is essential, it is customary to use a "bleeder" resistor in parallel with the load so as to maintain the conditions of Eq. (20-51), even if the useful current is small.

A more efficient method than using a small bleeder resistor, with its consequent power dissipation, is to make use of the fact that the inductance of an iron-core reactor depends, among other things, upon the magnitude of the direct current in the winding. Reactors for which the inductance is high at low values of direct current and decreases markedly with increased direct currents are called *swinging chokes*. Typically, such a reactor might have an inductance which drops from 30 H at zero current to 4 H at 100 mA. A choke whose inductance is constant at 30 H requires much more iron in order to avoid saturation, and hence is bulkier and more expensive than the swinging choke.

† If A represents the amplitude of the first ac term in the Fourier series of a wave and $B = 0.1A$ represents the amplitude of the second term, then $A + B = 1.1A$. A 10 percent error is made if B is neglected in calculating the sum. It is this general process that is involved in the calculation of L_c. However, the calculation of the ripple factor requires an evaluation of an expression of the form $\sqrt{A^2 + B^2} = \sqrt{A^2 + (0.1A)^2} = 1.005A$. Hence, if B is neglected, this results in an error of only 0.5 percent.

In designing an L-section filter, an inductance must be chosen so as to satisfy Eq. (20-52) for the specified bleeder resistance. Then a capacitance is chosen at least as large as that determined from Eq. (20-50) for the specified tolerable ripple. If a swinging choke is used, the minimum value of its inductance must be used in the calculation of the capacitance value needed.

EXAMPLE A full-wave rectifier is to supply 100 mA at 350 V with a ripple that must be less than 10 V. Specify the elements of a rectifier using a single L-section filter that will provide the desired results.

Solution The effective resistance of the load is

$$R_L = \frac{350}{0.100} = 3,500\ \Omega$$

The ripple factor is

$$r = \tfrac{10}{350} = 0.0286$$

From Eq. (20-53), the critical inductance for such a filter is

$$L_c = \frac{3,500}{1,130} = 3.1\ \text{H}$$

According to Eq. (20-50), the product LC must be at least as large as

$$LC = \frac{0.830}{0.0286} = 29$$

These calculations specify the minimum values of L and LC that may be used to accomplish the desired filtering. The actual values that will be used are determined by the commercially available inductors and capacitors. The desirability of using standard commercial components is dictated both by availability and by economic considerations.

Since 10-H chokes having the desired current rating are readily available, such an inductance will be chosen. The capacitance must therefore be about 3 μF. Since a 4-μF capacitance is readily available commercially, it is chosen.

A search through a tube manual reveals several rectifier tubes having the proper ratings. One such tube is the 5Y3-GT with a maximum dc output current rating of 125 mA, a maximum plate voltage per plate of 500 V rms, and a peak inverse voltage of 1,400 V. The plate characteristic of this tube (Fig. D-1) shows that the tube voltage is 50 V at 100 mA, corresponding to a resistance of approximately 500 Ω.

The resistance of a 10-H choke capable of carrying 100 mA is found in a manufacturer's catalog. A reasonable value is 200 Ω. Similarly, a reasonable value for the transformer resistance is 200 Ω. Hence the total resistance in series with the inductor is $R = 500 + 200 + 200 = 900\ \Omega$. From Eq. (20-46) the peak transformer voltage is

$$V_m = \frac{\pi}{2}\,(V_{\text{dc}} + I_{\text{dc}}R) = \frac{\pi}{2}\,[350 + (0.1)(900)] = 690\ \text{V}$$

and

$$V_{\text{rms}} = \frac{690}{\sqrt{2}} = 488 \text{ V}$$

A stock transformer would be purchased whose current rating is at least 100 mA and whose voltage to center tap is close to 488 V, say 500 V. If the exact value of choke and transformer resistances were known, a more accurate calculation of the transformer voltage needed could be made.

The peak inverse voltage is $2V_m = (2)(690) = 1,380$ V. Since the rated peak inverse voltage of the 5Y3-GT tube is 1,400 V, it is safe to use this tube in this application.

If the load should be removed accidentally, the circuit will behave as if it has a capacitor input filter, and the voltage will rise to the peak transformer voltage to center tap or to 690 V. Hence the insulation rating of the filament heating transformer should be at least this high.

The inequalities used in the derivation of the expression for the ripple factor are now checked: $R_L = 3,500$; $X_L = 4\pi f L = 7,540$; and $X_C = 1/4\pi f C = 332 \ \Omega$. Hence $X_C \ll R_L$, $X_L \gg X_C$, thus verifying the inequalities assumed.

20-10   MULTIPLE L–SECTION FILTER

The filtering may be made much more complete through the use of two L-section filters in cascade, as shown in Fig. 20-18. An approximate solution that is sufficiently accurate for practical purposes can be obtained by proceeding according to the development in Sec. 20-9.

It is assumed that the reactances of all the chokes are much larger than the reactances of the capacitors. Also, it is assumed that the reactance of the last capacitor is small compared with the resistance of the load. Under these circumstances, the impedance between A_3 and B_3 is effectively X_{C2}. The impedance between A_2 and B_2 is effectively X_{C1}, and the impedance between A_1 and B_1 is effectively X_{L1}. The alternating current I_1 is, approximately, from Eq. (20-47),

$$I_1 = \frac{\sqrt{2} \, V_{\text{dc}}}{3} \frac{1}{X_{L1}}$$

The ac voltage across C_1 is approximately

$$V_{A2B2} = I_1 X_{C1}$$

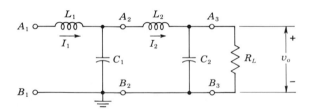

Fig. 20-18 A multiple (two-section) L-section filter.

The alternating current I_2 is, approximately,

$$I_2 = \frac{V_{A2B2}}{X_{L2}}$$

The ac voltage across C_2 and hence across the load is, approximately,

$$I_2 X_{C2} = I_1 \frac{X_{C2}X_{C1}}{X_{L2}} = \frac{\sqrt{2}\,V_{dc}}{3} \frac{X_{C2}}{X_{L2}} \frac{X_{C1}}{X_{L1}}$$

The ripple factor is given by dividing this expression by V_{dc}. Hence

$$r = \frac{\sqrt{2}}{3} \frac{X_{C1}}{X_{L1}} \frac{X_{C2}}{X_{L2}} \tag{20-54}$$

A comparison of this equation with Eq. (20-49) indicates the generalization which should be made in order to obtain an expression valid for any number of sections. For example, a multiple L filter of n similar sections has a ripple factor that is given by

$$r = \frac{\sqrt{2}}{3}\left(\frac{X_C}{X_L}\right)^n = \frac{\sqrt{2}}{3}\frac{1}{(16\pi^2 f^2 LC)^n} \tag{20-55}$$

For a multiple L filter of n similar sections, the product LC for a specified ripple factor may be evaluated from Eq. (20-55). The result is, at 60 Hz,

$$LC = 1.76\left(\frac{0.471}{r}\right)^{1/n} \tag{20-56}$$

To the approximation that the impedance between A_1 and B_1 is simply X_{L1}, the critical inductance is the same for the first inductor of a multisection filter as for a single-section unit. The remaining inductors may have any values, since they play no part in determining the cutout condition.

20-11   Π–SECTION FILTER

A very smooth output may be obtained by using a filter that consists of two capacitors separated by an inductor, as shown in Fig. 20-19. Such filters are characterized by highly peaked tube currents and by poor regulation, as for the simple capacitor input filter. They are used if, for a given transformer, higher voltage than can be obtained from an L-section filter is needed and if

Fig. 20-19 A Π-section filter.

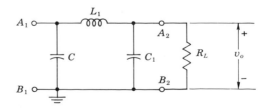

lower ripple than can be obtained from a simple capacitor or an L-section filter is desired.

The action of a Π-section filter can best be understood by considering the inductor and the second capacitor as an L-section filter that acts upon the triangular output-voltage wave from the first capacitor. The output potential is then approximately that from the input capacitor [Eq. (20-44)], decreased by the dc voltage drop in the inductor. The ripple contained in this output is reduced by the L-section filter.

The ripple voltage can be calculated by analyzing the triangular wave of Fig. 20-14a into a Fourier series and then multiplying each component by X_{C1}/X_{L1} for this harmonic. This procedure leads to rather involved expressions. An upper limit to the ripple can, however, be more easily obtained. If it is assumed that cutout takes place for the entire half cycle (for a full-wave rectifier), Fig. 20-14a becomes a triangular wave with vertical sides. The Fourier analysis of this waveform is given by

$$v = V_{dc} - \frac{V_r}{\pi}\left(\sin 2\omega t - \frac{\sin 4\omega t}{2} + \frac{\sin 6\omega t}{3} - \cdots\right) \qquad (20\text{-}57)$$

From Eq. (20-42b),

$$V_r = \frac{I_{dc}}{2fC}$$

The rms second-harmonic voltage is

$$V_2' = \frac{V_r}{\pi\sqrt{2}} = \frac{I_{dc}}{2\pi fC\sqrt{2}} = \sqrt{2}\,I_{dc}X_C \qquad (20\text{-}58)$$

where X_C is the reactance of C at the second-harmonic frequency.

A second method of obtaining the same result, due to Arguimbau,[4] is instructive. If the instantaneous current to the filter is i, then the rms second-harmonic current I_2' is given by the Fourier component

$$\sqrt{2}\,I_2' = \frac{1}{\pi}\int_0^{2\pi} i\cos 2\alpha\, d\alpha$$

The current i is in the form of pulses near the peak value of the cosine curve, and hence not too great an error is made by replacing $\cos 2\alpha$ by unity. Since the maximum value of the cosine is unity, this will give the maximum possible value of I_2'. Thus

$$\sqrt{2}\,I_2' \le \frac{1}{\pi}\int_0^{2\pi} i\, d\alpha = 2I_{dc}$$

because, by definition,

$$I_{dc} \equiv \frac{1}{2\pi}\int_0^{2\pi} i\, d\alpha$$

Hence the upper limit of the rms second-harmonic voltage is

$$V_2' = I_2'X_C = \sqrt{2}\,I_{dc}X_C$$

which agrees with the first method of analysis, in which it was assumed that the cutout took place over the complete half cycle. If this were true, the charging current could exist only for an infinitesimally small time near the peak of the input voltage or at the points for which $\cos 2\alpha = 1$. This shows the consistency of the two methods of attack.

The voltage V_2' is impressed on an L section, and by using the same logic as in Sec. 20-9 the output ripple is $V_2'X_{C1}/X_{L1}$. Hence the ripple factor is

$$r = \frac{V_{rms}'}{V_{dc}} = \frac{\sqrt{2}\,I_{dc}X_C}{V_{dc}}\frac{X_{C1}}{X_{L1}} = \sqrt{2}\,\frac{X_C}{R_L}\frac{X_{C1}}{X_{L1}} \tag{20-59}$$

where all reactances are calculated at the second-harmonic frequency. This expression gives the second-harmonic ripple, but, just as for the simple inductor filter, very little error is made in neglecting the higher harmonics, and we may consider this as the total ripple.

For 60 Hz, Eq. (20-59) reduces to

$$r = \frac{3{,}300}{CC_1L_1R_L} \tag{20-60}$$

where the capacitances are in microfarads, the inductances in henrys, and the resistances in ohms.

If the Π section is followed by an L section whose parameters are L_2 and C_2, then the above reasoning leads to the expression

$$r = \sqrt{2}\,\frac{X_C}{R_L}\frac{X_{C1}}{X_{L1}}\frac{X_{C2}}{X_{L2}} \tag{20-61}$$

This analysis can be extended in an obvious fashion to include any number of sections.

If a half-wave circuit is used, it can be shown that Eqs. (20-59) and (20-61) are still valid provided that all reactances are calculated at the fundamental instead of the second-harmonic frequency. Thus, for a single Π section, the half-wave ripple is eight times that for a full-wave circuit. The dc output voltage is that corresponding to the half-wave simple capacitor filter, minus the dc voltage drop in the inductor.

EXAMPLE Design a power supply using a Π-section filter to give dc output of 25 V at 100 mA with a ripple factor not to exceed 0.01 percent.

Solution The load resistance is $R_L = 25/(100 \times 10^{-3}) = 250\ \Omega$. From Eq. (20-60), with $C = C_1$, $r = 3{,}300/C^2LR_L$, or

$$C^2L = \frac{3{,}300}{10^{-4} \times 250} = 1.32 \times 10^5$$

There is no unique way of solving this equation for C and L. A reasonable commercially available value of L is chosen, and then C is calculated. If we choose a choke which has an inductance of 20 H at 100 mA and a dc resistance of 375 Ω, the corresponding capacitances required have values

$$C = \left(\frac{1.32 \times 10^5}{20}\right)^{\frac{1}{2}} = 81.2 \ \mu F$$

Tantulum electrolytic capacitors are available in this range. For example, a 100-μF capacitance at 100 V dc would be suitable.

The dc voltage drop in the choke is $(100 \times 10^{-3})(375) = 37.5$ V. Hence the dc voltage across the first capacitor is $25 + 37.5 = 62.5$ V. The peak transformer voltage to center tap V_m is given by Eq. (20-44), or

$$V_m = V_{dc} + \frac{I_{dc}}{4fC} = 62.5 + \frac{0.100}{(4)(60)(100 \times 10^{-6})} = 66.7 \text{ V}$$

Thus

$$V_{rms} = \frac{V_m}{\sqrt{2}} = 47 \text{ V}$$

Hence a 50-0-50-V transformer would be used. A suitable diode for this application would be the 1N485. It is rated at 125 mA average rectified current and a peak inverse voltage of 175 V. The peak inverse for this circuit is $2V_m = 133.4$ V, which is well within the diode rating.

20-12   Π–SECTION FILTER WITH A RESISTOR REPLACING THE INDUCTOR

Consider the network of Fig. 20-19 with the choke L replaced by a resistor R. This type of filter is analyzed in the same manner as in Sec. 20-11. The dc output is the value given in Eq. (20-44) for a simple capacitor filter minus the $I_{dc}R$ drop in the resistor. The ripple factor is given by Eq. (20-59), with X_L replaced by R. Thus, for a single section,

$$r = \sqrt{2} \frac{X_C}{R_L} \frac{X_{C1}}{R} \tag{20-62}$$

Hence, if the resistor R is chosen equal to the reactance of the choke which it replaces, the ripple remains unchanged. Since this means a saving in the expense, weight, and space of the choke, it is desirable to use the resistor wherever possible. Such a replacement of a resistor for an inductor is often practical only for low-current power supplies. Thus, for example, if in a full-wave circuit with an output current of 100 mA, a 20-H choke is to be replaced by a resistor to give the same ripple, its value must be

$$R = X_L = 4\pi fL = 15,000 \ \Omega$$

The voltage drop in this resistor would be $(15,000)(0.1) = 1,500$ V! The dc power dissipated would be $I_{dc}^2 R = (0.1)^2(15,000) = 150$ W! Hence such a substitution would not be a sensible one. However, if the rectifier is to furnish only 10 mA (perhaps for a cathode-ray-tube supply), the drop in the resistor is only 150 V, and the power loss in this resistor is 1.5 W. The resistor rather than the inductor should be used in such an application.

Since very large capacitances (100 μF or more) are available, the Π-section filter with a resistor replacing the inductor is quite popular even for high current supplies. Consider, for example, a load current of 100 mA at 300 V. If $R = 100$ Ω, the drop in this resistor is 10 V and the power loss is 1 W, which are reasonable values. The load resistance is $R_L = 3,000$. If two 100-μF capacitors are used, we calculate from Eq. (20-62) that the ripple is 0.083 percent, which may be satisfactory for some purposes.

20-13   SUMMARY OF FILTERS

Table 20-1 contains a compilation of the more important information relating to the various types of filters, when used with full-wave circuits. In all cases, diode, transformer, and filter-element resistances are considered negligible, and a 60-Hz power line is assumed.

20-14   REGULATED POWER SUPPLIES

An unregulated power supply consists of a transformer, a rectifier, and a filter. There are three reasons why such a simple system is not good enough for some applications. The first is its poor regulation; the output voltage is far from constant as the load varies. The second is that the dc output voltage

TABLE 20-1   Summary of filter information†

	Filter				
	None	L	C	L-section	Π-section
V_{dc}—no load..........	$0.636V_m$	$0.636V_m$	V_m	V_m	V_m
V_{dc}—load I_{dc}........	$0.636V_m$	$0.636V_m$	$V_m - \dfrac{4,170I_{dc}}{C}$	$0.636V_m$	$V_m - \dfrac{4,170I_{dc}}{C}$
Ripple factor r........	0.48	$\dfrac{R_L}{16,000L}$	$\dfrac{2,410}{CR_L}$	$\dfrac{0.83}{LC}$	$\dfrac{3,300}{CC_1L_1R_L}$
Peak inverse..........	$2V_m$	$2V_m$	$2V_m$	$2V_m$	$2V_m$

† C is in microfarads, L in henrys, R_L in ohms, V_m in volts, and I_{dc} in amperes.

varies directly with the ac input. In many locations the line voltage (of nominal value 115 V) may vary over as wide a range as 90 to 130 V, and yet it is necessary that the dc voltage remain essentially constant. The third is that the dc output voltage varies with the temperature, particularly if semiconductor devices are used. An electronic feedback or control circuit is used in conjunction with an unregulated power supply to overcome the above three shortcomings and also to reduce the ripple voltage. Such a system is called a *regulated power supply*.[5]

Stabilization Since the output dc voltage V_o depends on the input unregulated dc voltage V_i, load current I_L, and temperature T, then the change ΔV_o in output voltage of a power supply can be expressed as follows:

$$\Delta V_o = \frac{\partial V_o}{\partial V_i} \Delta V_i + \frac{\partial V_o}{\partial I_L} \Delta I_L + \frac{\partial V_o}{\partial T} \Delta T \tag{20-63}$$

or

$$\Delta V_o = S_V \, \Delta V_i + R_o \, \Delta I_L + S_T \, \Delta T \tag{20-64}$$

where the three coefficients are defined as

Stability factor:

$$S_V = \frac{\Delta V_o}{\Delta V_i}\bigg|_{\substack{\Delta I_L = 0 \\ \Delta T = 0}} \tag{20-65}$$

Output resistance:

$$R_o = \frac{\Delta V_o}{\Delta I_L}\bigg|_{\substack{\Delta V_i = 0 \\ \Delta T = 0}} \tag{20-66}$$

Temperature coefficient:

$$S_T = \frac{\Delta V_o}{\Delta T}\bigg|_{\substack{\Delta V_i = 0 \\ \Delta I_L = 0}} \tag{20-67}$$

The smaller the value of the three coefficients, the better the regulation of the power supply. The input-voltage change ΔV_i may be due to a change in ac line voltage or may be ripple because of inadequate filtering. For the present we assume constant temperature, and thus the third term in Eqs. (20-63) and (20-64) is zero. The temperature effect is considered below [Eq. (20-77)].

Emitter-follower Regulator If a power supply has poor regulation, it possesses a high internal impedance. This difficulty may be avoided by using an emitter follower to convert from high to low internal impedance. Refer to Fig. 20-20. If the output resistance of the unregulated supply is called r_o, then the output resistance R_o after the emitter follower has been added is

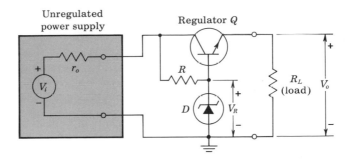

Fig. 20-20   An emitter-follower regulator.

approximately (Fig. 12-11c)

$$R_o = \frac{R_z + h_{ie}}{1 + h_{fe}} \tag{20-68}$$

where R_z represents the dynamic resistance of the Zener or avalanche reference diode D. A reasonable value of r_o is 100 Ω (10 V drop for each 100 mA change in load). If $1 + h_{fe} = 100$, $h_{ie} = 1,000$ Ω, and $R_z = 20$ Ω, then $R_o = 1,020/100 = 10.2$ Ω, which is a significant improvement over the 100-Ω output resistance of the unregulated power supply.

For the simple emitter-follower regulator the voltage stabilization ratio is, approximately,

$$S_V = \frac{\Delta V_o}{\Delta V_i} \approx \frac{R_z}{R_o + R} \tag{20-69}$$

From Eq. (20-69) we see that improving S_V requires increasing R, with attendant increase in V_{CE} and power dissipated in the transistor. Other disadvantages of this circuit are the following: (1) no provision exists for varying the output voltage since it is almost equal to the reference voltage V_R of the avalanche diode, and (2) changes in V_{BE} and V_R due to temperature variations appear at the output. A voltage regulator which is far superior to the simple emitter follower is discussed in the next section.

20-15   SERIES VOLTAGE REGULATOR

The physical reason for the improvement in voltage regulation with the circuit of Fig. 20-20 lies in the fact that a large fraction of the increase in input voltage appears across the control transistor, so that the output voltage tries to remain constant. If the input increases, the output must also increase (but to a much smaller extent), because it is this increase in output that acts to bias the control transistor toward less current. This additional bias causes an increase in collector-to-emitter voltage which tends to compensate for the increased input.

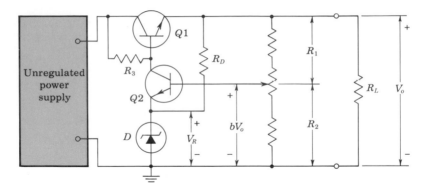

Fig. 20-21 A semiconductor-regulated power supply. The series pass element or series regulator is $Q1$, the difference amplifier is $Q2$, and the reference avalanche diode is D.

From the foregoing explanation it follows that if the change in output were amplified before being applied to the control transistor, better stabilization would result. The improvement is demonstrated with reference to Fig. 20-21. Here a fraction of the output voltage bV_o is compared with the reference voltage V_R. The difference $bV_o - V_R$ is amplified by $Q2$. If the input voltage increases by ΔV_i (say, because the power-line voltage increases), then V_o need increase only slightly, and yet $Q2$ may cause a large current change in R_3. Thus it is possible for almost all of ΔV_i to appear across R_3 (and since the base-to-emitter voltage is small, also across $Q1$) and for V_o to remain essentially constant. These considerations are now made more quantitative.

Simplified Analysis   From Fig. 20-22 the output dc voltage V_o is given by

$$V_o = V_R + V_{BE2} + \frac{R_1}{R_1 + R_2} V_o$$

or

$$V_o = (V_R + V_{BE2})\left(1 + \frac{R_1}{R_2}\right) \tag{20-70}$$

Hence a convenient method for changing the output is adjusting the ratio R_1/R_2 by means of a resistance divider as indicated in Fig. 20-21.

An approximate expression for S_V (sufficiently accurate for most applications) is obtained as follows: The input-voltage change v_i is very much larger than the output change v_o. Also, by the definition of Eq. (20-65), $\Delta I_L = 0$, and to a first approximation we can neglect the ac voltage drop across r_o. Hence $\Delta V_i = v_i$ appears as shown in Fig. 20-22. Neglecting the small change in base-to-emitter voltage of $Q1$, the current change $\Delta I = i$ in

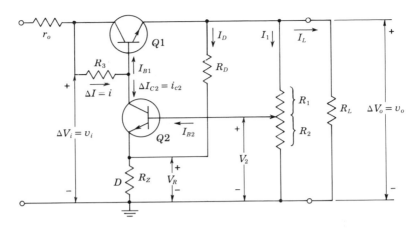

Fig. 20-22   Analysis of the series-regulated power supply.

R_3 is given by

$$i = \frac{v_i - v_o}{R_3} \approx \frac{v_i}{R_3} \qquad (20\text{-}71)$$

Since R_L is fixed, constant output voltage requires that I_L, and hence I_{B1}, remain constant.   Hence, for constant I_{B1},

$$i = \Delta I_{C2} = i_{c2} \qquad (20\text{-}72)$$

In Prob. 20-30 we find that, for small values of R_3,

$$i_{c2} \approx h_{fe2} \frac{R_2}{R_1 + R_2} \frac{v_o}{(R_1\|R_2) + h_{ie2} + (1 + h_{fe2})R_z} \equiv G_m v_o \qquad (20\text{-}73)$$

Using Eqs. (20-71) to (20-73), we find

$$S_V = \frac{v_o}{v_i} = \frac{R_1 + R_2}{R_2} \frac{(R_1\|R_2) + h_{ie2} + (1 + h_{fe2})R_z}{h_{fe2}R_3} \qquad (20\text{-}74)$$

In Prob. 20-31 the output impedance R_o of the circuit of Fig. 20-22 is found to be

$$R_o \approx \frac{r_o + \dfrac{R_3 + h_{ie1}}{1 + h_{fe1}}}{1 + G_m(R_3 + r_o)} \qquad (20\text{-}75)$$

where $G_m \equiv i_{c2}/v_o$ is obtained from Eq. (20-73).   A design procedure is indicated in the following illustrative example.

EXAMPLE   (a) Design a series-regulated power supply to provide a nominal output voltage of 25 V and supply load current $I_L \leq 1$ A.   The unregulated power supply has the following specifications: $V_i = 50 \pm 5$ V and $r_o = 10\ \Omega$.   (b) Find the stability factor S_V.   (c) Find the output resistance R_o.   (d) Compute the change in output voltage ΔV_o due to input-voltage changes of ± 5 V and load current I_L variation from zero to 1 A.

Solution   *a.* Select a silicon reference diode with $V_R \approx V_o/2$. Two 1N755 diodes in series provide $V_R = 7.5 + 7.5 = 15$ V and $R_z = 12$ Ω at $I_z = 20$ mA. Refer to Figs. 20-22 and 20-23. Choose $I_{C2} \approx I_{E2} = 10$ mA. The Texas Instruments 2N930 silicon transistor can provide the collector current of 10 mA. For this transistor the manufacturer specifies $I_C(\max) = 30$ mA and $V_{CE}(\max) = 45$ V.

At $I_{C2} = 10$ mA, the following parameters were measured:

$$h_{FE2} = 220 \qquad h_{fe2} = 200 \qquad h_{ie2} = 800 \ \Omega$$

Choose $I_D = 10$ mA, so that $D1$, $D2$ operate at $I_z = 10 + 10 = 20$ mA. Then

$$R_D = \frac{V_o - V_R}{I_D} = \frac{25 - 15}{10} = 1 \text{ K}$$

The ratio R_1/R_2 may be found from Eq. (20-70). Each resistor is determined as follows:

$$I_{B2} = \frac{I_{C2}}{h_{FE2}} = \frac{10 \text{ mA}}{220} = 45 \ \mu\text{A}$$

Since we require $I_1 \gg I_{B2}$, we select $I_1 = 10$ mA; then, since $V_{BE} = 0.6$ V,

$$V_2 = V_{BE2} + V_R = 15.6 \text{ V}$$

$$R_1 = \frac{V_o - V_2}{I_1} = \frac{25 - 15.6}{10 \times 10^{-3}} = 940 \ \Omega$$

$$R_2 \approx \frac{V_2}{I_1} = \frac{15.6}{10 \times 10^{-3}} = 1,560 \ \Omega$$

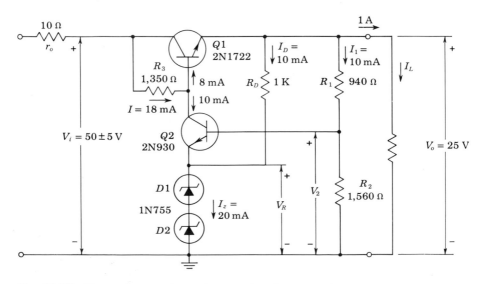

Fig. 20-23   The series regulator discussed in the example.

If we select the Texas Instruments 2N1722 silicon power transistor for $Q1$, we measure at $I_{C1} = 1$ A the following parameters:

$$h_{FE1} = 125 \qquad h_{fe1} = 100 \qquad h_{ie1} = 20 \ \Omega$$

We thus have

$$I_{B1} = \frac{I_L + I_1 + I_D}{h_{FE1}} = \frac{1{,}000 + 10 + 10}{125} \approx 8 \text{ mA}$$

The current I through resistor R_3 is $I = I_{B1} + I_{C2} = 8 + 10 = 18$ mA. The value for R_3 corresponding to $V_i = 45$ and to $I_L = 1$ A is given by

$$R_3 = \frac{V_i - (V_{BE1} + V_o)}{I} = \frac{50 - 25.6}{18 \times 10^{-3}} = 1{,}360 \ \Omega$$

The complete circuit is shown in Fig. 20-23.

$b.$ From Eq. (20-74) we find

$$S_V = \frac{2.50}{1.56} \times \frac{586 + 800 + (201)(12)}{(200)(1{,}360)} = 0.022$$

$c.$ The output resistance is found from Eqs. (20-73) and (20-75). Since

$$G_m = \frac{(200)(1.56)}{2.50} \times \frac{1}{586 + 800 + (201)(12)} = 0.033$$

$$R_o = \frac{10 + (1{,}360 + 20)/101}{1 + (0.033)(1{,}360 + 10)} - 0.51 \ \Omega$$

$d.$ The net change in output voltage, assuming constant temperature, is obtained using Eq. (20-63):

$$\Delta V_o = S_V \, \Delta V_i + R_o \, \Delta I_L = 0.022 \times 10 + 0.51 \times 1 = 0.22 + 0.51 = 0.73 \text{ V}$$

The circuit designed in this example was built in the laboratory, and excellent agreement between measured and calculated values was obtained.

Very often it is necessary to design a power supply with much smaller value for S_V. From Eq. (20-74) we see that S_V can be improved if R_3 is increased. Since $R_3 \approx (V_i - V_o)/I$, we can increase R_3 by decreasing I. The current I can be decreased by using a Darlington pair (Fig. 12-15) for $Q1$. For even greater improvement in S_V, R_3 is replaced by a constant-current source (so that $R_3 \to \infty$), as shown in Fig. 20-24 (see also Sec. 12-12). For this circuit, which incorporates a Darlington pair, values of $S_V = 0.00014$ and $R_o = 0.1 \ \Omega$ have been obtained.[6] The constant-current source in Fig. 20-24 is often called a *transistor preregulator.* Other types of preregulators (Prob. 20-35) are possible.[6] The 0.01-μF capacitor in Fig. 20-24 is added to prevent high-frequency oscillation.

Practical Considerations The maximum dc load current of the power supply shown in Fig. 20-22 is restricted by the maximum allowable collector

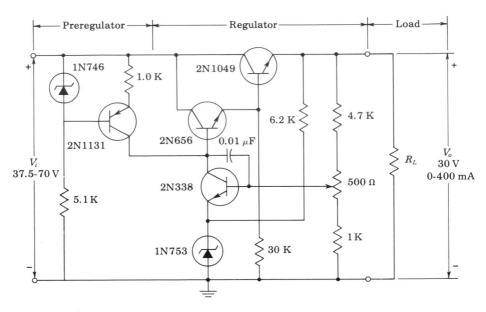

Fig. 20-24 Typical series regulator using preregulator and Darlington pair. (Courtesy of Texas Instruments, Inc.)

current of the series transistor.   The difference between the output and input voltages of the regulator is applied across $Q1$, and thus the maximum allowable V_{CE} for a given $Q1$ and specified output voltage determines the maximum input voltage to the regulator.   The product of the load current and V_{CE} is approximately equal to the power dissipated in the series transistor.   Consequently, the maximum allowable power dissipated in the series transistor further limits the combination of load current and input voltage of the regulator.

The reverse saturation current I_{CO} of $Q1$ plays an important role in determining the minimum load of the regulator.   If $I_{B1} = 0$, then $I_{E1} = I_{CO1}/(1 - \alpha_1)$.   Hence, if the total emitter current of $Q1$ $(I_L + I_D + I_1)$ falls below $I_{CO1}/(1 - \alpha_1)$, then V_{CE1} cannot be controlled by I_{B1}, and the regulator cannot function properly.   We thus see that, at high temperatures, where I_{CO} is high and $1 - \alpha$ may be small, the regulator may fail when the load current falls below a certain minimum level.   Various techniques have been proposed[7] to reduce this minimum-load restriction due to I_{CO}.   The 30-K resistor in Fig. 20-24 is added to allow operation at low load currents.

A power supply must be protected further from the possibility of damage through overload.   In simple circuits protection is provided by using a fusible element in series with r_o.   In more sophisticated equipment the series transistor is such that it can permit operation at any voltage from zero to the maximum output voltage.   In case of an overload or short circuit, the circuit of Fig. 20-25 can provide protection.   Here the diodes $D1$, $D2$ are nonconducting until the voltage drop across the sensing resistor R_S exceeds their forward

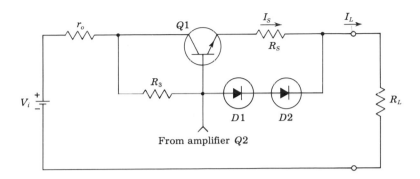

Fig. 20-25   Short-circuit overload-protection circuit.

threshold voltage V_γ. Thus, in the case of a short circuit, the current I_S would only increase up to a limiting point determined by

$$I_S = \frac{V_{\gamma 1} + V_{\gamma 2} - V_{BE1}}{R_S}$$

Under short-circuit conditions the load current would be, approximately,

$$I_L \approx \frac{V_i}{R_2} + \frac{V_{\gamma 1} + V_{\gamma 2} - V_{BE1}}{R_S} \tag{20-76}$$

Finally, an important practical consideration is the variation in output voltage with temperature. From Eq. (20-70) we see that, approximately,

$$\frac{\Delta V_o}{\Delta T} \approx \left(\frac{\Delta V_R}{\Delta T} + \frac{\Delta V_{BE2}}{\Delta T}\right)\left(1 + \frac{R_1}{R_2}\right) \tag{20-77}$$

Thus cancellation of temperature coefficients between the reference diode $D1$ and the transistor $Q2$ can result in a very low $\Delta V_o/\Delta T$. The GE reference amplifiers RA-1, RA-2, and RA-3 have been designed for this purpose. They are integrated devices composed of a reference diode and n-p-n transistor in a single chip. Typical temperature coefficients for these units are better than ± 0.002 percent/°C.

20-16   VACUUM–TUBE–REGULATED POWER SUPPLY

In many practical applications it is necessary to regulate voltages as high as 500 V and currents in the range of 50 to 200 mA. For this application the vacuum-tube-regulated power supply shown in Fig. 20-26 is often used. An approximate expression for S_V is obtained as follows: The input-voltage change v_i is very much larger than the output change v_o. If v_o is very small, the change in current is very small. Hence, to a first approximation, we can neglect the current change, and the ac voltage across r_o may be taken as zero. Furthermore, from the definition of μ it follows that the change in plate volt-

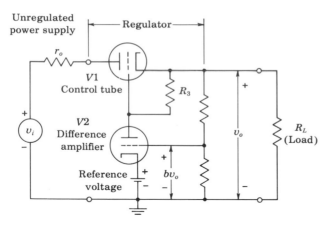

Fig. 20-26 A regulated vacuum-tube power supply.

age across the control tube is μ times the change in grid voltage. If b is the fraction of the output voltage v_o fed to the grid of the amplifier $V2$, the output of the amplifier is A_2bv_o, where A_2 is the *magnitude* of the amplification of $V2$. Since the amplifier output is approximately the grid-to-cathode voltage of $V1$, then the plate-to-cathode voltage of $V1$ is $\mu_1A_2bv_o$. This voltage is approximately equal to v_i. Hence

$$S_V = \frac{v_o}{v_i} \approx \frac{1}{\mu_1A_2b} \tag{20-78}$$

For a single-pentode amplifier an amplification of 150 is reasonable. If $b = 0.5$ and $\mu_1 = 2$, then $S_V = \frac{1}{150}$, so that any input-voltage change is divided by 150 before it appears at the output.

To find the output impedance of the power supply, assume a voltage v_o applied to the output (with $v_i = 0$) and find the current i_o drawn from v_o. The current in R_3 may be neglected because R_3 is very high (~ 1 M) compared with the output impedance (~ 10 Ω). If $\mu_1A_2b \gg 1$, the output resistance $R_o \equiv v_o/i_o$ is found (Prob. 20-38) to be

$$R_o \approx (r_{p1} + r_o)S_V \tag{20-79}$$

For the numerical values used above, $r_{p1} = 300$ Ω, $r_o = 1$ K, and $S_V = \frac{1}{150}$, we find $R_o = 1,300/150 = 8.7$ Ω.

Practical Considerations A commercial form of an electronically regulated power supply is indicated in Fig. 20-27. Specific numerical values for components and voltages are available in the literature.[8] The important components in the circuit are as follows:

1. The reference voltage, which in the preceding diagrams was shown as a battery, is usually a VR tube[9] connected to the regulated output through a dropping resistor. The 0.1-μF capacitor across the VR tube tends to prevent high-frequency oscillations. The most stable reference tube available is the 5651. An avalanche diode may be used in place of the VR tube.

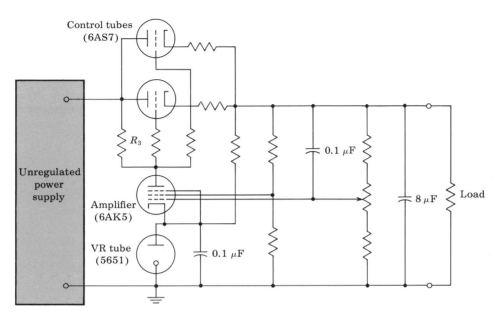

Fig. 20-27　A complete regulated vacuum-tube power supply.

2. The amplifier must have high gain, and hence a pentode (6AK5, 6SJ7, 6SH7) is used. If better stabilization is desired, a multistage direct-coupled difference amplifier is used.

3. The control tube must pass all the load current. If the rating of a single tube is exceeded, several tubes are connected in parallel. Two are indicated in Fig. 20-27. The small resistances in series with the cathodes of the control tubes tend to equalize the currents drawn by these tubes. The small resistors in series with the grids tend to suppress parasitic high-frequency oscillations. The unregulated voltage must exceed the regulated voltage by the drop in the control tube. Hence the ideal control tube is one which has a high perveance, so that it can supply large currents at low voltages. The 6AS7 has been designed for this purpose. It is a double triode, each section of which is rated at 125 mA. The tube drop is less than 40 V at 125 mA and zero grid voltage. The plate resistance is only 300 Ω. Unfortunately, the amplification factor is only 2, and a high-gain amplifier must be used if a large-voltage stabilization is to be obtained. Other tubes suitable for control tubes are the 2A3, 6B4, 6L6, 6V6, and 6Y6, the last three being triode-connected.

4. The 8-μF capacitor across the output lowers the ac output impedance. It also prevents the circuit from oscillating at a high frequency by reducing the loop gain below unity at that frequency for which the loop phase shift is zero.

5. The potentiometer controls the value of the dc output voltage at some definite current, say 100 mA. Thus the output voltage may be set at some specific value, say 300 V. The limits are set by the fact that if the potenti-

ometer is too far to one end, grid current will be drawn, and if it is too far to the other end, the tube may be cut off.

6. The 0.1-μF capacitor from the output terminal to the center of the potentiometer gives improved stabilization for fast changes in input voltage or lowered output impedance for fast changes in load. The reason for this improvement is that the voltage across a capacitor cannot change instantaneously. Hence, for a fast change in output voltage, this voltage appears instantaneously from the grid of the amplifier to ground. In other words, $b = 1$ for fast changes. On the other hand, if the potentiometer is set at its center value, $b = 0.5$ for slow changes. As a result, for example, the 120-Hz ripple from the power supply is cut in half by the addition of the 0.1-μF capacitor.

REFERENCES

1. Waidelich, D. L.: The Full-wave Voltage-doubling Rectifier Circuit, *Proc. IRE*, vol. 29, pp. 554–558, October, 1941.
   Waidelich, D. L., and C. L. Shackelford: Characteristics of Voltage-multiplying Rectifiers, *ibid.*, vol. 33, pp. 470–476, August, 1944.
   Waidelich, D. L., and H. A. K. Taskin: Analyses of the Voltage-tripling and Quadrupling Rectifier Circuits, *ibid.*, vol. 33, pp. 449–457, July, 1945.

2. Stout, M. B.: Analysis of Rectifier Circuits, *Elec. Eng.*, vol. 54, pp. 977–984, September, 1935.

3. Waidelich, D. L.: Diode Rectifying Circuits with Capacitance Filters, *Trans. AIEE*, vol. 60, pp. 1161–1167, 1941.
   Schade, O. H.: Analysis of Rectifier Operation, *Proc. IRE*, vol. 31, pp. 341–361, July, 1943.

4. Arguimbau, L. B.: "Vacuum Tube Circuits," pp. 21–28, John Wiley & Sons, Inc., New York, 1956.

5. Wilson, E. C., and R. T. Windecker: DC Regulated Power Supply Design, *Solid State J.*, November, 1961, pp. 37–46.

6. Texas Instruments, Inc.: "Transistor Circuit Design," chap. 9, McGraw-Hill Book Company, New York, 1963.
   General Electric Co.: "Transistor Manual," chap. 10, Syracuse, N.Y., 1964.

7. Moores, H. T.: Design Procedure for Power Transistors, Part 2, *Electron. Design*, September, 1955, pp. 43–45.

8. "Handbook of Preferred Circuits, Navy Aeronautical Electronic Equipment," U.S. National Bureau of Standards, NAVAER 16-1-519, September, 1955.

9. Millman, J.: "Vacuum-tube and Semiconductor Electronics," chap. 13, McGraw-Hill Book Company, New York, 1958.

PROBABLE VALUES OF GENERAL PHYSICAL CONSTANTS†

Constant	Symbol	Value
Electronic charge	e	1.602×10^{-19} C
Electronic mass	m	9.109×10^{-31} kg
Ratio of charge to mass of an electron	e/m	1.759×10^{11} C/kg
Mass of atom of unit atomic weight (hypothetical)	.....	1.660×10^{-27} kg
Mass of proton	m_p	1.673×10^{-27} kg
Ratio of proton to electron mass	m_p/m	1.837×10^3
Planck's constant	h	6.626×10^{-34} J-sec
Boltzmann constant	k	1.381×10^{-23} J/°K
	k	8.620×10^{-5} eV/°K
Stefan-Boltzmann constant	σ	5.670×10^{-8} W/(m²)(°K⁴)
Avogadro's number	N_A	6.023×10^{23} molecules/mole
Gas constant	R	8.314 J/(deg)(mole)
Velocity of light	c	2.998×10^8 m/sec
Faraday's constant	F	9.649×10^3 C/mole
Volume per mole	V_o	2.241×10^{-2} m³
Acceleration of gravity	g	9.807 m/sec²

† E. A. Mechtly, "The International System of Units: Physical Constants and Conversion Factors," National Aeronautics and Space Administration, NASA SP-7012, Washington, D.C., 1964.

B / CONVERSION FACTORS AND PREFIXES

1 ampere (A)	$= 1$ C/sec	mega (M)	$= \times 10^6$
1 angstrom unit (Å)	$= 10^{-10}$ m	1 meter (m)	$= 39.37$ in.
1 atmosphere pressure	$= 760$ mm Hg	micro (μ)	$= \times 10^{-6}$
1 coulomb (C)	$= 1$ A-sec	1 micron	$= 10^{-6}$ m
1 electron volt (eV)	$= 1.60 \times 10^{-19}$ J	1 mil	$= 10^{-3}$ in.
1 farad (F)	$= 1$ C/V	1 mile	$= 5{,}280$ ft
1 foot (ft)	$= 0.305$ m		$= 1.609$ km
1 gram-calorie	$= 4.185$ J		
giga (G)	$= \times 10^9$	milli (m)	$= \times 10^{-3}$
1 henry (H)	$= 1$ V-sec/A	nano (n)	$= \times 10^{-9}$
1 hertz (Hz)	$= 1$ cycle/sec	1 newton (N)	$= 1$ kg-m/sec^2
1 inch (in.)	$= 2.54$ cm	Permeability of free	
1 joule (J)	$= 10^7$ ergs	space (μ_0)	$= 4\pi \times 10^{-7}$ H/m
	$= 1$ W-sec	Permittivity of free	
	$= 6.25 \times 10^{18}$ eV	space (ϵ_0)	$= (36\pi \times 10^9)^{-1}$ F/m
	$= 1$ N-m	pico (p)	$= \times 10^{-12}$
	$= 1$ C-V	1 pound (lb)	$= 453.6$ g
kilo (k)	$= \times 10^3$	1 tesla (T)	$= 1$ Wb/m^2
1 kilogram (kg)	$= 2.205$ lb	1 ton	$= 2{,}000$ lb
1 kilometer (km)	$= 0.622$ mile	1 volt (V)	$= 1$ W/A
1 lumen	$= 0.0016$ W	1 watt (W)	$= 1$ J/sec
	(at 0.55 μ)	1 weber (Wb)	$= 1$ V-sec
1 lumen per square		1 weber per square	
foot	$= 1$ ft-candle	meter (Wb/m^2)	$= 10^4$ gauss

PERIODIC TABLE
OF THE ELEMENTS†

Period	Group IA	Group IIA	Group IIIB	Group IVB	Group VB	Group VIB	Group VIIB	Group VIII			Group IB	Group IIB	Group IIIA	Group IVA	Group VA	Group VIA	Group VIIA	Inert gases
1	H 1 1.01																	He 2 4.00
2	Li 3 6.94	Be 4 9.01											B 5 10.81	C 6 12.01	N 7 14.01	O 8 16.00	F 9 19.00	Ne 10 20.18
3	Na 11 22.99	Mg 12 24.31											Al 13 26.98	Si 14 28.09	P 15 30.97	S 16 32.06	Cl 17 35.45	Ar 18 39.95
4	K 19 39.10	Ca 20 40.08	Sc 21 44.96	Ti 22 47.90	V 23 50.94	Cr 24 52.00	Mn 25 54.94	Fe 26 55.85	Co 27 58.93	Ni 28 58.71	Cu 29 63.54	Zn 30 65.37	Ga 31 69.72	Ge 32 72.59	As 33 74.92	Se 34 78.96	Br 35 79.91	Kr 36 83.80
5	Rb 37 85.47	Sr 38 87.62	Y 39 88.90	Zr 40 91.22	Nb 41 92.91	Mo 42 95.94	Tc 43 (99)	Ru 44 101.07	Rh 45 102.90	Pd 46 106.4	Ag 47 107.87	Cd 48 112.40	In 49 114.82	Sn 50 118.69	Sb 51 121.75	Te 52 127.60	I 53 126.90	Xe 54 131.30
6	Cs 55 132.90	Ba 56 137.34	La 57 138.91	Hf 72 178.49	Ta 73 180.95	W 74 183.85	Re 75 186.2	Os 76 190.2	Ir 77 192.2	Pt 78 195.09	Au 79 196.97	Hg 80 200.59	Tl 81 204.37	Pb 82 207.19	Bi 83 208.98	Po 84 (210)	At 85 (210)	Rn 86 (222)
7	Fr 87 (223)	Ra 88 (226)	Ac 89 (227)	Th 90 232.04	Pa 91 (231)	U 92 238.04	Np 93 (237)	Pu 94 242)	Am 95 (243)	Cm 96 (247)	Bk 97 (247)	Cf 98 (251)	Es 99 (254)	Fm 100 (253)	Nd 101 (256)	No 102 (254)	Lw 103 (257)	

The Rare Earths

Ce 58 140.12	Pr 59 140.91	Nd 60 144.24	Pm 61 (147)	Sn 62 150.35	Eu 63 151.96	Gd 64 157.25	Tb 65 158.92	Dy 66 162.50	Ho 67 164.93	Er 68 167.26	Tm 69 168.93	Yb 70 173.04	Lu 71 174.97

† The number to the right of the symbol for the element gives the atomic number. The number below the symbol for the element gives the atomic weight.

TUBE CHARACTERISTICS†

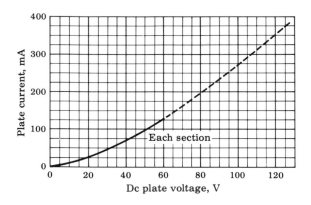

Fig. D-1   5Y3-GT diode (6087).

Each section

Plate current, mA

Dc plate voltage, V

† Courtesy of General Electric Company.

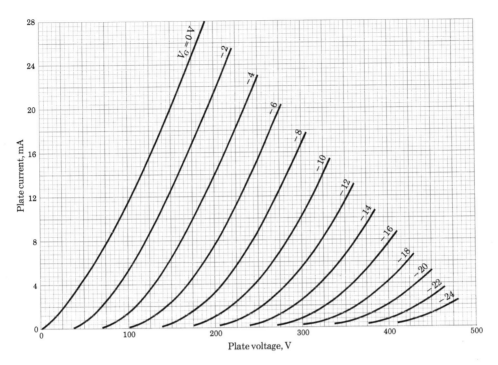

Fig. D-2 6CG7 (6SN7) negative-grid characteristics (each section).

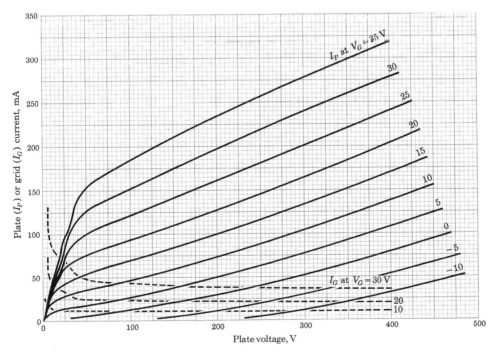

Fig. D-3 6CG7 (6SN7) positive-grid characteristics (each section).

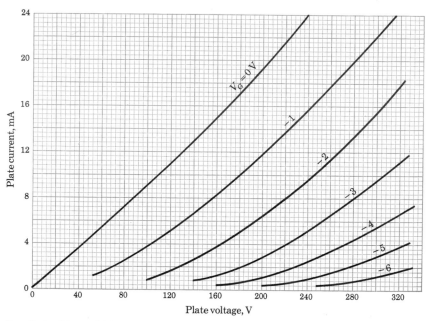

Fig. D-4   12AT7 (6664 and 7898) negative-grid characteristics (each section).

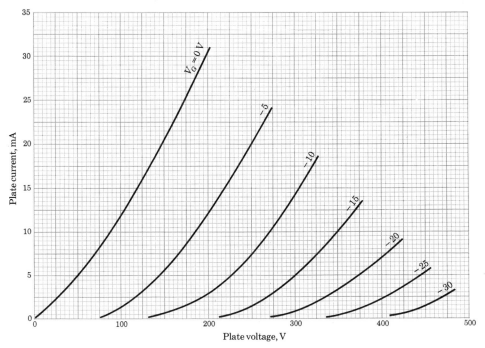

Fig. D-5   12AU7 (5814, 5963, and 6135) negative-grid characteristics (each section).

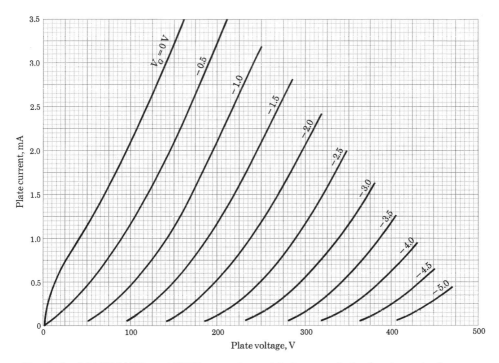

Fig. D-6   12AX7 (6681 and 7058) negative-grid characteristics (each section).

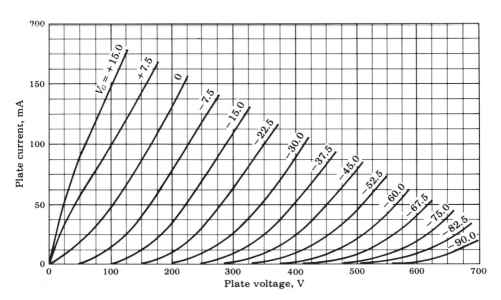

Fig. D-7   6L6 triode (screen grid connected to plate).

PROBLEMS

CHAPTER 1

1-1 *a.* An electron is emitted from a thermionic cathode with a negligible initial velocity and is accelerated by a potential of 1,000 V. Calculate the final velocity of the particle.

b. Repeat the problem for the case of a deuterium ion (heavy hydrogen ion—atomic weight 2.01) that has been introduced into the electric field with an initial velocity of 10^5 m/sec.

1-2 *a.* The distance between the plates of a plane-parallel capacitor is 1 cm. An electron starts at rest at the negative plate. If a direct voltage of 1,000 V is applied, how long will it take the electron to reach the positive plate?

b. If a 60-Hz sinusoidal voltage of peak value 1,000 V is applied, how long will the time of transit be? Assume that the electron is released with zero velocity at the instant of time when the applied voltage is passing through zero. HINT: Expand the sine function into a power series. Thus $\sin \theta = \theta - \theta^3/3! + \theta^5/5! - \cdots$.

1-3 An electron having an initial kinetic energy of 10^{-16} J at the surface of one of two parallel-plane electrodes and moving normal to the surface is slowed down by the retarding field caused by a 400-V potential applied between the electrodes.

a. Will the electron reach the second electrode?

b. What retarding potential would be required for the electron to reach the second electrode with zero velocity?

1-4 The plates of a parallel-plate capacitor are d (meters) apart. At $t = 0$, an electron is released at the bottom plate with a velocity v_o (meters per second) normal to the plates. The potential of the top plate with respect to the bottom is $-V_m \sin \omega t$.

a. Find the position of the electron at any time t.

b. Find the value of the electric field intensity at the instant when the velocity of the electron is zero.

1-5 An electron is released with zero initial velocity from the lower of a pair of horizontal plates which are 3 cm apart. The accelerating potential between these plates increases from zero linearly with time at the rate of 10 V/μsec. When the electron is 2.8 cm from the bottom plate, a reverse voltage of 50 V replaces the linearly rising voltage.

a. What is the instantaneous potential between the plates at the time of the potential reversal?

b. With which electrode does the electron collide?

c. What is the time of flight?

d. What is the impact velocity of the electron?

1-6 A 100-eV hydrogen ion is released in the center of the plates, as shown in the figure. The voltage between the plates varies linearly from 0 to 50 V in 10^{-7} sec and then drops immediately to zero and remains at zero. The separation between the plates is 2 cm. If the ion enters the region between the plates at time $t = 0$, how far will it be displaced from the X axis upon emergence from between the plates?

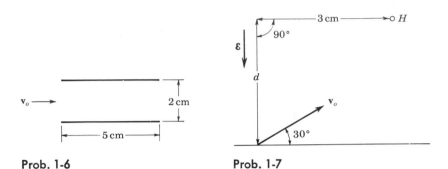

Prob. 1-6   **Prob. 1-7**

1-7 Electrons are projected into the region of constant electric field intensity of magnitude 5×10^3 V/m that exists vertically. The electron gun makes an angle of 30° with the horizontal. It ejects the electrons with an energy of 100 eV.

a. How long does it take an electron leaving the gun to pass through a hole H at a horizontal distance of 3 cm from the position of the gun? Refer to the figure. Assume that the field is downward.

b. What must be the distance d in order that the particles emerge through the hole?

c. Repeat parts *a* and *b* for the case where the field is upward.

1-8 In a certain plane-parallel diode the potential V is given as a function of the distance x between electrodes by the equation

$$V = kx^{\frac{4}{3}}$$

where k is a constant. Find an expression for the time it will take an electron that leaves the cathode with zero initial velocity to reach the anode, a distance d away.

1-9 *a.* Through what potential must an electron fall if relativistic corrections are not made, in order that it acquire a speed equal to that of light?

b. What speed does the electron actually acquire in falling through this potential?

1-10 Calculate the ratio m/m_o for 2-MeV electrons and also for 2-MeV deuterons (atomic weight 2.01).

1-11 An electron starts at rest in a constant electric field. Using the relativistic expression for the mass, find the velocity and the displacement of the particle at any time t.

1-12 The electrons emitted from the thermionic cathode of a cathode-ray-tube gun are accelerated by a potential of 400 V. The essential dimensions in Fig. 1-4 are

$$L = 19.4 \text{ cm} \qquad l = 1.27 \text{ cm} \qquad d = 0.475 \text{ cm}$$

a. Compare the electrostatic sensitivity of this tube obtained from the theoretical expression with the experimental value of 0.89 mm/V.

b. What must be the magnitude of a transverse magnetic field acting over the whole length of the tube in order to produce the same deflection as that produced by a deflecting potential of 30 V? The distance from the anode to the screen is 23.9 cm.

c. Repeat part b for the case where the transverse magnetic field exists only in the region between the deflecting plates instead of over the entire length of the tube.

1-13 What transverse magnetic field acting over the entire length of a cathode-ray tube must be applied to cause a deflection of 3 cm on a screen that is 15 cm away from the anode if the accelerating voltage is 2,000 V?

1-14 A cathode-ray tube has the following dimensions:
Length of plates, 2.0 cm
Separation of plates, 1.0 cm
Distance from electron gun to center of plates, 5.0 cm
Distance from center of plates to the screen, 20.0 cm
Assume that there is only one set of plates in the tube. The accelerating voltage is 1,000 V, and the beam leaving the gun is well focused. An ac voltage applied to the plates produces a straight line 4.0 cm in length on the screen if no magnetic field is present.

A uniform axial magnetic field is now applied over the entire length of the cathode-ray tube.

a. Assuming that a virtual cathode exists at the center of the plates (Sec. 1-8), calculate the minimum magnetic field that will reduce the line to a point on the screen.

b. If the magnetic field is reduced to half the value found in part a, a line is observed on the screen. Why? Calculate the length of this line and the angle it makes with the direction of the 4.0-cm line that was observed for zero magnetic field.

1-15 A 100-V electron is introduced in the XY plane into the region of uniform magnetic field intensity of 5 mWb/m², as shown.

a. At what point does the electron strike the XZ plane?

b. What are the velocity components with which the electron strikes the XZ plane?

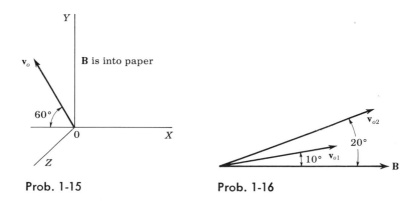

Prob. 1-15   Prob. 1-16

1-16 Two 50-eV electrons enter a magnetic field of 2.0 mWb/m² as shown, one at 10°, the other at 20°. How far apart are these electrons when they have traversed (a) one revolution of their helical paths, (b) two revolutions of their helical paths?

1-17 An electron is injected into a magnetic field with a velocity of 10^7 m/sec in a direction lying in the plane of the paper and making an angle of 30° with **B**, as shown in the figure. If the length L is 0.1 m, what must be the value of **B** in order that the electron pass through the point Q?

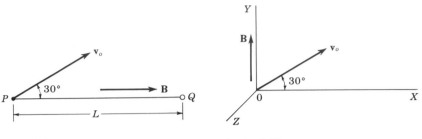

Prob. 1-17   Prob. 1-18

1-18 An electron having a speed $v_o = 10^7$ m/sec is injected in the XY plane at an angle of 30° to the X axis. A uniform magnetic field parallel to the Y axis and with flux density $B = 5.10$ mWb/m² exists in the region. Find the position of the electron in space at $t = 5$ nsec after entering the magnetic field.

1-19 Consider the cathode-ray tube shown. A dc potential is applied to the plates of this cathode-ray tube. In addition, a solenoid is placed over the tube, giving a uniform magnetic field parallel to the axis of the tube. Describe in words the exact motion of an electron starting at rest at the cathode K in the following sections of the tube:

    a. Between cathode K and anode A. Assume that the field is uniform in this region.

    b. Between anode A and the edge of the plates O.

    c. In the region between the plates.

    d. In the region beyond the plates.

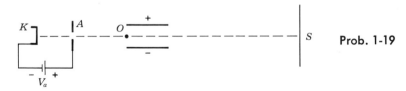

Prob. 1-19

1-20 The accelerating voltage of a cathode-ray tube is 1,000 V. A sinusoidal voltage is applied to a set of deflecting plates. The axial length of the plates is 2 cm.

    a. What is the maximum frequency of this voltage if the electrons are not to remain in the region between the plates for more than one-half cycle?

    b. For what fraction of a cycle does the electron remain in the region between the plates if the frequency is 60 Hz?

1-21 The electric field in the region between the plates of a cathode-ray tube is produced by the application of a deflecting potential given by

$$V_d = 60 \sin (2\pi \times 10^8 t)$$

The important tube dimensions are

$$L = 19.4 \text{ cm} \qquad l = 1.27 \text{ cm} \qquad d = 0.475 \text{ cm}$$

The accelerating voltage is 200 V.   Where will an electron strike the screen if it enters the region between the plates at an instant when the phase of the deflecting voltage is zero?

1-22   Solve Prob. 1-21 if the applied deflecting potential is given by

$$V_d = 4 \times 10^{10}t$$

1-23   *a.* A sinusoidal voltage of frequency ω is applied to the deflecting plates of a cathode-ray tube.   The transit time between the plates is τ.   The length of the line on the screen is A.   If A_o is the line length when the transit time is negligible compared with the period of the applied voltage, show that

$$A = A_o \frac{\sin (\omega\tau/2)}{\omega\tau/2}$$

b. If $V_a = 1,000$ V and $l = 1$ cm, at what frequency will $A/A_o = 0.9$?

1-24   Show that the magnetic deflection in a TV tube having a screen diameter comparable with the length of the tube neck is given by

$$D = lLB \sqrt{\frac{e/m}{2V_a - (e/m)(Bl)^2}}$$

The symbols have the meaning given in Sec. 1-14.

1-25   Electrons emerge from a hole in an anode of a cathode-ray tube in a diverging cone of small angle.   With 900 V between the cathode and the anode, the minimum longitudinal magnetic field required to cause the electron beam to come to a focus on the screen is 2.5 mWb/m². If the anode voltage is decreased to 400 V, what minimum magnetic field will now be necessary to focus the beam?   What is the next higher value of magnetic field at which a focus will be obtained?

1-26   Electrons emerge from the hole in the anode of a cathode-ray tube in all directions within a cone of small angle.   The accelerating voltage is 300 V.   The distance from the anode to the screen is 22.5 cm.

The tube is placed in a 40-cm-long solenoid having a diameter of 12 cm and wound with 24 turns of wire per inch.   The tube and solenoid axes coincide.   The maximum current rating of the solenoid is 5 A.   For what values of current in the solenoid will the beam of electrons come to a focus as a spot on the screen?

1-27   *a.* Refer to Sec. 1-15 on magnetic focusing.   Show that the coordinates of the electron *on the screen* are

$$x = \frac{v_{ox}L}{v_{oy}\alpha} \sin \alpha \quad \text{and} \quad z = \frac{v_{oz}L}{v_{oy}\alpha} (1 - \cos \alpha)$$

where $\alpha = eBL/mv_{oy}$ and the other symbols have the meanings given in the text.

b. Let $x' = (\pi v_{oy}/Lv_{ox})x$ and $z' = (\pi v_{oy}/Lv_{oz})z$, and plot z' versus x' for intervals of α equal to $\pi/4$.   This will give the path the electrons will trace out on the screen as the magnetic field intensity is increased from zero.   Plot enough points so that the path corresponding to two complete spirals will be obtained.

1-28   Given a uniform electric field of 5×10^3 V/m parallel to and in the same direction as a uniform magnetic field of 1.2 mWb/m²; 300-eV electrons enter the region where these fields exist, at an angle of 30° with the direction of the fields.   A photographic plate is placed normal to the direction of the fields at a distance of 1.6 cm from the electron gun, as shown in the figure.

    a. At what point do the electrons strike the plate?

    b. With what velocity components do they strike the plate?

    c. Repeat parts *a* and *b* for the case where the direction of the electric field is reversed.

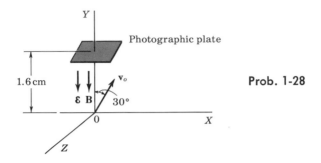

Prob. 1-28

1-29   An electron is injected with an initial velocity $v_{ox} = 4 \times 10^6$ m/sec halfway between two large parallel plates 0.5 cm apart. The XZ plane is parallel to the plates. There is a voltage of 200 V impressed between the plates, and a magnetic field of 10 mWb/m² perpendicular to the plates, directed from the positive to the negative plate.

    a. Where does the electron strike the positive plate?

    b. With what velocity components does the electron strike?

1-30   A positive hydrogen ion enters a region containing parallel electric and magnetic fields in a direction perpendicular to the lines of force. The electric field strength is 10^4 V/m, and the magnetic field strength is 0.1 Wb/m². How far along the direction of the fields will the ion travel during the second revolution of its helical path?

1-31   Given a uniform electric field of 10^4 V/m parallel to and in the same direction as a uniform magnetic field of B Wb/m²; 300-V electrons enter the region where these fields exist at an angle of 60° with the direction of the fields. If the electron reverses its direction of travel along the lines of force at the end of the first revolution of its helical path, what must be the strength of the magnetic field?

1-32   In Fig. 1-14 what must be the relationship between $\mathcal{E}$, B, φ, v_o if the electron is to return to the origin?

1-33   Given a uniform electric field of 2×10^4 V/m and a uniform magnetic field of 0.03 Wb/m² parallel to each other and in the same direction. Into this region are

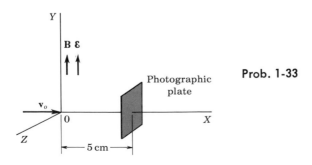

Prob. 1-33

released 150-eV hydrogen ions in a direction normal to the fields. A photographic plate is placed normal to the initial direction of the ions at a distance of 5.0 cm from the gun, as shown in the figure.

a. How long after leaving the gun will the ions hit the plate?

b. What are the coordinates of the point at which the photographic plate is exposed?

c. Repeat the problem for the case where the photographic plate is perpendicular to the Y axis and 5.0 cm from the origin (instead of perpendicular to the X axis).

d. Repeat the problem for the case where the photographic plate is perpendicular to the Z axis and 5.0 cm from the origin.

1-34 An electron starts from rest at the center of the negative plate of a parallel-plate capacitor across which is a voltage of 100 V. Parallel to the plates is a constant magnetic field of 1.68 mWb/m².

a. If the distance between the plates is 1 cm, how far from the center does the electron strike the positive plate?

b. How long will it take the electron to reach the positive plate?

1-35 An electron is released at the point O with a velocity v_o parallel to the plates of a parallel-plate capacitor. The distance between the plates is 1 cm, and the applied potential is 100 V.

a. What magnitude and direction of magnetic field will cause the electron to move in the cycloidal path indicated? Note that O is midway between the plates and that the cusps are on the negative plate.

b. What must be the value of v_o in order that this path be followed?

Prob. 1-35

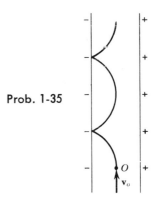

1-36 Consider the configuration of perpendicular electric and magnetic fields shown in the figure. An ion gun fires 100-eV hydrogen ions along the Y axis as shown. $B = 0.05$ Wb/m², and $\mathcal{E} = 5 \times 10^3$ V/m.

a. What are the coordinates of the point at which the photographic plate is exposed?

b. Repeat the problem for the case where the photographic plate is perpendicular to the X axis (and at a distance of 14 cm from the origin) instead of perpendicular to the Y axis.

c. Repeat the problem for the case where the photographic plate is perpendicular to the negative Z axis and at a distance of 14 cm from the origin.

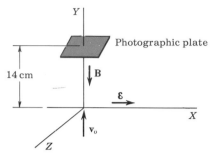

Prob. 1-36

Magnetic field **B** perpendicular to paper

Prob. 1-37

1-37 An apparatus for verifying the relativistic variation of mass with velocity [Eq. (1-27)] is shown in the sketch. The electronic source S of high-velocity electrons is situated between the two very closely spaced capacitor plates CC'. The entire apparatus (the source, the capacitor plates, and the photographic plate PP') is subjected to a transverse magnetic field of intensity B Wb/m². Show that if the electric field intensity between the plates is $\mathcal{E}$ V/m, only those electrons having a speed $v = \mathcal{E}/B$ will leave the region between the plates. Show that for the electrons with this particular speed the ratio of charge to mass (in mks units) is

$$\frac{e}{m} = \frac{\mathcal{E}}{B^2 R}$$

where the radius of the circular path R is given by $R = (L^2 + D^2)/2D$.

By changing either B or $\mathcal{E}$, a new value of v and the corresponding value of e/m are obtained, etc.

1-38 An electron starts at rest in perpendicular electric and magnetic fields. Show that the speed at any instant is given by

$$v = 2u \sin \frac{\theta}{2}$$

and that the distance d traveled *along the cycloidal path* is

$$d = 4Q \left(1 - \cos \frac{\theta}{2} \right)$$

The symbols have the meaning given in Sec. 1-17.

1-39 In Sec. 1-17 the equations of motion in perpendicular electric and magnetic fields are considered, the initial velocities v_{ox} and v_{oz} being taken as zero. Show, by direct integration of Eqs. (1-54), that if arbitrary initial velocities are assumed, the position of the electron at any time t is given by the equations

$$x = \frac{v_{ox}}{\omega} \sin \omega t + \left(\frac{u}{\omega} - \frac{v_{oz}}{\omega} \right) (1 - \cos \omega t)$$

$$y = v_{oy} t$$

$$z = \frac{v_{ox}}{\omega} (1 - \cos \omega t) - \left(\frac{u}{\omega} - \frac{v_{oz}}{\omega} \right) \sin \omega t + ut$$

1-40 A uniform magnetic field **B** exists parallel to the Y axis. A uniform electric field exists parallel to the XY plane and has components $\mathcal{E}_x$ and $\mathcal{E}_y$. An electron is injected parallel to the Z axis with an initial speed v_{oz}.

  a. What must be the value of v_{oz} in order that the electron remain forever in the YZ plane?

  b. What are the Y and Z coordinates of the electron at any time t if v_{oz} is chosen as in part *a*?

  c. What is the resultant path?

1-41 An electron starts at rest at the origin of the field configuration shown. The plane determined by **B** and $\mathcal{E}$ is chosen as the XY plane. Describe the motion of the particle.

Prob. 1-41

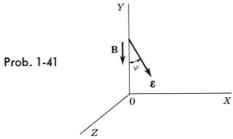

1-42 The fields in Prob. 1-41 have the following values:

$$\mathcal{E} = 5 \text{ kV/m} \qquad B = 1 \text{ mWb/m}^2 \qquad \varphi = 20°$$

If an electron is released with zero velocity at the origin, where will it expose a photographic plate which is perpendicular to the Z axis at a distance of 8.00 cm from the origin?

1-43 A uniform magnetic field of **B** Wb/m² exists in the Y direction, and a uniform electric field of 10^4 V/m makes an angle of 60° with **B** and lies in the XY plane as indicated. A 400-eV electron starts at the origin, moving up to the Y axis.

  a. Describe clearly the exact motion of the electron, including a sketch of the path.

  b. Calculate the value (or values) of B which will cause the electron to return to the XZ plane at some point along the Z axis.

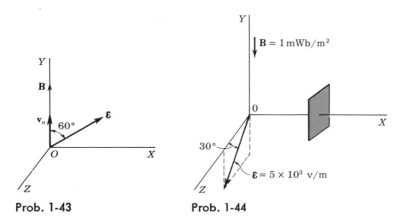

Prob. 1-43   Prob. 1-44

1-44 An electron which was at rest at the origin at time $t = 0$ strikes the photographic plate at time $t = 5$ nsec. Find the x, y, and z coordinates of the point where it hits the plate.   (In the figure, $\boldsymbol{\varepsilon}$ is parallel to the YZ plane, $\mathbf{B}$ is parallel to the negative Y axis, and the plate is perpendicular to the X axis.)

1-45   Uniform electric and magnetic fields of 10^5 V/m and 10 mWb/m², respectively, are inclined at an angle of 30° with respect to each other.   If an electron is released with zero initial velocity, how far from its initial position will it be at the end of 1 nsec?

1-46   a. If the potential at any point in space is $V(x, y, z)$, write down the differential equations of motion of an electron in this field.

b. If the magnetic field components $B_x(x, y, z)$, $B_y(x, y, z)$, and $B_z(x, y, z)$ are added to the electric field in part a, write the modified equations.

1-47   The magnetic field strength is 0.9 Wb/m² in a certain cyclotron.   Light hydrogen ions (protons) are used.

a. What must be the frequency of the oscillator supplying the power to the dees?

b. If each passage of the ions across the accelerating gap increases the energy of the ion by 60,000 V, how long does it take for the ion introduced at the center of the spiral to emerge at the rim of the dee with an energy of 6 Mev?

c. Calculate the radius of the last semicircle before emergence.

1-48   Protons are accelerated in a small cyclotron.   The magnetic field strength is 1.3 Wb/m², and the radius of the last semicircle is 0.5 m.

a. What must be the frequency of the oscillator supplying the power to the dees?

b. What is the final energy acquired by the proton?

c. If the total transit time of the proton is 3.3 μsec, how much energy is imparted to the particle in each passage from one dee to the other?

CHAPTER 2

2-1   For the hydrogen atom show that

a. The possible radii in meters are given by

$$r = \frac{h^2 \epsilon_o n^2}{\pi m e^2}$$

where n is any integer but not zero.   For the ground state ($n = 1$) show that the radius is 0.53 Å.

b. The energy levels in joules are given by

$$W_n = -\frac{me^4}{8h^2\epsilon_o^2}\frac{1}{n^2}$$

c. The reciprocal of the wavelength (called the *wave number*) of the spectral lines is given in waves per meter by

$$\frac{1}{\lambda} = R\left(\frac{1}{n_2^2} - \frac{1}{n_1^2}\right)$$

where n_1 and n_2 are integers, with n_1 greater than n_2, and $R = me^4/8\epsilon_o^2h^3c = 1.10 \times 10^7$ m⁻¹ is called the *Rydberg constant*.

If $n_2 = 1$, this formula gives a series of lines in the ultraviolet, called the *Lyman series*.   If $n_2 = 2$, the formula gives a series of lines in the visible, called the *Balmer series.* Similarly, the series for $n_2 = 3$ is called the *Paschen series.* These predicted lines are observed in the hydrogen spectrum.

2-2 Show that Eq. (2-7) follows from Eq. (2-4).

2-3 Show that the time for one revolution of the electron in the hydrogen atom in a circular path about the nucleus is

$$T = \frac{m^{\frac{1}{2}}e^2}{4\sqrt{2}\,\epsilon_o(-W)^{\frac{3}{2}}}$$

where the symbols are as defined in Sec. 2-1.

2-4 A photon of wavelength 1,400 Å is absorbed by cold mercury vapor, and two other photons are emitted. If one of these is the 1,850-Å line, what is the wavelength of the second photon?

2-5 Cold mercury vapor is bombarded with radiation, and as a result the fluorescent lines 2,537 and 4,078 Å appear. What wavelength must have been present in the bombarding radiation?

2-6 The six lowest energy levels of hydrogen are 0, 10.19, 12.07, 12.73, 13.04, and 13.20 eV. If cold hydrogen vapor absorbs the ultraviolet 972-Å line, what possible fluorescent lines may appear?

2-7 The seven lowest energy levels of sodium vapor are 0, 2.10, 3.19, 3.60, 3.75, 4.10, and 4.26 eV. A photon of wavelength 3,300 Å is absorbed by an atom of the vapor, and three other photons are emitted.

a. If one of these is the 11,380-Å line, what are the wavelengths of the other two photons?

b. Between what energy states do the transitions take place in order to produce these lines?

2-8 What might happen if cold mercury vapor is bombarded with (*a*) one 5.00-eV photon, (*b*) one 5.00-eV electron, (*c*) one 5.46-eV photon?

2-9 *a.* With what speed must an electron be traveling in a sodium-vapor lamp in order to excite the yellow line whose wavelength is 5,893 Å?

b. Could electrons with this speed excite the 2,537-Å line of Hg?

2-10 *a.* What is the minimum speed with which an electron must be traveling in order that a collision between it and an unexcited neon atom may result in ionization of this atom? The ionization potential of neon is 21.5 V.

b. What is the minimum frequency that a photon can have and still be able to cause photoionization of a neon atom?

2-11 An x-ray tube is essentially a high-voltage diode. The electrons from the hot filament are accelerated by the plate supply voltage so that they fall upon the anode with considerable energy. They are thus able to effect transitions among the tightly bound electrons of the atoms in the solid of which the target (the anode) is constructed.

a. What is the minimum voltage that must be applied across the tube in order to produce x-rays having a wavelength of 0.5 Å?

b. What is the minimum wavelength in the spectrum of an x-ray tube across which is maintained 60 kV?

2-12 An electron, after falling through a potential of 10 V, collides with a mercury atom that is in its lowest metastable state. As a result of the impact, the atom is elevated to its 7.73-eV level. What is the energy in joules of the impinging electron after the collision? Assume that the kinetic energy of the atom is unaffected by the collision.

2-13 Argon resonance radiation corresponding to an energy of 11.6 eV falls upon sodium vapor. If a photon ionizes an unexcited sodium atom, with what speed is the electron ejected?   The ionization potential of sodium is 5.12 eV.

2-14 A radio transmitter radiates 1,000 W at a frequency of 10 MHz.

a. What is the energy of each radiated quantum in electron volts?

b. How many quanta are emitted per second?

c. How many quanta are emitted in each period of oscillation of the electromagnetic field?

d. If each quantum acts as a particle, what is its momentum?

2-15 What is the wavelength of (*a*) a mass of 1 kg moving with a speed of 1 m/sec, (*b*) an electron which has been accelerated from rest through a potential difference of 10 V?

2-16 Classical physics is valid as long as the physical dimensions of the system are much larger than the De Broglie wavelength.   Determine whether the particle is classical in each of the following cases:

a. An electron in a vacuum tube (plate-cathode potential = 300 V).

b. An electron in the electron beam of a cathode-ray tube (anode-cathode voltage = 25 kV).

c. The electron in a hydrogen atom.

2-17 The Schrödinger equation must be solved subject to the following restrictions:

a. The wave function Ψ must be single-valued and continuous.

b. The first spatial derivatives of Ψ must be continuous.

c. The integral of $|\Psi|^2$ over all space must equal unity.

d. Ψ must be finite everywhere.

Give a physical explanation for each of these conditions.   HINT: For *b*, refer to the Schrödinger equation.

2-18 An electron with a total energy W moves in a one-dimensional region 1, where the potential energy may be taken as zero, $U = 0$ for $x < 0$.   At $x = 0$ there is a potential-energy barrier of height $U_0 > W$, and as indicated in the figure, the potential energy remains constant in region 2 for $x > 0$.

a. Verify that the solution of the Schrödinger equation in region 1 is

$$\Psi_1 = C \sin ax + D \cos ax$$

and in region 2 is

$$\Psi_2 = A \epsilon^{-x/2d_o} + B \epsilon^{+x/2d_o}$$

where a and d_o are real numbers.   Find a and d_o.

b. Using the constraints on Ψ given in Prob. 2-17, evaluate B, C, and D in terms of A.

c. What is the physical meaning of the fact that $|\Psi_2| > 0$?

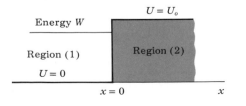

Prob. 2-18

CHAPTER 3

3-1 Prove that the concentration n of free electrons per cubic meter of a metal is given by

$$n = \frac{d\nu}{AM} = \frac{A_o d\nu \times 10^3}{A}$$

where d = density, kg/m^3
     ν = valence, free electrons per atom
     A = atomic weight
     M = weight of atom of unit atomic weight, kg (Appendix A)
     A_o = Avogadro's number, molecules/mole

3-2 Compute the conductivity of copper for which $\mu = 34.8$ cm^2/V-sec and $d = 8.9$ g/cm^3. Use the result of Prob. 3-1.

3-3 Compute the mobility of the free electrons in aluminum for which the density is 2.70 g/cm^3 and the resistivity is 3.44×10^{-6} Ω-cm. Assume that aluminum has three valence electrons per atom. Use the result of Prob. 3-1.

3-4 The resistance of No. 18 copper wire (diameter = 1.03 mm) is 6.51 Ω per 1,000 ft. The concentration of free electrons in copper is 8.4×10^{28} electrons/m^3. If the current is 2 A, find the (a) drift velocity, (b) mobility, (c) conductivity.

3-5 A diode consists of a plane emitter and a plane-parallel anode separated by a distance of 0.5 cm. The anode is maintained at a potential of 10 V negative with respect to the cathode.

a. If an electron leaves the emitter with a speed of 10^6 m/sec and is directed toward the anode, at what distance from the cathode will it intersect the potential-energy barrier?

b. With what speed must the electron leave the emitter in order to be able to reach the anode?

3-6 A particle when displaced from its equilibrium position is subject to a linear restoring force $f = -kx$, where x is the displacement measured from the equilibrium position. Show by the energy method that the particle will execute periodic vibrations with a maximum displacement which is proportional to the square root of the total energy of the particle.

3-7 A particle of mass m is projected vertically upward in the earth's gravitational field with a speed v_o.

a. Show by the energy method that this particle will reverse its direction at the height of $v_o^2/2g$, where g is the acceleration of gravity.

b. Show that the point of reversal corresponds to a "collision" with the potential-energy barrier.

3-8 A triode consists of plane-parallel elements. The grid is located 0.2 cm, and the anode is 1.0 cm, from the cathode. The grid is maintained at a potential of -1.0 V, and the plate at a potential of 100 V, with respect to the cathode. Assume that the potential varies linearly from the cathode to the grid and also linearly from the grid to the plate. Assume that the grid offers no mechanical hindrance to the flow of electrons.

a. If the electron leaving the cathode surface in the perpendicular direction collides with the potential-energy barrier after it has traveled a distance of 0.05 cm, with what energy was it emitted?

b. With what energy must it leave the cathode in order to be able to reach the anode?

The foregoing assumptions are not strictly valid in a practical triode.

3-9 a. If the cathode and plate of Prob. 3-8 are maintained at zero potential and if the potential of the grid is 4 V (positive), will the electron collide with a potential-energy barrier at any point of its path if its initial velocity is zero?

b. How long will it take the particle to reach the anode?

c. With what velocity will the electron strike the plate?

3-10 Consider the following model of an atom: The nucleus consists of a positive point charge Ze, where Z is the atomic number and e is the numerical value of the charge of the electron. This is surrounded by Z electrons, of which $Z - 1$ may be considered to be located on the surface of an imaginary sphere of radius r_o.

a. If the potential at infinity is taken as zero, show that the potential-energy function of the remaining (valence) electron is given by

$$4\pi\epsilon_o U = -\frac{e^2}{r} \qquad \text{if } r > r_o$$

$$4\pi\epsilon_o U = -\frac{Ze^2}{r} + (Z - 1)\frac{e^2}{r_o} \qquad \text{if } r < r_o$$

In the equations above, r is expressed in meters, e in coulombs, U in joules, and ϵ_0 is the permittivity of free space in the mks rationalized system.

b. Consider three such atoms in a row. The first is separated from the second by a distance of $4r_o$, and the second is separated from the third by the same amount. Assuming that sodium atoms ($Z = 11$) are under consideration, plot to scale the potential energy of the valence electron. Make the transformations

$$y = \frac{4\pi\epsilon_o U r_o}{e^2} \qquad \text{and} \qquad x = \frac{r}{r_o}$$

and plot y versus x instead of U versus r.

3-11 How many electrons per cubic meter in metallic tungsten have energies between 8.5 and 8.6 eV (a) at 0°K, (b) at 2500°K?

3-12 a. Calculate the maximum energy of the free electrons in metallic aluminum at absolute zero. Assume that there are three free electrons per atom. The specific gravity of aluminum is 2.7.

b. Repeat part a for the electrons in metallic silver. The specific gravity of silver is 10.5. Assume that there is one free electron per atom.

3-13 a. Show that the average energy E_{av} of the electrons in a metal is given by

$$E_{av} = \frac{\int E \, dn_E}{\int dn_E}$$

b. Prove that the average energy at absolute zero is $3E_F/5$.

3-14 If the emission from a certain cathode is 10,000 times as great at 2000° as at 1500°K, what is the work function of this surface?

3-15 a. If the temperature of a tungsten filament is raised from 2300 to 2320°K, by what percentage will the emission change?

b. To what temperature must the filament be raised in order to double its emission at 2300°K?

3-16 *a.* Draw the potential-energy diagram of two metals in contact (Fig. 3-15), assuming that the barriers at the two surfaces *A* and *B* are vertical lines and that metal 1 has a lower work function than metal 2.

b. From the diagram in part *a* verify Eq. (3-32).

3-17 If 10 percent of the thermionic-emission current is collected (under space-charge-free conditions), what must be the retarding voltage at the surface of the metal? The filament temperature is 2000°K.

3-18 What fraction of the thermionic current will be obtained with zero applied voltage between the cathode and anode of a diode? The work function of the cathode is 4.50 V, and the work function of the anode is 4.75 V. The cathode temperature is 2000°K.

3-19 A plane cathode having a work function of 3.00 V is connected directly to a parallel-plane anode whose work function is 5.00 V. The distance between anode and cathode is 2.00 cm. If an electron leaves the cathode with a normal-to-the-surface velocity of 5.93×10^5 m/sec, how close to the anode will it come?

3-20 A diode has an oxide-coated cathode operating at a temperature of 1000°K. With zero plate voltage the anode current is essentially zero, indicating that the contact potential is high enough to keep most of the electrons from reaching the plate. The applied voltage is increased so that a small current is drawn. Show that there is a tenfold increase in current for every 0.2-V increase in voltage.

3-21 A diode with plane-parallel electrodes is operated at a temperature of 1500°K. The filament is made of tungsten, the area being such that a saturation current of 10 μA is obtained. The contact difference of potential between cathode and anode is 0.5 V, with the cathode at the higher potential.

a. What current is obtained with zero applied voltage?

b. What applied voltage will yield a current of 1 μA?

c. What fraction of the electrons emitted from this filament can move against an *applied retarding* field of 1 V?

3-22 What accelerating field must be applied to the surface of a tungsten emitter operating at 2500°K in order to increase the zero-field thermionic emission by 1 percent?

3-23 Indicate by letter which of the following statements are true:

a. The work function of a metal is always less than the potential barrier at the surface of a metal.

b. The potential barrier at the surface of a metal is a solid hill made up of the material of the metal.

c. The ionic structure of a metal shows that the inside of the metal is not an equipotential volume.

d. At absolute zero the electrons in a metal all have zero energy.

e. The energy method of analyzing the motion of a particle can be applied to uncharged as well as to charged particles.

f. The ionic structure of a metal shows that the surface of a metal is not at a specific location.

g. For an electron to escape from a metal, the potential barrier at the surface of the metal must first be broken down.

h. The distribution function for the electrons in a metal shows how many electrons are close to a nucleus and how many are far away.

i. The number of secondary electrons which leave a metal is always greater than the number of primary electrons striking the metal surface.

3-24 Indicate by letter which of the following statements are true:

a. The potential energy as a function of distance along a row of ions *inside* a metal varies very rapidly in the immediate neighborhood of an ion but is almost constant everywhere else inside the metal.

b. The potential-energy barrier at the surface of a metal *cannot* be explained on the basis of the modern crystal-structure picture of a metal, but it can be explained on the basis of classical electrostatics (image forces).

c. In order to remove any one of the free electrons from a metal, it is necessary only to give this electron an amount of energy equal to the work function of the metal.

d. The symbol E_F used in the energy distribution function represents the maximum number of free electrons per cubic meter of metal at absolute zero.

e. The area under the energy distribution curve represents the total number of free electrons per cubic meter of metal at any temperature.

f. The Dushman equation of thermionic emission gives the current that is obtained from a heated cathode as a function of applied plate voltage.

CHAPTER 4

4-1 The saturation current from a certain tungsten filament operated at 1840°K is 143 μA. What would be the emission from a thoriated-tungsten filament of the same area operating at the same temperature?

4-2 The radiated power density necessary to maintain an oxide-coated filament at 1100°K is found to be 5.80×10^4 W/m². Assume that the heat loss due to conduction is 10 percent of the radiation loss. Calculate the total emission current and the cathode efficiency in milliamperes per watt of the cathode. Take $E_W = 1.0$ eV, $A_o = 100$ A/(m²)(°K²), and $S = 1.8$ cm².

4-3 A triode is provided with a ribbon filament of cross section 0.014 by 0.004 in., and it is 4.5 in. long. Calculate the total cathode emission expected from this oxide-coated cathode when operated at 1200°K. Assume the following values for the thermionic-emission constants: $E_W = 1.0$ eV, and $A_o = 100$ A/(m²)(°K²).

4-4 A tungsten cathode is heated to a temperature of 2300°K. What must the retarding voltage be in order to limit the current density to 10^{-2} A/m²? Neglect contact potential.

4-5 Given a diode with zero voltage applied between cathode and anode. The work function of the anode is 4.75 eV. The cathode temperature is 2000°K. The plate current flowing is 23.5 percent of the thermionic current. Presuming that space-charge effects can be neglected, what is the work function of the cathode?

4-6 Prove that the following relationships are valid for a plane-parallel diode operating under space-charge-limited conditions:

$$V = V_P \left(\frac{x}{d}\right)^{\frac{4}{3}}$$

$$v = v_P \left(\frac{x}{d}\right)^{\frac{2}{3}}$$

$$\rho = \rho_P \left(\frac{x}{d}\right)^{-\frac{2}{3}}$$

where $v_P = (2eV_P/m)^{\frac{1}{2}}$ is the speed with which the electrons strike the plate, and $\rho_P = V_P/(81\pi d^2 \times 10^9)$ is the charge density at the plate. The other symbols have the meanings assigned in the text.

4-7 Show that the transit time of an electron from the cathode to the anode of a plane-parallel space-charge-limited diode is $T = 3d/v_P$, where d is the cathode-anode spacing, and $v_P = (2eV_P/m)^{\frac{1}{2}}$ is the speed with which the electron strikes the plate. The electron is assumed to leave the cathode with zero initial velocity.

Show that, if the space charge is negligibly small, the transit time is $T = 2d/v_P$. This is only two-thirds of the time taken under space-charge conditions.

4-8 Show that the tangent to the potential distribution curve at the anode of a plane-parallel space-charge-limited diode passes through the zero of potential at one-fourth the cathode-plate distance.

4-9 A diode having plane-parallel electrodes is operating under space-charge conditions. The plate current is 10 mA at 100 V plate voltage.

a. What must be the plate voltage in order that the plate current be doubled?

b. What current will be obtained if the voltage is doubled ($V_P = 200$ V)?

c. If another diode is constructed having half the cathode-anode spacing and twice the electrode area, what current will be obtained if a potential of 100 V is applied?

4-10 A plane-parallel diode having a 2-cm spacing is operated under space-charge conditions. The plate voltage is 100 V. What is the space-charge density at a point halfway between the cathode and anode?

4-11 In a plane-parallel vacuum diode the applied voltage is 50 V. Under the assumption of zero-emission velocity the minimum cathode temperature for which the field at the cathode is zero is 1000°K. If the cathode is heated to 1200°K, what is the maximum value of the plate voltage for which the field at the cathode is zero? Assume that $E_W/k = 12,000$°K.

4-12 The space-charge-limited current of a certain plane-parallel type of vacuum diode is 20 mA at a plate voltage of 100 V. The temperature-limited current of the same type is 20 mA at a filament temperature of 2300°K.

Two identical diodes of this type are connected in series across a dc supply with the proper polarity for both tubes to conduct. Find the plate current through the tubes and the voltage across each tube if the supply voltage is

a. 50 V and if both tubes are operated at the same filament temperature of 2300°K.

b. 300 V and if both tubes are operated at the same filament temperature of 2300°K.

c. 300 V and if one tube is operated at a filament temperature of 2300°K while the other is operated at a filament temperature of 3000°K.

4-13 *a.* Show that a plot of log I_P versus log V_P is a straight line for a space-charge-limited diode, and find the slope of this line.

b. Determine whether or not the 5Y3-GT diode whose volt-ampere characteristic is plotted in Appendix D satisfies Eq. (4-12). Determine the exponent of V_P in Eq. (4-12) for this diode.

4-14 *a.* A plane-parallel diode with a cathode-anode spacing of 1 cm operates under space-charge-limited conditions at a plate voltage of 100 V. How much power per square meter must the plate dissipate?

b. If the voltage is increased to 400 V, by what factor is the dissipation multiplied?

4-15 In a certain space-charge-limited diode a current of 5 mA results from the application of 100 V. What is the maximum plate voltage that can be applied before the plate dissipation exceeds 16 W?

4-16 In a plane-parallel diode all the dimensions are enlarged by the same factor. If the voltage remains constant, show that the space-charge current is unchanged.

4-17 Evaluate the static resistance R and the dynamic plate resistance $R_f = r_p$ of the 5Y3-GT diode (Appendix D) at a plate voltage of 50 V.

4-18 (a) A 5Y3-GT tube in series with a 250-Ω load is excited from a 60-V dc source. What is the tube current? What is the tube voltage? Repeat the problem if the load is (b) 50 Ω, (c) zero, (d) infinity.

4-19 The 120-V dc mains are impressed across a 5Y3-GT diode in series with a resistor R. Find the tube current and voltage if R equals (a) 500 Ω, (b) 200 Ω, (c) zero, (d) infinity.

4-20 Plot (from zero to 100 V input) the dynamic characteristic of the 5Y3-GT diode for a 250-Ω load.

4-21 A plane-parallel diode operating under space-charge-limited conditions delivers a plate current of 100 mA at a plate voltage of 100 V.

a. What are $R = V_P/I_P$ and r_p at $V_P = 100$ V?

b. What are $R = V_P/I_P$ and r_p at 50 V?

CHAPTER 5

5-1 Consider intrinsic germanium at room temperature (300°K). By what percent does the conductivity increase per degree rise in temperature?

5-2 Repeat Prob. 5-1 for intrinsic silicon.

5-3 Evaluate n given by Eq. (5-8). HINT: Refer to a table of definite integrals.

5-4 Verify the expression for p in Eq. (5-14). HINT: Refer to a table of definite integrals.

5-5 If the effective mass of an electron is equal to twice the effective mass of a hole, find the distance (in electron volts) of the Fermi level in an intrinsic semiconductor from the center of the forbidden band at room temperature.

5-6 a. Verify the numerical values in Eqs. (5-20) and (5-21).

b. From Eq. (5-21) and the numerical values given in Table 5-1 evaluate $m_n m_p/m^2$.

5-7 (a) Prove that the resistivity of intrinsic germanium at 300°K is 45 Ω-cm. (b) If a donor-type impurity is added to the extent of 1 atom per 10^8 germanium atoms, prove that the resistivity drops to 3.7 Ω-cm.

5-8 (a) Find the resistivity of intrinsic silicon at 300°K. (b) If a donor-type impurity is added to the extent of 1 atom per 10^8 silicon atoms, find the resistivity.

5-9 a. Determine the concentration of free electrons and holes in a sample of germanium at 300°K which has a concentration of donor atoms equal to 2×10^{14} atoms/cm³ and a concentration of acceptor atoms equal to 3×10^{14} atoms/cm.³ Is this p- or n-type germanium? In other words, is the conductivity due primarily to holes or to electrons?

b. Repeat part a for equal donor and acceptor concentrations of 10^{15} atoms/cm³. Is this p- or n-type germanium?

c. Repeat part a for a temperature of 400°K, and show that the sample is essentially intrinsic.

5-10 Find the concentration of holes and of electrons in p-type germanium at 300°K if the conductivity is 100 $(\Omega\text{-cm})^{-1}$.

5-11 Repeat Prob. 5-10 for n-type silicon if the conductivity is 0.1 $(\Omega\text{-cm})^{-1}$.

5-12 A sample of germanium is doped to the extent of 10^{14} donor atoms/cm³ and 7×10^{13} acceptor atoms/cm³. At the temperature of the sample the resistivity of pure (intrinsic) germanium is 60 Ω-cm. If the applied electric field is 2 V/cm, find the total conduction current density.

5-13 *a.* In *n*-type germanium the donor concentration corresponds to 1 atom per 10^8 germanium atoms. Assume that the effective mass of the electron equals one-half the true mass. At room temperature, how far from the edge of the conduction band is the Fermi level? Is E_F above or below E_C?

b. Repeat part *a* if impurities are added in the ratio of 1 donor atom per 10^3 germanium atoms.

c. Under what circumstances will E_F coincide with E_C?

5-14 *a.* In *p*-type silicon the acceptor concentration corresponds to 1 atom per 10^8 silicon atoms. Assume that $m_p = 0.6m$. At room temperature, how far from the edge of the valence band is the Fermi level? Is E_F above or below E_V?

b. Repeat part *a* if impurities are added in the ratio of 1 acceptor atom per 5×10^3 silicon atoms.

c. Under what condition will E_F coincide with E_V?

5-15 In *n*-type silicon the donor concentration is 1 atom per 2×10^8 silicon atoms. Assume that the effective mass of the electron equals the true mass. At what temperature will the Fermi level coincide with the edge of the conduction band?

5-16 In *p*-type germanium at room temperature (300°K), for what doping concentration will the Fermi level coincide with the edge of the valence band? Assume $m_p = 0.4m$.

CHAPTER 6

6-1 *a.* Consider a *p-n* alloy-junction germanium diode with $N_D = 10^3 N_A$ and with N_A corresponding to 1 donor atom per 10^9 germanium atoms. Calculate the height E_o of the potential-energy barrier in electron volts at room temperature.

b. Repeat part *a* for a silicon *p-n* junction.

6-2 *a.* The resistivities of the two sides of an abrupt germanium diode are 2 Ω-cm (*p* side) and 1 Ω-cm (*n* side). Calculate the height E_o of the potential-energy barrier.

b. Repeat part *a* for a silicon *p-n* junction.

6-3 *a.* Sketch logarithmic and linear plots of carrier concentration vs. distance for an abrupt silicon junction if $N_D = 10^{15}$ atoms/cm³ and $N_A = 10^{16}$ atoms/cm³. Give numerical values for ordinates. Label the *n*, *p*, and depletion regions.

b. Sketch the space-charge electric field and potential as a function of distance for this case (Fig. 6-1).

6-4 Repeat Prob. 6-3 for an abrupt germanium junction.

6-5 Starting with Eq. (6-19) for I_{pn} and the corresponding expression for I_{np}, prove that the ratio of hole to electron current crossing a *p-n* junction is given by

$$\frac{I_{pn}(0)}{I_{np}(0)} = \frac{\sigma_p L_n}{\sigma_n L_p}$$

where σ_p (σ_n) = conductivity of *p* (*n*) side. Note that this ratio depends upon the ratio of the conductivities. For example, if the *p* side is much more heavily doped than the *n* side, the hole current will be much larger than the electron current crossing the junction.

6-6 Starting with Eq. (6-27), verify that the reverse saturation current is given by

$$I_o = A V_T \frac{b \sigma_i^2}{(1 + b)^2} \left(\frac{1}{L_p \sigma_n} + \frac{1}{L_n \sigma_p} \right)$$

where σ_n (σ_p) = conductivity of n (p) side

σ_i = conductivity of intrinsic material

$b = \mu_n/\mu_p$

6-7 Using the result of Prob. 6-6, find the reverse saturation current for a germanium p-n junction diode at room temperature, 300°K. The cross-sectional area is 4.0 mm², and

$$\sigma_p = 1.0 \ (\Omega\text{-cm})^{-1} \qquad \sigma_n = 0.1 \ (\Omega\text{-cm})^{-1} \qquad L_n = L_p = 0.15 \ \text{cm}$$

Other physical constants are given in Table 5-1.

6-8 Repeat Prob. 6-7 for a silicon p-n junction diode. Assume $L_n = L_p = 0.01$ cm and $\sigma_n = \sigma_p = 0.01 \ (\Omega\text{-cm})^{-1}$.

6-9 Find the ratio of the reverse saturation current in germanium to that in silicon, using the result of Prob. 6-6. Assume $L_n = L_p = 0.1$ cm and $\sigma_n = \sigma_p = 1.0$ $(\Omega\text{-cm})^{-1}$ for germanium, whereas the corresponding values are 0.01 cm and 0.01 $(\Omega\text{-cm})^{-1}$ for silicon. See also Table 5-1.

6-10 *a.* For what voltage will the reverse current in p-n junction germanium diode reach 90 percent of its saturation value at room temperature?

b. What is the ratio of the current for a forward bias of 0.05 V to the current for the same magnitude, reverse bias?

c. If the reverse saturation current is 10 μA, calculate the forward currents for voltages of 0.1, 0.2, and 0.3 V, respectively.

6-11 *a.* Calculate and plot the volt-ampere characteristics of an ideal p-n junction diode at room temperature. The reverse saturation current is 10 μA. Assume input voltages in the range from -0.2 to $+0.2$ V.

b. The diode has an ohmic resistance of 25 Ω. Plot the new volt-ampere diode characteristic, taking the ohmic drop into account. Use the same graph sheet and the same current range as in part *a.*

6-12 *a.* Evaluate η in Eq. (6-31) from the slope of the plot in Fig. 6-9 for $T = 25°C$. Draw the best-fit line over the current range 0.01 to 10 mA.

b. Repeat for $T = -55$ and 150°C.

6-13 A reverse-biasing voltage of 100 V is applied through a resistor R to a type 1N270 diode (Fig. 6-10a). The diode operates at 25°C. Determine the diode current and voltage for the cases $R = 10$ M, $R = 1$ M, and $R = 100$ K.

6-14 A resistor of 100 Ω is placed in series with a germanium diode whose reverse saturation current at 25°C is 5 μA. Make a semilog plot of the volt-ampere characteristic of the series combination over the range from 10 μA to 50 mA in the forward direction.

6-15 *a.* Use Eq. (6-35) to calculate the anticipated factor by which the reverse saturation current of a germanium diode is multiplied when the temperature is increased from 25 to 80°C.

b. Repeat part *a* for a silicon diode over the range 25 to 150°C.

6-16 It is predicted from Eq. (6-35) that, for germanium, the reverse saturation current should increase by 0.11 °C^{-1}. It is found experimentally in a particular diode that at a reverse voltage of 10 V, the reverse current is 5 μA and the temperature dependence is only 0.07 °C^{-1}. What is the leakage resistance shunting the diode?

6-17 A diode is mounted on a chassis in such a manner that, for each degree of temperature rise above ambient, 0.1 mW is thermally transferred from the diode to its surroundings. (The "thermal resistance" of the mechanical contact between the diode and its surroundings is 0.1 mW/°C.) The ambient temperature is 25°C. The diode temperature is not to be allowed to increase by more than 10°C above ambient. If the reverse saturation current is 5.0 μA at 25°C and increases at the rate 0.07 °C^{-1}, what is the maximum reverse-bias voltage which may be maintained across the diode?

6-18 *a.* Consider a diode biased in the forward direction at a fixed voltage V. Prove that the fractional change in current with respect to temperature is

$$\frac{1}{I}\frac{dI}{dT} = \frac{V_{GO} - V}{\eta T V_T}$$

b. Find the percentage change in current per degree centigrade for Ge at $V = 0.2$ V and for Si at $V = 0.6$ V.

6-19 A silicon diode operates at a forward voltage of 0.4 V. Calculate the factor by which the current will be multiplied when the temperature is increased from 25 to 150°C. Compare the result with the plot of Fig. 6-9.

6-20 An ideal germanium *p-n* junction diode has a reverse saturation current of 30 μA. At a temperature of 125°C find the dynamic resistance for a 0.2-V bias in (*a*) the forward direction, (*b*) the reverse direction.

6-21 Each diode is described by a linearized volt-ampere characteristic, with incremental resistance r and offset voltage V_γ. Diode *D1* is germanium with $V_\gamma = 0.2$ V and $r = 20$ Ω, whereas *D2* is silicon with $V_\gamma = 0.6$ V and $r = 15$ Ω. Find the diode currents if (*a*) $R = 10$ K, (*b*) $R = 1$ K.

Prob. 6-21

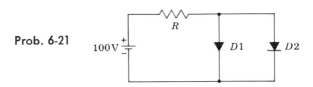

6-22 Reverse-biased diodes are frequently employed as electrically controllable variable capacitors. The transition capacitance of an abrupt junction diode is 20 pF at 5 V. Compute the decrease in capacitance for a 1.0-V increase in bias.

6-23 Prove that, for an alloy *p-n* junction (with $N_A \ll N_D$), the width W of the depletion layer is given by

$$W = \left(\frac{2\epsilon\mu_p V_o}{\sigma_p}\right)^{\frac{1}{2}}$$

where V_o is the contact junction potential.

6-24 *a.* Prove that, for an alloy silicon *p-n* junction (with $N_A \ll N_D$), the depletion-layer capacitance in picofarads per square centimeter is given by

$$C_T = 2.9 \times 10^{-4} \left(\frac{N_A}{V_B}\right)^{\frac{1}{2}}$$

b. If the resistivity of the *p* material is 3.5 Ω-cm, the barrier height V_o is 0.35 V, the applied reverse voltage is 5 V, and the cross-sectional area is circular of 40 mils diameter, find C_T.

6-25 Calculate the barrier capacitance of a germanium *p-n* junction whose area is 1 by 1 mm and whose space-charge thickness is 2×10^{-4} cm. The dielectric constant of germanium (relative to free space) is 16.

6-26 For an alloy junction for which N_A is not negligible compared with N_D, verify that Eq. (6-47) remains valid provided that W is interpreted as the total space-charge width and $1/N_A$ is replaced by $1/N_A + 1/N_D$.

6-27 The zero-voltage barrier height at an alloy germanium p-n junction is 0.2 V. The concentration N_A of acceptor atoms in the p side is much smaller than the concentration of donor atoms in the n material, and $N_A = 3 \times 10^{20}$ atoms/m^3. Calculate the width of the depletion layer for an applied reverse voltage of (a) 10 V, (b) 0.1 V, and (c) for a forward bias of 0.1 V. (d) If the cross-sectional area of the diode is 1 mm^2, evaluate the space-charge capacitance corresponding to the values of applied voltage in (a) and (b).

6-28 a. Consider a grown junction for which the uncovered charge density ρ varies linearly. If $\rho = ax$, prove that the barrier voltage V_o is given by

$$V_o = \frac{aW^3}{12\epsilon}$$

b. Verify that the barrier capacitance C_T is given by Eq. (6-49).

6-29 Given a forward-biased silicon diode with $I = 1$ mA. If the diffusion capacitance is $C_D = 1$ μF, what is the diffusion length L_p? Assume that the doping of the p side is much greater than that of the n side.

6-30 The derivation of Eq. (6-54) for the diffusion capacitance assumes that the p side is much more heavily doped than the n side, so that the current at the junction is entirely due to holes. Derive an expression for the total diffusion capacitance when this approximation is not made. Note that the total capacitive current is the sum of hole and electron capacitive currents.

6-31 a. The voltage impressed on a junction diode is $V = V_1 + V_m\epsilon^{j\omega t}$. This expression represents a dc voltage V_1 and a sinusoidal voltage of peak value V_m. Assume that $V_m \ll V_1$. The current may be expected to consist of a dc term plus an ac term. Hence assume that the concentration is given by an expression of the form

$$p_n - p_{no} = p_{no}(\epsilon^{V_1/V_T} - 1)\epsilon^{-x/L_p} + F(x)V_m\epsilon^{j\omega t}$$

Show that this form satisfies the equation of continuity (Sec. 5-9) and that $F(x)$ is given by

$$F(x) = K\epsilon^{-(1+j\omega\tau_p)^{\frac{1}{2}}x/L_p} = K \exp\left(-\sqrt{1+j\omega\tau_p}\,\frac{x}{L_p}\right)$$

b. At $x = 0$,

$$p_n - p_{no} = p_{no}\left(\exp\frac{V_1 + V_m\epsilon^{j\omega t}}{V_T} - 1\right)$$

Show that if $V_m/V_T \ll 1$,

$$p_n - p_{no} = p_{no}(\epsilon^{V_1/V_T} - 1) + p_{no}\frac{V_m}{V_T}\epsilon^{V_1/V_T}\epsilon^{j\omega t}$$

Comparing this expression with that given in part a, evaluate K.

c. Prove that the diffusion current at $x = 0$ is

$$I_{pn}(0) = I_1 + eD_pA\frac{p_{no}}{V_TL_p}\epsilon^{V_1/V_T}(1 + j\omega\tau_p)^{\frac{1}{2}}V_m\epsilon^{j\omega t}$$

where I_1 is the direct current corresponding to V_1.

d. If $\omega\tau_p \ll 1$, prove that

$$I_{pn}(0) = I_1 + g_p V_m \epsilon^{j\omega t} + j\omega C_{Dp} V_m \epsilon^{j\omega t}$$

where g_p is the zero-frequency conductance, and $C_{Dp} = (\tau_p/2)g_p$ is the diffusion capacitance for holes.

e. If $\omega\tau_p \gg 1$, prove that

$$I_{pn}(0) = I_1 + g_p \left(\frac{\omega\tau_v}{2}\right)^{\frac{1}{2}} V_m \epsilon^{j\omega t} + j\omega C_{Dp} V_m \epsilon^{j\omega t}$$

where $C_{Dp} = (\tau_p/2\omega)^{\frac{1}{2}}g_p$.

Note that the conductance, as well as the capacitance, varies with frequency.

6-32 **a.** Prove that the maximum electric field $\mathcal{E}_m$ at an alloy junction is given by

$$\mathcal{E}_m = \frac{2V_B}{W}$$

b. It is found that Zener breakdown occurs when $\mathcal{E}_m = 2 \times 10^7$ V/m $\equiv \mathcal{E}_Z$. Prove that Zener voltage V_z is given by

$$V_s = \frac{\epsilon\mathcal{E}_Z{}^2}{2eN_A}$$

Note that the Zener-breakdown voltage can be controlled by controlling the concentration of acceptor ions.

6-33 **a.** Zener breakdown occurs in germanium at a field intensity of 2×10^7 V/m. Prove that the breakdown voltage is $V_B = 51/\sigma_p$, where σ_p is the conductivity of the p material in $(\Omega\text{-cm})^{-1}$. Assume that $N_A \ll N_D$.

b. If the p material is essentially intrinsic, calculate V_Z.

c. For a doping of 1 part in 10^8 of p-type material, the resistivity drops to 3.7 Ω-cm. Calculate V_Z.

d. For what resistivity of the p-type material will $V_Z = 1$ V?

6-34 **a.** Two p-n germanium diodes are connected in series opposing. A 5-V battery is impressed upon this series arrangement. Find the voltage across each junction at room temperature. Assume that the magnitude of the Zener voltage is greater than 5 V.

Note that the result is independent of the reverse saturation current. Is it also independent of temperature?

HINT: Assume that reverse saturation current flows in the circuit, and then justify this assumption.

b. If the magnitude of the Zener voltage is 4.9 V, what will be the current in the circuit? The reverse saturation current is 5 μA.

Prob. 6-34

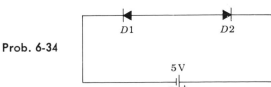

6-35 *a.* In the circuit of Prob. 6-34, the Zener breakdown voltage is 2.0 V. The reverse saturation current is 5 μA. If the diode resistance could be neglected, what would be the current?

b. If the ohmic resistance is 100 Ω, what is the current?

6-36 A *p-n* germanium junction diode at room temperature has a reverse saturation current of 10 μA, negligible ohmic resistance, and a Zener breakdown voltage of 100 V. A 1-K resistor is in series with this diode, and a 30-V battery is impressed across this combination. Find the current (*a*) if the diode is forward-biased, (*b*) if the battery is inserted into the circuit with the reverse polarity. (*c*) Repeat parts *a* and *b* if the Zener breakdown voltage is 10 V.

6-37 The Zener diode can be used to prevent overloading of sensitive meter movements without affecting meter linearity. The circuit shown represents a dc voltmeter which reads 20 V full scale. The meter resistance is 560 Ω, and $R_1 + R_2 = 99.5$ K. If the diode is a 16-V Zener, find R_1 and R_2 so that, when $V_i > 20$ V, the Zener diode conducts and the overload current is shunted away from the meter.

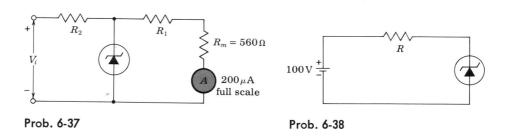

Prob. 6-37   **Prob. 6-38**

6-38 The breakdown diode is a 5.7-V reference diode. From the characteristics of Fig. 6-19, find the value of R for which the reference voltage will have a zero-temperature coefficient.

6-39 A series combination of a 15-V avalanche diode and a forward-biased silicon diode is to be used to construct a zero-temperature-coefficient voltage reference. The temperature coefficient of the silicon diode is -1.7 mV/°C. Express in percent per degree centigrade the required temperature coefficient of the Zener diode.

6-40 The saturation currents of the two diodes are 1 and 2 μA. The breakdown voltages of the diodes are the same and are equal to 100 V.

a. Calculate the current and voltage for each diode if $V = 90$ V and $V = 110$ V.

b. Repeat part *a* if each diode is shunted by a 10-M resistor.

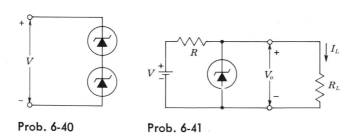

Prob. 6-40   **Prob. 6-41**

6-41　*a.* The avalanche diode regulates at 50 V over a range of diode current from 5 to 40 mA. The supply voltage $V = 200$ V. Calculate R to allow voltage regulation from a load current $I_L = 0$ up to I_{max}, the maximum possible value of I_L. What is I_{max}?

b. If R is set as in part a and the load current is set at $I_L = 25$ mA, what are the limits between which V may vary without loss of regulation in the circuit?

6-42　Consider a tunnel diode with $N_D = N_A$ and with the impurity concentration corresponding to 1 atom per 10^3 germanium atoms. At room temperature calculate (a) the height of the potential-energy barrier under open-circuit conditions (the contact potential energy), (b) the width of the space-charge region.

6-43　Repeat Prob. 6-42 if the semiconductor is silicon instead of germanium.

6-44　From Fig. 6-23, it is clear that the Fermi level in the n material must be at least equal to E_C in order for tunneling to take place. For a symmetrically doped tunnel diode calculate the minimum impurity concentration required if the material is (a) silicon, (b) germanium.

6-45　*a.* A tunnel diode has the idealized piecewise linear characteristic shown, with $I_P = 10I_V$, $V_V = 7V_P$, and $V_F = 8.5V_P$. Reproduce the characteristic on graph paper, and deduce, by graphical means, the resultant volt-ampere characteristic of two such diodes in series. HINT: The current is the same in the two diodes, whereas the composite voltage is the sum of the two individual tunnel-diode voltages. Note that the composite characteristic will display more than one peak and more than one valley.

b. Repeat part a if the diodes are placed in parallel.

Prob. 6-45

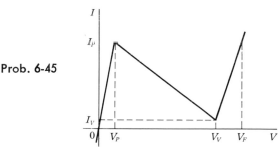

6-46　*a.* Two tunnel diodes have the idealized form given in Prob. 6-45. However, the diodes have different peak currents, I_{P1} and I_{P2}. Find graphically the composite volt-ampere characteristic which results if the diodes are placed in series. Assume $I_{P2} = 0.8I_{P1}$.

b. Generalize the results of part a if n diodes are operated in series.

6-47　Two tunnel diodes with characteristics as given in Prob. 6-45 are operated in series opposing. Find graphically the composite volt-ampere characteristic. Assume that in the reverse direction the characteristic continues, as shown, to be a straight line passing through the origin.

6-48　A resistance $R = 2V_V/I_P$ is placed in series with a tunnel diode whose volt-ampere characteristic is given in Prob. 6-45. Draw a plot of the volt-ampere characteristic of the combination.

6-49 The composite characteristic for the tunnel-diode pair shown is a plot of i (the resistor current) versus v_1. Note that $v_2 = 2V_S - v_1$.

a. Plot the composite curve if each tunnel diode has the volt-ampere characteristic given in Prob. 6-45, with $V_P = 0.1$ V, $I_P = 5$ mA, and $V_S = 0.4$ V.

b. Draw a load line on the composite characteristic, and find the current in each diode and the voltage across each diode.

c. Find V_S if the current in one tunnel diode is to be zero.

d. Repeat parts a and b if $V_S = 0.5$ V.

e. Repeat parts a and b if $V_S = 0.2$ V.

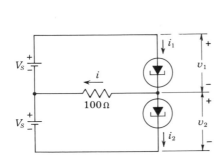

Prob. 6-49   Prob. 6-50

6-50 A germanium tunnel diode has the characteristic shown, with $I_P = 10$ mA, $I_V = 1.0$ mA, $V_P = 50$ mV, $V_V = 350$ mV, and $V_F = 475$ mV. A resistor R is placed in parallel with the tunnel diode, and this combination is called a *tunnel resistor*. Find the value of the resistance R so that the tunnel-resistor volt-ampere characteristic exhibits no negative-resistance region. Plot this composite characteristic.

CHAPTER 7

7-1 a. From the plate characteristics of the 6CG7 triode (Appendix D), obtain the transfer, or mutual, characteristics for $V_P = 100$, 200, and 300 V.

b. Obtain the constant-current characteristics of the 6CG7. Plot v_P versus v_G for $I_P = 6$, 12, and 18 mA.

7-2 a. From the plate characteristics of the 12AX7 triode (Appendix D), obtain the mutual, or transfer, characteristics for $V_P = 100$, 200, and 300 V.

b. Obtain the constant-current characteristics for the 12AX7. Plot v_P versus v_G for $I_P = 0.7$, 1.4, and 2.1 mA.

7-3 If the plate current in a triode can be represented by Eq. (7-1), show that r_p is proportional to $i_P{}^{-m}$ and that g_m is proportional to $i_P{}^m$, where $m = (n-1)/n$. Note that if the three-halves-power law is valid, then $m = \frac{1}{3}$.

7-4 The plate resistance of a triode is 10 K, and the amplification factor is 20. The tube is operated at the quiescent point $V_P = 250$ V, $V_G = -8$ V, and $I_P = 8$ mA.

a. To what value must the grid voltage be changed if the plate current is to change to 12 mA? The plate voltage is maintained at 250 V.

b. To what value must the plate voltage be changed if the plate current is to be brought back to its previous value? The grid voltage is maintained constant at the value found in part *a.*

7-5 *a.* Calculate μ, r_p, and g_m from the plate characteristics of the 6CG7 tube (Appendix D) at the quiescent point $V_P = 250$ V, $V_G = -8$ V.

b. Plot μ, r_p, and g_m for a 6CG7 as a function of I_P with $V_P = 250$ V.

c. Plot μ, r_p, and g_m for a 6CG7 as a function of V_G with $V_P = 250$ V.

7-6 Given the transfer characteristics of a triode. Explain clearly how to determine r_p, μ, and g_m at a specified quiescent point.

7-7 Show that if the triode plate characteristic can be approximated by straight lines, the equation of these lines is

$$i_P = \frac{1}{r_p}(\mu v_G + v_P - v_o)$$

where v_o is the voltage intercept at zero current of the $v_G = 0$ curve.

7-8 *a.* Starting with the definitions of g_m and r_p, show that if two identical tubes are connected in parallel, g_m is doubled and r_p is halved. Since $\mu = r_p g_m$, then μ remains unchanged.

b. If the two tubes are not identical, show that

$$g_m = g_{m1} + g_{m2}$$

that

$$\frac{1}{r_p} = \frac{1}{r_{p1}} + \frac{1}{r_{p2}}$$

and that

$$\mu = \frac{\mu_1 r_{p2} + \mu_2 r_{p1}}{r_{p1} + r_{p2}}$$

7-9 Plot i_P for a 6AU6 pentode (Fig. 7-12) as a function of v_{G1} at $V_P = 250$ V, $V_{G2} = 150$ V, and $V_{G3} = 0$ in the range -0.5 V $\leq v_{G1} \leq -4$ V.

7-10 Plot g_m for a 6AU6 as a function of v_{G1} at $V_P = 250$ V, $V_{G2} = 150$ V, $V_{G3} = 0$ in the range -0.5 V $\leq v_{G1} \leq -4$ V.

7-11 A 6AU6 pentode (Fig. 7-12) is operated at the quiescent point $V_{G1} = -2.5$ V, $V_{G2} = 150$ V, and $V_P = 200$ V.

a. What is the plate resistance r_p?

b. What is the transconductance g_m for an increase in plate current?

c. Repeat part *b* for a decrease in plate current.

d. Find the average value of g_m.

e. Find μ, using the results of parts *a* and *d*. Why can μ not be found directly from the plate characteristics?

7-12 A type 6AU6 pentode (Fig. 7-12) is operated from a 300-V supply with a bias of -2 V and $V_{G2} = 150$ V. The load resistance is 20 K.

a. What are the quiescent current and voltage values?

b. If the peak-to-peak signal voltage is 1 V, what is the peak-to-peak output swing?

7-13 An adjustable resistance R_L is connected in series with the plate of a 6CG7 triode and a plate supply of 250 V. The grid is maintained at -4 V with respect to the cathode. Determine by graphical methods, using the plate characteristics in Appendix D,

    a. The plate current, when R_L has values 0, 10, and 50 K.

    b. The plate voltage corresponding to the resistances in part *a.*

    c. The load resistance that will give a plate current of 10 mA.

    d. The voltage drop across R_L if the bias is changed to -8 V and if the load resistance is 10 K.

    7-14 A 12AX7 triode is operated at the quiescent point $V_P = 250$ V, $V_G = -2$ V. The plate characteristics of this tube are given in Appendix D.

    a. Calculate the plate supply voltage that must be used for the following values of load resistance: 50, 100, and 200 K.

    b. If the grid excitation is sinusoidal with a peak value of 2 V, find the maximum and minimum currents obtainable with each of the load resistances of part *a.*

    c. Plot the dynamic transfer characteristic for $R_L = 100$ K.

    7-15 From the plate characteristic of a 6L6 (Fig. 7-15), draw the transfer characteristics for a screen voltage of 250 V and the following values of plate voltage: $V_P = 100$, 200, and 300 V.

    7-16 A 6L6 tetrode (Fig. 7-15) is operated at the quiescent point $V_G = -15$ V, $V_P = 300$ V. Draw the dynamic curves for the following values of load resistance: 0.3, 1, and 3 K.

    7-17 A 6AU6 pentode (Fig. 7-12) is operated at the quiescent point $V_{G1} = -2.0$ V, $V_{G2} = 150$ V, and $V_P = 200$ V.

    a. Plot the static transfer characteristic.

    b. Plot the dynamic transfer characteristic for a load resistance of 20 K.

    7-18 Given a cathode follower with $V_{PP} = 250$ V, $V_{GG} = 0$ V, $V_{KK} = 0$ V, and $R_k = 100$ K; the tube is one section of a 12AX7. Find the input voltage v_i and the output voltage v_o for (*a*) cutoff, (*b*) zero grid-to-cathode voltage. (*c*) Calculate and plot v_o versus v_i for values between the extremes in parts *a* and *b*. Observe how linear this curve is. (*d*) Calculate the amplification.

    7-19 *a.* The supply V_{KK} is adjusted from zero to 150 V in 50-V steps. Calculate the output voltage V_o for each value of V_{KK}.

    b. Repeat part *a* if the grid-to-ground voltage is 50 V instead of zero.

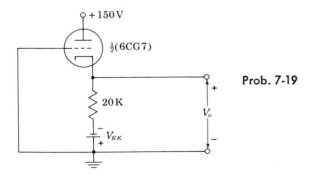

Prob. 7-19

    7-20 What is (*a*) v_i when the output is zero, (*b*) v_o if $v_i = -100$ V, (*c*) the grid-to-cathode voltage when $v_o = +50$ V?

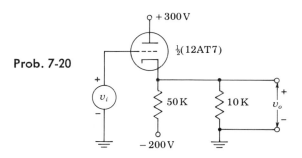

Prob. 7-20

7-21   Design an ac cathode follower using a 12AX7 tube and a 300-V supply using self-bias.   The circuit must operate quite linearly over an input voltage range of ± 75 V.

7-22   The reactance of C and the impedance of the generator are both negligible, $R_1 + R_2 = 10$ K.   The input signal v_i is symmetrical with respect to ground.   Find R_1 and R_2 if the tube is to handle, without distortion and without drawing grid current, the largest possible amplitude of signal.   What is the maximum signal the tube will handle in this case?

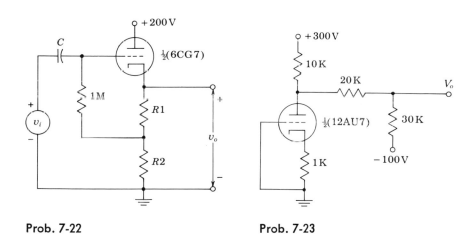

Prob. 7-22   Prob. 7-23

7-23   *a.* Find the quiescent plate current.   HINT: Apply Thévenin's theorem between the plate and ground to the elements external to the tube.

b. Find the quiescent output voltage V_o with respect to ground.

CHAPTER 8

8-1   The plate current in amperes of a certain triode is given by the equation

$$i_P = 4 \times 10^{-4}(v_G + 0.1v_P)^{1.5}$$

a. Find the plate resistance and the amplification factor when the plate voltage is 450 V and the grid bias is -20 V.

b. The plate load consists of a 10-K resistor and a 0.016-μF capacitor in parallel. What must be the value of the plate supply voltage in order that the tube operate under the conditions of part *a?*

c. If a 2-V rms 1,000-Hz signal is impressed on the amplifier, draw the equivalent circuit and calculate the output voltage across the load.

8-2   *a.* If v_i is a small input signal, derive an expression for the output-signal voltage v_{op} from the plate in the circuit shown.

b. Show that the Thévenin's equivalent circuit looking into the plate is a generator $-\mu v_i$ in series with an output impedance $R_o = r_p + (\mu + 1)R_k$.

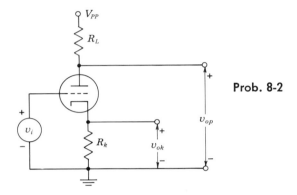

Prob. 8-2

8-3   *a.* If v_i is a small input signal, derive an expression for the output-signal voltage v_{ok} from the cathode in the circuit shown in Prob. 8-2.

b. Show that the Thévenin's equivalent circuit looking into the cathode is a generator $\mu v_i/(\mu + 1)$ in series with an output resistance $R_o = (r_p + R_L)/(\mu + 1)$.

8-4   If an input signal V_i is impressed between the grid and ground, find the amplification $A = V_o/V_i$.   The tube parameters are $\mu = 30$ and $r_p = 5$ K.

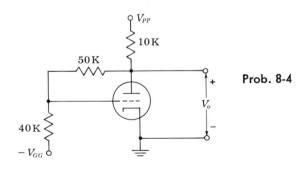

Prob. 8-4

8-5   If in Prob. 8-4 the signal is impressed in series with the 40-K resistor (instead of from grid to ground), find A.

8-6 A triode is operated as shown. Calculate the voltage gain $A_V = V_o/V_i$ at 1,000 Hz. The tube parameters are $\mu = 20$ and $r_p = 10$ K.

Prob. 8-6

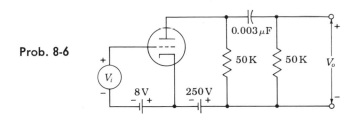

8-7 The triode shown has a plate resistance of 2.5 K and an amplification factor of 5. If the rms-reading voltmeter M has a resistance of 10 K and negligible reactance, what will it read? The input signal V_i is 12 V rms at a frequency of 1,000 Hz. The reactance of the capacitor C may be neglected in comparison with the voltmeter resistance.

Prob. 8-7

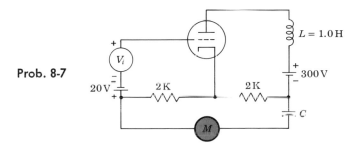

8-8 Find an expression for the signal voltage v_o across R_L. The two tubes are identical and have parameters μ, r_p, and g_m.

Prob. 8-8

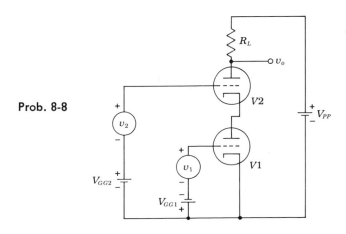

8-9   Each tube has a plate resistance $r_p = 10$ K and an amplification factor $\mu = 20$. Find the gain (a) v_o/v_1 if $v_2 = 0$, (b) v_o/v_2 if $v_1 = 0$.

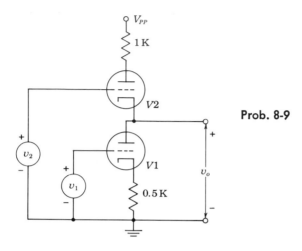

Prob. 8-9

8-10   a. Prove that the magnitude of the signal current is the same in both tubes provided that

$$r = \frac{1}{g_m} + \frac{2R_L}{\mu}$$

Neglect the reactance of the capacitors.

b. If r is chosen as in part a, prove that the voltage gain is given by

$$A = \frac{-\mu^2}{\mu + 1} \frac{R_L}{R_L + r_p/2}$$

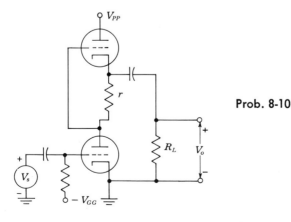

Prob. 8-10

8-11 *a.* If the positive supply voltage changes by $\Delta V_{PP} = v_a$, how much does the plate-to-ground voltage change?

b. How much does the cathode voltage change under the conditions in part *a*?

c. Repeat parts *a* and *b* if V_{PP} is constant but V_{KK} changes by $\Delta V_{KK} = v_k$.

d. If $R_L = 0$ so that the circuit is a cathode follower, show that, if $(\mu + 1)R_k \gg r_p$, the cathode voltage changes by $v_a/(\mu + 1)$ or $v_k[(r_p/R_k)/(\mu + 1)]$. What is the physical significance of these results?

Prob. 8-11

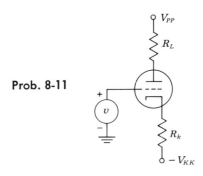

8-12 If $R_1 = R_2$ and the two tubes have identical parameters, verify that the voltage amplification $v_o/v_s = -\mu/2$ and the output impedance is $\frac{1}{2}[r_p + (\mu + 1)R]$.

Prob. 8-12

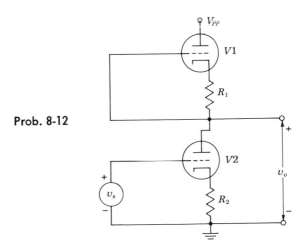

8-13 In the circuit of Prob. 8-12 the triodes are the two sections of a 12AX7 with $r_p = 62$ K and $\mu = 100$. If $v_s = 5$ V, $R_1 = 2$ K, and $R_2 = 1$ K, find the output voltage v_o and the output impedance.

8-14   The triodes are the two sections of a 5965 with $\mu = 47$ and $r_p = 7.2$ K.   If the plate supply ripple voltage is $v_a = 1$ mV, what is the ripple voltage at the plate of $V2$?

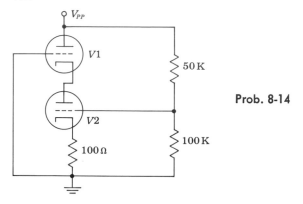

Prob. 8-14

8-15   *a.* The circuit shown is that of a dc vacuum-tube voltmeter.   The dc meter M measures the input voltage V.   The resistance r is used to adjust the range of the instrument.   Compute the value of r such that a 200-μA meter will read full scale when the input voltage is 10 V.   The triodes are the two sections of a 6CG7 for which $\mu = 20$ and $r_p = 7.7$ K.   First obtain an approximate solution by assuming that each triode is an ideal cathode follower.   Then use the exact equivalent circuit, looking into each cathode to obtain a more accurate value for r.

b. Consider that, because of aging, the g_m has increased by 10 percent, the r_p has decreased by 10 percent, and μ has remained constant.   Compute the correction (in percent) which must be applied to the instrument readings.   HINT: Since the correction is small, use the binomial expansion and neglect higher-order terms.

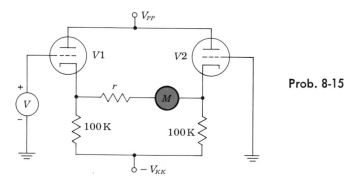

Prob. 8-15

8-16   Given a cathode follower with a 25-K cathode resistor using a 6CG7.   The input voltage swings over such a large range that the plate resistance varies between 24 and 8 K.   Assume that μ is constant over this range.   Prove that the gain remains constant to within about 3 percent.

8-17   In the cathode-coupled phase-inverter circuit of Fig. 8-16 solve for the current by drawing the equivalent circuit looking into the cathode of $V1$.   Then replace $V2$ by the Thévenin's equivalent, looking into its plate.   The cathode resistor R_k may be taken to have an arbitrarily large resistance.

8-18 In the circuit of Fig. 8-16, $R_L = r_p = 10$ K, $R_k = 1$ K, and $\mu = 19$. If the output is taken from the plate of $V2$, find (a) the voltage gain, (b) the output impedance.

8-19 a. Prove that in the phase-inverter circuit of Fig. 8-16 the signal current i_1 is always larger than i_2 in magnitude.

b. Prove that, if i_1 is to exceed i_2 by less than 10 percent,

$$R_k > 10 \frac{r_p + R_L}{\mu + 1}$$

8-20 a. In the phase-inverter circuit of Fig. 8-16, show that the voltage across R_k is

$$\frac{1}{2} \frac{\mu v}{\mu + 1} \frac{1}{1 + (r_p + R_L)/2(\mu + 1)R_k} \approx \frac{v}{2}$$

b. Assume that the amplification factors of the two sections are identical and constant but that the plate resistances r_{p1} and r_{p2} are functions of plate current. Show that the single-ended gain at the plate of $V1$, assuming that R_k is large compared with $(R_{L2} + r_{p2})/(\mu + 1)$, is

$$A \approx \frac{\mu R_{L1}}{R_{L1} + r_{p1} + r_{p2} + R_{L2}}$$

Explain why this circuit tends to keep amplitude distortion low.

8-21 a. A signal voltage v_a is applied in series with the plate of $V1$ in Fig. 8-16 and $v = 0$. Assuming that R_k is very large, prove that the output voltage v_{o2} is given by

$$v_{o2} = \frac{R_L v_a}{2(R_L + r_p)}$$

b. Prove that the output impedance Z_o at the plate of $V2$ is given by

$$Z_o = \frac{R_L(R_L + 2r_p)}{2(R_L + r_p)}$$

8-22 Calculate the signal current I in terms of the signal voltage V_1 and V_2. The parameters of each tube are $\mu = 70$ and $r_p = 44$ K.

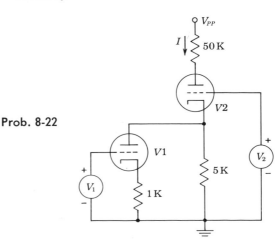

Prob. 8-22

8-23 *a.* If $\mu = 19$ and $r_p = 10$ K for each tube in Fig. 8-16 and $R_L = 30$ K and $R_k = 2$ K, find the voltage gain $A = v_{o2}/v$.

b. Find the output impedance.

8-24 Prove that the input impedance is $(r_p + R_L)/(\mu + 1)$ for the grounded-grid amplifier.

8-25 *a.* Given a cathode follower with the grid resistor R_g connected from grid to cathode. Prove that the input impedance Z_i is greater than R_g and is given by

$$Z_i = \frac{R_g}{1 - A}$$

where A is the voltage gain.

b. For a 12AU7 (Table 7-1) with $R_k = 20$ K and $R_g = 1$ M, find the value of Z_i.

8-26 Solve Prob. 8-8 by replacing $V2$ by its Thévenin's equivalent, looking into its cathode (Prob. 8-3*b*).

8-27 Solve Prob. 8-9 by replacing $V1$ by its Thévenin's equivalent, looking into its plate (Prob. 8-2*b*), and by replacing $V2$ by its Thévenin's equivalent, looking into its cathode (Prob. 8-3*b*).

8-28 In the cascode circuit of Fig. 8-18 the triodes are the two sections of a 12AT7, $R = 10$ K, $V' = 125$ V, $V_{PP} = 250$ V, and $V_{GG} = 2$ V. Find the quiescent current and the voltage at K_2.

8-29 *a.* Find the minimum value of V_{PP} so that the top tube does not draw grid current.

b. Plot i_P versus V_{PP} from this minimum value of V_{PP} to $V_{PP} = 500$ V, and show that this volt-ampere characteristic resembles that of a pentode.

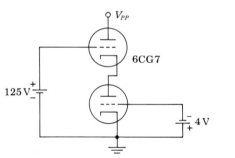

Prob. 8-29

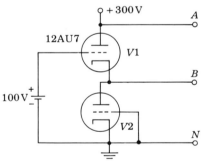

Prob. 8-30

8-30 (*a*) Find the quiescent current in the circuit shown. Find the effective impedance seen (*b*) between terminals A and N, (*c*) between B and N.

8-31 In the circuit shown, the triode is used as an adjustable impedance element by varying the dc bias, and thereby the g_m of the triode.

a. Assume that there is a generator V between the terminals A and B. Draw the equivalent circuit. Neglect interelectrode capacitances.

b. Show that the input admittance between A and B is

$$Y_i = Y_p + (1 + g_m R)Y_{CR}$$

where Y_p is the admittance corresponding to r_p, and Y_{CR} is the admittance corresponding to R and C in series.

c. If $g_m R \gg 1$, show that the effective input capacitance is

$$C_i = \frac{g_m \alpha}{\omega(1 + \alpha^2)}$$

and the effective input resistance is

$$R_i = \frac{(1 + \alpha^2) r_p}{1 + \alpha^2 (1 + \mu)}$$

where $\alpha \equiv \omega C R$.

Prob. 8-31

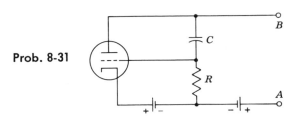

d. At a given frequency, show that the maximum value of C_i (as either C or R is varied) is obtained when $\alpha = 1$, and

$$(C_i)_{max} = \frac{g_m}{2\omega}$$

Also show that the value of R_i corresponding to this C_i is

$$(R_i)_{max} = \frac{2 r_p}{2 + \mu}$$

which, for $\mu \gg 2$, reduces to $(R_i)_{max} = 2/g_m$.

e. The tube is a 6CG7 (Fig. 7-8) operated at 5,000 Hz. If the bias is adjusted so that the tube current can be varied over the range from 2 to 20 mA, over what range do $(C_i)_{max}$ and $(R_i)_{max}$ vary? Assume that $V_p = 250$ V.

8-32 Solve for the quantities analogous to those asked for in Prob. 8-31 if the capacitor C is replaced by an inductor L.

8-33 a. A 6SF5 triode works into a 100-K resistive load. Calculate the complex voltage gain and the input admittance of the system for frequencies of 100 and 100,000 Hz. Take the interelectrode capacitances into consideration. The tube parameters are $\mu = 100$, $r_p = 66$ K, $g_m = 1.5$ mA/V, $C_{gk} = 4.0$ pF, $C_{pk} = 3.6$ pF, and $C_{gp} = 2.4$ pF.

Compare these results with those obtained when the interelectrode capacitances are neglected.

b. Calculate the input resistance and capacitance.

8-34 Calculate the input admittance of a triode at 10^3 and 10^6 Hz when the total plate-circuit impedance is (a) a resistance of 50 K, (b) an inductive reactance of 50 K at each frequency. Take the interelectrode capacitances into consideration. The tube parameters are $\mu = 20$, $r_p = 10$ K, $g_m = 2.0$ mA/V, $C_{gk} = 3.0$ pF, $C_{pk} = 11.0$ pF, and $C_{gp} = 2.0$ pF. Express the results in terms of the input resistance and capacitance.

8-35   A 6CG7 is incorporated in a simple grounded-cathode amplifier circuit.   It is to be operated at the recommended point.   Starting with a zero load, how much resistance must be introduced as load in order to multiply the input capacitance by a factor of 6? $C_{pk} = 2.2$ pF, $C_{gk} = 2.3$ pF, $C_{gp} = 4$ pF, $\mu = 20$, $r_p = 7.7$ K.

8-36   Draw the equivalent circuit of a pentode, including all interelectrode capacitances.   Show that to a very good approximation the input capacitance is equal to C_{gk} and C_{gs} in parallel and that the output capacitance is equal to C_{pk}, C_{ps}, and C_{p3} in parallel.   The symbols are as defined in Sec. 8-13.

8-37   Verify Eq. (8-52) for the gain of a cathode follower.

8-38   Verify Eq. (8-58) for the output impedance of a cathode follower.

CHAPTER 9

9-1   Show that the ratio of hole to electron currents I_{pE}/I_{nE} crossing the emitter junction of a p-n-p transistor is proportional to the ratio of the conductivity of the p-type material to that of the n-type material.

9-2   Derive expressions (9-22) for the parameters a_{21} and a_{22} in terms of the physical constants of the transistor.

9-3   a. If it is not assumed that $W/L_B \ll 1$, prove that Eqs. (9-19) and (9-21) remain valid provided that

$$a_{11} = Ae \left(D_p \frac{p_{no}}{L_B} \coth \frac{W}{L_B} + \frac{D_n n_{EO}}{L_E} \right)$$

$$a_{12} = a_{21} = -AeD_p \frac{p_{no}}{L_B} \operatorname{csch} \frac{W}{L_B}$$

$$a_{22} = Ae \left(D_p \frac{p_{no}}{L_B} \coth \frac{W}{L_B} + \frac{D_n n_{CO}}{L_C} \right)$$

b. Show that if $W/L_B \ll 1$, these expressions reduce to those given by Eqs. (9-20) and (9-22).

9-4   Show that Eq. (9-27) follows from Eq. (9-26).

9-5   Using the results of Prob. 9-3a, verify that $\alpha = \beta^* \gamma$, where γ is given by Eq. (9-28) and β^* by Eq. (9-29).

9-6   If $W/L_B \ll 1$, verify that Eqs. (9-30) and (9-31) follow from Eqs. (9-28) and (9-29), respectively.

9-7   a. The reverse saturation current of the germanium transistor in Fig. 9-10 is 2 μA at room temperature (25°C) and increases by a factor of 2 for each temperature increase of 10°C.   The bias $V_{BB} = 5$ V.   Find the maximum allowable value for R_B if the transistor is to remain cut off at a temperature of 75°C.

b. If $V_{BB} = 1.0$ V and $R_B = 50$ K, how high may the temperature increase before the transistor comes out of cutoff?

9-8   Using $\beta' = h_{fe}$ and $\beta \approx h_{FE}$, show that Eq. (9-47) becomes

$$h_{fe} = \frac{h_{FE}}{1 - (I_{CBO} + I_B)(\partial h_{FE}/\partial I_C)}$$

9-9   a. If $I_B \gg I_{CBO}$, show that

$$\frac{h_{fe} - h_{FE}}{h_{fe}} \approx \frac{I_C}{h_{FE}} \frac{\partial h_{FE}}{\partial I_C}$$

b. From Fig. 9-12 verify that at $I_C = 80$ mA, h_{fe} is approximately 20 percent less than h_{FE}.

9-10 From the characteristic curves for the type 2N404 transistor given in Fig. 9-11, find the voltages V_{BE}, V_{CE}, and V_{RC} for the circuit shown.

Prob. 9-10

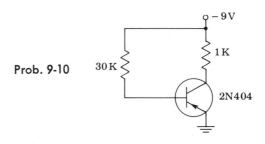

9-11 a. Derive the Ebers-Moll equations [Eqs. (9-51) and (9-52)] from Eqs. (9-49) and (9-50).

b. Derive Eqs. (9-55) and (9-56) from Eqs. (9-49) and (9-50).

9-12 Draw the Ebers-Moll model for an n-p-n transistor.

9-13 a. Show that the exact expression for the CE output characteristics of a p-n-p transistor is

$$V_{CE} = V_T \ln \frac{\alpha_I}{\alpha_N} + V_T \ln \frac{I_{CO} + \alpha_N I_B - I_C(1 - \alpha_N)}{I_{EO} + I_B + I_C(1 - \alpha_I)}$$

b. Show that this reduces to Eq. (9-57) if $I_B \gg I_{EO}$ and $I_B \gg I_{CO}/\alpha_N$.

9-14 a. A transistor is operating in the cutoff region with both the emitter and collector junctions reverse-biased by at least a few tenths of a volt. Prove that the currents are given by

$$I_E = \frac{I_{EO}(1 - \alpha_N)}{1 - \alpha_N \alpha_I}$$

$$I_C = \frac{I_{CO}(1 - \alpha_I)}{1 - \alpha_N \alpha_I}$$

b. Prove that the emitter-junction voltage required just to produce cutoff ($I_E = 0$ and the collector back-biased) is

$$V_E = V_T \ln (1 - \alpha_N)$$

9-15 a. Find the collector current for a transistor when both emitter and collector junctions are reverse-biased. Assume $I_{CO} = 5$ μA, $I_{EO} = 3.57$ μA, and $\alpha_N = 0.98$.

b. Find the emitter current I_E under the same conditions as in part a.

9-16 Show that the emitter volt-ampere characteristic of a transistor in the active region is given by

$$I_E \approx I_0 \epsilon^{V_E/V_T}$$

where $I_0 = -I_{EO}/(1 - \alpha_N \alpha_I)$. Note that this characteristic is that of a p-n junction diode.

9-17 *a.* Given an *n-p-n* transistor for which (at room temperature) $\alpha_N = 0.98$, $I_{CO} = 2\ \mu\text{A}$, and $I_{EO} = 1.6\ \mu\text{A}$. A common-emitter connection is used, and $V_{CC} = 12$ V and $R_L = 4.0$ K. What is the minimum base current required in order that the transistor enter its saturation region?

b. Under the conditions in part *a*, find the voltages across each junction between each pair of terminals if the base-spreading resistance $r_{bb'}$ is neglected.

c. Repeat part *b* if the base current is 200 μA.

d. How are the above results modified if $r_{bb'} = 250\ \Omega$?

9-18 Plot emitter current vs. emitter-to-base voltage for a transistor for which $\alpha_N = 0.98$, $I_{CO} = 2\ \mu\text{A}$, and $I_{EO} = 1.6\ \mu\text{A}$ if (*a*) $V_C = 0$, (*b*) V_C is back-biased by more than a few tenths of a volt. Neglect the base-spreading resistance.

9-19 Plot carefully to scale the common-emitter characteristic I_C/I_B versus V_{CE} for a transistor with $\alpha_N = 0.90 = \alpha_I$.

9-20 A common method of calculating α_N and α_I is by measurement of I_{CO}, I_{CEO}, and I_{CES}. Show that

$$(a)\quad \alpha_N = \frac{I_{CEO} - I_{CO}}{I_{CEO}} \qquad (b)\quad \alpha_I = \frac{1 - I_{CO}/I_{CES}}{1 - I_{CO}/I_{CEO}}$$

9-21 The collector leakage current is measured as shown in the figure, with the emitter grounded and a resistor R connected between base and ground. If this current is designated as I_{CER}, show that

$$I_{CER} = \frac{I_{CO}(1 + I_{EO}R/V_T)}{1 - \alpha_N\alpha_I + (I_{EO}R/V_T)(1 - \alpha_N)}$$

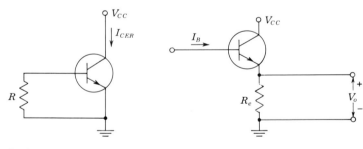

Prob. 9-21   Prob. 9-22

9-22 For the circuit shown, verify that $V_o = V_{CC}$ when

$$I_B = \frac{V_{CC}}{R_e}\left(1 + \frac{\alpha_N}{\alpha_I}\frac{1 - \alpha_I}{1 - \alpha_N}\right) = \frac{V_{CC}}{R_e}\left(1 + \frac{\beta_N}{\beta_I}\right)$$

Under these conditions the base current exceeds the emitter current.

9-23 For the circuit shown, $\alpha_1 = 0.98$, $\alpha_2 = 0.96$, $V_{CC} = 24$ V, $R_c = 120\ \Omega$, and $I_E = -100$ mA. Neglecting the reverse saturation currents, determine (*a*) the currents I_{C1}, I_{B1}, I_{E1}, I_{C2}, I_{B2}, and I_C; (*b*) V_{CE}; (*c*) I_C/I_B, I_C/I_E.

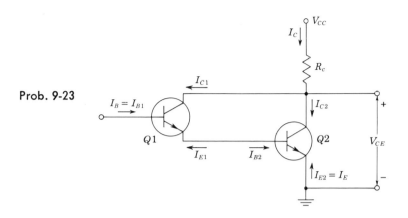

Prob. 9-23

9-24 For the circuit shown, prove that the floating emitter-to-base voltage is given by

$$V_{EBF} = V_T \ln (1 - \alpha_N)$$

Neglect $r_{bb'}$.

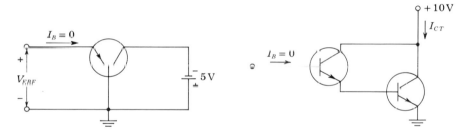

Prob. 9-24   Prob. 9-25

9-25 For the "floating-base" connection shown, prove that

$$I_{CT} = \frac{2 - \alpha_N}{(1 - \alpha_N)^2} I_{CO}$$

Assume that the transistors are identical.

9-26 *a.* Show that if the collector junction is reverse-biased with $|V_{CB}| \gg V_T$, the voltage V_{BE} is related to the base current by

$$V_{BE} = I_B \left(r_{bb'} + \frac{R_E}{1 - \alpha_N} \right)$$
$$+ \left\{ \frac{I_{CO}R_E}{1 - \alpha_N} + V_T \ln \left[1 + \frac{I_B(1 - \alpha_N\alpha_I)}{I_{EO}(1 - \alpha_N)} + \frac{\alpha_N(1 - \alpha_I)}{\alpha_I(1 - \alpha_N)} \right] \right\}$$

where $r_{bb'}$ is the base-spreading resistance, and R_E is the emitter-body resistance.

b. Show that $V_{BE} = I_B(r_{bb'} + R_E) + V_T(1 + I_B/I_{EO})$, if the collector is open-circuited.

9-27 If $\alpha = 0.98$ and $V_{BE} = 0.6$ V, find R_1 in the circuit shown for an emitter current $I_E = -2$ mA. Neglect the reverse saturation current.

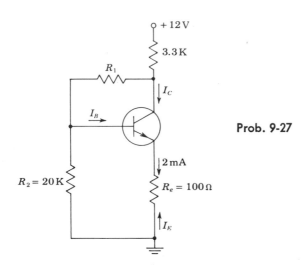

Prob. 9-27

9-28 A transistor is operated at a forward emitter current of 2 mA and with the collector open-circuited. Find (*a*) the junction voltages V_C and V_E, (*b*) the collector-to-emitter voltage V_{CE}. Assume $I_{CO} = 2$ μA, $I_{EO} = 1.6$ μA, $\alpha_N = 0.98$. Is the transistor operating in saturation, at cutoff, or in the active region?

9-29 *a.* Show that, for an *n-p-n* silicon transistor of the alloy type in which the resistivity ρ_B of the base is much larger than that of the collector, the punch-through voltage V is given by $V = 6.10 \times 10^3 W^2/\rho_B$, where V is in volts, ρ_B in ohm-centimeters, and the base width W in mils.

b. Calculate the punch-through voltage if $W = 1$ micron and $\rho_B = 0.5$ Ω-cm.

CHAPTER 10

10-1 An *n-p-n* transistor with $\beta = 50$ is used in a common-emitter circuit with $V_{CC} = 10$ V and $R_c = 2$ K. The bias is obtained by connecting a 100-K resistance from collector to base. Assume $V_{BE} = 0$. Find (*a*) the quiescent point, (*b*) the stability factor *S*.

10-2 A transistor with $\beta = 100$ is to be used in a CE configuration with collector-to-base bias. The collector circuit resistance is $R_c = 1$ K and $V_{CC} = 10$ V. Assume $V_{BE} = 0$. (*a*) Choose R_b so that the quiescent collector-to-emitter voltage is 4 V. (*b*) Find the stability factor *S*.

10-3 For the two-battery transistor circuit shown, prove that the stabilization factor *S* is given by

$$S = \frac{1 + \beta}{1 + \beta R_e/(R_e + R_b)}$$

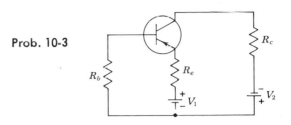

Prob. 10-3

10-4 *a.* Verify Eq. (10-17).
b. Show that S may be put in the form

$$S = \frac{G_e + G_1 + G_2}{G_e/(1 + \beta) + G_1 + G_2}$$

where the G's are the conductances corresponding to the R's shown in Fig. 10-6a.

10-5 (*a*) Determine the quiescent currents and the collector-to-emitter voltage for a germanium transistor with $\beta = 50$ in the self-biasing arrangement of Fig. 10-6. The circuit component values are $V_{CC} = 20$ K, $R_c = 2$ K, $R_e = 0.1$ K, $R_1 = 100$ K, and $R_2 = 5$ K. (*b*) Find the stability factor S.

10-6 A *p-n-p* germanium transistor is used in the self-biasing arrangement of Fig. 10-6. The circuit-component values are $V_{CC} = 4.5$ V, $R_c = 1.5$ K, $R_e = 0.27$ K, $R_2 = 2.7$ K, and $R_1 = 27$ K. If $\beta = 44$, find (*a*) the stability factor S, (*b*) the quiescent point. (*c*) Recalculate these values if the base spreading resistance of 690 Ω is taken into account.

10-7 (*a*) A germanium transistor is used in the self-biasing arrangement of Fig. 10-0 with $V_{CC} = 16$ V and $R_c = 1.5$ K. The quiescent point is chosen to be $V_{CE} = 8$ V and $I_C = 4$ mA. A stability factor $S = 12$ is desired. If $\beta = 50$, find R_1, R_2, and R_e. (*b*) Repeat part *a* for $S = 3$. (*c*) What is the "price" paid for the improved stability in part *b*?

10-8 A *p-n-p* germanium transistor is used in a common-collector circuit (Fig. 10-6 with $R_c = 0$). The circuit-component values are $V_{CC} = 3.0$ V, $R_e = 1$ K, $R_1 = R_2 = 5$ K. If $\beta = 44$, find (*a*) S, (*b*) the quiescent point. (*c*) Recalculate these values, taking the base-spreading resistance of 690 Ω into account.

10-9 Determine the stability factor S for the circuit shown.

Prob. 10-9

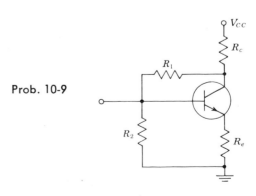

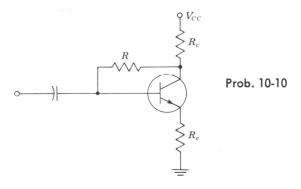

Prob. 10-10

10-10 In the circuit shown, $V_{CC} = 24$ V, $R_c = 10$ K, and $R_e = 270$ Ω. If a silicon transistor is used with $\beta = 45$ and if under quiescent conditions $V_{CE} = 5$ V, determine (a) R, (b) the stability factor S.

10-11 In the transformer-coupled amplifier stage shown, $V_{BE} = 0.5$ V, $\beta = 50$, and the quiescent voltage is $V_{CE} = 4$ V. Determine (a) R_e, (b) the stability factor S.

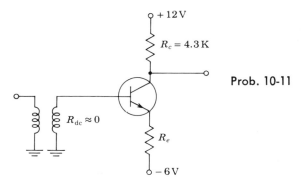

Prob. 10-11

10-12 In the two-stage circuit shown, assume $\beta = 100$ for each transistor. (a) Determine R so that the quiescent conditions are $V_{CE1} = -4$ V and $V_{CE2} = -6$ V. (b) Explain how quiescent-point stabilization is obtained. Assume $V_{BE} = 0.2$ V.

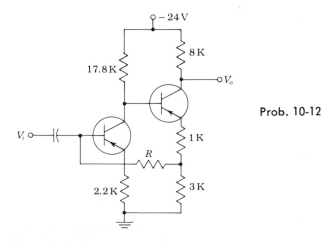

Prob. 10-12

10-13   In the Darlington stage shown, $V_{CC} = 24$ V, $\beta_1 = 24$, $\beta_2 = 39$, $V_{BE} = 0.6$ V, $R_c = 330$ Ω, and $R_e = 120$ Ω.   If at the quiescent point $V_{CE2} = 6$ V, determine (a) R, (b) the stability factor defined as $S \equiv dI_C/dI_{CO1}$.

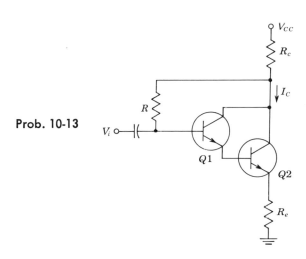

Prob. 10-13

10-14   Derive Eq. (10-29) in the text.

10-15   In the circuit of Fig. 10-6, let $V_{CC} = 27.5$ V, $R_c = 5.6$ K, $R_e = 1$ K, $R_1 = 90$ K, $R_2 = 10$ K, $I_C = 1.5$ mA.   Using the transistor of Table 10-1, find I_C at $+175$ and   65°C.

10-16   Repeat Prob. 10-15 for the transistor of Table 10-2 at $+75$ and -65°C.

10-17   In the emitter-follower circuit shown, $R_e = 1$ K, V_{CC}, and V_{BB} are adjusted to give $I_C = 1.5$ mA.   Using the transistor of Table 10-1, find I_C at $+175$ and -65°C. Compare the results with those of Prob. 10-15.

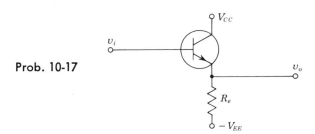

Prob. 10-17

10-18   Repeat Prob. 10-17 for the transistor of Table 10-2 at $+75$ and -65°C. Compare these results with those of Prob. 10-16.

10-19   For the self-bias circuit of Fig. 10-6a, $R_e = 1$ K and $R_b = R_1 \| R_2 = 7.75$ K. The collector supply voltage and R_c are adjusted to establish a collector current of 1.5 mA.   Determine the variation of I_C in the temperature range -65 to $+175$°C when the silicon transistor of Table 10-1 is used.

10-20   Repeat Prob. 10-19 for the range -65 to $+75$°C when the germanium transistor of Table 10-2 is used.

10-21 If in Eq. (10-24) we do not assume $\beta \gg 1$ so that V' is now a function of β, verify that Eq. (10-29) is given by

$$S'' = \frac{(I_c - I_{co})S}{\beta(1 + \beta)}$$

10-22 If in Eq. (10-24) we do not assume $\beta \gg 1$, so that V' is now a function of β, verify that Eq. (10-34) is given by

$$S'' = \frac{(I_{c1} - I_{co1})S_2}{(\beta_1)(1 + \beta_2)}$$

HINT: Write the expression for $(I_{c2} - I_{co2})/(I_{c1} - I_{co1})$ and then subtract unity from both sides of the equation.

10-23 Two identical silicon transistors with $\beta = 48$, $V_{BE} = 0.6$ V at $T = 25°C$, $V_{CC} = 20.6$ V, $R_1 = 10$ K, and $R_c = 5$ K are used in Fig. 10-13a.

  a. Find the currents I_{B1}, I_{B2}, I_{c1}, and I_{c2} at $T = 25°C$.

  b. Find I_{c2} at $T = 175°C$ when $\beta = 98$ and $V_{BE} = 0.22$ V.

  HINT: Assume $I_{B1} = I_{B2}$.

10-24 Prove Eq. (10-41).

10-25 a. Calculate the thermal resistance for the 2N338 transistor for which the manufacturer specifies $P_C(\text{max}) = 125$ mW at 25°C free-air temperature and maximum junction temperature $T_j = 150°C$.

  b. What is the junction temperature if the collector dissipation is 75 mW?

10-26 Show that the load line tangent to the constant-power-dissipation hyperbola of Fig. 10-16 is bisected by the tangency point; that is, $AC = BC$.

10-27 The transistor used in the circuit shown is at cutoff.

  a. Show that runaway will occur for values of I_{co} in the range

$$\frac{V_{CC} - \sqrt{V_{CC}^2 - 8R_c/0.07\Theta}}{4R_c} \leq I_{co} \leq \frac{V_{CC} + \sqrt{V_{CC}^2 - 8R_c/0.07\Theta}}{4R_c}$$

  b. Show that if runaway is not destructive, the collector current I_{co} after runaway can never exceed $I_{co} = V_{CC}/2R_c$.

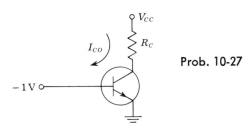

Prob. 10-27

10-28 A germanium transistor with $\Theta = 250°C/W$, $I_{co} = 10\ \mu A$ at 25°C, $R_c = 1$ K, and $V_{CC} = 30$ V is used in the circuit of Prob. 10-27.

  a. Find I_{co} at the point of runaway.

  b. Find the ambient temperature at which runaway will occur.

CHAPTER 11

11-1 The transistor whose input characteristics are shown in Fig. 9-14a is biased at $V_{CE} = 8$ V and $I_B = 300\ \mu A$.

a. Compute graphically h_{fe} and h_{oe} at the quiescent point specified above.

b. Using the h parameters computed in part *a*, calculate h_{fb} and h_{ob}.

11-2 *a.* Show that the exact expression for h_{fe} in terms of the CB hybrid parameters is

$$h_{fe} = - \frac{h_{fb}(1 - h_{rb}) + h_{ib}h_{ob}}{(1 + h_{fb})(1 - h_{rb}) + h_{ob}h_{ib}}$$

b. From this exact formula obtain the approximate expression for h_{fe} in Table 11-3.

11-3 *a.* Show that the exact expression for h_{fb} in terms of the CE hybrid parameters is

$$h_{fb} = - \frac{h_{fe}(1 - h_{re}) + h_{ie}h_{oe}}{(1 + h_{fe})(1 - h_{re}) + h_{oe}h_{ie}}$$

b. From this exact formula obtain the approximate expression for h_{fb} in Table 11-3.

11-4 Find, in terms of the CC hybrid parameters, the CE hybrid parameters. Note that the expressions in Table 11-3 are exact for this conversion.

11-5 For the circuit shown, verify that the modified h parameters (indicated by primes) are

(a) $h'_{ie} \approx h_{ie} + \dfrac{(1 + h_{fe})R_e}{1 + h_{oe}R_e}$ (b) $h'_{re} = \dfrac{h_{re} + h_{oe}R_e}{1 + h_{oe}R_e}$

(c) $h'_{fe} = \dfrac{h_{fe} - h_{oe}R_e}{1 + h_{oe}R_e}$ (d) $h'_{oe} = \dfrac{h_{oe}}{1 + h_{oe}R_e}$

(e) To what do these expressions reduce if $h_{oe}R_e \ll 1$?

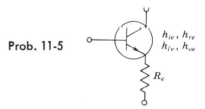

Prob. 11-5

h_{ie}, h_{re}
h_{fe}, h_{oe}

R_e

11-6 Show that the overall h parameters of the accompanying two-stage cascaded amplifier are

(a) $h_{11} = h'_{11} - \dfrac{h'_{12}h'_{21}}{1 + h''_{22}h''_{11}} h''_{11}$ (b) $h_{12} = \dfrac{h'_{12}h''_{12}}{1 + h''_{22}h''_{11}}$

(c) $h_{21} = - \dfrac{h'_{21}h''_{21}}{1 + h''_{22}h''_{11}}$ (d) $h_{22} = h''_{22} - \dfrac{h''_{12}h''_{21}}{1 + h'_{22}h''_{11}} h'_{22}$

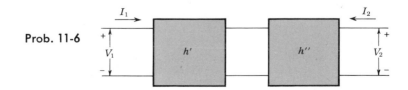

Prob. 11-6

I_1 I_2

$+$
V_1 h' h'' $+$ V_2
$-$ $-$

11-7 Show that the overall h parameters for the composite transistor shown are

(a) $h_{ie} = h_{ie1} + \dfrac{(1 - h_{re1})(1 + h_{fe1})h_{ie2}}{1 + h_{oe1}h_{ie2}}$ (b) $h_{fe} = h_{fe1} + \dfrac{(h_{fe2} - h_{oe1}h_{ie2})(1 + h_{fe1})}{1 + h_{oe1}h_{ie2}}$

(c) $h_{oe} = h_{oe2} + \dfrac{(1 + h_{fe2})(1 - h_{re2})h_{oe1}}{1 + h_{oe1}h_{ic2}}$ (d) $h_{re} = h_{re2} + \dfrac{(h_{ie2}h_{oe1} + h_{re1})(1 - h_{re2})}{1 + h_{oe1}h_{ie2}}$

(e) Obtain numerical values for the h parameters of the composite transistor by assuming identical transistors $Q1$ and $Q2$ and using Table 11-2.

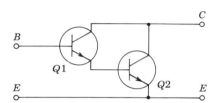

Prob. 11-7

11-8 Given a single-stage transistor amplifier with the h parameters specified in Table 11-2, calculate A_I, A_V, A_{Vs}, R_i, and R_o for the CC transistor configuration, with $R_s = R_L = 10$ K. Check your results with Figs. 11-14 to 11-17.

11-9 a. Draw the equivalent circuit for the CE and CC configurations subject to the restriction that $R_L = 0$. Show that the input impedances of the two circuits are identical.

b. Draw the circuits for the CE and CC configurations subject to the restriction that the input is open-circuited. Show that the output impedances of the two circuits are identical.

11-10 For any transistor amplifier prove that

$$R_i = \frac{h_i}{1 - h_r A_V}$$

11-11 Verify expression (11-34) for the output admittance Y_o by evaluating Y_o as the ratio of the short-circuit current to the open-circuit voltage.

11-12 Prove that

$$Y_o = h_o \left(\frac{R_s + R_{i\infty}}{R_s + R_{io}} \right)$$

where $R_{i\infty} \equiv R_i$ for $R_L = \infty$, and $R_{io} \equiv R_i$ for $R_L = 0$.

11-13 Verify the extreme points ($R_s = 10$ and 10^7 Ω, $R_L = 10$ and 10^7 Ω) of the curves given in Figs. 11-14 to 11-17, using the h parameters given in Table 11-2, (a) for the CE connection, (b) for the CB connection, (c) for the CC connection.

11-14 Find the output impedance Z_o for the example in Sec. 11-6 by evaluating the current I_a drawn from an auxiliary voltage source V_a impressed across the output terminals (with zero input voltage and $R_L = \infty$). Then $Z_o = V_a/I_a$.

11-15 Find the voltage gain A_V for the example in Sec. 11-6 directly as the ratio V_o/V_i (without finding A_I or Z_i).

11-16 For the amplifier shown with transistor parameters specified in Table 11-2, calculate A_V, A_{Vs}, R_i, and $A_I = -I_2/I_1$. HINT: Follow the rules given in Sec. 11-8.

Prob. 11-16

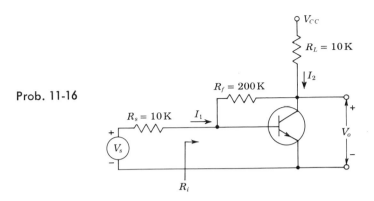

11-17 *a.* For a CE configuration, what is the maximum value of R_L for which R_i differs by no more than 10 percent of its value at $R_L = 0$? Use the transistor parameters given in Table 11-2.

  b. What is the maximum value of R_s for which R_o differs by no more than 10 percent of its value for $R_s = 0$?

11-18 *a.* In the circuit shown, find the input impedance R_i in terms of the CE h parameters, R_L and R_e. HINT: Follow the rules given in Sec. 11-8.

  b. If $R_L = R_e = 1$ K and the h parameters are as given in Table 11-2, what is the value of R_i?

Prob. 11-18

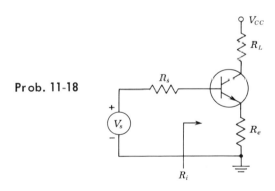

11-19 (a) For the two-transistor amplifier circuit shown (supply voltages are not indicated) calculate A_I, A_V, A_{Vs}, and R_i. The transistors are identical, and their parameters are given in Table 11-2. HINT: Follow the rules given in Sec. 11-8. (b) Repeat part *a* using the results given in Prob. 11-6.

Prob. 11-19

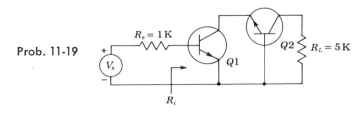

11-20 The transistor amplifier shown uses a transistor whose h parameters are given in Table 11-2. Calculate $A_I = I_o/I_i$, A_V, A_{Vs}, R_o, and R_i.

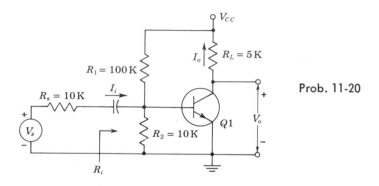

Prob. 11-20

11-21 *a.* Calculate R_i, A_V, and $A_I = -I_o/I_i$ for the circuit shown. Use the h parameter values given in Table 11-2. HINT: Follow the rules given in Sec. 11-8.
b. Repeat part a using the results in Prob. 11-7.

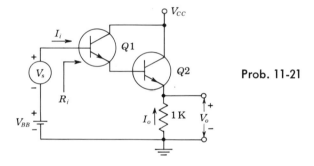

Prob. 11-21

11-22 For the amplifier shown, using a transistor whose parameters are given in Table 11-2, compute $A_I = I_o/I_i$, A_V, A_{Vs}, and R_i. HINT: Follow the rules given in Sec. 11-8.

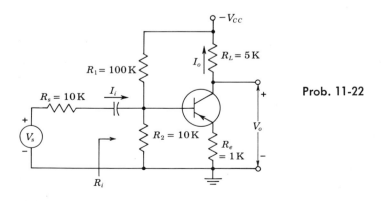

Prob. 11-22

11-23 For the circuit shown, with the transistor parameters specified in Table 11-2, calculate $A_I = I_o/I_i$, A_V, A_{Vs}, and R_i.   HINT: Follow the rules given in Sec. 11-8.

Prob. 11-23

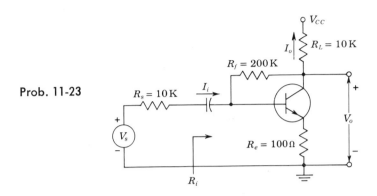

11-24 For the CB configuration, what is the maximum value of R_L for which R_i does not exceed 50 Ω?   Use the transistor parameters given in Table 11-2.

11-25 Draw Fig. 11-20 in a CE configuration.   Then prove that this circuit is equivalent to that shown where $a_e = a/(1 - a)$ and $r_d = (1 - a)r_c$.

Prob. 11-25

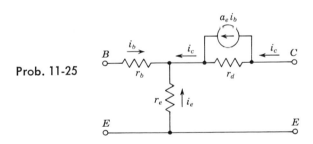

11-26 Obtain the CB h parameters given in Table 11-3 in terms of the parameters of the T model of Fig. 11-20.

11-27 Verify the transformation equations in Table 11-7.

CHAPTER 12

NOTE: *Unless otherwise specified, all transistors in these problems are identical and the numerical values of their h parameters are given in Table 11-2. Also assume that all capacitances are arbitrarily large.*

12-1   *a.* For the two-stage cascade shown, compute the input and output imped-ances and the individual and overall voltage and current gains, using the exact pro-cedure of Sec. 12-1.   See note on bottom of page 691.
   b. Repeat part *a* using the approximate formulas in Table 12-2.

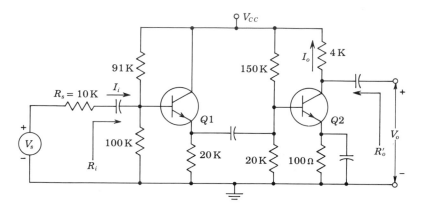

Prob. 12-1

12-2   *a.* Compute A_I, A_V, A_{Vs}, R_i, and R'_o for the two-stage cascade shown, using the exact procedure of Sec. 12-1.   See note on bottom of page 691.
   b. Repeat part *a* using the approximate formulas in Table 12-2.

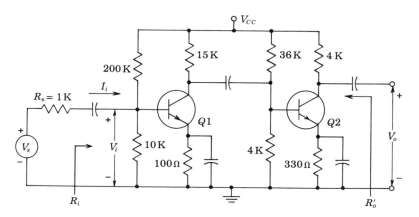

Prob. 12-2

12-3   A common decibel scale used in the measurement of amplifier gains is the dBm scale.   By definition, 0 dBm is the power level corresponding to a 1-mW dissipa-tion in a 600-Ω resistance.

a. What does 0 dBm correspond to in voltage across a 600-Ω resistor?

b. What voltage would correspond to 20 dBm in a 60-Ω resistance? In a 600-K resistance?

12-4 For the circuit shown, compute A_I, A_V, A_{Vs}, R_i, and R'_o. See note on bottom of page 691.

Prob. 12-4

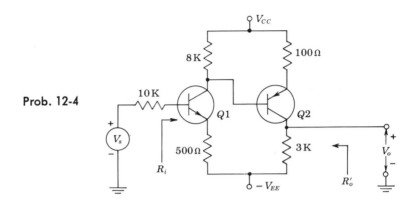

12-5 a. Consider a CB connection with $R_s = 2$ K and $R_L = 4$ K. Find the exact and approximate values of A_I, A_V, A_{Vs}, R_i, and R'_o.

b. Repeat part a for the CE connection.

c. Repeat part a for the CC connection. See note on bottom of page 691.

12-6 Find A_V, A_{Vs}, R_i, and R'_o for the amplifier of Fig. 12-4. Neglect the effect of all capacitances.

12-7 The three-stage amplifier shown contains identical transistors. Calculate the voltage gain of each stage and the overall voltage gain V_o/V_s. See note on bottom of page 691.

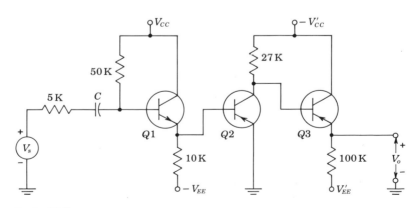

Prob. 12-7

12-8   Find the voltage gain A_{Vs} of the amplifier shown.   Assume $h_{ie} = 1,000\ \Omega$, $h_{re} = 10^{-4}$, $h_{fe} = 50$, $h_{oe} = 10^{-8}$ A/V.

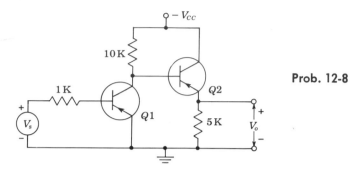

Prob. 12-8

12-9   For the two-stage cascade shown, find A_I, A_V, R_i, and R'_o.   See note on bottom of page 691.

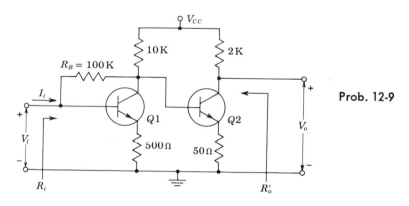

Prob. 12-9

12-10   Design a two-stage cascade using the configuration of Prob. 12-9, with $R_B = 100$ K, to meet the following specifications (see note on bottom of page 691):

$$125 \geq A_V \geq 100 \qquad 10\text{ K} \geq R_i \geq 5\text{ K} \qquad R'_o \leq 3\text{ K}$$

12-11   For the two-stage cascade shown, calculate A_I, A_V, R_i, and R'_o.   See note on bottom of page 691.

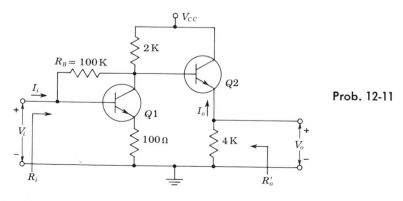

Prob. 12-11

12-12 Design a two-stage amplifier using the configuration of Prob. 12-11, with $R_B = 100$ K, to meet the following specifications (see note on bottom of page 691):

$$|A_V| \geq 15 \qquad R_i \geq 2 \text{ K} \qquad R_o' \leq 100 \; \Omega$$

12-13 For the circuit shown, find the voltage gain V_o/V_s and input impedance as a function of R_s, b, R_e, and R_L. Assume that $h_{oe}(R_e + R_L) \leq 0.1$.

Prob. 12-13

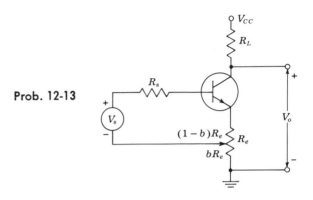

12-14 Using the exact expressions of Eq. (12-48) for A_I and Eq. (12-49) for R_i, calculate the output resistance R_o in Fig. 12-12a as the ratio of open-circuit voltage V to short-circuit current I. Verify that R_o is given by Eq. (12-51). HINT: Note that

$$V = \lim_{R_L \to \infty} A_V V_s.$$

12-15 Do Prob. 11-16 using Miller's theorem.

12-16 The amplifier shown is made up of an *n-p-n* and a *p-n-p* transistor. The h parameters of the two transistors are identical, and are given as $h_{ie} = 1$ K, $h_{fe} - 100$, $h_{oe} = 0$, and $h_{re} = 0$.

a. With the switch open, find $A_V = V_o/V_i$.

b. With the switch closed, find (with the aid of Miller's theorem) A_V, A_{Vs}, R_i, and $A_I \equiv -I_o/I_i$.

Prob. 12-16

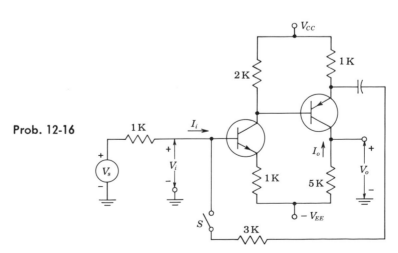

12-17   For the bootstrap circuit shown, calculate $A_I \equiv I_o/I_i$, R_i, and A_V.   The transistor parameters are $h_{ie} = 2$ K, $h_{fe} = 100$, $1/h_{oe} = 40$ K, and $h_{re} = 2.5 \times 10^{-4}$.

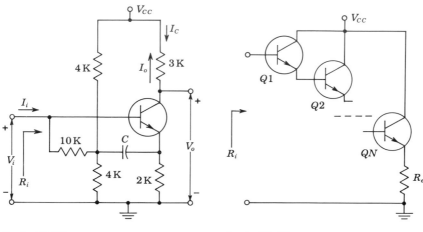

Prob. 12-17   Prob. 12-18

12-18   The cascade configuration shown is known as the tandem emitter follower. Find the input resistance R_i if $h_{ie} = h_{re} = 0$, $h_{oe} = 0$, and h_{fe} is the same for each of the transistors $Q1$ to QN.

12-19   The bootstrapped Darlington pair uses identical transistors with the following h parameters: $h_{ie} = 1$ K, $h_{re} = 2.5 \times 10^{-4}$, $h_{oe} = 2.5 \times 10^{-5}$ A/V, and $h_{fe} = 100$.   Find I_{e1}/I_{b1}, V_{o2}/V_i, R_i, and V_{o1}/V_i.

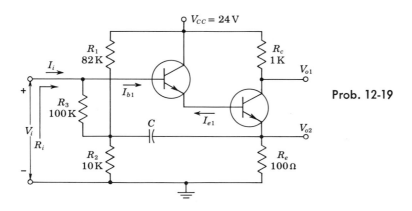

Prob. 12-19

12-20   Calculate $A_I = I_o/I_i$, $A_V = V_o/V_i$, $R_i = V_i/I_i$, and R_o' for the circuit shown.   See note on bottom of page 691.

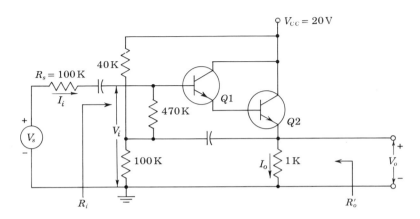

Prob. 12-20

12-21   Verify Eq. (12-77).

12-22   Calculate R_i and A_V for the circuit shown in Fig. 12-18, with $R_{e1} = 100$ K and $R_{e2} = 1$ K.   See note on bottom of page 691.

12-23   For the circuit shown, find $A_V = V_o/V_i$, $A_{Vs} = V_o/V_s$, $A_I = I_o/I_i$, $R_i = V_i/I_i$, and R_o'.   See note on bottom of page 691.

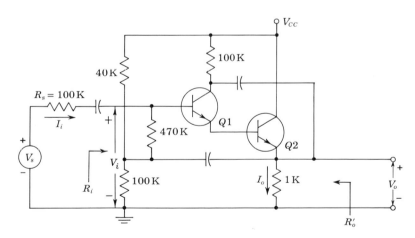

Prob. 12-23

12-24 Calculate $A_I = I_o/I_i$, A_V, A_{Vs}, R_i, and R_o' for the cascode circuit shown. See note on bottom of page 691.

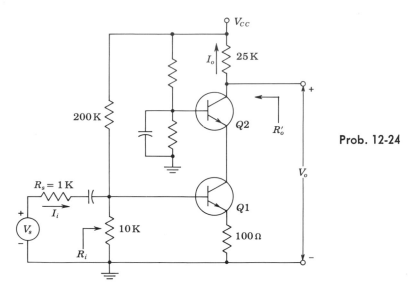

Prob. 12-24

12-25 The circuit shown is an amplifier using a p-n-p and an n-p-n transistor in parallel. The two transistors have identical characteristics. Find the expression for the voltage gain and the input resistance of the amplifier, using the simplified hybrid model.

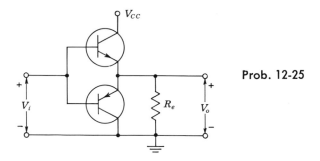

Prob. 12-25

12-26 For the emitter-coupled differential amplifier of Fig. 12-21, compute A_c, A_d, ρ, A_1, and A_2. The resistance values are $R_s = 1$ K, $R_c = 4$ K, and $R_e = 20$ K.

12-27 Repeat Prob. 12-26 when the emitter resistor is replaced by the transistor constant-current source of Fig. 12-23, with $R_1 = 100$ K, $R_2 = 10$ K, and $R_3 = 1$ K.

12-28 Verify Eqs. (12-91) and (12-92) for the difference amplifier.

CHAPTER 13

13-1 The emitter efficiency γ is usually quite close to unity and is essentially independent of frequency up to frequencies of the order of f_α. Hence assume that

$\alpha = \beta^*$, and from Eqs. (5-56) and (9-29), verify that α is given as

$$\alpha(\omega) = \mathrm{sech}\,\frac{W}{L_B}(1 + j\omega\tau_B)^{\frac{1}{2}}$$

where τ_B and L_B are the mean lifetime and diffusion length of minority carriers in the base.

  a. Using $W/L_B \ll 1$, expand the hyperbolic secant in a power series and obtain Eq. (13-4).

  b. Show that, under the above conditions,

$$\omega_\alpha = \frac{2D_B}{W^2\alpha_o} \qquad \text{where } \alpha_o = \frac{1}{1 + \frac{1}{2}W^2/L_B^2}$$

Compare with Eq. (13-13).

  13-2 a. Show that the magnitude and phase of $\alpha(\omega)$ given in Prob. 13-1 at $\omega = \omega_\alpha$ are 0.775 and 50°, respectively. Assume $W/L_B \ll 1$ and $\alpha_o = 1$.

  b. Compute the magnitude and phase of $\alpha(\omega)$ as given by Eq. (13-4) at $\omega = \omega_\alpha$, and compare with the results of part a.

  13-3 a. Show that the magnitude and phase of $\alpha(\omega)$ given in Prob. 13-1 are 0.707 and 58° at the frequency $\omega_\alpha = 2.43D_B/W^2\alpha_o$. Assume $W/L_B \ll 1$ and $\alpha_o = 1$.

  b. Compute the magnitude and phase of $\alpha(\omega)$ as given by Eq. (13-4) at $\omega = \omega_\alpha$, and compare with the results of part a.

  c. What must be the excess phase factor m in Eq. (13-7) if the phase of α at $\omega = \omega_\alpha$ is to be 58° as in part a?

  13-4 Consider the CB circuit of Fig. 13-2, with the output short-circuited and with a step of current I into the emitter at $t = 0$. Prove that the output current for $t \geq 0$ is given by

$$\frac{i_L}{I} = \alpha_o + \left(1 + \frac{\alpha_o\omega_\alpha}{\omega' - \omega_\alpha}\right)\epsilon^{-\omega' t} - \frac{\alpha_o\omega'}{\omega' - \omega_\alpha}\epsilon^{-\omega_\alpha t}$$

where $\omega' r_{bb'}C_c \equiv 1$.

  13-5 Refer to the result in Prob. 13-4. Show that if

$$\omega_\alpha = \frac{1}{r_e'C_e} \ll \omega' = \frac{1}{r_{bb'}C_c}$$

then

$$i_L \approx \alpha_o I(1 - \epsilon^{-\omega_\alpha t}) \qquad \text{for } t > 0$$

  13-6 Given a germanium p-n-p transistor whose base width is 5×10^{-4} cm. At room temperature and for a dc emitter current of 2 mA, find (a) the emitter resistance, (b) the alpha cutoff frequency, (c) the emitter diffusion capacitance, (d) the base transit time. Use Table 5-1.

  13-7 A silicon p-n-p transistor has an alpha cutoff frequency of 100 kHz. What is the base thickness? Use Table 5-1.

  13-8 Given an n-p-n germanium transistor with $W = 1$ mil and a mean lifetime $\tau_n = 4$ μsec. Using Table 5-1, Eq. (5-51), and the expression for α_o given in Prob. 13-1, calculate (a) f_α, (b) f_β.

  13-9 From the expression for α_o given in Prob. 13-1 and using Eq. (5-51), prove that the common-emitter cutoff frequency f_β is given by $f_\beta = 1/2\pi\tau_B$, where τ_B is the mean lifetime of minority carriers in the base.

13-10 *a.* Starting with Fig. 13-4, prove that the short-circuit CE current gain is

$$A_{ie} = \frac{-\alpha Z_c + Z_e}{(1 - \alpha)Z_c + Z_e}$$

where Z_c is the parallel impedance of r_c' and C_c, and Z_e is the parallel impedance of r_e' and C_e.

b. Since $|Z_e| \ll |(1 - \alpha)Z_c|$, show that $A_{ie} = -\alpha(\omega)/[1 - \alpha(\omega)]$.

13-11 Prove that the CC short-circuit current gain as a function of frequency is given by

$$A_{ic} = \frac{\alpha_{co} + jf/f_{ac}}{1 + jf/f_{ac}} \approx \frac{\alpha_{co}}{1 + jf/f_{ac}}$$

where $\alpha_{co} = 1/(1 - \alpha_o)$ and $f_{ac} = f_{ae} = f_\beta$.

HINT: Redraw Fig. 13-2 with the collector as the common terminal.

13-12 *a.* Verify that f_β obtained from the hybrid-Π model is given by

$$f_\beta = \frac{1 - \alpha_o}{2\pi r_e'(C_e + C_c)}$$

b. Show that this expression is essentially the same as that obtained from the high-frequency T model.

13-13 The following low-frequency parameters are known for a given transistor at $I_C = 10$ mA, $V_{CE} = 10$ V, and at room temperature.

$$h_{ie} = 500 \ \Omega \qquad h_{oe} = 4 \times 10^{-5} \ \text{A/V}$$
$$h_{fe} = 100 \qquad h_{re} = 10^{-4}$$

At the same operating point, $f_T = 50$ MHz and $C_{ob} = 3$ pF, compute the values of all the hybrid-Π parameters.

13-14 Given the following transistor measurements made at $I_C = 5$ mA, $V_{CE} = 10$ V, and at room temperature:

$$h_{fe} = 100 \qquad\qquad h_{ie} = 600 \ \Omega$$
$$|A_{ie}| = 10 \text{ at } 10 \text{ MHz} \qquad C_c = 3 \text{ pF}$$

Find f_β, f_T, f_α, C_e, $r_{b'e}$, and $r_{bb'}$.

13-15 Use the Ebers-Moll equations to show that the transconductance of a transistor in the active region is given by

$$g_m = \frac{dI_C}{dV_E}\bigg|_{V_C = \text{const}} \approx \frac{1}{V_T}\left[I_C - \frac{(1 - \alpha_I)I_{co}}{1 - \alpha_N\alpha_I}\right] \approx \frac{I_C}{V_T}$$

HINT: Assume $\epsilon^{V_C/V_T} \ll 1$.

13-16 *a.* At low frequencies the short-circuit CE current gain β is related to the short-circuit CB current gain α by

$$\alpha = \frac{\beta}{1 + \beta}$$

Assuming that this relationship remains valid at high frequencies and using $\beta = -A_i$ in Eq. (13-17), verify that α is given by Eq. (13-5), where

$$\alpha_o = \frac{h_{fe}}{1 + h_{fe}} \qquad \text{and} \qquad f_\alpha = \frac{f_\beta}{1 - \alpha_o}$$

b. Using the results of part *a*, verify that, for $\alpha_o \approx 1$, $f_\alpha \approx f_\beta h_{fe}$.

c. Verify that

$$A_i = \frac{-\alpha_o}{1 - \alpha_o + jf/f_\alpha}$$

d. To account for "excess phase" replace α_o by $\alpha_o \epsilon^{-jmf/f_\alpha}$. Prove that f_T, the frequency at which $|A_i| = 1$, is given implicitly by

$$1 + x^2 = 2\alpha_o(\cos mx - x \sin mx)$$

where $x = f_T/f_\alpha$.

e. If $mx \ll 1$, expand the trigonometric functions and prove that

$$f_T \approx \frac{\alpha_o f_\alpha}{[1 + 2\alpha_o(m + m^2/2)]^{\frac{1}{2}}}$$

f. If $\alpha_o = 1$ and $m = 0.2$, show that $f_T = f_\alpha/1.2$.

13-17 *a.* Redraw the CE hybrid-Π equivalent circuit with the base as the common terminal and the output terminals, collector and base, short-circuited. Taking account of typical values of the transistor parameters, show that C_c, $r_{b'c}$, and r_{ce} may be neglected.

b. Using the circuit in part *a*, prove that the CB short-circuit current gain is

$$A_{ib} = \frac{g_m}{g_{b'e} + g_m + j\omega C_e} = \frac{\alpha_o}{1 + jf/f_\alpha}$$

where

$$\alpha_o = \frac{h_{fe}}{1 + h_{fe}} \qquad \text{and} \qquad f_\alpha = \frac{g_m}{2\pi C_{g'Y_n}} \approx \frac{f_\beta}{1 - \alpha_o}$$

13-18 Verify Eq. (13-57) for the gain-bandwidth product of a single-stage transistor amplifier. HINT: Use Eqs. (13-51) to (13-53) and (13-45).

13-19 For the transistor whose hybrid-Π parameters are given in Sec. 13-5, driven from a source with an output resistance $R_s = 1$ K, evaluate f_2, A_{Vso}, and A_{Iso} for the following values of load: $R_L = 0$, 1 K, and 2 K.

13-20 *a.* Consider the hybrid-Π circuit at low frequencies, so that C_e and C_c may be neglected. Omit none of the other elements in the circuit. If the load resistance is $R_L = 1/g_L$, prove that

$$K \equiv \frac{V_{ce}}{V_{b'e}} = \frac{-g_m + g_{b'c}}{g_{b'c} + g_{ce} + g_L}$$

HINT: Use the theorem that the voltage between C and E equals the short-circuit current times the impedance seen between C and E, with the input voltage $V_{b'e}$ shorted [Eq. (8-22)].

b. Using Miller's theorem, draw the equivalent circuit between C and E. Applying KCL to this network, show that the above value of K is obtained.

c. Using Miller's theorem, draw the equivalent circuit between B and E. Prove that the current gain under load is

$$A_I = \frac{g_L}{(g_{b'c} + g_{b'e})/K - g_{b'c}}$$

d. Using the results of parts *a* and *c* and the relationships between the hybrid-Π and the *h* parameters, prove that

$$A_I = \frac{-h_{fe}}{1 + h_{oe}R_L}$$

which is the result [Eq. (11-22)] obtained directly from the low-frequency *h*-parameter model. HINT: Neglect $g_{b'c}$ compared with g_m or $g_{b'e}$ in A_I and in K. Justify these approximations.

13-21 Consider a single-stage CE transistor amplifier with the load resistor R_L shunted by a capacitance C_L.

a. Prove that the internal voltage gain $K = V_{ce}/V_{b'e}$ is

$$K \approx \frac{-g_m R_L}{1 + j\omega(C_c + C_L)R_L}$$

b. Prove that the 3-dB frequency is given by

$$f_2 \approx \frac{1}{2\pi(C_c + C_L)R_L}$$

provided that the following condition is valid:

$$g_{b'e}R_L(C_c + C_L) \gg C_e + C_c(1 + g_m R_L)$$

13-22 For a single-stage CE transistor amplifier whose hybrid-Π parameters have the average values given in Sec. 13-5, what value of source resistance R_s will give a 3-dB frequency f_2 which is (*a*) half the value for $R_s = 0$, (*b*) twice the value for $R_s = \infty$? Do these values of R_s depend upon the magnitude of the load R_L?

CHAPTER 14

14-1 For a *p*-channel silicon FET with $a = 2 \times 10^{-4}$ cm and channel resistivity $\rho = 10\ \Omega$-cm, (*a*) find the pinch-off voltage; (*b*) repeat (*a*) for a *p*-channel germanium FET with $\rho = 2\ \Omega$-cm.

14-2 *a.* Plot the transfer characteristic curve of a FET as given by Eq. (14-8), with $I_{DSS} = 10$ mA and $V_P = -4$ V.

b. The magnitude of the slope of this curve at $V_{GS} = 0$ is g_{mo} and is given by Eq. (14-19). If the slope is extended as a tangent, show that it intersects the V_{GS} axis at the point $V_{GS} = V_P/2$.

14-3 *a.* Show that the transconductance g_m of a JFET is related to the drain current I_{DS} by

$$g_m = \frac{2}{|V_P|}\sqrt{I_{DSS}I_{DS}}$$

b. If $V_P = -4$ V and $I_{DSS} = 4$ mA, plot g_m versus I_{DS}.

14-4 Show that for small values of V_{GS} compared with V_P, the drain current is given approximately by $I_D \approx I_{DSS} + g_{mo}V_{GS}$.

14-5 (*a*) For the FET whose characteristics are plotted in Fig. 14-3, determine r_d and g_m graphically at the quiescent point $V_{DS} = 10$ V and $V_{GS} = -1.5$ V. Also evaluate μ. (*b*) Determine $r_d(\text{ON})$ for $V_{GS} = 0$.

14-6 (a) Verify Eq. (14-20) for the voltage gain of the CS amplifier, taking inter-electrode capacitances into account. (b) Using Miller's theorem, verify Eq. (14-22) for the input admittance.

14-7 If an input signal V_i is impressed between gate and ground, find the amplification $A_V = V_o/V_i$. Apply Miller's theorem to the 50-K resistor. The FET parameters are $\mu = 30$ and $r_d = 5$ K. Neglect capacitances.

Prob. 14-7

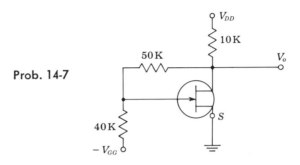

14-8 If in Prob. 14-7 the signal is impressed in series with the 40-K resistor (instead of from gate to ground), find A_V.

14-9 Calculate the voltage gain $A_V = V_o/V_i$ at 1 kHz for the circuit shown. The FET parameters are $g_m = 2$ mA/V and $r_d = 10$ K.

Prob. 14-9

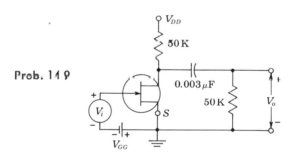

14-10 (a) Starting with the circuit model of Fig. 14-9, verify Eq. (14-25) for the voltage gain of the source follower, taking interelectrode capacitances into account. (b) Using Miller's theorem, verify Eq. (14-27) for the input admittance. (c) Verify Eq. (14-28) for the output admittance.

14-11 Starting with the circuit model of Fig. 14-9, show that, for the CG amplifier stage with $R_s = 0$ and $C_{ds} = 0$,

(a) $A_V = \dfrac{(g_m + g_d)R_d}{1 + R_d(g_d + j\omega C_{gd})}$ (b) $Y_i = g_m + g_d(1 - A_V) + j\omega C_{sg}$

(c) Repeat (a), taking the source resistance R_s into account. (d) Repeat (b), taking the source resistance R_s into account.

14-12 (a) Starting with the circuit model of Fig. 14-9 and neglecting interelectrode capacitances, verify Eq. (14-30) for the voltage gain of the CS amplifier with a source resistance R_s. (b) Verify Eq. (14-31) for the output resistance.

14-13 (*a*) Starting with the circuit model of Fig. 14-9 and neglecting interelectrode capacitances, verify Eq. (14-32) for the voltage gain of the CG amplifier with a source resistance R_s. (*b*) Verify Eq. (14-33) for the input resistance.

14-14 (*a*) Starting with the circuit model of Fig. 14-9 and neglecting interelectrode capacitances, verify Eq. (14-34) for the voltage gain of the CD amplifier. (*b*) Verify Eq. (14-35) for the output resistance.

14-15 Find an expression for the signal voltage across R_L. The two FETs are identical, with parameters μ, r_d, and g_m. HINT: Use the equivalent circuits in Fig. 14-19 at S_2 and D_1.

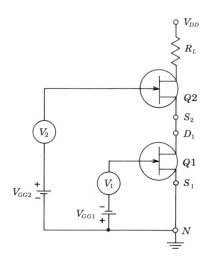

Prob. 14-15

14-16 Each FET shown has the parameters $r_d = 10$ K and $g_m = 2$ mA/V. Using the equivalent circuits in Fig. 14-19 at S_2 and D_1, find the gain (*a*) v_o/v_1 if $v_2 = 0$, (*b*) v_o/v_2 if $v_1 = 0$.

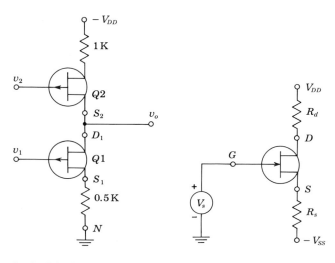

Prob. 14-16   **Prob. 14-17**

14-17   *a.* If in the amplifier stage shown the positive supply voltage V_{DD} changes by $\Delta V_{DD} = v_a$, how much does the drain-to-ground voltage change?

b. How much does the source-to-ground voltage change under the conditions in part *a*?

c. Repeat parts *a* and *b* if V_{DD} is constant but V_{SS} changes by $\Delta V_{SS} = v_s$.

14-18   (*a*) The circuit shown is a difference amplifier.   Replace each FET by its equivalent circuit as seen from its source.   Assuming that the FETs have identical parameters and that R_s is arbitrarily large, verify that $V_{o2} = I_2 R_d$ is proportional to $V_1 - V_2$, and find the difference gain $A_d \equiv V_{o2}/(V_1 - V_2)$.   (*b*) Verify that $V_{o1} = -V_{o2}$.

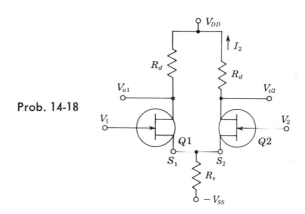

Prob. 14-18

14-19   If in the circuit of Prob. 14-18, $V_2 = 0$, then this circuit becomes a source coupled phase inverter, since $V_{o1} = -V_{o2}$.   Solve for the current I_2 by drawing the equivalent circuit, looking into the source of $Q1$ (Fig. 14-19).   Then replace $Q2$ by the equivalent circuit, looking into its drain.   The source resistance R_s may be taken as arbitrarily large.

14-20   In the circuit of Prob. 14-18, assume that $V_2 = 0$, $R_d = r_d = 10$ K, $R_s = 1$ K, and $\mu = 19$.   If the output is taken from the drain of $Q2$, find (*a*) the voltage gain, (*b*) the output impedance.   HINT: Use the equivalent circuits in Fig. 14-19.

14-21   *a.* In the circuit of Prob. 14-18, assume that $V_1 = V_2 = 0$ and that a signal V_a is applied in series with R_d in the drain branch of $Q1$.   If R_s may be taken as arbitrarily large, prove that

$$V_{o2} = \frac{R_d V_a}{2(R_d + r_d)}$$

HINT: Use the equivalent circuits in Fig. 14-19.

b. Prove that the output resistance R_o at the drain of $Q2$ is given by

$$R_o = \frac{R_d(R_d + 2r_d)}{2(R_d + r_d)}$$

14-22   In the circuit of Prob. 14-18, $V_2 = 0$, $R_d = 30$ K, $R_s = 2$ K, $\mu = 19$, and $r_d = 10$ K.   Find (*a*) the voltage gain $A_V = V_{o2}/V_1$, (*b*) the output resistance.   HINT: Use the equivalent circuits in Fig. 14-19.

14-23   The CS amplifier stage shown in Fig. 14-20 has the following parameters: $R_d = 12$ K, $R_g = 1$ M, $R_s = 470$ Ω, $V_{DD} = 30$ V, C_s is arbitrarily large, $I_{DSS} = 3$ mA, $V_P = -2.4$ V, and $r_d \gg R_d$.   Determine (a) the gate-to-source bias voltage V_{GS}, (b) the drain current I_D, (c) the quiescent voltage V_{DS}, (d) the small-signal voltage gain A_V.

14-24   The amplifier stage shown uses an n-channel FET having $I_{DSS} = 1$ mA, $V_P = -1$ V.   If the quiescent drain-to-ground voltage is 10 V, find R_1.

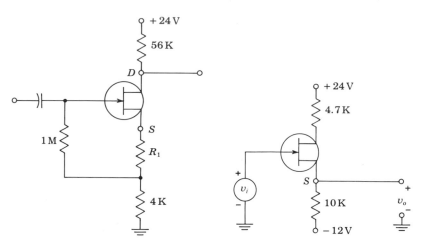

Prob. 14-24   **Prob. 14-25**

14-25   The FET shown has the following parameters: $I_{DSS} = 5.6$ mA and $V_P = -4$ V.   (a) If $v_i = 0$, find v_o.   (b) If $v_i = 10$ V, find v_o.   (c) If $v_o = 0$, find v_i. NOTE: v_i and v_o are constant voltages (and not small-signal voltages).

14-26   If $|I_{DSS}| = 4$ mA, $V_P = 4$ V, calculate the quiescent values of I_D, V_{GS}, and V_{DS}.

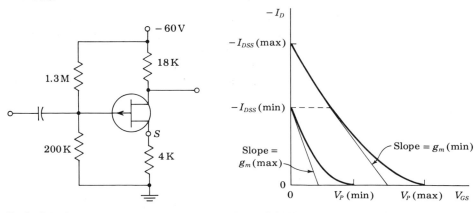

Prob. 14-26   **Prob. 14-27**

14-27   In the figure shown, two extreme transfer characteristics are indicated. The values of $V_P(\text{max})$ and $V_P(\text{min})$ are difficult to determine accurately.   Hence these values are calculated from the experimental values of $I_{DSS}(\max)$, $I_{DSS}(\min)$, $g_m(\max)$, and $g_m(\min)$. Note that g_m is the slope of the transfer curve and that both $g_m(\max)$ and $g_m(\min)$ are measured at a drain current corresponding to $I_{DSS}(\min)$. Verify that

(a) $V_P(\max) = -\dfrac{2}{g_m(\min)} [I_{DSS}(\max)I_{DSS}(\min)]^{\frac{1}{2}}$ (b) $V_P(\min) = -\dfrac{2I_{DSS}(\min)}{g_m(\max)}$

(c) If for a given FET, $I_{DSS}(\min) = 2$ mA, $I_{DSS}(\max) = 6$ mA, $g_m(\min) = 1.5$ mA/V, and $g_m(\max) = 3$ mA/V, evaluate $V_P(\max)$ and $V_P(\min)$.

14-28   The drain current in milliamperes of the enhancement-type MOSFET shown is given by

$$I_D = 0.2(V_{GS} - V_P)^2$$

in the region $V_{DS} \geq V_{GS} - V_P$. If $V_P = +3$ V, calculate the quiescent values I_D, V_{GS}, and V_{DS}.

Prob. 14-28

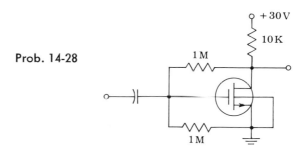

14-29   Show that if $R_L \ll 1/h_{ob2}$, the voltage gain of the hybrid cascode amplifier stage in Fig. 14-28 is given to a very good approximation by

$$A_V = g_m h_{fb} R_L$$

where g_m is the FET transconductance.

14-30   If $h_{ie} \ll R_d$, $h_{ie} \ll r_d$, $h_{fe} \gg 1$, and $\mu \gg 1$ for the circuit shown, show that

(a) $A_{V1} = \dfrac{v_{o1}}{v_i} \approx \dfrac{g_m h_{fe} R_s}{1 + g_m h_{fe} R_s}$ (b) $A_{V2} = \dfrac{v_{o2}}{v_i} \approx \dfrac{g_m h_{fe}(R_s + R_c)}{1 + g_m h_{fe} R_s}$

where g_m is the FET transconductance.

Prob. 14-30

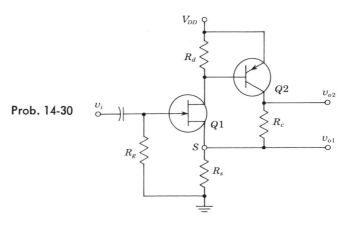

14-31 If $r_d \gg R_1$, $R_2 \gg h_{ib3}$, $1/h_{oe2} \gg h_{ib3}$, $R' \gg R_3$, and $1/h_{ob3} \gg R_3$, show that the voltage gain at low frequencies is given by

$$A_o = \frac{v_o}{v_i} = g_m(1 + h_{fe2})h_{fb3} \frac{R_1 R_3}{R_1 + h_{ie2} + h_{ib3}(1 + h_{fe2})}$$

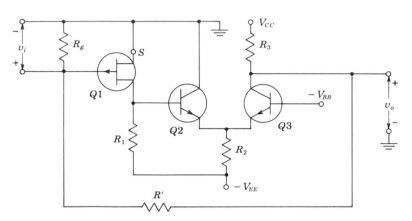

Prob. 14-31

CHAPTER 15

15-1 (*a*) Verify that Eq. (15-3) meets the stated boundary conditions. (*b*) Verify that Eq. (15-5) satisfies the diffusion equation (15-2) and that it meets the stated boundary conditions.

15-2 A silicon wafer is uniformly doped with phosphorus to a concentration of 10^{15} cm^{-3}. Refer to Table 5-1 on page 98. At room temperature (300°K) find

a. The percentage of phosphorus by weight in the wafer.

b. The conductivity and resistivity.

c. The concentration of boron, which, if added to the phosphorus-doped wafer, would halve the conductivity.

15-3 *a.* Using the data of Fig. 15-8, calculate the percent maximum concentration of arsenic (atoms per cubic centimeter) that can be achieved in solid silicon. The concentration of pure silicon may be calculated from the data in Table 5-1 on page 98.

b. Repeat part *a* for gold.

15-4 *a.* How long would it take for a fixed amount of phosphorus distributed over one surface of a 25-μ-thick silicon wafer to become substantially uniformly distributed throughout the wafer at 1300°C? Consider that the concentration is sufficiently uniform if it does not differ by more than 10 percent from that at the surface.

b. Repeat part *a* for gold, given that the diffusion coefficient of gold in silicon is 1.5×10^{-6} cm^2/sec at 1300°C.

c. Comment briefly on the significance of these results in transistor and monolithic integrated-circuit fabrication.

15-5 Show that the junction depth x_j resulting from a Gaussian impurity diffusion into an oppositely doped material of background concentration N_{BC} is given by

$$x_j = \left(2Dt \ln \frac{Q^2}{N_{BC}{}^2 \pi Dt}\right)^{\frac{1}{2}}$$

15-6 A uniformly doped n-type silicon substrate of 0.1 Ω-cm resistivity is to be subjected to a boron diffusion with constant surface concentration of 4.8×10^{18} cm^{-3}. The desired junction depth is 2.7 microns.

a. Calculate the impurity concentration for the boron diffusion as a function of distance from the surface.

b. How long will it take if the temperature at which this diffusion is conducted is 1100°C?

c. An n-p-n transistor is to be completed by diffusing phosphorus at a surface concentration of 10^{21} cm^{-3}. If the new junction is to be at a depth of 2 microns, calculate the concentration for the phosphorus diffusion as a function of distance from the surface.

d. Plot the impurity concentrations (log scale) vs. distance (linear scale) for parts a and c, assuming that the boron stays put during the phosphorus diffusion. Indicate emitter, base, and collector on your plot.

e. If the phosphorus diffusion takes 30 min, at what temperature is the apparatus operated?

15-7 List in order the steps required in fabricating a monolithic silicon integrated transistor by the epitaxial-diffused method. Sketch the cross section after each oxide growth. Label materials clearly. No buried layer is required.

15-8 Sketch *to scale* the cross section of a monolithic transistor fabricated on a 5-mil-thick silicon substrate. HINT: Refer to Sec. 15-1 and Figs. 15-12 and 15-13 for typical dimensions.

15-9 Sketch the five basic diode connections (in circuit form) for the monolithic integrated circuits. Which will have the lowest forward voltage drop? Highest breakdown voltage?

15-10 If the base sheet resistance can be held to within ± 10 percent and resistor line widths can be held to ± 0.1 mil, plot approximate tolerance of a diffused resistor as a function of line width w in mils over the range $0.5 \leq w \leq 5.0$. (Neglect contact-area and contact-placement errors.)

15-11 A 1-mil-thick silicon wafer has been doped uniformly with phosphorus to a concentration of 10^{16} cm^{-3}, plus boron to a concentration of 2×10^{15} cm^{-3}. Find its sheet resistance.

15-12 a. Calculate the resistance of a diffused crossover 4 mils long, 1 mil wide, and 2 microns thick, given that its sheet resistance is 2.2 Ω/square.

b. Repeat part a for an aluminum metalizing layer 0.5 micron thick of resistivity 2.8×10^{-6} Ω-cm. Note the advantage of avoiding diffused crossovers.

15-13   *a.* What is the minimum number of isolation regions required to realize in monolithic form the logic gate shown?

b. Draw a monolithic layout of the gate in the fashion of Fig. 15-24b.

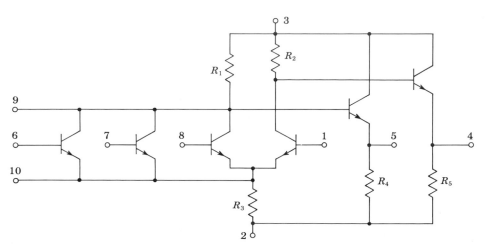

Prob. 15-13

15-14   Repeat Prob. 15-13 for the difference amplifier shown.

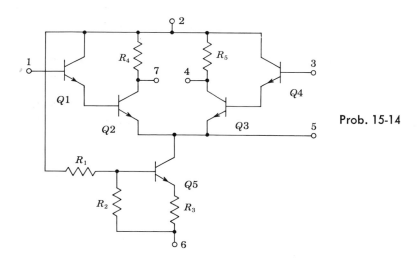

Prob. 15-14

15-15   For the circuit shown, find (*a*) the *minimum* number, (*b*) the *maximum* number, of isolation regions.

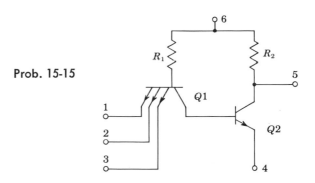

Prob. 15-15

15-16 For the circuit shown, (a) find the minimum number of isolation regions, and (b) draw a monolithic layout in the fashion of Fig. 15-25, given that (i) $Q1$, $Q2$, and $Q3$ should be single-base-stripe, 1- by 2-mil emitter transistors, (ii) $R_1 = R_2 = R_3 = 400 \ \Omega$, $R_4 = 600 \ \Omega$. Use 1-mil-wide resistors.

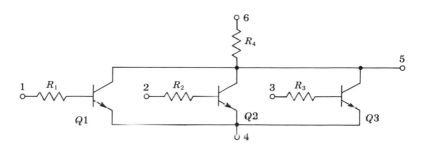

Prob. 15-16

15-17 An integrated junction capacitor has an area of 1,000 mils² and is operated at a reverse barrier potential of 1 V. The acceptor concentration of 10^{15} atoms/cm³ is much smaller than the donor concentration. Calculate the capacitance.

15-18 A thin-film capacitor has a capacitance of 0.4 pF/mil². The relative dielectric constant of silicon dioxide is 3.5. What is the thickness of the SiO_2 layer in angstroms?

15-19 The n-type epitaxial isolation region shown is 8 mils long, 6 mils wide, and 1 mil thick and has a resistivity of 0.1 Ω-cm. The resistivity of the p-type substrate is 10 Ω-cm. Find the parasitic capacitance between the isolation region and the substrate under 5-V reverse bias. Assume that the sidewalls contribute 0.1 pF/mil².

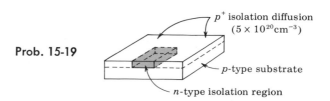

Prob. 15-19

p^+ isolation diffusion
$(5 \times 10^{20} \text{cm}^{-3})$

p-type substrate

n-type isolation region

NOTE: *In the problems that follow indicate your answer by giving the letter of the statement you consider correct.*

15-20 The typical number of diffusions used in making epitaxial-diffused silicon integrated circuits is (*a*) 1, (*b*) 2, (*c*) 3, (*d*) 4, (*e*) 5.

15-21 Repeat Prob. 15-20 for silicon MOS integrated circuits.

15-22 Epitaxial growth is used in integrated circuits (*IC*s)

a. To grow selectively single-crystal *p*-doped silicon of one resistivity on a *p*-type substrate of a different resistivity.

b. To grow single-crystal *n*-doped silicon on a single-crystal *p*-type substrate.

c. Because it yields back-to-back isolating *p-n* junctions.

d. Because it produces low parasitic capacitance.

15-23 Silicon dioxide (SiO_2) is used in *IC*s

a. Because it facilitates the penetration of diffusants.

b. Because of its high heat conduction.

c. To control the location of diffusion and to protect and insulate the silicon surface.

d. To control the concentration of diffusants.

15-24 The *p*-type substrate in a monolithic circuit should be connected to

a. The most positive voltage available in the circuit.

b. The most negative voltage available in the circuit.

c. Any dc ground point.

d. Nowhere, i.e., be left floating.

15-25 Monolithic integrated-circuit systems offer greater reliability than discrete-component systems because

a. There are fewer interconnections.

b. High-temperature metalizing is used.

c. Electric voltages are low.

d. Electric elements are closely matched.

15-26 The collector-substrate junction in the epitaxial collector structure is, approximately,

a. An abrupt junction.

b. A linearly graded junction.

c. An exponential junction.

d. None of the above.

15-27 The sheet resistance of a semiconductor is

a. An undesirable parasitic element.

b. An important characteristic of a diffused region, especially when used to form diffused resistors.

c. A characteristic whose value determines the required area for a given value of integrated capacitance.

d. A parameter whose value is important in a thin-film resistance.

15-28 Isolation in *IC*s is required

a. To make it simpler to test circuits.

b. To protect the components from mechanical damage.

c. To protect the transistor from possible "thermal runaway."

d. To minimize electrical interaction between circuit components.

15-29 Almost all resistors are made in a monolithic *IC*

a. During the emitter diffusion.

b. While growing the epitaxial layer.

c. During the base diffusion.

d. During the collector diffusion.

15-30 Increasing the yield of an integrated circuit

a. Reduces individual circuit cost.

b. Increases the cost of each good circuit.

c. Results in a lower number of good chips per wafer.

d. Means that more transistors can be fabricated on the same size wafer.

15-31 In a monolithic-type IC

a. Most isolation problems are eliminated.

b. Resistors and capacitors of any value may be made.

c. All components are fabricated into one piece of material.

d. Each transistor is diffused into a separate isolation region.

15-32 The main purpose of the metalization process is

a. To interconnect the various circuit elements.

b. To protect the chip from oxidation.

c. To act as a heat sink.

d. To supply a bonding surface for mounting the chip.

15-33 The presence of a positive-charge layer on the surface of an oxide-coated wafer may cause inversion of the wafer if the material is

a. Lightly doped n type.

b. Heavily doped n type.

c. Lightly doped p type.

d. Heavily doped p type.

CHAPTER 16

16-1 *a.* To show the effect of phase shift on the image seen on a cathode-ray screen, consider the following: The sinusoidal voltages applied to both sets of plates should be equal in phase and magnitude so that the maximum displacement in either direction on the screen is 2 in. Because of frequency distortion in the horizontal amplifier, the phase of the horizontal voltage is shifted 5° but the magnitude is changed inappreciably. Plot to scale the image that actually appears on the screen, and compare with the image that would be seen if there were no phase shift.

b. If the phase shift in both amplifiers were the same, what would be seen on the cathode-ray screen?

16-2 The input to an amplifier consists of a voltage made up of a fundamental signal and a second-harmonic signal of half the magnitude and in phase with the fundamental. Plot the resultant.

The output consists of the same magnitude of each component, but with the second harmonic shifted 90° (on the fundamental scale). This corresponds to perfect frequency response but bad phase-shift response. Plot the output and compare it with the input waveshape.

16-3 Verify Eqs. (16-5) and (16-6).

16-4 It is desired that the voltage gain of an RC-coupled amplifier at 60 Hz should not decrease by more than 10 percent from its midband value. Show that the coupling capacitance must be at least equal to $5.5/R'$, where $R' \equiv R'_o + R'_i$ is expressed in kilohms.

16-5 An RC-coupled amplifier stage uses a 12AX7 (Table 7-1) with $R_p = 15$ K, $R_g = 1$ M, $C_b = 0.02$ μF, and $C_s = 50$ pF. Evaluate (a) f_1, (b) f_2, (c) the midband voltage gain in decibels, (d) the phase shift at 20 Hz, (e) the phase shift at 200 kHz.

16-6 An *RC*-coupled amplifier stage uses a FET with $\mu = 70$, $r_d = 44$ K, $R_d = 50$ K, and $R_g = 1$ M. Assume a total shunting capacitance of 100 pF. Find (a) the midband amplification in decibels, (b) f_2, (c) C_b if $f_1 = 50$ Hz.

16-7 The bandwidth of an amplifier extends from 20 Hz to 20 kHz. Find the frequency range over which the voltage gain is down less than 1 dB from its midband value.

16-8 Prove that over the range of frequencies from $10f_1$ to $0.1f_2$ the voltage amplification is constant to within 0.5 percent and the phase shift to within ±0.1 rad.

16-9 *a.* Verify Eq. (16-19) for the maximum 3-dB frequency of a CE stage in an infinite cascade of stages.

b. Find the value of $(f_2)_{max}$ for the typical transistor whose parameters are given on page 370.

16-10 The transistor whose parameters are given on page 370 is used in a cascade of identical CE stages. A gain of 15 per stage is desired. Evaluate R_c and f_2.

16-11 A 2N1141 transistor whose parameters at $I_E = 10$ mA and $V_{CE} = 10$ V are $r_{bb'} = 80\ \Omega$, $r_{b'e} = 100\ \Omega$, $C_c = 1.5$ pF, and $C_e = 85$ pF is used in an infinite CE cascade. For each stage find (a) f_T, (b) $(R_c)_{opt}$ and the corresponding $|A_o f_2|$, (c) f_2 for $A_o = 10$, (d) f_2 for $R_c = 2$ K, (e) the maximum possible value of f_2.

16-12 For the amplifier of Prob. 16-11, find the gain if a rise time of 20 nsec/stage is desired.

16-13 Consider an infinite cascade of CE stages, using 2N247 transistors whose parameters are $g_{b'e} = 0.39$ mA/V, $g_m = 54$ mA/V, $r_{bb'} = 45\ \Omega$, $C_e = 780$ pF, and $C_c = 3.5$ pF.

a. Find the load resistance $(R_c)_{opt}$ for which the gain-bandwidth product $|A_o f_2|$ is a maximum.

b. Find $|A_o f_2|$ for $R_c = 100\ \Omega$, 1 K, 10 K, and $(R_c)_{opt}$.

16-14 For the amplifier of Prob. 16-13, find the values of R_c and A_o which will give a rise time of 1 μsec/stage.

16-15 For a cascade of CE stages, find the asymptotic values of A_o, f_2, and $|A_o f_2|$ as $R_c \to \infty$. For the typical transistor whose parameters are given on page 370, evaluate these quantities.

16-16 Verify Eq. (16-17) for $(R_c)_{opt}$. What is the significance of a value of x which is less than unity?

16-17 An ideal 1-μsec pulse is fed into an amplifier. Plot the output if the band-pass is (a) 10 MHz, (b) 1.0 MHz, and (c) 0.1 MHz.

16-18 *a.* Given a single-stage *RC*-coupled FET or tube amplifier with $C_b = 0.2\ \mu$F, $R_g = 0.5$ M, and an output-circuit resistance $R_y = 3$ K. Calculate the percentage tilt in the output if the input is a 100-Hz square wave.

b. Repeat part *a* for a transistor stage with $C_b = 10\ \mu$F, $R'_i = 2$ K, and $R_y = 3$ K.

c. For each amplifier, what is the lowest-frequency square wave which will suffer less than a 1 percent tilt?

16-19 *a.* Prove that the response of a two-stage (identical) amplifier to a unit step is

$$v_o = A_o{}^2[1 - (1 + x)\epsilon^{-x}]$$

where A_o is the midband gain and $x \equiv t/R_2C_2$.

b. For $t \ll R_2C_2$, show that the output varies quadratically with time.

16-20 If the upper 3-dB frequency of a single stage is f_2 and the rise time of a two-stage amplifier is $t_r^{(2)}$, show that $f_2 t_r^{(2)} = 0.53$. HINT: Use the result given in Prob. 16-19.

16-21 If two cascaded stages have very unequal bandpasses, show that the combined bandwidth is essentially that of the smaller.

16-22 Three identical cascaded stages have an overall upper 3-dB frequency of 20 kHz and a lower 3-dB frequency of 20 Hz. What are f_1 and f_2 of each stage?

16-23 A two-stage FET RC-coupled amplifier has the following parameters: $g_m = 10$ mA/V, $r_d = 5.5$ K, $R_d = 10$ K, $R_g = 0.5$ M, and $C_s = 50$ pF for each stage.

  a. What must be the value of C_b in order that the frequency characteristic of each stage be flat within 1 dB down to 10 Hz?

  b. Repeat part *a* if the overall gain of both stages is to be down 1 dB at 10 Hz.

  c. At what high frequency is the overall gain down 1 dB?

  d. What is the overall midband voltage gain?

16-24 A three-stage RC-coupled amplifier uses field-effect transistors with the following parameters: $g_m = 2.6$ mA/V, $r_d = 7.7$ K, $R_d = 10$ K, $R_g = 0.1$ M, $C_b = 0.005$ μF, and $C_s = 60$ pF for each stage. Evaluate (*a*) the overall midband voltage gain in decibels, (*b*) f_1, (*c*) the overall lower 3-dB frequency, (*d*) f_2, (*e*) the overall upper 3-dB frequency.

16-25 Given two RC-coupled stages connected as shown and using a 12AU7 double-triode tube. The circuit parameters are: quiescent current $= 10$ mA, $g_m = 2.2$ mA/V, $r_p = 7.7$ K, $C_{pg} = 1.5$ pF, $C_{gk} = 1.6$ pF, $C_{pk} = 0.5$ pF, and shunt wiring capacitance per stage $= 20$ pF. Find (*a*) the resistance R_p, (*b*) the midband gain of each stage and the overall gain, (*c*) the input capacitance, (*d*) f_1, (*e*) f_2 for each stage. Why do the two stages have different values of f_2 whereas f_1 is the same for both stages? (*f*) How are the foregoing results modified if the output is observed on an oscilloscope whose input impedance is a 1-M resistance in parallel with a 20 pF capacitance?

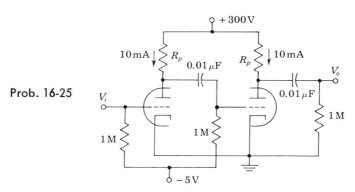

Prob. 16-25

16-26 An RC-coupled amplifier uses a 6AK5 pentode stage ($g_m = 5.1$ mA/V and $C_o + C_i = 6.8$ pF). If $R_g = 1$ M, $C_b = 0.01$ μF, and a voltage gain of 15 per stage is desired, calculate (assume that stray wiring capacitance from signal lead to ground in each stage is 10 pF) (*a*) R_p, (*b*) f_1, (*c*) f_2.

If 6CG7 (Table 7-1) triode tubes are used instead of the pentodes, repeat parts *a* to *c*. Assume $C_{gp} = 3.9$ pF, $C_{gk} = 2.4$ pF, and $C_{pk} = 0.7$ pF.

16-27 A tube amplifier consists of two identical stages. The total effective shunt capacitance across each stage is the same and is equal to 20 pF. The 3-dB bandwidth of the complete amplifier is 10 MHz.   If the tubes used have $g_m = 10$ mA/V, find the gain of the complete amplifier.

   16-28   A pentode amplifier consists of two identical stages.   The total effective shunt capacitance across each stage is the same and is equal to 20 pF.   The circuit parameters are $g_m = 10$ mA/V, $r_p = 1$ M, $R_p = 2.5$ K, $R_g = 1$ M, and $C_b = 0.5$ μF. Calculate for the overall amplifier (a) the gain, (b) the rise time, (c) the frequency of a square-wave signal which will suffer a 10 percent tilt when transmitted through this amplifier.

   16-29   a. Show that the relative voltage gain of an amplifier with an emitter resistor R_e bypassed by a capacitor C_z may be expressed in the form

$$\frac{A_1}{A_o} = \frac{1 + j\omega R_e C_z}{B + j\omega R_e C_z}$$

where $B = 1 + R'/R$, $R' = R_e(1 + h_{fe})$, and $R = R_s + h_{ie}$.
   b. Prove that the lower 3-dB frequency is

$$f_1 = \frac{\sqrt{B^2 - 2}}{2\pi R_e C_z}$$

What is the physical meaning of the condition $B < \sqrt{2}$?
   c. If $B \gg 1$, show that $f_1 \approx f_p$, the pole frequency as defined in Eqs. (16-35).

   16-30   a. For the circuit of Fig. 16-15, with a bypassed cathode resistor, verify that the gain is

$$A_V = \frac{-g_m R_L}{1 + g_m Z_k}$$

where Z_k is the parallel impedance of R_k and C_k.
   b. Prove that the midband gain is $A_o = -g_m R_L$.
   c. Verify Eq. (16-38) for A_V/A_o.

   16-31   A pentode amplifier stage has the following parameters: $g_m = 5$ mA/V, $R_L = 2$ K, $R_k = 100$ Ω, $C_k = 500$ μF, $C_b = 0.25$ μF, and $R_g = 0.5$ M.   If a 200-Hz square wave is applied to the input, find the percentage tilt in the output waveform.

   16-32   Find the percentage tilt in the output of a transistor stage caused by a capacitor C_z bypassing an emitter resistor R_e.   Use the following method: If V is the magnitude of the input step, then from Fig. 16-13b (and using lowercase letters for instantaneous values),

$$v_o = -h_{fe} i_b R_c = -h_{fe} R_c \frac{V - v_{en}}{R}$$

where $R \equiv R_s + h_{ie}$.   Take as a first approximation $v_{en} = 0$.   Calculate the corresponding current, and assuming that all the emitter current passes through C_z, calculate v_{en}, and then show that

$$v_o = -\frac{h_{fe} R_c V}{R}\left[1 - \frac{(1 + h_{fe})t}{R C_z}\right]$$

From this result verify Eq. (16-37).

16-33   *a.* Find the noise bandwidth B for an amplifier for which $A_{Vo} = 1$, $f_1 = 0$ Hz, and

$$|A_V(f)| = \frac{1}{\sqrt{1 + (f/f_2)^2}}$$

b. Compute B if $f_2 = 10$ kHz.

16-34   *a.* Find the mean-square value $V_o{}^2$ of the output noise voltage for the circuit shown.   The circle represents a generator supplying Johnson noise to the RC combination.

   b. Prove that

$$\tfrac{1}{2}CV_o{}^2 = \tfrac{1}{2}kT$$

This result is known as the *equipartition theorem.*

Prob. 16-34

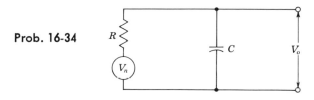

CHAPTER 17

17-1   For the circuit shown in Fig. 17-2b, with $R_c = 4$ K, $R_L = 4$ K, $R_b = 20$ K, $R_s = 1$ K, and the transistor parameters given in Table 11-2, find
   a. The current gain I_L/I_s.
   b. The voltage gain V_o/V_s, where $V_s = I_s R_s$.
   c. The transconductance I_L/V_s.
   d. The transresistance V_o/I_s.
   e. The input resistance seen by the source.
   f. The output resistance seen by the load.
Make reasonable approximations.   Neglect all capacitive effects.

17-2   Repeat Prob. 17-1 for the circuit shown, with $g_m = 5$ mA/V and $r_d = 100$ K

Prob. 17-2

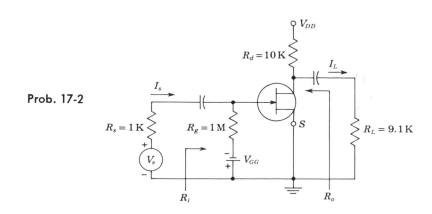

17-3 *a.* For the circuit shown in Fig. 17-7c, find the ac voltage V_i as a function of V_s and V_f. Assume that the noninverting amplifier input resistance is infinite, that $A = A_V = 1,000$, $\beta = V_f/V_o = 1/100$, $R_s = R_e = R_c = 1$ K, $h_{ie} = 1$ K, and $h_{fe} = 100$.

b. Find $A_{Vf} = V_o/V_s = AV_i/V_s$.

17-4 Repeat Prob. 17-3 for the circuit of Fig. 17-7d, with $R_s = 0$, $R_{c1} = R_{c2} = 1$ K, and $R_e = 10$ K. Assume that the transistors are identical and that $h_{ie} = 1$ K, $h_{fe} = 100$, $h_{re} = 0$, and $1/h_{oe} = 40$ K.

17-5 An amplifier consists of three identical stages connected in cascade. The output voltage is sampled and returned to the input in series opposing. If it is specified that the relative change dA_f/A_f in the closed-loop voltage gain A_f must not exceed Ψ_f, show that the minimum value of the open-loop gain A of the amplifier is given by

$$A = 3A_f \frac{|\Psi_1|}{|\Psi_f|}$$

where $\Psi_1 \equiv dA_1/A_1$ is the relative change in the voltage gain of each stage of the amplifier.

17-6 An amplifier with open-loop voltage gain $A_V = 1,000 \pm 100$ is available. It is necessary to have an amplifier whose voltage gain varies by no more than ±0.1 percent.

a. Find the reverse transmission factor β of the feedback network used.

b. Find the gain with feedback.

17-7 An amplifier without feedback gives a fundamental output of 36 V with 7 percent second-harmonic distortion when the input is 0.028 V.

a. If 1.2 percent of the output is fed back into the input in a negative voltage-series feedback circuit, what is the output voltage?

b. For an output of 36 V with 1 percent second-harmonic distortion, what is the input voltage?

17-8 An amplifier with an open-loop voltage gain of 1,000 delivers 10 W of output power at 10 percent second-harmonic distortion when the input signal is 10 mV. If 40 dB negative voltage-series feedback is applied and the output power is to remain at 10 W, determine (*a*) the required input signal, (*b*) the percent harmonic distortion.

17-9 A single-stage *RC*-coupled amplifier with a midband voltage gain of 1,000 is made into a feedback amplifier by feeding 10 percent of its output voltage in series with the input opposing.

a. As the frequency is varied, to what value does the voltage gain of the amplifier without feedback fall before the gain of the amplifier with feedback falls 3 dB?

b. What is the ratio of the half-power frequencies with feedback to those without feedback?

c. If $f_1 = 20$ Hz and $f_2 = 50$ kHz for the amplifier without feedback, what are the corresponding values after feedback has been added?

17-10 Assume that the parameters of the circuit are $r_d = 10$ K, $R_g = 1$ M, $R_1 = 40\ \Omega$, $R_d = 50$ K, and $g_m = 6$ mA/V. Neglect the reactances of all capacitors. Find the voltage gain and output impedance of the circuit at the terminals (*a*) AN, (*b*) BN.

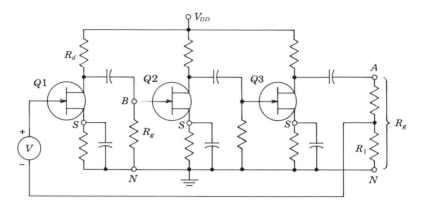

Prob. 17-10

17-11 Prove that for voltage-series feedback, with $R_s = 0$,

$$A_{If} = A_I$$

HINT: $A_V = A_I R_L / R_i$.

17-12 The circuit shown represents a dc feedback amplifier consisting of a differential input pair $Q1$-$Q2$ followed by two stages, $Q3$ and $Q4$.

All transistors are identical, and their parameters are

$$h_{ie} = 1 \text{ K} \qquad h_{oe} = 10 \text{ } \mu\text{mhos} \qquad h_{re} = 2.5 \times 10^{-4} \qquad h_{fe} = 100$$

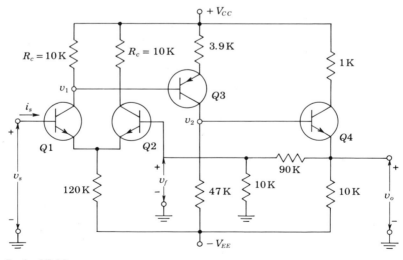

Prob. 17-12

Make reasonable approximations resulting in errors of no more than 10 percent.   Compute the following quantities at low frequencies:

    a. The difference gain A_d and common-mode gain A_c for the differential amplifier defined by the equation

$$v_1 = A_d(v_f - v_s) + A_c \frac{v_f + v_s}{2}$$

Make use of the symmetry of the circuit (Sec. 12-12).

    b. v_2/v_1, v_o/v_2, and $A = v_o/v_1$.   Assume that $Q3$ does not load the 10-K resistance.

    c. $A_V = v_o/v_s$.

17-13   The transistors in the feedback amplifier shown are identical, and their h parameters are as given in Table 11-2.   Make reasonable approximations whenever appropriate, and neglect the reactance of the capacitors.

    a. With switch S in position A, calculate $R_i = V_i'/I_i$, $A_I = -I/I_i$, $A_V = V_o/V_i'$, $A_{Vs} = V_o/V_s$, and R_o.

    b. Repeat part a with switch S in position B.

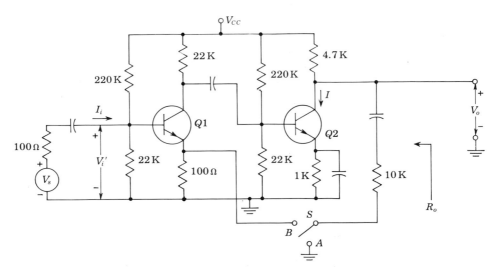

Prob. 17-13

17-14   A modified second-collector to first-emitter feedback pair is shown with dc biasing omitted for simplicity.   All transistors are identical.   Neglecting h_{re}, h_{rb}, h_{oe}, h_{ob}, and assuming that $h_{fe} \gg 1$, $h_{fe}R_1 \gg R_s + h_{ie}$, and $R_2 \gg h_{ib3}$, show that

    a. The voltage gain $A_V = V_o/V_i \approx R_2/R_1$.

    b. The output resistance $R_o \approx R_c \| (R_2/h_{fe})$.

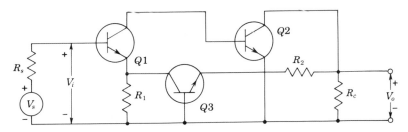

Prob. 17-14

17-15 Consider the transistor stage of Fig. 17-21a.

a. Neglecting h_{re} and h_{oe} and assuming that $h_{fe} \gg 1$, show that the voltage gain is

$$A_f = \frac{V_o}{V_s} \approx \frac{-h_{fe}R_L}{R_s + h_{ie} + h_{fe}R_e}$$

b. If the relative change dA_f/A_f of the voltage gain A_f must not exceed a specified value Ψ_f due to variations of h_{fe}, show that the minimum required value of the emitter resistor R_e is given by

$$R_e = \frac{R_s + h_{ie}}{h_{fe}} \left(\frac{dh_{fe}/h_{fe}}{\Psi_f} - 1 \right)$$

17-16 Find an expression for the output resistance of the transistor amplifier stage shown in Fig. 17-21a, using Eq. (17-32). The result should be identical with Eq. (12-51), with $h_{re} = 0$.

17-17 Verify Eq. (17-32) for the output resistance of the current-series feedback amplifier of Fig. 17-19 by the following method: Let $V_s = 0$, apply a voltage V to the output, and calculate the current I drawn from V. Then $R_{of} = V/I$.

17-18 In the two-stage feedback amplifier shown, the transistors are identical and have the following parameters: $h_{fe} = 50$, $h_{ie} = 2$ K, $h_{re} = 0$, and $h_{oe} = 0$. Calculate (a) $A'_V = V'_o/V_i$, (b) R_{if}, (c) $A_V = V_o/V_i$, (d) $A_{Vf} = V_o/V_s$. (e) Evaluate A_{Vf} from Eq. (17-49). Compare with the result obtained in part d.

Prob. 17-18

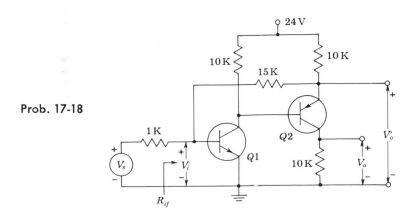

17-19 Repeat Prob. 17-18 for the amplifier shown.

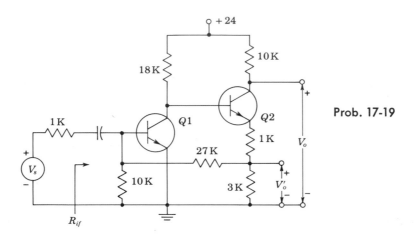

Prob. 17-19

17-20 *a.* Verify Eq. (17-53).

b. Evaluate R_{of} for the voltage-shunt feedback circuit discussed in the example of Sec. 17-9.

17-21 For the transistor feedback-amplifier stage shown, $h_{fe} = 100$, $h_{ie} = 1$ K, while h_{re} and h_{oe} are negligible. Determine with $R_e = 0$ the following: (*a*) $A_V = V_o/V_i$, (*b*) $A_{Vs} = V_o/V_s$, (*c*) R_{if}, (*d*) R_{of}. (*e*) Repeat the four preceding calculations if $R_e = 1$ K.

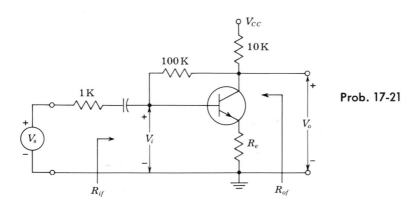

Prob. 17-21

17-22 The transistors in the feedback amplifier shown are identical, and their h parameters are given in Table 11-2. Make reasonable approximations where appropriate, and neglect the reactances of the capacitors. With the switch open, (*a*) calculate R_i, $A_I = -I_o/I_i$, $A_V = V_o/V_i$, $A_{Vs} = V_o/V_s$, and R_o. (*b*) Repeat part *a* with the switch closed.

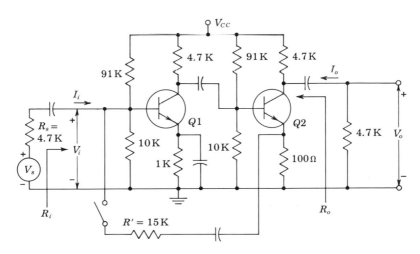

Prob. 17-22

17-23 Let h_{fe} of $Q1$ and $Q2$ of Prob. 17-22 increase to 100. If all other parameters remain constant, compute R_i, A_I, A_V, A_{Vs}, and R_o with the switch closed.

17-24 For the circuit shown, prove that

$$A_{Vf} = \frac{V_o}{V_s} = -\frac{R'}{R} \frac{1}{1 + \dfrac{R'}{R_m}\left(\dfrac{R_i + R'}{R'} + \dfrac{R_i}{R}\right)}$$

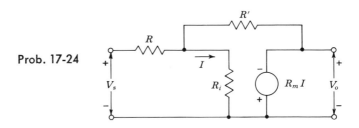

Prob. 17-24

17-25 For the CB feedback amplifier shown, assume that $h_{ib} = 0$, $h_{rb} = 0$, and $h_{ob} = 0$.

  a. Prove that

$$A_{Vf} = \frac{v_o}{v_i} = \frac{\dfrac{1}{R_f} - \dfrac{h_{fb}}{R_b}}{\dfrac{1 + h_{fb}}{R_c} + \dfrac{1}{R_f}}$$

b. For a specified value of A_{Vf}, show that

$$\frac{R_f}{R_b} = \frac{1}{h_{fb}}\left\{1 - A_{Vf}\left[(1 + h_{fb})\frac{R_f}{R_c} + 1\right]\right\}$$

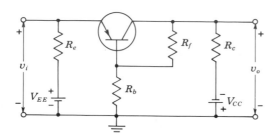

Prob. 17-25

17-26 a. Prove that the circuit shown is another equivalent circuit of the operational amplifier of Fig. 17-26b, where

$$\alpha \equiv \frac{Y}{Y' + Y + Y_i}$$

and

$$\beta \equiv \frac{-Y'}{Y' + Y + Y_i}$$

HINT: Use the principle of superposition.

b. Show that

$$A_{Vf} = \frac{V_o}{V_s} = \frac{YA_V/(Y' + Y + Y_i)}{1 - Y'A_V/(Y' + Y + Y_i)}$$

where $A_V \equiv V_o/V_i$.

c. Show that A_{Vf} in part b reduces to Eq. (17-56).

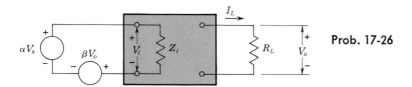

Prob. 17-26

17-27 The differential-input operational amplifier shown consists of a base amplifier with infinite gain. Terminals 1 and 2 are inverting and noninverting, respectively. (The output at 4 is in phase with the input at 2.) Show that

$$A_{Vf} = \frac{V_o}{V_s} = 1 + \frac{R_2}{R_1}$$

HINT: $V_{12} = V_i = 0$. Why?

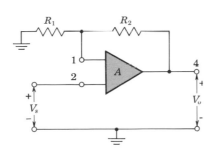

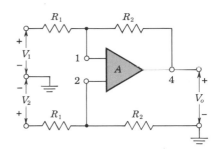

Prob. 17-27   Prob. 17-28

17-28 The differential-input operational amplifier shown consists of a base amplifier of infinite gain. Terminals 1 and 2 are inverting and noninverting, respectively. Show that

$$V_o = \frac{R_2}{R_1} (V_2 - V_1)$$

17-29 Repeat Prob. 17-28 for the amplifier shown, where V_o is the differential output.

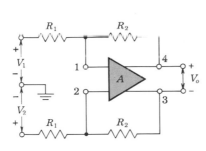

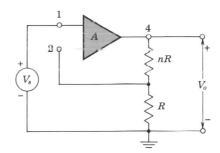

Prob. 17-29   Prob. 17-30

17-30 In the base differential-input amplifier of the circuit shown, 1 and 2 are inverting and noninverting terminals, respectively. Assuming infinite input resistance, zero output resistance, and finite gain A,

    a. Obtain an expression of the gain $A_{Vf} = V_o/V_s$.

    b. Show that $\lim_{A \to \infty} A_{Vf} = n + 1$.

17-31 Derive the exact formula (17-56) for the voltage gain of an operational amplifier from the equivalent circuit of Fig. 17-28.

17-32 Design an operational amplifier whose output (for a sinusoidal signal) is equal in magnitude to its input and leads the input by 45°.

17-33 Consider a single-stage operational amplifier with a gain of -100. If $Z = R$ and $Z' = -jX_C$, with $R = X_C$, calculate the gain as a complex number.

17-34 Given an operational amplifier consisting of R and L in series for Z, and C for Z'. If the input is a constant V, find the output v_o as a function of time. Assume an infinite open-loop gain.

17-35 For the circuit shown, prove that the output voltage is given by

$$-v_o = \frac{R_2}{R_1} v + \left(R_2 C + \frac{L}{R_1} \right) \frac{dv}{dt} + LC \frac{d^2 v}{dt^2}$$

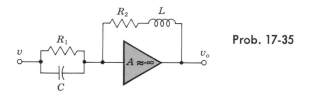

Prob. 17-35

17-36 Given an operational amplifier with Z consisting of a resistor R in parallel with a capacitor C, and Z' consisting of a resistor R'. The input is a sweep voltage $v = \alpha t$. Prove that the output is a sweep voltage that starts with an initial step. Thus show that

$$v_o = -\alpha R'C - \alpha \frac{R'}{R} t$$

Assume an infinite open-loop gain.

17-37 Given an operational amplifier with infinite open-loop gain consisting of a 100-K resistance for Z and a series combination of a 50-K resistance and a 0.001 μF capacitance for Z'. If the capacitor is initially uncharged, and if at $t = 0$ the input voltage $v_s = 10\epsilon^{-t/\tau}$, with $\tau = 5 \times 10^{-4}$ sec, is applied, find $v_o(t)$.

17-38 Sketch an operational amplifier circuit having an input v and an output which is approximately $-5v - 3dv/dt$.

17-39 *a.* The input to the operational integrator of Fig. 17-30 is a step voltage of magnitude V. Prove that the output is

$$v_o = A V (1 - \epsilon^{-t/RC(1-A)})$$

b. Compare this result with that obtained if the step voltage is impressed upon a simple RC integrating network (without the use of an amplifier). Show that, for large values of RC, both solutions represent a voltage which varies approximately linearly with time. Verify that if $-A \gg 1$, the slope of the ramp output is approximately the same for both circuits. Also prove that the deviation from linearity for the amplifier circuit is $1/(1 - A)$ times that of the simple RC circuit.

17-40 *a.* The input to an operational differentiator whose open-loop gain A is finite is a ramp voltage $v = \alpha t$. Show that the output is

$$v_o = \frac{A}{1 - A} \alpha RC (1 - \epsilon^{-t(1-A)/RC})$$

b. Compare this result with that obtained if the same input is impressed upon a simple RC differentiating network (without the use of an amplifier). Show that, approximately, the same final constant output $RC\, dv/dt$ is obtained. Also show that the operational-amplifier output reaches this correct value of the differentiated input much more quickly than does the simple RC circuit.

17-41　Given an operational amplifier with Z consisting of R in series with C, and Z' consisting of R' in parallel with C'. The input is a step voltage of magnitude V.

　　a. Show by qualitative argument that the output voltage must start at zero, reach a maximum, and then again fall to zero.

　　b. Show that if $R'C' \neq RC$, the output is given by

$$v_o = \frac{R'CV}{R'C' - RC} (\epsilon^{-t/RC} - \epsilon^{-t/R'C'})$$

17-42　Sketch in block-diagram form a computer, using operational amplifiers, to solve the differential equation

$$\frac{dv}{dt} + 0.5v + 0.1 \sin \omega t = 0$$

An oscillator is available which will provide a signal $\sin \omega t$. Use only resistors and capacitors.

17-43　Set up a computer in block-diagram form, using operational amplifiers, to solve the following differential equation:

$$\frac{d^3y}{dt^3} + 2\frac{d^2y}{dt^2} - 4\frac{dy}{dt} + 2y = x(t)$$

where

$$y(0) = 0 \qquad \frac{dy}{dt}\bigg|_{t=0} = -2 \qquad \text{and} \qquad \frac{d^2y}{dt^2}\bigg|_{t=0} = 3$$

Assume that a generator is available which will provide the signal $x(t)$.

17-44　An operational amplifier has a base amplifier whose *unloaded* open-loop gain and impedance are A_v and Z_o, respectively. These are the values of gain and output impedance with the impedance Z' omitted. Assume zero input admittance.

　　a. Draw the equivalent circuit of the operational amplifier. Include an external impedance Z_L across the output terminals.

　　b. Find the expression for the ratio V_o/V_i which gives the gain without feedback but with the amplifier loaded with Z'.

　　c. From part *b* deduce that the open-loop loaded gain A and output impedance Z'_o (with the base amplifier loaded by Z') are given by

$$A = A_v \frac{Z' + Z_o/A_v}{Z_o + Z'} \qquad \text{and} \qquad Z'_o = \frac{Z_o Z'}{Z_o + Z'}$$

HINT: Write

$$\frac{V_o}{V_i} = \frac{AZ_L}{Z_L + Z_o}$$

　　d. Find the expression for V_o/V_s which gives the gain with feedback. Write

$$\frac{V_o}{V_s} = \frac{A_{Vf}Z_L}{Z_L + Z_{of}}$$

and prove that A_{Vf} is given by Eq. (17-56) and that the output impedance with feedback Z_{of} is given by

$$Z_{of} = \frac{Z'_o}{1 - AZ/(Z + Z')}$$

17-45   Prove that the polar plot of the loop gain of an RC-coupled amplifier is a circle in the complex plane located as in Fig. 17-35.

17-46   *a.* The possibility of oscillation is to be avoided in the three-stage RC-coupled amplifier of Prob. 17-10.   Prove that the midband loop gain must be kept below 8.

   b. What is the maximum possible value of R_1 if all other component values are as specified in Prob. 17-10?

17-47   Verify Eq. (17-64) for the feedback factor of the phase-shift network of Fig. 17-39, assuming that this network does not load the amplifier.   Prove that the phase shift of V_o/V_i is 180° for $\alpha^2 = 6$ and that at this frequency $\beta = \frac{1}{29}$.

17-48   *a.* For the network of Prob. 17-47, show that the input impedance is given by

$$Z_i = R\frac{1 - 5\alpha^2 - j(6\alpha - \alpha^3)}{3 - \alpha^2 - j4\alpha}$$

   b. Show that the input impedance at the frequency of the oscillator, $\alpha = \sqrt{6}$, is $(0.83 - j2.70)R$.

   Note that if the frequency is varied by varying C, the input impedance remains constant.   However, if the frequency is varied by varying R, the impedance is varied in proportion to R.

17-49   Design a phase-shift oscillator to operate at a frequency of 5 kHz.   Use one of the triodes in Table 7-1.   The phase-shift network is not to load down the amplifier.

   a. Which tubes in Table 7-1 *cannot* be used?

   b. Find the minimum value of the plate-circuit resistance R_p for which the circuit will oscillate.

   c. Find the product RC.

   d. Choose a reasonable value for R, and find C.

17-50   *a.* A two-stage FET oscillator uses the phase-shifting network shown. Prove that

$$\frac{V_o}{V_i} = \frac{1}{3 + j(\omega RC - 1/\omega RC)}$$

   b. Show that the frequency of oscillation is $f = 1/2\pi RC$ and that the gain must exceed 3.

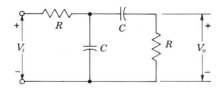

Prob. 17-50

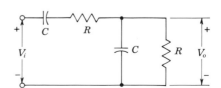

Prob. 17-51

17-51   a. Find V_o/V_i for the network shown.

b. Sketch the circuit of a phase-shift oscillator, using this feedback network.

c. Find the expression for the frequency of oscillation, assuming that the network does not load down the amplifier.

d. Find the minimum gain required for oscillation.

17-52   Consider the two-section RC network shown.   Find the V_o/V_i function, and verify that it is not possible to obtain $180°$ phase shift with a finite attenuation.

Prob. 17-52

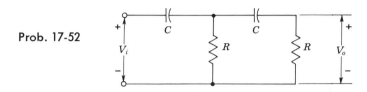

17-53   For the feedback network shown find (a) the transfer function, (b) the input impedance.   (c) If this network is used in a phase-shift oscillator, find the frequency of oscillation and the minimum amplifier voltage gain.   Assume that the network does not load down the amplifier.

Prob. 17-53

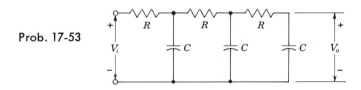

17-54   Take into account the loading of the RC network in the phase-shift oscillator of Fig. 17-39.   If R_o is the output impedance of the amplifier (assume that C_s is arbitrarily large), prove that the frequency of oscillation f and the minimum gain A are given by

$$f = \frac{1}{2\pi RC}\frac{1}{\sqrt{6 + 4(R_o/R)}} \qquad A = 29 + 23\frac{R_o}{R} + 4\left(\frac{R_o}{R}\right)^2$$

17-55   For the FET oscillator shown, (a) find V_o/V_i, (b) the frequency of oscillations, (c) the minimum gain of the source follower required for oscillations.

Prob. 17-55

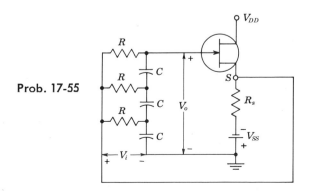

17-56   Verify Eqs. (17-65) and (17-66) for the transistor phase-shift oscillator of Fig. 17-40.

17-57   Apply the Barkhausen criterion to the tuned-plate oscillator, and verify Eqs. (17-67) and (17-68).

17-58   *a.* At what frequency will the circuit shown oscillate, if at all?

b. Find the minimum value of R needed to sustain oscillations.   The FETs are identical with $g_m = 1.6$ mA/V and $r_d = 44$ K.

HINT: Assume a voltage V from gate G_1 of $Q1$ to ground but with the point G' not connected to the gate G_1.   Calculate the loop gain from the equivalent circuit, obtained by looking into each source.

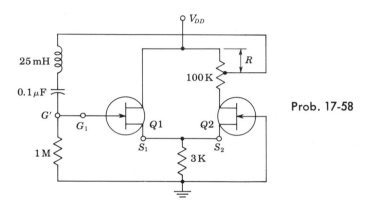

Prob. 17-58

17-59   In the cathode-coupled oscillator circuit shown, Z represents a parallel *RLC* combination.   Assume that R_k, R_g, and C_b are arbitrarily large.

a. At what frequency will the circuit oscillate, if at all?

b. Prove that the minimum value of R is $2r_p/(\mu - 1) \approx 2/g_m$ if the circuit is to oscillate.

HINT: Assume a voltage V from the grid G_2 of $V2$ to ground, but with the point G' not connected to the grid G_2.   Calculate the loop gain from the equivalent circuit, obtained by looking into each cathode.

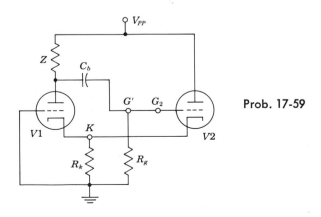

Prob. 17-59

17-60 In the circuit of Prob. 17-59, the impedance Z consists of an inductor L in parallel with a capacitance C. The series resistance of the inductor is r. Prove that the frequency of oscillation is given by

$$\omega^2 = \frac{1}{LC}\left(1 - \frac{r^2 C}{L}\right)$$

and the minimum transconductance is given by

$$g_m = \frac{2\mu r C}{(\mu - 1)L}$$

17-61 Verify Eq. (17-69) by the two methods outlined in the text.

17-62 *a.* Consider a vacuum-tube Colpitts oscillator, taking into account the resistance r in series with the inductor L. Prove that the frequency of oscillation is given by

$$\omega^2 = \frac{1}{L}\left[\frac{1}{C_1} + \frac{1}{C_2}\left(1 + \frac{r}{r_p}\right)\right]$$

b. If $r/r_p \ll 1$, prove that the minimum transconductance is given by

$$g_m = \frac{r\mu C_2 (C_1 + C_2)}{L(\mu C_2 - C_1)}$$

17-63 *a.* Consider the Hartley oscillator of Fig. 17-43a, with the addition of a cathode resistor R_k. If the resistances of the inductors are r_1 and r_2, respectively, find the frequency of oscillation.

b. Find the value of R_k for which the loop gain will just equal unity.

17-64 The Hartley oscillator of Fig. 17-43a is modified by placing C_3 across L_2 and by allowing a mutual inductance M between L_1 and L_2. Find the frequency of oscillation.

17-65 *a.* Verify Eq. (17-75) for the reactance of a crystal.

b. Prove that the ratio of the parallel- to series-resonant frequencies is given approximately by $1 + \frac{1}{2}C/C'$.

c. If $C = 0.04$ pF and $C' = 2.0$ pF, by what percent is the parallel-resonant frequency greater than the series-resonant frequency?

17-66 A crystal has the following parameters: $L = 0.33$ H, $C = 0.065$ pF, $C' = 1.0$ pF, and $R = 5.5$ K.

a. Find the series-resonant frequency.

b. By what percent does the parallel-resonant frequency exceed the series-resonant frequency?

c. Find the Q of the crystal.

CHAPTER 18

18-1 *a.* Nonlinear distortion results in the generation of frequencies in the output that are not present in the input. If the dynamic curve can be represented by Eq. (18-6), and if the input signal is given by

$$x = X_1 \cos \omega_1 t + X_2 \cos \omega_2 t$$

show that the output will contain a dc term and sinusoidal terms of (angular) frequency ω_1, ω_2, $2\omega_1$, $2\omega_2$, $\omega_1 + \omega_2$, and $\omega_1 - \omega_2$.

b. Generalize the results of part *a* by showing that if the dynamic curve must be represented by higher-order terms in *x*, the output will contain intermodulation frequencies, given by the sum and difference of integral multiples of ω_1 and ω_2, for example, $2\omega_1 \pm 2\omega_2$, $2\omega_1 \pm \omega_2$, $3\omega_1 \pm \omega_2$, etc.

18-2 A type 6L6 tube (Fig. D-7) is operated as a triode with a load resistance of 2 K and a plate supply of 300 V. The grid bias is -15 V, and the peak grid signal is 15 V.

    a. What is the fundamental current output?

    b. What is the percent second-harmonic distortion?

    c. What is the direct current?

18-3 A 6CG7 (Table 7-1 and Fig. D-2) is to be operated from a plate supply voltage of 240 V. A voltage gain of approximately 10 is desired. The peak-to-peak 2,000-Hz sinusoidal input voltage is 12 V. If the grid is never to swing positively, specify (*a*) the load resistance, (*b*) the bias voltage, (*c*) the quiescent current, (*d*) the percent second-harmonic distortion, (*e*) the fundamental voltage and power gains.

18-4 A transistor supplies 0.85 W to a 4-K load. The zero-signal dc collector current is 31 mA, and the dc collector current with signal is 34 mA. Determine the percent second-harmonic distortion.

18-5 The input excitation of an amplifier is $x = X_m \sin \omega t$. Prove that the output current can be represented by a Fourier series which contains only odd sine components and even cosine components.

18-6 Supply the missing steps in the derivation of Eqs. (18-18).

18-7 Obtain a five-point schedule for determining B_o, B_1, B_2, B_3, and B_4 in terms of I_{max}, $I_{0.707}$, I_b, $I_{-0.707}$, and I_{min}.

18-8 A power triode feeds a load resistance R_L through an ideal transformer of turns ratio *n*. Assuming that the small-signal model is valid, show that the voltage gain is

$$A = \frac{n\mu\delta}{n^2 + \delta}$$

where $\delta \equiv R_L/r_p$

    μ = amplification factor

    r_p = plate resistance of tube

Show that for a fixed value of δ and μ the maximum gain is $n\mu/2$, and is obtained when the turns ratio is adjusted to equal $\delta^{\frac{1}{2}}$.

18-9 The *p-n-p* transistor whose input and output characteristics are given in Fig. 18-5 is used in the circuit of Fig. 18-4, with $R_s = 0$ and $R'_L = (N_1/N_2)^2 R_L = 10$ Ω. The quiescent point is $I_C = -1.1$ A and $V_{CE} = -7.5$ V. The peak-to-peak 2,000-Hz sinusoidal base-to-emitter voltage is 140 mV.

    a. What is the fundamental current output?

    b. What is the percent second-, third-, and fourth-harmonic distortion?

    c. What is the output power?

    d. What is the rectification component B_o of the collector current?

Neglect any changes in the operating point.

18-10 Verify the data plotted in Fig. 18-6 for $R'_L = 20$ Ω.

18-11 For the operating conditions indicated in Fig. 18-5, calculate the fundamental power P_1 for (*a*) $R'_L = 5$ Ω, (*b*) $R'_L = 30$ Ω.

18-12 Repeat Prob. 18-9, but now assume a current drive (large R_s) so that the base current is sinusoidal, with a peak-to-peak value of 30 mA.

18-13   A power transistor operating class A in the circuit of Fig. 18-4 is to deliver
a maximum of 5 W to a 4-Ω load ($R_L = 4\ \Omega$).   The quiescent point is adjusted for
symmetrical clipping, and the collector supply voltage is $V_{CC} = 20$ V.   Assume ideal
characteristics, as in Fig. 18-10, with $V_{min} = 0$.

    a. What is the transformer turns ratio $n = N_2/N_1$?

    b. What is the peak collector current I_m?

    c. What is the quiescent operating point I_C, V_{CE}?

    d. What is the collector-circuit efficiency?

18-14   A 6L6 power triode (Fig. D-7) operates at $V_P = 250$ V.   The maximum
allowable plate dissipation is 10 W.   Calculate the power output and second-harmonic
distortion for an effective load resistance R'_L of (*a*) 3 K, (*b*) 7 K.

18-15   Calculate the output power, the plate-circuit efficiency, and the percent
second-harmonic distortion of a 6L6 connected as a triode (Fig. D-7) when supplying
power to an effective 4,000-Ω load from a 300-V supply, with $V_G = -22.5$ V, if (*a*) the
load is series-fed, (*b*) the load is transformer-coupled to the tube.   A 22.5-V peak sinusoidal signal is impressed on the grid of the tube.

18-16   Draw three transistor collector characteristics to correspond to base cur-
rents $I_B + I_{bm}$, I_B, $I_B - I_{bm}$.   Draw the load line through the point $i_C = 0$, $v_{CE} = V_{CC}$,
and the quiescent point $i_B = I_B$, $i_C = I_C$, and $v_{CE} = V_C$.   This corresponds to a series-
fed resistance load.

    a. Assuming that the input signal is zero, indicate on the i_C-v_{CE} plane the areas that
represent the total input power to the collector circuit, the collector dissipation, and
the power loss in the load resistance.

    b. Repeat part *a* if the input signal is sinusoidal, with a peak value equal to I_{bm}.
Also, indicate the area that represents the output power.

    c. The ratio of what two areas gives the collector-circuit efficiency?

    d. Repeat parts *a* to *c* for a shunt-fed load.   Assume that the static resistance is
small but not zero.

18-17   A 6L6 is operated at the quiescent point $V_{G1} = -14$ V, $V_P = 250$ V, and
$V_{G2} = 250$ V.   The peak grid swing is 14 V.   Use Fig. 7-15.

    a. What must the load resistance be in order to eliminate second-harmonic
distortion?

    b. For a load resistance of 2.5 K, calculate the percent third-harmonic distortion.

18-18   A 6L6 (Fig. 7-15) operates at the quiescent point $V_{G1} = -15$ V, $V_P =$
200 V, $V_{G2} = 250$ V.   The grid signal is sinusoidal, with a peak value of 15 V.   The
load is shunt-fed.   (*a*) Calculate the effective load resistance for which there will be
zero second-harmonic distortion.   With the load as determined in part *a*, calculate
(*b*) the output power, (*c*) the power dissipated in the plate, (*d*) the plate-circuit efficiency.

18-19   Verify the data plotted in Fig. 18-8 for (*a*) $R'_L = 1$ K, (*b*) $R'_L = 4$ K.

18-20   In a push-pull system the input (base current) to transistor Q1 is $x_1 =$
$X_m \cos \omega t$, and the input to transistor Q2 is $x_2 = -X_m \cos \omega t$.   The collector current
in each transistor may be expressed in terms of the input excitation by a series of the
form

$$i_C = I_C + a_1 x + a_2 x^2 + a_3 x^3 + \cdots$$

    a. With the aid of this series, show that the output current contains only odd
cosine terms.

    b. Show that the collector supply current contains only even harmonics, in addition
to a dc term.

18-21 Prove, without recourse to a Fourier series, that mirror symmetry [Eq. (18-37)] exists in a push-pull amplifier. Start with $i = k(i_1 - i_2)$ and make use of Eq. (18-34).

18-22 A single transistor is operating as an ideal class B amplifier with a 1-K load. A dc meter in the collector circuit reads 10 mA. How much signal power is delivered to the load?

18-23 Given an ideal class B transistor amplifier whose characteristics are as in Fig. 18-12. The collector supply voltage V_{CC} and the effective load resistance $R'_L = (N_1/N_2)^2 R_L$ are fixed as the base-current excitation is varied. Show that the collector dissipation P_C is zero at no signal ($V_m = 0$), rises as V_m increases, and passes through a maximum [given by Eq. (18-42)] at $V_m = 2V_{CC}/\pi$.

18-24 The idealized push-pull class B power amplifier shown in Fig. 18-11 has $R_2 = 0$, $V_{CC} = 20$ V, $N_2 = 2 N_1$, and $R_L = 20$ Ω, and the transistors have $h_{FE} = 20$. The input is a sinusoid. For the maximum output signal at $V_m = V_{CC}$, determine (a) the output signal power, (b) the collector dissipation in each transistor.

18-25 The power transistor whose characteristics are shown in Fig. 18-5 is used in the class B push-pull circuit of Fig. 18-11, with $R_2 = 0$ and $V_{CC} = -20$ V. If the base current is sinusoidal, with a peak value of 20 mA and $R'_L = (N_1/N_2)^2 R_L = 15$ Ω, calculate (a) the third-harmonic distortion, (b) the power output, (c) the collector-circuit efficiency.

18-26 Repeat Prob. 18-25, using $V_{CC} = -15$ V, $R'_L = 7.5$ Ω, and a peak base current of 30 mA.

18-27 The power transistor whose characteristics are shown in Fig. 18-5 is used in the class B push-pull circuit of Fig. 18-11, with $R_2 = 0$ and $V_{CC} = -20$ V and $R'_L = 15$ Ω. If the base voltage is sinusoidal, with a peak value of 0.4 V, plot the output collector current. Note the crossover distortion.

18-28 Sketch the circuit of a push-pull class B transistor amplifier in the common-collector configuration (a) with an output transformer, (b) without an output transformer.

18-29 Discuss the push-pull complementary circuit of Fig. 18-14. In particular, show that no even harmonics are present.

18-30 The circuit shown represents a transformerless class B single-ended complementary-symmetry push-pull power amplifier. Transistors $Q2$ and $Q3$ are

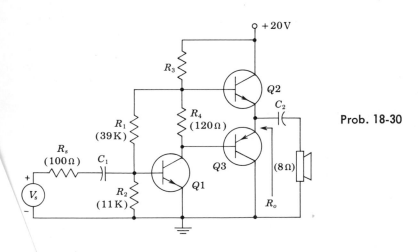

Prob. 18-30

matched silicon devices, with $h_{FE} \approx h_{fe} = 100$ and $h_{ie} = 50\ \Omega$. $Q1$ is a silicon transistor whose small-signal h parameters are given in Table 11-2, and $h_{FE} = 50$.

a. Explain the operation of this circuit. Note especially the role of the capacitor
C_2. Neglect the reverse saturation currents.

b. Calculate the quiescent currents in all the resistors, and determine the value of
R_3 so that

$$|V_{CE3}| = |V_{CE2}|$$

c. Find the output resistance R_o, assuming ideal class B operation.

d. Calculate the maximum power that can be delivered to the 8-Ω speaker. Take
the output resistance R_o into account, and assume $V_{CE}(\text{sat}) \approx 0$.

HINT: In parts c and d, assume that for class B operation $R_4 = 0$.

CHAPTER 19

19-1 Find the maximum speed with which the photoelectrons will be emitted
(if at all) when radiation of wavelength 5,893 Å falls upon (a) a cesium surface, for
which the work function is 1.8 eV, (b) a platinum surface, for which the work function
is 6.0 eV. (c) Repeat parts a and b if the surfaces are illuminated with neon resonance
radiation (743 Å) instead of the yellow sodium line.

19-2 What is the minimum energy, expressed in joules and in electron volts,
required to remove an electron from the surface of metallic potassium, the photoelectric threshold wavelength of which is 5,500 Å?

19-3 A cesium surface for which the work function is 1.8 eV is illuminated with
argon resonance radiation (1,065 Å). What retarding potential must be applied in
order that the plate current in this photocell drop to zero? Assume that the contact
potential is 0.50 V, with the plate negative with respect to the cathode.

19-4 When a certain surface is irradiated by the 2,537-Å mercury line, it is found
that no current flows until at least 0.54 V accelerating potential is applied. Assume
that the contact potential is 1.00 V, the cathode being positive with respect to the anode.

a. What is the work function of the surface?

b. What is the threshold wavelength of the surface?

19-5 A certain photosurface has a spectral sensitivity of 6 mA/W of incident
radiation of wavelength 2,537 Å. How many electrons will be emitted photoelectrically
by a pulse of radiation consisting of 10,000 photons of this wavelength?

19-6 The photoelectric sensitivity of a photocell is 14 μA/lumen when the anode
potential is 90 V. The window area of the photocell is 0.9 in.² A 100-W electric-
light bulb has a mean horizontal candlepower of 120 cp. What will be the photocurrent
if the cell is placed 3 ft from the lamp?

19-7 The energy-distribution curve of a light source is known. The spectral-
sensitivity curves of several of the commercially available photosurfaces are supplied
by the tube manufacturer and are shown in Fig. 19-7. Explain exactly how to determine which tube should be used with this particular light source in order to obtain the
maximum photocurrent.

19-8 Devise a circuit for determining automatically the correct exposure time in
the photographic printing process. Use a photocell, a relay, and any other auxiliary
apparatus needed. The blackening of a photographic emulsion is determined by the

product of the luminous intensity falling on the plate and the time of exposure.   The instrument must trip the relay at the same value of this product, regardless of what light source is used.

19-9   Plot curves of photocurrent vs. light intensity for the photocell whose characteristics are given in Fig. 19-6b for load resistances of 1 and 10 M, respectively. The supply voltage is held constant at 80 V.

19-10   In Fig. 19-8a, the tube has the characteristics given in Fig. 19-6a, $V_{PP} = 80$ V, and an electronic switch is placed across R_L.   The switch closes at 20 V or above and has an infinite input impedance.

a. What minimum light intensity is required to close the switch if $R_L = 2$ M?

b. If the maximum voltage across the switch may not exceed 50 V and if the maximum intensity of light is 208 ft-c, what is the maximum allowable value of R_L?

19-11   Calculate the number of stages required in a secondary-emission multiplier to give an amplification of 10^6 if the secondary-emission ratio is 3.5.

19-12   In a nine-stage secondary-emission phototube multiplier, the incident photocurrent is 10 nA and the output current from the multiplier is 0.1 A.   What is the secondary-emission ratio of the target material?

19-13   In the secondary-emission multiplier of Fig. 19-11, the distance between a target and its plate is 1.0 cm.   The potential between these two elements is 100 V. Assume that there is no field between targets and that the electrons leave each target with zero velocity, so that the resultant motion is truly cycloidal.

a. Find the minimum magnetic field required in order that this tube operate properly.

b. If the tube were designed to operate with a field of 5 mWb/m², what would be the distance between centers of adjacent targets?   Assume that the path remains cycloidal.

19-14   The photoconductor used in the circuit of Fig. 19-8c, with $V_{PP} = 40$ V and $R_L = 4$ K, is the Sylvania type 8347 (Fig. 19-16), designed to dissipate 300 mW safely.

a. What common light intensity is required so that the voltage V_o across R_L is at least 20 V?

b. What is the power dissipated in the photoconductor when $V_o = 20$ V?

c. If the maximum intensity of light is 100 ft-c, what is the minimum allowable value of R_L so that the power rating of the photoconductor is not exceeded?

19-15   The photocurrent I in a p-n junction photodiode as a function of the distance x of the light spot from the junction is given in Fig. 19-21.   Prove that the slopes of the lines are $-1/L_p$ and $-1/L_n$, respectively, on the n and p sides.   Note that L_p represents the diffusion length for holes in the n material.

19-16   Photodiode 1N77 (Fig. 19-19) is used in the circuit of Fig. 19-8b, with $V_{PP} = 40$ V.   Plot curves of photocurrent vs. light intensity for load resistances of 100 K, 50 K, and 0.

19-17   Diode 1N2175 (Fig. 19-23) is used in the circuit shown. R_L represents the coil resistance of a relay for which the current required to close the relay is 1.2 mA. The transistor used is silicon with $V_{BE} = 0.6$ V and $h_{FE} = 100$.

a. Find the voltage V_D at which switching of the relay occurs.

b. Find the minimum illumination required to close the relay.

c. Find the current through the relay coil when the illumination intensity is 300 ft-c.

HINT: Assume that the transistor does not load the 50-K resistor, and verify the assumption.

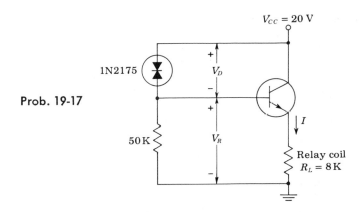

1N2175

$V_{CC} = 20$ V

V_D

V_R

50 K

I

Relay coil
$R_L = 8$ K

Prob. 19-17

19-18 The circuit shown represents the sound detector for a movie projector (lens system not indicated). The output of the transistor preamplifier is cascaded with a power amplifier which feeds a loudspeaker. Assume that the load on the LS223 represents essentially a short circuit, as can be verified from Fig. 19-24. For the transistor used, $h_{ie} = 1$ K, $h_{fe} = 25$, $h_{re} = 0$, and $h_{oe} = 0$. Neglect the reactance of all capacitors.

   a. If the light intensity changes from 2,000 to 2,500 ft-c, find the change in input voltage to the transistor.

   b. Find the peak-to-peak output voltage.

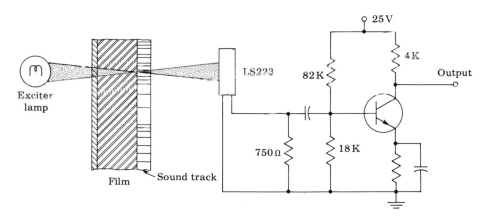

Exciter lamp

Film

Sound track

LS223

82 K

750 Ω

18 K

25 V

4 K

Output

Prob. 19-18

19-19 *a.* For the type LS223 photovoltaic cell whose characteristics are given in Fig. 19-24, plot the power output vs. the load resistance R_L.

   b. What is the optimum value of R_L?

CHAPTER 20

20-1 A diode whose internal resistance is 20 Ω is to supply power to a 1,000-Ω load from a 110-V (rms) source of supply. Calculate (*a*) the peak load current, (*b*) the dc load current, (c) the ac load current, (d) the dc diode voltage, (e) the total input power to the circuit, (f) the percentage regulation from no load to the given load.

20-2 Show that the maximum dc output power $P_{dc} \equiv V_{dc}I_{dc}$ in a half-wave single-phase circuit occurs when the load resistance equals the diode resistance R_f.

20-3 The efficiency of rectification η_r is defined as the ratio of the dc output power $P_{dc} \equiv V_{dc}I_{dc}$ to the input power $P_i = (1/2\pi)\int_0^{2\pi} v_i i \, d\alpha$.

a. Show that, for the half-wave rectifier circuit,

$$\eta_r = \frac{40.6}{1 + R_f/R_L}\%$$

b. Show that, for the full-wave rectifier, η_r has twice the value given in part a.

20-4 Prove that the regulation of both the half-wave and the full-wave rectifier is given by

$$\% \text{ regulation} = \frac{R_f}{R_L} \times 100\%$$

20-5 A full-wave single-phase rectifier consists of a double-diode vacuum tube, the internal resistance of each element of which may be considered to be constant and equal to 500 Ω. These feed into a pure resistance load of 2,000 Ω. The secondary transformer voltage to center tap is 280 V. Calculate (a) the dc load current, (b) the direct current in each tube, (c) the ac voltage across each diode, (d) the dc output power, (e) the percentage regulation.

20-6 In the full-wave single-phase bridge, can the transformer and the load be interchanged? Explain carefully.

20-7 A 1-mA dc meter whose resistance is 10 Ω is calibrated to read rms volts when used in a bridge circuit with semiconductor diodes. The effective resistance of each element may be considered to be zero in the forward direction and infinite in the inverse direction. The sinusoidal input voltage is applied in series with a 5-K resistance. What is the full-scale reading of this meter?

20-8 The circuit shown is a half-wave voltage doubler. Analyze the operation of this circuit. Calculate (a) the maximum possible voltage across each capacitor, (b) the peak inverse voltage of each diode. Compare this circuit with the bridge voltage doubler of Fig. **20-6**. In this circuit the output voltage is negative with respect to ground. Show that if the connections to the cathode and anode of each diode are interchanged, the output voltage will be positive with respect to ground.

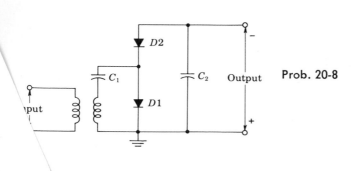

Prob. **20-8**

20-9 The circuit of Prob. 20-8 can be extended from a doubler to a quadrupler by adding two diodes and two capacitors as shown. In the figure, (a) and (b) are alternative ways of drawing the same circuit.

a. Analyze the operation of this circuit.

b. Answer the same questions as asked in Prob. 20-8.

c. Generalize the circuit of this and of Prob. 20-8 so as to obtain n-fold multiplication when n is any even number. In particular, sketch the circuit for sixfold multiplication.

d. Show that n-fold multiplication, with n odd, can also be obtained provided that the output is properly chosen.

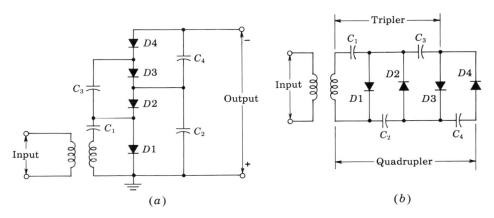

(a)   (b)

Prob. 20-9

20-10 By connecting two half-wave doublers of the type illustrated in Prob. 20-8 to the same input, show that it is possible to obtain a full-wave quadrupler. Explain the operation of this circuit.

20-11 a. Prove that the general solution of the differential equation in Eq. (20-24) is

$$i = - \frac{V_m}{\sqrt{R_L{}^2 + \omega^2 L^2}} [\sin (\omega t - \psi) + e^{-R_L t/L} \sin \psi]$$

where $\tan \psi = \omega L / R_L$.

b. The angle of cutout ωt_2 is that angle at which the current becomes zero. Show that, at cutout,

$$\sin (\omega t_2 - \psi) + e^{-(R_L/\omega L)\omega t_2} \sin \psi = 0$$

Plot a semilog curve of ωt_2 versus $\omega L / R_L$, with $\omega L / R_L$ in the range from 0.1 to 1,000.

c. Verify the curves of Fig. 20-8. In particular, check the value for $\omega L / R_L = 5$.

20-12 A single-phase full-wave rectifier uses semiconductor diodes. The voltage drop and internal resistance of the diodes may be neglected. Assume an ideal transformer.

a. Prove that one diode conducts for one half cycle and that the other diode conducts for the remaining half cycle of the input line voltage if the load consists of a resistor R in series with an inductor L.

b. Find the analytic expression for the load current in the interval

$$0 \leq \alpha = 2\pi ft \leq \pi$$

HINT: Set up the differential equation for the load current i in this interval. The solution of this equation will consist of a steady-state ac term added to a "transient" term. Evaluate the arbitrary constant in the "transient" term by noting that the current repeats itself at intervals of π in α, so that $i(0) = i(\pi)$.

c. Evaluate the direct current I_{dc} by averaging the instantaneous current.

d. Evaluate the first term in the Fourier series for the current, and compare with Eq. (20-25).

20-13   Prove that the rms value of the triangular voltage depicted in Fig. 20-14 is given by Eq. (20-41).

20-14   A single-phase full-wave rectifier uses a semiconductor diode. The transformer voltage is 35 V rms to center tap. The load consists of a 40-μF capacitance in parallel with a 250-Ω resistor. The diode and the transformer resistances and leakage reactance may be neglected.

a. Calculate the cutout angle.

b. Plot to scale the output voltage and the diode current as in Fig. 20-13. Determine the cutin point graphically from this plot, and find the peak diode current corresponding to this point.

c. Repeat parts a and b, using a 160-μF instead of a 40-μF capacitance.

20-15   The circuit of Fig. 20-15 can be analyzed by the methods of elementary ac theory without making the approximations used in Sec. 20-9. Assuming that the input voltage to the filter is given by Eq. (20-45), prove that the ripple factor is

$$r = \frac{\sqrt{2/3}}{\sqrt{(X_L/R_L)^2 + (X_L/X_C - 1)^2}}$$

Under what condition does this reduce to the simpler equation (20-49)?

20-16   By error, the capacitor of an L-section filter is connected to the input side of the inductor. Examine this filter analytically, and derive an expression for (a) the regulation of the system, (b) the ripple factor. Compare these results with those in Sec. 20-9.

20-17   The output of a full-wave rectifier is fed from a 40-0-40-V transformer. The load current is 0.1 A. Two 40-μF capacitances are available. The circuit resistance exclusive of the load is 50 Ω.

a. Calculate the value of inductance for a two-stage L-section filter. The inductances are to be equal. The ripple factor is to be 0.0001.

b. Calculate the dc output voltage.

20-18   Given two equal capacitors C and two equal inductors L. Under what circumstances will it be better to use a double-L-section filter than to use a single section with the inductors in series and the capacitors in parallel?

20-19   An L-section filter is used in the output of a full-wave rectifier that is fed from a 40-0-40-V transformer. The load current is 0.2 A. Two 40-μF capacitances and two 2-H chokes are available. The diodes used are ideal.

a. Calculate the 120-Hz ripple voltage if a single-section filter is used, with the two chokes in series and the two capacitors in parallel.

b. Repeat part a for a two-section filter.

c. Calculate the 240-Hz ripple voltage if a single-section filter is used.

20-20 Given a full-wave rectifier circuit, a 375-0-375-V transformer, $R_L = 2,000\ \Omega$, each diode has a forward resistance of 100 Ω, two 20-H chokes, and two 16-μF capacitors. The transformer resistance to center tap and each choke resistance is 200 Ω. Calculate the approximate output voltage and ripple factor under the following filter arrangements:

   a. The two chokes are connected in series with the load.

   b. The two capacitors are connected in parallel across the load.

   c. A single-section L filter, consisting of the two inductors in series and the two capacitors in parallel.

   d. A two-section L filter.

   e. A Π-section filter, using both inductors.

20-21 Derive an expression for the ripple in a Π-section filter when used with a half-wave rectifier, subject to the same approximations as those in Sec. 20-11 for the full-wave case.

20-22 A full-wave single-phase rectifier employs a Π-section filter consisting of two 4-μF capacitances and a 20-H choke. The transformer voltage to center tap is 300 V rms. The load current is 50 mA. Calculate the dc output voltage and the ripple voltage. The resistance of the choke is 200 Ω.

20-23 The voltage at the input capacitor of a Π-section filter is given to a close approximation by $v(t) = 525 - 40 \sin 745t$. The output capacitance of the filter is 10 μF. If the filter dc output voltage is 500 V for a 100-mA load with a ripple factor of 0.001, determine the inductance and dc resistance of the filter choke.

20-24 Given a full-wave rectifier using ideal elements (i.e., no resistance or leakage reactance in the transformer, no diode drop, and no resistance in the chokes). The voltage on each side of the center tap of the transformer is 300 V rms.

   Answer the following questions for *each* type of filter: (1) no filter, (2) a 10-μF capacitance filter, (3) a 20-H inductance filter, (4) an L-section filter consisting of a 10-μF capacitance and a 20-H choke.

   a. What is the no-load dc voltage? (List your answers as $u1$, $u2$, $u3$, and $u4$.)

   b. What is the dc voltage at 100 mA?

   c. Does the ripple increase, decrease, or stay constant with increasing load current?

   d. What is the peak inverse voltage across each diode?

20-25 A single center-tapped transformer (60-0-60 V) is to supply power at two different voltages for certain service. The negative is to be grounded on each system. The low voltage is full-wave and is filtered with a two-section L filter. The high voltage is half-wave and has a capacitor input filter. Show the schematic diagram for such a system. What is the nominal output voltage of each unit?

20-26 What voltages are available from the rectifier circuit shown? A 40-0-40-V transformer is used. Label the polarities of the output voltages.

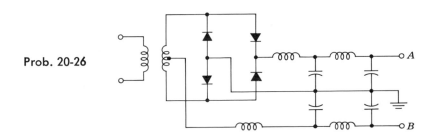

Prob. 20-26

20-27   The circuit shown is to be used to supply power for an amplifier and also for the accelerating voltage of an associated cathode-ray tube.   What output voltages are obtained if a 350-0-350-V center-tapped transformer is used?   HINT: See Prob. 20-8.

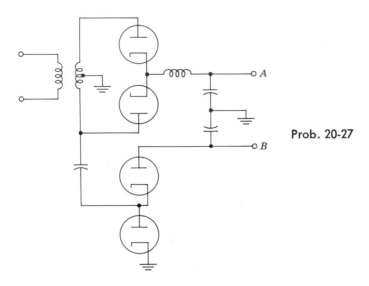

Prob. 20-27

20-28   The circuit shown operates from a 30-0-30-V transformer.
   a. What are the magnitude and polarity of the dc voltage at *A*?   At *B*?   Under no load?
   b. What is the peak inverse on each diode?
   c. If the load current at *A* is 100 mA, what is the voltage at *A*?
   d. If the load current at *B* is 20 mA, what is the voltage at *B*?

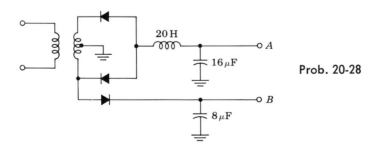

Prob. 20-28

20-29   Verify Eqs. (20-68) and (20-69).
20-30   Verify Eqs. (20-73) and (20-74).
   20-31   Find the output resistance of the series-regulated power supply as given by Eq. (20-75).   HINT: Short-circuit the input, $V_i = 0$, and derive the expression for the output current, using an auxiliary voltage source.
   20-32   Design a regulated power supply as shown in Fig. 20-21 with the following specifications:

Nominal unregulated input voltage $V_i = 30$ V and $r_o = 8\ \Omega$

Nominal regulated output voltage $V_o = 12$ V

Maximum load current $I_L(\text{max}) = 200$ mA

Control transistor $Q1$ (silicon): $h_{FE} = h_{fe} = 100$, $h_{ie} = 200\ \Omega$

Amplifier transistor $Q2$ (silicon): $h_{FE} = h_{fe} = 200$, $h_{ie} = 1$ K

Reference avalanche diode $D1$: $V_R = 6$ V, $R_Z = 10\ \Omega$ at $I_z = 20$ mA

    a. Sketch the complete circuit and obtain reasonable values for R_1, R_2 and R_3.

    b. Calculate the voltage stabilization factor S_V.

    c. Calculate the output impedance R_o.

    20-33 In the circuit of Fig. 20-22, the control transistor $Q1$ is replaced by a Darlington pair $Q1$-$Q3$. The junction of R_3 and the collector of $Q2$ is connected to the base of $Q3$.

    a. Discuss the possible improvement in S_V over the value for the circuit of Fig. 20-22.

    b. Show that the output resistance is

$$R_o \approx \frac{r_o + \dfrac{R_3 + h_{fe3}h_{ie1}}{h_{fe1}h_{fe3}}}{1 + G_m(R_3 + r_o)}$$

where G_m is as given by Eq. (20-73).

    20-34 Repeat Prob. 20-32, using the circuit of Prob. 20-33. Assume that $Q2$ and $Q3$ are identical.

    20-35 The circuit shown employs a Zener diode preregulator.

    a. Explain carefully the operation of the circuit.

    b. Obtain an approximate expression for the voltage stabilization factor S_V. HINT: Assume $\Delta V_o \approx 0$ when $\Delta V_i \gg \Delta V_o$.

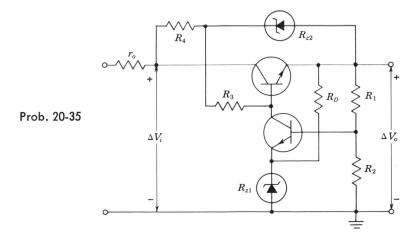

Prob. 20-35

    20-36 Sketch the circuit of a regulated semiconductor power supply whose output is positive with respect to ground, using (*a*) *p-n-p* transistors, (*b*) complementary transistors.

20-37   Sketch the circuit of a regulated semiconductor power supply whose output is negative with respect to ground, using (a) *p-n-p* transistors, (b) *n-p-n* transistors, (c) complementary transistors.

20-38   Verify Eq. (20-79).

20-39   Prove that if no approximations are made in the derivation of Eq. (20-78), the exact value of S_V is given by

$$S_V = \cfrac{1}{\cfrac{r_o + r_{p1}}{R_L} + 1 + \mu_1 + \mu_1 A_2 b}$$

20-40   In the regulated power supply of Fig. 20-26, the resistor R_3 is connected to the input side of the series tube.   Prove that the output resistance is

$$R_o = (r_{p1} + r_o) S_V$$

with

$$S_V = \frac{1 + \mu_1 \gamma}{\mu_1 b A_2}$$

where

$$\gamma = \frac{r_{p2}}{r_{p2} + R_3}$$

INDEX